Practical Mathematics
for Home Study

BOOKS BY
C. I. PALMER

(Published by the McGraw-Hill Book Company, Inc.)

PALMER AND BIBB'S
Practical Mathematics

    Part I—Arithmetic with Applications

    Part II—Algebra with Applications

    Part III—Geometry with Applications

    Part IV—Trigonometry and Logarithms

PALMER'S
Practical Mathematics for Home Study

PALMER'S
Practical Calculus for Home Study

PALMER AND LEIGH'S
Plane and Spherical Trigonometry with Tables

PALMER AND KRATHWOHL'S
Analytic Geometry

PALMER AND MISER'S
College Algebra

(Published by Scott, Foresman and Company)

PALMER, TAYLOR, AND FARNUM'S
Plane Geometry

PALMER, TAYLOR, AND FARNUM'S
Solid Geometry

PALMER, TAYLOR, AND FARNUM'S
Plane and Solid Geometry

Practical Mathematics
for Home Study

Being the essentials of ARITHMETIC, GEOMETRY, ALGEBRA AND TRIGONOMETRY

BY

CLAUDE IRWIN PALMER
Late Professor of Mathematics and Dean of Students, Armour Institute of Technology

AND

SAMUEL FLETCHER BIBB
Associate Professor of Mathematics, Illinois Institute of Technology Armour College of Engineering

THIRD EDITION
THIRD IMPRESSION

McGRAW-HILL BOOK COMPANY, Inc.
NEW YORK AND LONDON
1942

THE MAPLE PRESS COMPANY, YORK, PA.

CLAUDE IRWIN PALMER

Claude Irwin Palmer, passed away suddenly on April 8, 1931, just after completing the second edition of this book. That his passing is mourned by thousands is no exaggeration. Many persons who felt the urge to advance their education, and to improve the talents with which their Creator endowed them, found the solution of their problem in the study of the textbooks which he wrote. He had the faculty of analyzing a problem and presenting its solution so simply that anyone with the proper preparation could understand its presentation.

About the year 1905, President Raymond, who was then the Dean of the Armour Institute of Technology, suggested to Professor Palmer that he give in the evening classes a course on practical mathematics for men employed in various trades in Chicago. The course was begun in a modest way with only a few men. Professor Palmer studied their needs and found that he must begin with arithmetic. He suggested to his students that they bring to him problems which actually arose in their work, and which they had to solve. He offered to solve these problems without any charge. In addition he offered a bonus of half a dollar for each exceptionally good problem. How many half dollars he had to pay he never said, but he very rapidly accumulated quite a collection of problems. Studying these problems showed him not only the necessity for studying algebra, geometry and trigonometry, but also the portions of those subjects which occurred most frequently in actual practice. These problems, their solutions and the necessary explanations were then mimeographed.

Probably no course has ever been revised and rewritten as often as this one, and probably no course has ever been built up so closely in contact with the actual daily experience of the students who took it. Finally he decided that it would be a considerable saving of time if the notes on this course could be printed, and that is how the Home Study Course in Practical Mathematics came to be published.

Dean Palmer, as he finally came to be known, was born on May 31, 1871, in Barry County, Michigan. His early life was spent on a farm near Lake View, in Montcalm County, Michigan. Always eager to improve his education, he worked his way through normal college and the University of Michigan. From the latter, in 1903, he achieved one of his ambitions which was the bachelor of arts degree. In that year he joined the faculty of the Armour Institute of Technology as instructor of mathematics and rose successively through the grades of assistant professor, associate professor and finally professor and head of the department of mathematics. His success as a teacher and the high esteem in which he was held by all his students made him the logical candidate for the office of dean. In 1927, President Raymond appointed him to the position as Dean of Students at the Armour Institute of Technology, and thus he fulfilled what was undoubtedly another ambition. He was so modest and retiring that no one really knew what his heart most desired.

Probably the fact that whatever honors he attained were secured not by gift, but by merit, and that he earned every success by sheer hard work and ability, made him so kindly and sympathetic toward others. His correspondence was very heavy. Every reader who asked him for information received an answer. In his later years, when he should have worked less, he gradually gave up many of his recreations and worked more, in order that those who wished help might have it.

With the passing of this kindly man who was never too busy or too weary to help another, his students and readers have lost a great friend and a great teacher.

WILLIAM CHARLES KRATHWOHL.

CHICAGO, ILLINOIS,
August, 1931.

PREFACE TO THE THIRD EDITION

This third edition consists largely of a reproduction of the second edition insofar as the reading matter is concerned. However, the exercises in this new edition have been completely revised. Some of the exercises that the late Dean Palmer selected with such great care have been changed but little, if at all. The data in the new problems have been brought up to date. A great many of them are entirely new in thought, and it is hoped that they may appeal to an even wider field of practical students. They conform to the present trend of practical applications of everyday problems in social science as well as technical science.

SAMUEL FLETCHER BIBB.

PREFACE TO THE FIRST EDITION

During the past fifteen years the author has taught classes in practical mathematics in the evening school at the Armour Institute of Technology, Chicago. These classes have been composed of men engaged in practical pursuits of various kinds. The needs of these men have been carefully studied; and, so far as possible, those mathematical subjects of interest to them have been taken up. The matter presented to the classes has necessarily been of an intensely practical nature. This has been worked over and arranged in a form that was thought most suitable for class use; and was printed in Palmer's Practical Mathematics, four volumes, in 1912 and appeared in a revised edition in 1918.

The four volume edition has been used by thousands of men for home study. It is to meet the needs especially of such men that this one volume edition has been made. The subject matter includes all that is in the four volumes; and to this has been added a few new topics together with many solutions of exercises, and suggestions that make the text more suitable for home study. It is hoped that it will find a place in the library of the man who applies elementary mathematics, and who wishes occasionally to brush up his mathematics.

Usually when the practical man appreciates the fact for himself that mathematics is a powerful tool that he must be able to use in performing his work, he finds that even the arithmetic that he learned at school has left him. A student of this kind is discouraged if required to pursue the study of mathematics in the ordinary text-books.

This work has been written for the adult. The endeavor has been to make the student feel that he is in actual touch with real things. The intention has been to lay as broad a foundation as is consistent with the scope of the work.

The nearly 3000 drill exercises and problems are, in most cases, new. Many of them are adapted from engineering and trade journals, from handbooks of various kinds, and from treatises on the steel square and other mechanical devices; other problems are from the author's experience; and a large number of the specially practical problems were proposed by members of the classes pursuing the course during its growth.

Much information on various matters to which mathematics is applied, is incidentally given in the problems. Many devices and methods used by the practical man are given. Care has been taken to make these true to practice; but, in so wide a range of matter, there are undoubtedly errors. It is thought that the answers to the exercises are given to a reasonable degree of accuracy. It is hoped that the volume, as a whole, will not be found unmathematical.

The main features of Part One are the concise treatment of various subjects in arithmetic and their applications, checks of processes, degree of accuracy possible in solutions, and contracted processes.

In Part Two, the endeavor has been to state definitions so as to give a clear idea of the term or object defined, and yet not to be too technical. Wherever possible, the attempt is made to discuss a fact or principle of geometry in such a way that its reasonableness will be apparent. While the subjects are treated in the mathematical order, many applications are given under separate headings. Such are brickwork, lumber, the steel square, screw threads, circular mils, belt pulleys, and gear wheels.

In Part Three, the intention is to give sufficient drill in algebra for one who wishes to make direct applications to practical problems. Much attention is given to formulas and their transformations. The equation is applied to many practical problems. Graphical methods are considered, and many articles on special subjects are given.

In Part Four, the intention is to give sufficient work in logarithms to secure a fair degree of skill in computations. In trigonometry, those parts are emphasized that may be applied directly to practical problems; while the portions chiefly necessary as an aid in the study of more advanced mathematical subjects, are either treated very slightly or omitted. Many applications are given. The tables are given to four decimal places.

The author wishes to acknowledge his great indebtedness to the more than 1000 men who made up his classes during the growth of this work, and to the hundreds of men from various parts of the country who have offered kindly criticisms and suggestions; for, without their help and sympathy, the present results would have been impossible.

Because of the remarkable success of the previous editions, it is with the greatest pleasure that this special edition is submitted to our practical men.

C. I. PALMER.

CHICAGO, ILLINOIS,
June, 1919.

A WORD WITH THE STUDENT

One of the lessons of the two Great Wars and the strenuous efforts necessary to carry them on has been to bring forcibly to our minds the great usefulness of mathematics. The war activities have exhibited the extensive mathematical needs of those who aim to render the most efficient service under the most trying circumstances. The young men of the country realize the need for a working knowledge of mathematics, and see clearly that the need so emphasized by the war conditions is being carried over into the days of peace and into the period of great industrial activity that is sure to follow.

This volume being entitled Practical Mathematics does not mean that all exercises are such as would be called practical. It means that, in the main, the exercises, outside of those intended for pure drill, are such as may arise in some practical field of work. The endeavor has been to utilize the material afforded by the shops and the laboratories as well as in the trades and in engineering.

The practical man realizes that, for him, mathematics is a chest of tools together with many more or less complicated pieces of machinery that he may use to accomplish his purpose. To apply mathematics, then, he must be able to run its machinery not only accurately but speedily. To do this a great deal of work must be done in the arithmetical processes themselves. The student must drill himself on the fundamental operations—addition, subtraction, multiplication, and division—both in whole numbers and in fractions, until the processes become to a large degree mechanical. That is, he should be able to do these operations with but little expenditure of mental energy. This drill is best gained by doing many exercises especially set for this purpose. Each student who is studying alone, that is, without being in a class, must of necessity be his own judge as to how much drill he needs. For most people such drill is tedious and uninteresting, and it requires a strong will to force oneself to do the proper amount of such work.

That these ideas are not new is evident from the following quotation in quaint old English, taken from an arithmetic printed more than two hundred years ago: "Therefore, Courteous Reader, if thou intendest to be a Proficient in the Mathematicks, begin cheerfully, proceed gradually, and with Resolution, and the end will crown thy Endeavours with Success, and be not so slothfully Studious, as at every Difficulty thou meetest withal to cry, *Ne plus ultra*, for Pains and Diligence will overcome the greatest Difficulty: To conclude, That thou may'st so read as to understand, and so understand, as to become a Proficient, is the hearty desire of him who wisheth thy Welfare, and the Progress of Arts. From my School at *St. George's* Church in *Southwark*, *October* 27, 1684."

CONTENTS

PART ONE

ARITHMETIC

CHAPTER I

Preliminary Work

CHAPTER II

Common Fractions

CHAPTER III

DECIMAL FRACTIONS

CHAPTER IV

SHORT METHODS AND CHECKS

CHAPTER V

WEIGHTS AND MEASURES

CHAPTER VI

PERCENTAGE AND APPLICATIONS

CHAPTER VII

RATIO AND PROPORTION

CHAPTER VIII

POWERS AND ROOTS

PART TWO

GEOMETRY

CHAPTER IX

FUNDAMENTAL IDEAS IN GEOMETRY

CHAPTER X

AREAS OF POLYGONS

CHAPTER XI

TRIANGLES

CHAPTER XII

THE CIRCLE

PART THREE

ALGEBRA

CHAPTER XIX

INTRODUCTION TO ALGEBRA

CHAPTER XX

ADDITION AND SUBTRACTION

CHAPTER XXI

EQUATIONS

CHAPTER XXII

MULTIPLICATION

CHAPTER XXVII

EQUATIONS AND APPLICATIONS

CHAPTER XXVIII

EQUATIONS WITH MORE THAN ONE UNKNOWN

CHAPTER XXIX

EXPONENTS, POWERS, AND ROOTS

CHAPTER XXX

QUADRATIC EQUATIONS

CHAPTER XXXI

VARIATION

CHAPTER XXXII

GRAPHICAL METHODS AND FUNCTIONS

CHAPTER XXXIII

LOGARITHMS

PART FOUR

TRIGONOMETRY

CHAPTER XXXIV

INTRODUCTION, ANGLES

CHAPTER XXXV

TRIGONOMETRIC FUNCTIONS

TABLES

PART ONE

Arithmetic

CHAPTER I

PRELIMINARY WORK

1. The language of mathematics is one of signs and symbols, and, in a sense, is an unspoken language. "There can be no more universal or more simple language, no language more exempt from error and obscurity." The language of mathematics is the same throughout the civilized world, though the people of each country translate it into their peculiar spoken language. For instance, the symbol 5 means the same to a person in England, Spain, Italy, or in any other country; but in each country it may be called by a different spoken word.

Failure to learn the language of mathematics and to memorize the definitions and technical terms keeps many students from mastering the mathematical subjects they take up. The language of mathematics is based upon an exact science which was formed slowly through many centuries and which never loses a principle that has once been established.

Some of the best known symbols of mathematics are the Arabic numerals, 1, 2, 3, 4, 5, 6, 7, 8, 9, 0, the signs of addition, +, subtraction, −, multiplication, ×, division, ÷, and equality, =, and the letters of the alphabet. Other symbols will be explained as used.

2. The study of mathematics.—In the study of mathematics much time should be devoted: (1) to the expressing of verbally stated facts in mathematical language, that is, in the signs and

1

symbols of mathematics; (2) to the translating of mathematical expressions into common language.

The signs and symbols of mathematics are used for convenience. They have gradually come into use by general agreement. In some cases the symbols are abbreviations of words, but often have no such relation to the thing they stand for. We cannot tell why they stand for what they do any more than we can tell why the words for cat and dog stand for the different animals they do. They mean what they do by *common agreement* or by *definition*.

One should thoroughly appreciate and should remember that the understanding of any subject in mathematics presupposes a clear and definite knowledge of what precedes. This is the reason that "there is no royal road" to mathematics, and that the study of mathematics is discouraging to weak and indolent minds, those who are not able and willing to master the subject as presented.

The application of mathematics has to do with things that are vital, with real happenings of life; and much time is spent in solving such problems.

3. Number.—Arithmetic deals with the relations and combinations of numbers, and by means of numbers deals with all practical problems to which it may be applicable. What then is a number? This question is not easily answered. Perhaps the best we can do is to urge that each person endeavor to make clear to himself the meaning of number, and whence came the numbers that are connected with a particular problem. A number may come from counting the individuals in a group of objects, or a number may be used in stating the amount or measure of something that has been measured. Thus, one measures the length of a room and finds that it is 30 feet. Geometrically, real numbers may be represented as distances from a fixed point on a straight line, provided a convenient unit of measure is chosen.

4. How to attack a problem.—A problem in mathematics should not be attacked as a puzzle. No guesswork has any place in its consideration. The statement of the problem should be clear and so leave but one solution possible. To state the problem clearly is the duty of the author or the one who proposes the problem. The following suggestions should be carefully observed by the student:

(1) *The problem should be read and analyzed so carefully that all conditions are well fixed in mind.* If the problem cannot be understood there is no use in trying to solve it. Of course, if the answer is given, a series of guess operations may obtain it, but the work is worse than useless.

(2) *In the solution there should be no unnecessary work.* Shorten the processes whenever possible.

(3) *Always apply some proof or check to the work if possible.* A wrong answer is valueless. Accuracy is of the highest importance, and to no one more than to the practical man. If a check can be applied, there is no need of an answer being given to the problem.

In this text the answers follow most of the exercises. They are given for the convenience of the student in checking his work, and great care must be taken not to misuse them. An answer should never assist in determining how to solve a problem. It is best, then, not to look at the answer till the problem is solved.

5. Definitions.—In order to be exact in ideas and statements, it is necessary to give certain definitions. It would seem, however, that for the practical man, technical terms should be omitted so far as possible. It is usually sufficient to make the term understood, though the definition may not be a good one technically. In mathematics more than in almost any other subject, each word used has a *definite* and *fixed meaning.*

The following definitions are inserted here to help to recall to mind some of the terms used:

(1) An **integer,** or an **integral number,** is a whole number.

(2) A **factor,** or a **divisor,** of a whole number is any whole number that will exactly divide it.

(3) An **even number** is a number that is exactly divisible by 2.

Thus, 4, 8, and 20 are even nunbers.

(4) An **odd number** is an integer that is not exactly divisible by 2.

Thus, 5, 11, and 47 are odd numbers.

(5) A **prime number** is a number that has no factors except itself and 1.

Thus, 1, 2, 7, 11, and 17 are prime numbers.

(6) A **composite number** is a number that has other factors than itself and 1.

Thus, 6, 22, 49, and 100 are composite numbers.

(7) A **common factor,** or **divisor,** of two or more numbers is a factor that will exactly divide each of them.   If this factor is the largest factor possible it is called the **greatest common divisor :** abbreviated to G. C. D.

Thus, 4 is a common divisor of 16 and 24, but 8 is the G. C. D. of 16 and 24.

(8) A **multiple** of a number is a number that is divisible by the given number.   If the same number is exactly divisible by two or more numbers it is a **common multiple** of them. The least such number is called the **least common multiple :** abbreviated to L. C. M.

Thus, 36 and 72 are common multiples of 12, 9, and 4, but 36 is the L. C. M.

6. Rules for finding divisor of numbers.—It is often convenient to be able to tell without performing the division, whether or not a given number is divisible by another.   The following rules will assist in this.

(1) A number is divisible by 2 if its right-hand figure is 0 or one divisible by 2.

(2) A number is divisible by 3 if the sum of its digits is divisible by 3.

Thus, 73,245 is divisible by 3 since $7 + 3 + 2 + 4 + 5 = 21$ is divisible by 3.

(3) A number is divisible by 4 if the number represented by its two last digits on the right is divisible by 4, or if it ends in two zeros.

Thus, 87,656 is divisible by 4 since 56 is divisible by 4.

(4) A number is divisible by 5 if the last figure on the right is 0 or 5.

(5) An even number the sum of whose digits is divisible by 3 is divisible by 6.

(6) No convenient rule can be given for 7; the best thing to do is to test by trial.

(7) A number is divisible by 8 if the number represented by the last three digits on the right is divisible by 8.

Thus, 987,672 is divisible by 8 since 672 is divisible by 8.

(8) A number is divisible by 9 if the sum of its digits is divisible by 9.

(9) A number is divisible by 11 if the difference between the sum of the odd digits and the even digits, counting from the right, is divisible by 11.

Thus, 47,679,291 is divisible by 11 since $(9 + 9 + 6 + 4) - (1 + 2 + 7 + 7) = 11$ is divisible by 11.

Note.—This rule is of little value since the division can be tried about as easily as the rule can be applied.

The following facts are of some value:

(10) A factor of a number is a factor of any of its multiples.

(11) A common factor of any two numbers is a factor of the sum or the difference of any two multiples of the numbers.

Remark.—The eleven statements above are not meant to be all-inclusive. They are principles that are found to be the most practical when *integral numbers* are being used in arithmetic.

EXERCISES

1. Name the even numbers and the odd numbers in the following: 4, 11, 20, 29, 555, 1166, 1939, 1940.

2. Which of the following are prime numbers and which are composite: 7, 11, 18, 21, 23, 46, 69, 71, 1492, 1777, 1939?

3. Some of the prime numbers are given (*a*) by $2 + 1, 4 + 1, 16 + 1, 256 + 1$, etc. ($2^n + 1$, n a power of 2); (*b*) by $2 - 1, 8 - 1, 32 - 1, 128 - 1$, etc. ($2^p - 1$, p itself a prime).

4. Give all the divisors besides 1 and itself of 6; of 24; of 120; of 720; of 5040; of 10; of 70; of 770.

5. Is 39,916,800 divisible by 2? by 3? by 4? by 5? by 6? by 7? by 8? by 9? by 10? by 11?

Find the common divisors and the G. C. D. of each of the following groups of numbers. If the numbers are small, one can usually determine the common divisors and also the G. C. D. by inspection. If they cannot be determined in this way, factor each number into its prime factors and then select those that are common to all.

6. 12, 16, 24.   *Ans.* 2, 4; 4.   **9.** 110, 220, 330.
                                                  Ans. 2, 5, 10, 11, 110; 110.

7. 16, 24, 32.   *Ans.* 2, 4, 8; 8.   **10.** 24, 720, 5040.
                                                  Ans. 2, 3, 4, 6, 8, 12, 24; 24.

8. 9, 27, 144.   *Ans.* 3, 9; 9.   **11.** 65, 780, 1190.   *Ans.* 5; 5.

Find the least common multiple of each of the following groups of numbers. A good way to find the L. C. M. of several numbers is to factor each number into its prime factors and then take the product of all the factors of the first number together with those of the second number that are not found in the first, and those in the third that are not found in the first two, and so on till all the numbers are used.

12. 2, 4, 6, 8, 10.   *Ans.* 120.   **15.** 3, 7, 63, 147.   *Ans.* 441.

13. 1, 3, 5, 7, 9.   *Ans.* 315.   **16.** 5, 15, 75, 225.   *Ans.* 225.

14. 3, 11, 99, 726.   *Ans.* 2178.   **17.** 7, 22, 186, 3388.
                                                  Ans. 315,084.

18. Find the prime factors of each of the following: 1188; 148,225; 89,964; 36,992,000.

```
2)1188
2)594
3)297
3)99
3)33
11)11
    1
```

Solution.—The work is best carried out by selecting the smallest prime factors, leaving the larger till later. The prime factors of the number are all of the divisors used. The prime factors of 1188 are 2, 2, 3, 3, 3, 11.

19. Tell which of the following numbers are exactly divisible by each of 2, 3, 4, 5, 6, 7, 8, and 9:91,008; 6,370,560; 12,731,040; 181,272; 32,670; 22,869,000.

20. Give three divisors of 252. Give three multiples of 75. Give three common multiples of 21, 28, 9. Give the L. C. M. of the last three numbers. Is there a G. C. M. of the last three numbers?

21. Is 360 multiplied by any integer n divisible by each of 2, 3, 4, 5, 6, 8, and 9?

22. Is 360 multiplied by $(a + b)$ divisible by each of 2, 3, 4, 5, 6, 8, and 9? Multiplied by $(a - b)$?

7. Relative importance of signs of operation.—(1) A series of additions may be taken in any order.

Thus, $4 + 5 + 7 + 3 = 19$, when added in any order.

(2) A series of subtractions *must* be taken as written.

Thus, $100 - 20 - 10 - 3 = 67$, when taken in the order written

(3) A series of multiplications may be taken in any order.

Thus, $2 \times 3 \times 5 \times 6 = 180$, when taken in any order.

(4) A series of divisions *must* be taken as written.

Thus, $100 \div 10 \div 2 = 5$, when taken in the order written.

(5) In a series of different operations the multiplications *must* be performed first, the divisions next, and then the additions and subtractions may be taken in the order written.

Example 1: $12 + 3 - 2 + 9 + 7 - 3 = 26$, by performing the operations in the order in which they occur.

Example 2: $120 \div 3 \times 5 \times 2 \div 2 = 2$, by first performing the multiplications and then the divisions in the order in which they occur.

Example 3: $12 \div 3 + 8 \times 2 - 6 \div 2 + 7 \times 2 \times 3 - 9$
$$= 12 \div 3 + 16 - 6 \div 2 + 42 - 9$$
$$= 4 + 16 - 3 + 42 - 9 = 50, \text{ by first per-}$$
forming the multiplications, then the divisions, and then the additions and subtractions.

Remark 1.—The above methods of operations will give the correct result, but in a series of subtractions the numbers that are to be subtracted could be subtracted one at a time in any order.

Thus, $100 - 20 - 10 - 3 = 100 - 3 - 20 - 10 = 100 - 3 - 10 - 20 = 67$.

Or all of the numbers that are to be subtracted could be added to form a single sum (number) and then this single number could be subtracted.

Thus, $100 - (20 + 10 + 3) = 100 - 33 = 67$.

Remark 2.—In a series of different operations the parentheses ( ) and brackets [ ] could be used to group the desired order of operations.

Thus, $120 \div 3 \times 5 \times 2 \div 2 = [120 \div (3 \times 5 \times 2)] \div 2 = [120 \div 30] \div 2 = 4 \div 2 = 2$.

NOTE.—The operation indicated by the shortest group is performed first.

It is here assumed that the student is familiar with the four fundamental operations, addition, subtraction, multiplication, and division, of arithmetic; and, therefore, no explanation of these processes is given. The exercises in multiplication and division are given for practice and review in testing the ability of the student to perform these operations rapidly and correctly. One should drill himself in these operations until he has attained the desired facility in performing them.

EXERCISES

In Exercises 1 to 8 remember that the operations indicated by the shortest group should be performed first.

1. $(18 + 19 - 8) + (12 - 8 - 4) = ?$ *Ans.* 29.

2. $[21 \div (7 \times 3)] + (4 \times 5) = ?$ *Ans.* 21.

3. $18 - [(3 + 6 + 9) \div (9 - 6)] - 12 = ?$ *Ans.* 0.

4. $[(25 - 4 - 6) \div (3 \times 5)] + 4 \times 3 = ?$ *Ans.* 13.

5. $(27 - 7) - [(2 \times 3) \div (3 \times 2)] - 3 \times 6 = ?$ *Ans.* 1.

6. $[(55 - 10) \times (3 \times 6 \times 9)] \div [(4 \times 10) + 5] = ?$ *Ans.* 162.

7. $[256 \div (16 \times 16)] + [225 \div (15 \times 1)] = ?$ *Ans.* 16.

8. $(720 \div 360) + (180 \times 2) + 1 = ?$ *Ans.* 363.

9. Time yourself in doing the following six multiplications:

(1) 135×246.

(2) 157×268.

(3) 790×281.

(4) 975×864.

(5) 793×682.

(6) 9753×6429.

10. Check your work in the above six multiplications by doing the multiplying, using the first number in each case as the multiplier.

11. Time yourself in doing the following divisions. Check your work by finding the product of the divisor and quotient and comparing it with the dividend.

(1) $549,198 \div 9$.

(2) $427,154 \div 7$.

(3) $5746 \div 26$.

(4) $29,375 \div 235$.

(5) $32,277 \div 371$.

(6) $876,543,210 \div 90$.

12. Do the following multiplications and check the work by dividing the product by the multiplier and comparing the result with the multiplicand:

(1) 384×923.

(2) 2374×879.

(3) 4943×4350.

(4) 8793×7329.

13. Do the following divisions and check the work by finding the product of the divisor and quotient, then adding the remainder and comparing the result with the dividend:

(1) $93,462 \div 79$.

(2) $637,842 \div 2327$.

(3) $647,847 \div 353$.

(4) $9,963,486 \div 573$.

14. Note the following interesting products:

Multiply 12,345,679 by

(1) 63, which is 7×9.

(2) 54, which is 6×9.

(3) 45, which is 5×9.

(4) 36, which is 4×9.

Write down the results for 27, 18, and 9.

15. If 650 airships cost $48,002,500, what is the cost per ship?

Ans. $73,850.

16. For 1938 the United States produced 5,008,000 fine ounces of gold valued at $175,280,000.   What is the value of 1 fine ounce?   *Ans.* $35.

17. There are 21 accidents in the United States per minute.   How many accidents will there be in the United States in 365 days?
Ans. 11,037,600.

18. In order to do satisfactory work, the teeth of a saw must travel about 9225 feet per minute.   A circular saw has 75 teeth 1 inch apart. How many revolutions per minute should the saw make?   *Ans.* 1476.

19. The circumference of a drive wheel of a locomotive is 22 feet. How many revolutions will it make in going 286 miles if there are 5280 feet in a mile?   *Ans.* 68,640.

20. The pressure at the center of the earth is estimated to be about 3,200,000 atmospheres.   If this is 32 times the greatest pressure ever produced in a laboratory, and if the atmospheric pressure is 15 pounds per square inch, find the greatest pressure ever produced in a laboratory.
Ans. 1,500,000 pounds per square inch.

21. If a man takes a step of 28 inches and can walk 7 miles in 2 hours, how many steps does he take per minute (5280 feet in a mile)?
Ans. 132.

22. A hog weighing 78 pounds requires 400 pounds of grain for each 100 pounds gain in weight.   If the price of 56 pounds of grain increases in price from 42 cents to $1.54, what should be the increase in price of hogs per 100 pounds?

Solution.—Since 56 pounds of grain increases in price from 42 cents to $1.54, the increase is $1.12 for each 56 pounds, or 2 cents per pound.   This is an increase of $8 for 400 pounds.   Since it takes 400 pounds of grain to increase a hog's weight 100 pounds, the price of hogs should be increased $8 per 100 pounds.

23. When 56 pounds of corn cost 56 cents, hogs sold at $5.60 per 100 pounds live weight; and when corn cost $1.82 for 56 pounds, they sold at $15.10 per 100 pounds.   How much more or less does the farmer make per hundred if it takes 400 pounds of corn for each 100 pounds increase in weight of hogs?   *Ans.* In second case 50 cents more.

24. How many tons of silage, 2000 pounds per ton, should be stored for 20 cows, the intention being to feed each cow 40 pounds per day for 5 months, then 30 pounds per day for 2 months, then 20 pounds per day for 2 months?   Consider 30 days to a month.   *Ans.* 90.

8. Cancellation.—Often in solving problems, a fractional form like the following is obtained:

$$\frac{64 \times 25 \times 8 \times 12 \times 17}{48 \times 15 \times 32 \times 17 \times 24}$$

If we do all the multiplications above the line and below the line, and then perform the division which the line indicates, we shall obtain the result. It is often easy to avoid much of this work, however, by applying a principle of fractions. The process which is explained below is called **cancellation.**

$$\frac{\overset{2}{\cancel{64}} \times \overset{5}{\cancel{25}} \times \cancel{8} \times \cancel{12} \times \cancel{17}}{\underset{6}{\cancel{48}} \times \underset{3}{\cancel{15}} \times \cancel{32} \times \cancel{17} \times \underset{2}{\cancel{24}}}$$

(1) It is seen that 17 is found both above and below the line; we draw a line through each of these. These numbers are then said to be canceled.

(2) Now notice that the numbers 64 and 32 are divisible by 32. Cancel 64 and 32 and place 2 above 64 which is the number of times 32 is contained in 64.

(3) Next, divide 48 and 8 by 8 and cancel them, writing the quotient 6 below 48.

(4) Divide 25 and 15 by 5 and cancel them, writing the quotient 5 above 25 and 3 below 15.

(5) In a similar manner 12 and 24 are canceled; also 2 and 2.

In this manner we have replaced the given form by the simpler one $\frac{5}{6 \times 3} = \frac{5}{18}$. This is the answer.

It should be noted that when no factor remains either above or below the line after the cancellation is finished, we retain one of the unit factors which we neglected to write when canceling.

Thus, $\dfrac{\cancel{4} \times \cancel{8} \times \cancel{16} \times \cancel{10}}{\underset{3}{\cancel{12}} \times \underset{10}{\cancel{80}} \times \underset{3}{\cancel{48}}} = \dfrac{1}{9}$ *Ans.*

These processes may be restated as follows:

RULE.—(1) *Any factor above may be divided into any factor below the line.*

(2) *Any factor below may be divided into any factor above the line.*

(3) *Any factor common to factors one above and one below may be divided into each.*

(4) *The answer is obtained by dividing the product of the numbers remaining above the line by the product of the numbers remaining below the line. If no number remains above or below, use* 1.

If one becomes familiar with the methods of cancellation and uses them in making computations wherever convenient, much time and labor will be saved. As will be found later on, cancellation can be used when decimals are involved.

Remark.—It should be remembered that this method of simplifying cannot be used when there are additions or subtractions indicated in the problem.

In such a case the operations above the line must be performed first, then those below, and lastly the result above must be divided by the result below.

Thus,
$$\frac{4 + 200 - 6 \times 2}{38 + 98 - 12 \times 6} = \frac{192}{64} = 3 \quad Ans.$$

EXERCISES

Use cancellation to find the results in the following:

1. $\dfrac{3 \times 9 \times 7 \times 18 \times 5}{9 \times 21 \times 15}.$ *Ans.* 6.

2. $\dfrac{30 \times 56 \times 24}{12 \times 14 \times 10}.$ *Ans.* 24.

3. $\dfrac{68 \times 121 \times 38}{17 \times 22 \times 19}.$ *Ans.* 44.

4. $\dfrac{88 \times 200 \times 16 \times 28}{12 \times 11 \times 10 \times 9 \times 8}.$ *Ans.* $82\frac{26}{27}.$

5. $\dfrac{36 \times 50 \times 26 \times 24}{15 \times 39 \times 10}.$ *Ans.* 192.

6. $\dfrac{12 \times 14 \times 16 \times 51}{34 \times 64 \times 28}.$ *Ans.* $2\frac{1}{4}.$

7. $\dfrac{99 \times 888 \times 77}{72 \times 777 \times 42}.$ *Ans.* $2\frac{37}{42}.$

8. $\dfrac{2100 \times 155 \times 60 \times 100}{700 \times 31 \times 28}.$ *Ans.* $3214\frac{2}{7}.$

9. $\dfrac{120 \times 135 \times 510 \times 57}{36 \times 33 \times 170 \times 30}.$ *Ans.* $77\frac{8}{11}.$

10. $\dfrac{570 \times 5400 \times 6250}{45 \times 60 \times 60 \times 90}$. *Ans.* $1319\dfrac{4}{9}$.

11. $\dfrac{288 \times 800 \times 5280}{48 \times 540 \times 5600}$. *Ans.* $8\dfrac{8}{21}$.

12. $\dfrac{1020 \times 234 \times 1212 - 1020 \times 101}{[180 + (3 \times 90) + 570]24 \times 101}$. *Ans.* $116\dfrac{23}{24}$.

13. $\dfrac{5 \times 15 + 3 \times 25}{3 \times 50}$. *Ans.* 1.

14. $\dfrac{(77 - 15) + 2 \times 19}{(2 \times 14) - (3 \times 8)}$. *Ans.* 25.

15. $\dfrac{(17 \times 33) - (17 \times 11) + (17 \times 44)}{(17 \times 11)[66 - (4 \times 15)]}$. *Ans.* 1.

16. $\dfrac{512 \times 6 + [256 \times 6 - (32 \times 12)]}{(6 \times 64)[(256 \times 6) - (16 \times 24)]}$. *Ans.* $\dfrac{11}{1152}$.

Analyze the following and shorten the computation as much as possible by cancellation.

17. If 18 men can do a piece of work in 14 days, how many men will do the work in 21 days?

Analysis.—If 18 men can do a piece of work in 14 days, one man can do the work in 18×14 days. It will take as many men to do the work in 21 days as 21 is contained times in 18×14.

Operation

$$\dfrac{\overset{6}{\cancel{18}} \times \overset{2}{\cancel{14}}}{\underset{3}{\cancel{21}}} = 12$$

Hence, it takes 12 men to do the work in 21 days.

18. If 48 electric fans cost \$312, what will 18 of these fans cost?

Ans. \$117.

19. If a man trades 27 dozen eggs valued at 12 cents per dozen for bacon valued at 18 cents per pound, how many pounds of bacon does he get? *Ans.* 18.

20. A man walks 28 miles in 8 hours. If he takes steps of 28 inches, how many steps per minute does he take? *Ans.* 132.

21. If 8 men, in 15 days of 10 hours each, can throw 1000 cubic yards of earth into wheelbarrows, how many men will be required to throw 2000 cubic yards of earth into wheelbarrows in 20 days of 8 hours each?

Ans. 15.

Suggestion.—Analyze the problem and state in the following form for cancellation:

$$\dfrac{8 \times 15 \times 10 \times 2000}{20 \times 8 \times 1000}$$

22. If six men drink 124 quarts of milk in 31 days, how many quarts will eight men drink in 24 days? *Ans.* 128.

23. A man drives 256 miles on gasoline that costs 18 cents per gallon and finds that he is getting 16 miles to the gallon. How many miles could he have traveled on a train at 3 cents per mile if the cost is the same as for the car trip?   *Ans.* 96.

24. A farmer trades corn valued at 72 cents a bushel for a tank of gasoline that holds 128 cubic feet. If the gasoline is valued at 18 cents per gallon, and if there are $7\frac{1}{2}$ gallons to the cubic foot, how many barrels of corn were traded if there are 5 bushels in a barrel?   *Ans.* 48.

25. If 24 men in 18 days of 8 hours each can dig a ditch 95 rods long, 12 feet wide, and 9 feet deep, how many men in 24 days of 12 hours each will be required to dig a ditch 380 rods long, 9 feet wide, and 6 feet deep?
Ans. 24.

26. If 24 men in 18 days of 8 hours each can dig a ditch 105 rods long, 12 feet wide, and 9 feet deep, how many men in 24 days of 12 hours each will be required to dig a ditch 420 rods long, 9 feet wide, and 6 feet deep?
Ans. 24.

27. A bookstore orders 36 books valued at $1.50 per book and 48 books valued at $2.10 per book. How many different books valued at $3.60 per book must the store return to pay for the books ordered? *Suggestion:* For the purpose of cancellation, think of $1.50 as 150 cents, etc.
Ans. 43.

28. A dealer orders 24 coats valued at $5.46 per coat and 36 pairs of shoes valued at $4.16 per pair. To pay for the coat and shoes, the dealer returns enough golf balls valued at 52 cents per ball. How many dozen golf balls were returned?   *Ans.* 45.

29. A room 30 feet long, 30 feet wide, and 10 feet high contains about 700 pounds of air. What is the weight of air in another room under conditions similar to the first if it is 120 feet long, 90 feet wide, and 12 feet high?   *Ans.* 10,080 pounds.

9. Applying rules.—The practical man often has to apply a rule in solving a problem. This rule may be given to him by a fellow workman, or it may be taken from a handbook. The rule may be one, the reasonableness of which is apparent, but often it is not. Many rules are the results of experience, others of experiment, and still others are mere "rules of thumb," that is, they merely state a combination of numbers which gives the result desired.

In the following problems, read the rule carefully before applying it.

EXERCISES

RULE.—To find the number of revolutions of a *driven* pulley in a *given* time, multiply the *diameter* of the *driving* pulley by its number of *revolutions* in the given time and divide by the *diameter* of the *driven* pulley.

   1. A pulley 45 inches in diameter and making 68 revolutions per minute (R. P. M.) is driving a pulley 51 inches in diameter. Find the number of R. P. M.   *Ans.* 60.

   2. Find the R. P. M. of a pulley 9 inches in diameter driven by a 24-inch pulley making 48 R. P. M.   *Ans.* 128.

   3. Find the R. P. M. of a pulley 52 inches in diameter driven by a 36-inch pulley making 78 R. P. M.   *Ans.* 54.

   4. In the train of pulleys in Fig. 1, *A* is the driving pulley. Find the revolutions per minute of *C*.   *Ans.* 392.

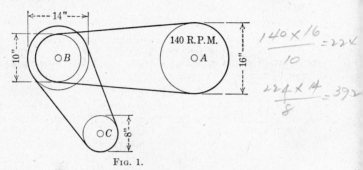

Fig. 1.

   5. In the pulley train of Fig. 2, find the revolutions per minute of the lathe pulley.

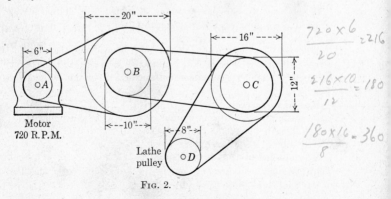

Fig. 2.

   Rule.—To determine the width of belt required to transmit a given **horsepower** at a given speed of the belt: For **single leather** or **four-ply**

rubber belts, multiply the number of horsepower to be transmitted by 33,000 and divide the product by the product of the speed of the belt, in feet per minute, multiplied by 60. The quotient will be width of the belt in inches.

6. What is the required width of belt to transmit 100 horsepower with a belt speed of 3500 feet per minute?

$$\textit{Solution:} \qquad \frac{\overset{110}{\underset{7}{\cancel{550}}}\cancel{100} \times \cancel{33000}}{\cancel{3500} \times \cancel{60}} = \frac{110}{7} = 15\frac{5}{7} \text{ inches.}$$

7. Find the width of a single leather belt to transmit 84 horsepower, with a belt speed of 4400 feet per minute.   *Ans.* $10\frac{1}{2}$ inches.

8. For heavy double leather of six-ply rubber belts, use 100 instead of 60 in the rule. Find the width of such a belt to transmit 120 horsepower with a belt speed of 3200 feet per minute.   *Ans.* $12\frac{3}{8}$ inches.

RULE.—To determine the horsepower a belt of given width will transmit when running at a given speed: For **single leather** or **four-ply rubber belts,** multiply width of belt in inches by 60 and the product by speed of belt in feet per minute and divide the product by 33,000. The quotient will be the number of horsepower that the belt will transmit with safety.

9. How many horsepower will an 8-inch single leather belt transmit if running at 4400 feet per minute?   *Ans.* 64.

10. How many horsepower will a 32-inch heavy double leather belt transmit if running at 4000 feet per minute? (Use 100 instead of 60 in the rule.)   *Ans.* $387\frac{29}{33}$.

The first letter of a word is often used in mathematics instead of the word itself. When two or more such letters are written together with no sign between them, it is understood that multiplication is indicated.

If

H = horsepower.

P = effective pressure in pounds of steam per square inch.

L = length of piston stroke in feet.

A = area of piston in square inches.

N = number of strokes per minute.

Then the **rule** for finding the horsepower of a steam engine may be stated in the following abbreviated form:

$$H = \frac{PLAN}{33,000}$$

11. Find H if $P = 55$ pounds per square inch, $L = 2$ feet, $A = 195$ square inches, and $N = 80$.

Solution: $$H = \frac{55 \times 2 \times 195 \times 80}{33,000} = 52$$

12. Find H if $P = 66$, $L = 2$, $A = 180$, and $N = 100$.   *Ans.* **72.**
13. Find H if $P = 99$, $L = 2$, $A = 85$, and $N = 190$.   *Ans.* $96\frac{9}{10}$.

CHAPTER II

COMMON FRACTIONS

DEFINITIONS AND GENERAL PROPERTIES

10. The number 6 when divided by 3 gives a quotient of 2. This may be written $\frac{6}{3} = 2$. If now we attempt to divide 6 by 7, we are unable to find the quotient as above. The division may be written $\frac{6}{7}$. This is called a **fraction.**

$\frac{1}{7}$ means that a unit is divided into 7 equal parts. The fraction $\frac{6}{7}$ indicates that 6 of the 7 equal parts are taken.

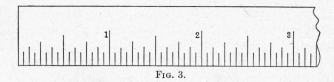

FIG. 3.

11. Definitions.—A **fraction** is an indicated division, which in a simple form expresses one or more of the equal parts into which a unit is divided.

The divisor, or the number below the line in the fraction, is called the **denominator** of the fraction. The denominator tells into how many parts the unit or the whole is divided.

The dividend, or the number above the line in the fraction, is called the **numerator** of the fraction. The numerator tells how many of the parts, into which the unit is divided, are taken.

If we are using a scale of inches and each inch is divided into halves, quarters, eighths, and sixteenths, $\frac{7}{16}$ of an inch means that the inch is divided into 16 equal parts and 7 of these parts are taken.

18

The numerator and the denominator are called **the terms** of the fraction.

The **value** of a fraction is the number that it represents.

Fractions may then be called fractional numbers; that is, there are numbers which are whole numbers and other numbers which are fractions. Thus, in speaking of $\frac{3}{4}$ of a dollar, we think of $\frac{3}{4}$ as a number just as we consider 5 a number when we say 5 dollars.

12. Mixed number.—Just as we have whole numbers and fractional numbers, so we have numbers made up of whole numbers and fractions.

Thus, we may have $2\frac{2}{3}$ which is read 2 and $\frac{2}{3}$ and means $2 + \frac{2}{3}$.
In the same way $2\frac{7}{8}$ in. means 2 in. and $\frac{7}{8}$ of an inch more.

A **mixed number** is one composed of a whole number and a fraction.

13. Proper and improper fractions.—If the fraction shows fewer parts taken than the unit is divided into, its value is evidently less than 1. If the fraction shows as many or more parts taken than the unit is divided into, the fraction is evidently equal to or greater than 1.

Thus, $\frac{6}{8}$ of an inch shows fewer parts taken than the unit, which is 1 in., is divided into. Its value is less than 1. We may speak of $\frac{8}{8}$ of an inch and here the fraction shows the same number of parts taken as the unit was divided into, and the value of the fraction is 1. Again we may speak of $\frac{11}{8}$ in., which is evidently more than 1 in. The first of these is a proper fraction and the last two are improper fractions.

A **proper fraction** is one in which the numerator is less than the denominator. An **improper fraction** is one in which the numerator is equal to or greater than the denominator.

The value of a proper fraction is always less than 1, and the value of an improper fraction is equal to or greater than 1.

Thus, $\frac{1}{2}$, $\frac{3}{4}$, $\frac{5}{8}$, and $\frac{10}{16}$ are proper fractions; and $\frac{3}{3}$, $\frac{7}{7}$, $\frac{9}{7}$, $\frac{13}{8}$, and $\frac{9}{2}$ are improper fractions.

It should be noted that an indicated division is often called a fraction, even though the division can be performed exactly, that is, without a remainder.

Thus, $\frac{12}{3}$, $\frac{24}{12}$, $\frac{44}{11}$ are fractions, though in each the indicated division may be performed.

14. Comparison of fractions.—If two fractions have equal numerators and equal denominators they are evidently equal in value.

If two fractions have *equal denominators*, the one that has the *larger numerator* is the *greater* in value.   Explain why.

Thus, of $\frac{5}{7}$ and $\frac{3}{7}$, $\frac{5}{7}$ is the larger.

If two fractions have *equal numerators*, the one that has the *larger denominator* is the *smaller* in value.   Explain why.

Thus, of $\frac{7}{8}$ and $\frac{7}{9}$, $\frac{7}{9}$ is the smaller.

If two fractions have *both numerators* and *denominators unequal*, their values cannot be compared so easily.

Thus, the values of $\frac{3}{4}$ and $\frac{5}{7}$ can be more easily compared when the fractions are changed to fractions that have the same denominator. (See Art. 20.)

15. General remarks.—In order to get the right viewpoint, it is well for the student to note that before he took up fractions he had learned to add, subtract, multiply, and divide whole numbers; here he has new numbers, fractions, to deal with.   It is now necessary to learn how to perform the fundamental operations on fractions.   They must be combined not only with other fractions but also with whole numbers.   The main thing in this chapter is to do these fundamental operations.   But to do them it is in all cases necessary to be able to change the fractional numbers in various ways, that is, to reduce to lower or higher terms, change fractions to common denominators, mixed numbers to improper fractions, and improper fractions to mixed numbers.

In order to work efficiently when making computations and using mathematics in any practical work, one must be able to work with fractions in a ready and accurate manner. To secure the necessary skill some students require more drill than others. Each should take the necessary amount of practice to secure ability to work accurately and quickly. Remember that fractions are numbers just as much as whole numbers are, but to work with them requires special rules and methods.

16. Principles.—Since a fraction is an indicated division the following principles may be stated for fractions:

(1) *Multiplying or dividing both numerator and denominator by the same number does not change the value of the fraction.*

(2) *Multiplying the numerator or dividing the denominator by a number multiplies the fraction by that number.*

(3) *Dividing the numerator or multiplying the denominator by a number divides the fraction by that number.*

17. Reduction of a whole or a mixed number to an improper fraction.

Example 1.—Reduce 5 to 6ths.
Since

$$1 = \tfrac{6}{6}, \ 5 = 5 \times \tfrac{6}{6} = \tfrac{30}{6} \quad Ans. \quad \text{By principle (2)}.$$

Example 2.—Reduce $7\tfrac{3}{5}$ to 5ths.
Since

$$1 = \tfrac{5}{5}, \ 7 = 7 \times \tfrac{5}{5} = \tfrac{35}{5}$$
$$\therefore \ 7\tfrac{3}{5} = \tfrac{35}{5} + \tfrac{3}{5} = \tfrac{38}{5} \quad Ans.$$

The three dots $\therefore$, as used above, form a symbol meaning hence or therefore.

RULE.—*To reduce a whole number to a fraction of a given denominator, first change 1 to a fraction of the given denominator and then multiply the numerator by the given whole number. With a mixed number, reduce the whole number to a fraction and then add to the numerator of this fraction the numerator of the fractional part of the mixed number.*

18. Reduction of an improper fraction to a whole or mixed number.

Example 1.—Reduce $\frac{32}{4}$ to a whole number.

$$\frac{32}{4} = 32 \div 4 = 8 \quad Ans.$$

Example 2.—Reduce $\frac{47}{9}$ to a mixed number.

$$\frac{47}{9} = 47 \div 9 = 5\frac{2}{9} \quad Ans.$$

Rule.—*To reduce an improper fraction to a whole or mixed number, perform the indicated division. The quotient is the number of units. If there is no remainder, it reduces to a whole number. If there is a remainder, it reduces to a mixed number of which the quotient is the whole number part and the remainder the numerator of the fractional part.*

EXERCISES

1. Reduce the following numbers to 5ths: 6; 10; 16; 18; 39. To 3ds. To 10ths.

2. Reduce the following mixed numbers to improper fractions: $3\frac{1}{4}$; $8\frac{2}{5}$; $10\frac{5}{8}$; $13\frac{4}{9}$; $18\frac{3}{7}$; $19\frac{1}{9}$; $23\frac{12}{13}$; $47\frac{13}{9}$.

3. Reduce the following improper fractions to whole or mixed numbers:

$\frac{19}{2}$	$\frac{62}{8}$	$\frac{514}{18}$
$\frac{20}{6}$	$\frac{73}{3}$	$\frac{9692}{574}$
$\frac{28}{8}$	$\frac{98}{17}$	$\frac{9728}{108}$
$\frac{33}{11}$	$\frac{48}{13}$	$\frac{101010}{555}$
$\frac{48}{7}$	$\frac{168}{28}$	$\frac{48795}{5420}$

19. Reduction of fractions to lowest terms.

Definition.—A fraction is in its **lowest terms** when the numerator and denominator are *prime* to each other, that is, when there is no integer that will divide both of them.

Example.—Reduce $\frac{75}{105}$ to its lowest terms.

$$\frac{75}{105} = \frac{15}{21} = \frac{5}{7} \quad Ans.$$

Since dividing both numerator and denominator by the same number does not change the value of the fraction, both terms may be divided by 5. Thus $\frac{15}{21}$ is obtained. Both terms of this fraction are divided by 3, and $\frac{5}{7}$ is obtained.

Since 5 and 7 are prime to each other, the fraction is in its lowest terms. Both terms could have been divided by 15 and the reduction made in one step.

RULE.—*To reduce a fraction to its lowest terms, divide both terms successively by their common factors, or divide by the greatest common divisor of the terms.*

EXERCISES

Reduce the following fractions to their lowest terms:

1. $\frac{5}{15}$, $\frac{4}{12}$, $\frac{15}{25}$, $\frac{8}{24}$.

2. $\frac{8}{40}$, $\frac{35}{45}$, $\frac{28}{35}$, $\frac{48}{64}$.

3. $\frac{18}{26}$, $\frac{19}{38}$, $\frac{23}{43}$, $\frac{28}{49}$.

4. $\frac{74}{100}$, $\frac{20}{155}$, $\frac{17}{51}$, $\frac{100}{225}$.

5. $\frac{448}{484}$. *Ans.* $\frac{112}{121}$.

6. $\frac{560}{630}$. *Ans.* $\frac{8}{9}$.

7. $\frac{270}{360}$. *Ans.* $\frac{3}{4}$.

8. $\frac{288}{432}$. *Ans.* $\frac{2}{3}$.

9. $\frac{120}{1680}$. *Ans.* $\frac{1}{14}$.

10. $\frac{252}{1008}$. *Ans.* $\frac{1}{4}$.

11. $\frac{231}{924}$. *Ans.* $\frac{1}{4}$.

12. $\frac{6030}{12060}$. *Ans.* $\frac{1}{2}$.

13. $\frac{3465}{4950}$. *Ans.* $\frac{7}{10}$.

14. $\frac{2222}{7777}$. *Ans.* $\frac{202}{707}$.

15. $\frac{3510}{2310}$. *Ans.* $\frac{117}{77}$.

16. $\frac{9378}{9873}$. *Ans.* $\frac{1042}{1097}$.

17. $\frac{78300}{837000}$. *Ans.* $\frac{29}{310}$.

18. $\frac{10395}{27951}$. *Ans.* $\frac{45}{121}$.

19. $\frac{10472}{11781}$. *Ans.* $\frac{8}{9}$.

20. $\frac{17703}{7266}$. *Ans.* $\frac{5901}{2422}$.

21. Reduce the following percentages to fractions in their lowest terms (the sign % takes the place of the denominator 100): 5%; 15%; 35%; 25%; 54%; 82%; 75%; 16%; 80%; 50%; 95%; 96%; 125%; 1000%; 28%.

20. Reduction of several fractions to fractions having the same denominator. *Definition.*—Fractions that have the same denominator are called **similar** fractions or fractions with a **common denominator**.

Example 1.—Reduce $\frac{1}{2}$ and $\frac{1}{3}$ to fractions which have 6 for a denominator.

The fraction $\frac{1}{2}$ may be changed to 6ths by multiplying both its terms by a number which will make the denominator 6. This will not change the value of the fraction. This multiplier is obtained by dividing 6 by 2 which gives 3.

$$\therefore \frac{1}{2} = \frac{1 \times 3}{2 \times 3} = \frac{3}{6} \quad Ans.$$

Likewise $\dfrac{1}{3} = \dfrac{1 \times 2}{3 \times 2} = \dfrac{2}{6}$ *Ans.*

Example 2.—Reduce $\frac{7}{9}$, $\frac{3}{8}$, and $\frac{5}{6}$ to 72ds.   •
Both terms of $\frac{7}{9}$ are multiplied by $72 \div 9 = 8$,
both terms of $\frac{3}{8}$ are multiplied by $72 \div 8 = 9$,
both terms of $\frac{5}{6}$ are multiplied by $72 \div 6 = 12$.

$\therefore \frac{7}{9} = \frac{56}{72}$ *Ans.*, $\frac{3}{8} = \frac{27}{72}$ *Ans.*, and $\frac{5}{6} = \frac{60}{72}$ *Ans.*

RULE.—*To reduce several fractions to fractions having a common denominator, multiply both terms of each fraction by a number found by dividing the common denominator by the denominator of that fraction.*

Fractions which have the same denominators are usually more easily compared as to size than are fractions with different denominators.   Thus, one can as readily tell which is the larger of $\frac{4}{7}$ and $\frac{6}{7}$ as he can tell how 6 apples compare with 4 apples; but $\frac{2}{7}$ and $\frac{4}{13}$ are not so easily compared in size.   However, if these are reduced to common denominators, they become $\frac{26}{91}$ and $\frac{28}{91}$ and can readily be compared in size.

21. Least common denominator.—In example 2 of the preceding article the common denominator, 72, was given. Usually the denominator is not given but we are asked to reduce the given fractions to fractions having a *least common denominator*.   When this is the case we find the least common multiple of the denominators of the given fractions, and this is the **least common denominator** (L. C. D.) for all the fractions.

Example.—Reduce $\frac{4}{9}$, $\frac{7}{12}$, and $\frac{13}{24}$ to fractions with a L. C. D.
The L. C. M. of 9, 12, and 24 is 72.   If we divide 72 by each of the given denominators we get the numbers to be used as multipliers.

$\therefore \frac{4}{9} = \frac{32}{72}$ *Ans.*, $\frac{7}{12} = \frac{42}{72}$ *Ans.*, and $\frac{13}{24} = \frac{39}{72}$ *Ans.*

Remark.—Usually the fractions dealt with have such denominators that their L. C. D. can be seen by inspection.

The student should endeavor to determine it in this way wherever possible. If it cannot be seen by inspection, a good way to find it is as follows:

RULE.—*Divide the given denominators by a prime number that will divide two or more of them, then divide the remaining numbers and the quotients by a prime number that will divide two or more of them. Continue this as long as possible. The L. C. D. is the continued product of all the divisors and the quotients or numbers left.*

Example.—Find the L. C. D. of $\frac{11}{30}$, $\frac{7}{45}$, $\frac{14}{135}$, and $\frac{13}{25}$.

Process:

$$\begin{array}{r} 5)\overline{30,\ 45,\ 135,\ 25} \\ 3)\overline{6,\quad 9,\quad 27,\quad 5} \\ 3)\overline{2,\quad 3,\quad 9,\quad 5} \\ \overline{2,\quad 1,\quad 3,\quad 5} \end{array}$$

L. C. D. $= 5 \times 3 \times 3 \times 2 \times 3 \times 5 = 1350$ *Ans.*

EXERCISES

Change as indicated:

1. $\frac{1}{2}$, $\frac{1}{3}$, and $\frac{1}{6}$ to 12ths.
Ans. $\frac{6}{12}$; $\frac{4}{12}$; $\frac{2}{12}$.

2. $\frac{1}{2}$, $\frac{1}{6}$, and $\frac{1}{7}$ to 42ds.

3. $\frac{2}{3}$, $\frac{4}{5}$, and $\frac{5}{6}$ to 30ths.

4. $\frac{3}{4}$, $\frac{5}{6}$, and $\frac{7}{8}$ to 24ths.
Ans. $\frac{21}{24}$; $\frac{20}{24}$; $\frac{18}{24}$.

5. 3, $\frac{3}{8}$, and $\frac{7}{9}$ to 72ds.

6. 4, 5, $\frac{3}{4}$, and $\frac{4}{5}$ to 20ths.

7. $\frac{2}{3}$, $\frac{3}{5}$, $\frac{5}{6}$, and $\frac{7}{15}$ to 90ths.
Ans. $\frac{60}{90}$; $\frac{54}{90}$; $\frac{75}{90}$; $\frac{42}{90}$.

8. $\frac{3}{5}$, $\frac{7}{4}$, $\frac{11}{20}$, and $\frac{15}{50}$ to 100ths.

9. $\frac{13}{16}$, $\frac{9}{11}$, $\frac{5}{8}$, and $\frac{1}{4}$ to 176ths.

10. $\frac{11}{24}$, $\frac{13}{17}$, $\frac{5}{6}$, and $\frac{2}{3}$ to 408ths.

Change the following to fractions having a L. C. D.:

11. $\frac{1}{2}$ and $\frac{3}{7}$. *Ans.* $\frac{7}{14}$; $\frac{6}{14}$.

12. $\frac{5}{6}$ and $\frac{14}{15}$. *Ans.* $\frac{25}{30}$; $\frac{28}{30}$.

13. $\frac{37}{39}$ and $\frac{11}{9}$. *Ans.* $\frac{111}{117}$; $\frac{143}{117}$.

14. $\frac{5}{7}$ and $\frac{11}{13}$. *Ans.* $\frac{65}{91}$; $\frac{77}{91}$.

15. $\frac{6}{11}$ and $\frac{13}{17}$. *Ans.* $\frac{102}{187}$; $\frac{143}{187}$.

16. $\frac{11}{17}$ and $\frac{13}{19}$. *Ans.* $\frac{209}{323}$; $\frac{221}{323}$.

17. $\frac{2}{3}$, $\frac{3}{4}$, $\frac{5}{6}$, and $\frac{77}{824}$.
Ans. $\frac{1648}{2472}$; $\frac{1854}{2472}$; $\frac{2060}{2472}$; $\frac{231}{2472}$.

18. $\frac{11}{30}$, $\frac{13}{60}$, $\frac{4}{81}$, and $\frac{35}{18}$.
Ans. $\frac{594}{1620}$; $\frac{351}{1620}$; $\frac{80}{1620}$; $\frac{3150}{1620}$.

19. $3\frac{5}{8}$, $5\frac{13}{12}$, and $7\frac{9}{40}$.
Ans. $3\frac{75}{120}$; $6\frac{10}{120}$; $7\frac{27}{120}$.

20. Change the following to 100ths and then write as per cents:

$\frac{1}{2}$	$\frac{1}{10}$	$\frac{19}{20}$	$\frac{7}{50}$
$\frac{1}{4}$	$\frac{7}{10}$	$\frac{1}{25}$	$\frac{13}{50}$
$\frac{3}{4}$	$\frac{9}{10}$	$\frac{3}{25}$	$\frac{47}{50}$
$\frac{1}{5}$	$\frac{1}{20}$	$\frac{21}{25}$	$\frac{77}{50}$
$\frac{3}{5}$	$\frac{7}{20}$	$\frac{23}{25}$	$\frac{98}{50}$
$\frac{6}{5}$	$\frac{13}{20}$	$\frac{1}{50}$	$\frac{125}{50}$

21. Which is the larger: $\frac{5}{8}$ or $\frac{11}{18}$? $\frac{2}{3}$ or $\frac{11}{16}$? $\frac{7}{11}$ or $\frac{20}{31}$?

22. A number of drills are, respectively, $\frac{5}{8}$; $\frac{11}{16}$; $\frac{1}{4}$; $\frac{19}{32}$; $\frac{23}{64}$; $\frac{13}{32}$; $\frac{27}{64}$; $\frac{1}{2}$; $\frac{17}{64}$; $\frac{3}{8}$; and $\frac{33}{64}$ inches in diameter.   Reduce the sizes to 64ths and arrange in order of size, with smallest first.

ADDITION OF FRACTIONS

22. *Example* 1.—Add $\frac{7}{12}$, $\frac{5}{12}$, and $\frac{11}{12}$.

Just as 7 apples + 5 apples + 11 apples = 23 apples, so 7 twelfths + 5 twelfths + 11 twelfths = 23 twelfths.

The work may be arranged as follows:

$$\frac{7}{12} + \frac{5}{15} + \frac{11}{12} = \frac{23}{12} = 1\frac{11}{12} \quad Ans.$$

Example 2.—Find the sum of $\frac{7}{12}$, $\frac{8}{15}$, $\frac{17}{30}$.

Here the fractions must first be reduced to fractions having a L. C. D.   The L. C. M. of 12, 15, and 30 is 60.

Then $\frac{7}{12} + \frac{8}{15} + \frac{17}{30} = \frac{35}{60} + \frac{32}{60} + \frac{34}{60} = \frac{101}{60} = 1\frac{41}{60} \quad Ans.$

Example 3.—Find the sum of $3\frac{3}{4}$, $5\frac{4}{7}$, $2\frac{9}{14}$, $7\frac{1}{2}$.

The whole numbers and the fractions may be added separately, and then these sums united.   The work may be written as here.

$$3\frac{3}{4} + 5\frac{4}{7} + 2\frac{9}{14} + 7\frac{1}{2} = 3\frac{21}{28} + 5\frac{16}{28} + 2\frac{18}{28} + 7\frac{14}{28} = 17\frac{69}{28} =$$
$$19\frac{13}{28} \quad Ans.$$

A more convenient way of writing the mixed numbers for adding, is to write them under each other, and add, similar to the method of adding whole numbers.

$$
\begin{aligned}
3\frac{3}{4} &= 3\frac{21}{28} \\
5\frac{4}{7} &= 5\frac{16}{28} \\
2\frac{9}{14} &= 2\frac{18}{28} \\
7\frac{1}{2} &= 7\frac{14}{28} \\
\hline
17\frac{69}{28} &= 19\frac{13}{28} \quad Ans.
\end{aligned}
$$

Rule.—*To add fractions that have a L. C. D., add the numerators of the fractions and place the sum over the L. C. D. If
this gives an improper fraction, it should be reduced to a whole
or mixed number. If the fractions do not have a L. C. D., first
reduce them to fractions with a L. C. D. To add mixed numbers,
add the whole numbers and fractions separately and then unite
the sums.*

EXERCISES

Add the following and express the sum in the simplest form:

1. $\frac{3}{7} + \frac{8}{7} + \frac{11}{7} + \frac{4}{7}$.

2. $\frac{2}{9} + \frac{5}{9} + \frac{19}{9} + \frac{23}{9}$.

3. $\frac{5}{14} + \frac{9}{14} + \frac{27}{14} + \frac{11}{14}$.

4. $\frac{4}{5} + \frac{5}{6} + \frac{7}{10}$.

5. $8 + \frac{7}{4} + \frac{8}{3} + \frac{7}{2}$.

6. $9\frac{1}{6} + 8\frac{5}{3} + 7$.

7. $14\frac{3}{4} + 30\frac{1}{2} + 4$.

8. $7\frac{2}{3} + 9\frac{3}{4} + 11\frac{1}{2}$.   *Ans.* $28\frac{11}{12}$.

9. $\frac{9}{10} + \frac{7}{12} + \frac{5}{4} + \frac{2}{3}$.   *Ans.* $3\frac{2}{5}$.

10. $\frac{7}{2} + \frac{2}{7} + \frac{9}{14} + \frac{11}{28}$.   *Ans.* $4\frac{23}{28}$.

11. $\frac{222}{3} + \frac{333}{2} + \frac{100}{6}$.   *Ans.* $257\frac{1}{6}$.

12. $\frac{13}{7} + \frac{23}{4} + \frac{111}{14}$.   *Ans.* $15\frac{15}{28}$.

13. $\frac{123}{3} + 231\frac{7}{32} + 321\frac{5}{8}$.   *Ans.* $593\frac{27}{32}$.

14. $5\frac{2}{3} + 71\frac{1}{4} + 82\frac{11}{12} + 5\frac{5}{6}$.   *Ans.* $166\frac{1}{6}$.

15. $\frac{2}{3} + \frac{3}{4} + \frac{5}{6} + \frac{7}{8} + \frac{11}{12} + \frac{13}{12}$.   *Ans.* $5\frac{1}{8}$.

16. $2\frac{2}{3} + 5\frac{3}{4} + 7\frac{5}{6} + 11\frac{11}{12} + 13\frac{13}{12}$.   *Ans.* $42\frac{1}{4}$.

17. $135\frac{17}{130} + 531\frac{71}{13} + 315\frac{19}{10}$.   *Ans.* $988\frac{32}{65}$.

18. $147\frac{5}{9} + 61\frac{7}{2} + \frac{22}{81} + 258 + \frac{73}{18}$.   *Ans.* $474\frac{31}{81}$.

19. $61\frac{3}{5} + 16\frac{11}{15} + 41\frac{2}{3} + 14\frac{13}{15} + 77\frac{7}{3} + 55\frac{2}{5}$.   *Ans.* $269\frac{3}{5}$.

20. $12\frac{1}{12} + 24\frac{1}{24} + 36\frac{1}{36} + 48\frac{1}{48} + 60\frac{1}{60}$.   *Ans.* $180\frac{137}{720}$.

21. $11\frac{2}{3} + 13\frac{11}{11} + 15\frac{5}{7} + 17\frac{17}{21} + 19\frac{19}{3}$.   *Ans.* $84\frac{1}{21}$.

22. A golf player drives a golf ball $253\frac{3}{4}$ yards, $189\frac{9}{10}$ yards, $33\frac{7}{8}$ yards, $5\frac{1}{2}$ yards, and $1\frac{1}{5}$ yards. Find the total number of yards that the ball was driven.   *Ans.* $484\frac{9}{40}$ yd.

23. At the end of each hour for 5 hours an airplane was noted to have flown $117\frac{5}{6}$, $166\frac{5}{8}$, $213\frac{5}{16}$, $258\frac{2}{3}$, and 160 miles, respectively. What was the total distance flown in 5 hours?   *Ans.* $916\frac{11}{16}$ miles.

24. A merchant sold to different customers $4\frac{1}{4}$, $7\frac{2}{3}$, $13\frac{5}{8}$, $15\frac{3}{4}$, and $2\frac{1}{2}$ yards of cloth, respectively. Find the total number yards sold.   *Ans.* $43\frac{19}{24}$ yd.

25. A brass rod was cut into five pieces of lengths $4\frac{1}{4}$, $3\frac{5}{8}$, $6\frac{1}{2}$, $7\frac{9}{16}$, and $2\frac{3}{4}$ inches, respectively? How long was the rod if $\frac{1}{16}$ inch was wasted in each cut.   *Ans.* $24\frac{15}{16}$ in.

26. One man can do $\frac{1}{5}$ of a certain piece of work in 1 day and a second man can do $\frac{1}{6}$ of it in 1 day. What part of the work can they both do in 1 day when working together?

27. *A* can do a piece of work in 4 days and *B* can do the same work in 3 days. What part of the work can both do in 1 day when working together?   *Ans.* $\frac{7}{12}$.

SUBTRACTION OF FRACTIONS

23. *Example* 1.—Subtract $\frac{4}{11}$ from $\frac{9}{11}$.

Since like numbers can be subtracted we can subtract 4 elevenths from 9 elevenths and have the remainder 5 elevenths. This may be written $\frac{9}{11} - \frac{4}{11} = \frac{5}{11}$.   *Ans.*

Example 2.—Subtract $\frac{7}{11}$ from $\frac{2}{3}$.

Here the fractions must first be reduced to fractions having the same denominator. It may be written

$$\frac{2}{3} - \frac{7}{11} = \frac{22}{33} - \frac{21}{33} = \frac{1}{33}.   Ans.$$

Example 3: $7\frac{2}{3} - 3\frac{3}{5} = $ what?

In this case the fractional part of the subtrahend is less than that of the minuend. The fractional parts of mixed numbers are reduced to fractions having the L. C. D., the fractional parts subtracted, and then the whole numbers.

Solution

$7\frac{2}{3} = 7\frac{10}{15}$

$3\frac{3}{5} = 3\frac{9}{15}$

Ans. $4\frac{1}{15}$

Example 4: $7\frac{1}{2} - 3\frac{2}{3} = $ what?

In this case the fractional part of the subtrahend is greater than the fractional part of the minuend. The fractions are changed to fractions having the L. C. D.

Solution

$7\frac{1}{2} = 7\frac{3}{6} = 6\frac{9}{6}$

$3\frac{2}{3} = 3\frac{4}{6} = 3\frac{4}{6}$

$\overline{\phantom{3\frac{2}{3} = 3\frac{4}{6} = }3\frac{5}{6}}$

as before. It is noticed that the fraction $\frac{4}{6}$ in the subtrahend is larger than $\frac{3}{6}$ in the minuend and so cannot be subtracted from it. To overcome this difficulty, we take 1 from the 7 and change it to sixths. This gives $6\frac{9}{6}$ instead of $7\frac{3}{6}$. The subtraction is then made as before.

RULE.—*To find the difference between two fractions having a common denominator, find the difference of the numerators and write it over the common denominator. If the fractions do not have a L. C. D., reduce them to such before subtracting. If the numbers are mixed numbers, subtract the fractional parts and then the whole numbers.*

EXERCISES

Subtract the following and give the results in the simplest forms:

1. $\frac{2}{3} - \frac{1}{3}$.   *Ans.* $\frac{1}{3}$.

2. $\frac{2}{3} - \frac{1}{6}$.   *Ans.* $\frac{1}{2}$.

3. $\frac{7}{8} - \frac{3}{4}$.   *Ans.* $\frac{1}{8}$.

4. $\frac{9}{10} - \frac{3}{5}$.   *Ans.* $\frac{3}{10}$.

5. $\frac{11}{16} - \frac{1}{2}$.   *Ans.* $\frac{3}{16}$.

6. $3\frac{1}{3} - 2\frac{2}{3}$.   *Ans.* $\frac{2}{3}$.

7. $7\frac{3}{5} - 3\frac{9}{10}$.   *Ans.* $3\frac{7}{10}$.

8. $13 - 12\frac{11}{12}$.   *Ans.* $\frac{1}{12}$.

9. $16 - 14\frac{23}{32}$.   *Ans.* $1\frac{9}{32}$.

10. $\frac{47}{18} - \frac{74}{90}$.   *Ans.* $1\frac{71}{90}$.

11. $\frac{19}{131} - \frac{2}{19}$.   *Ans.* $\frac{99}{2489}$.

12. $\frac{111}{36} - \frac{31}{72}$.   *Ans.* $2\frac{47}{72}$.

13. $6\frac{2}{9} - 2\frac{17}{90}$.   *Ans.* $4\frac{1}{30}$.

14. $77\frac{7}{8} - 11\frac{8}{9}$.   *Ans.* $65\frac{71}{72}$.

15. $18\frac{91}{100} - 15$.   *Ans.* $3\frac{91}{100}$.

16. $643\frac{3}{4}$
$346\frac{7}{8}$

17. $6491\frac{19}{33}$
$491\frac{10}{11}$

18. $320\frac{7}{8}$
$230\frac{2}{3}$

19. $309\frac{5}{6}$
$190\frac{3}{4}$

20. $189\frac{7}{17}$
$101\frac{7}{34}$

21. $171\frac{5}{8}$
$17\frac{2}{3}$

22. $164\frac{3}{10}$
$155\frac{3}{8}$

23. $2929\frac{29}{39}$
$929\frac{11}{78}$

24. $1111\frac{11}{10}$
$1001\frac{11}{30}$

Simplify the following, that is, do the operations indicated:

25. $21\frac{3}{14} + 19\frac{2}{7} - 10\frac{13}{28}$.   *Ans.* $30\frac{1}{28}$.

26. $6\frac{6}{7} + 5\frac{13}{20} - 10$.   *Ans.* $2\frac{71}{140}$.

27. $7\frac{3}{4} - \frac{4}{5} + 2\frac{17}{20}$.   *Ans.* $9\frac{4}{5}$.

28. $5\frac{12}{13} - \frac{5}{26} - 1\frac{1}{13} + 19$.   *Ans.* $23\frac{23}{26}$.

29. $13\frac{3}{5} + \frac{7}{8} - 7\frac{3}{4} - \frac{1}{8} + 2$.   *Ans.* $8\frac{3}{5}$.

30. $13 - (6\frac{7}{8} - \frac{3}{8}) + \frac{1}{2} - \frac{5}{8}$.   *Ans.* $6\frac{3}{8}$.

The parentheses indicate that the enclosed operations should be performed first. Thus, in the above, $\frac{3}{8}$ should be subtracted from $6\frac{7}{8}$ before they are subtracted from 13.

31. $\frac{7}{8} + 78 + \frac{31}{32} - (6 + 7\frac{8}{9})$.   *Ans.* $65\frac{275}{288}$.

32. $1\frac{2}{3} + 4\frac{5}{6} + 7\frac{8}{9} - (\frac{17}{18} + \frac{1}{3})$.   *Ans.* $13\frac{1}{9}$.

33. $2\frac{3}{4} + 5\frac{6}{7} - (1\frac{1}{2} - 1\frac{1}{7}) + 13\frac{1}{4}$.   *Ans.* $21\frac{1}{2}$.

34. $\frac{3}{8} + \frac{3}{7} + 21 - (\frac{5}{8} - \frac{11}{24})$.   *Ans.* $21\frac{107}{168}$.

35. $43 + (10\frac{18}{21} - 1\frac{1}{7} - \frac{3}{14})$.   *Ans.* $52\frac{1}{2}$.

Do as many of the following as you can without a pencil:

36. A man had $\frac{6}{7}$ of a debt to pay and paid $\frac{1}{2}$ of it. How much did he have left to pay?

37. A man had $\frac{3}{4}$ of a dollar and lost $\frac{7}{10}$ of it. How much money did he have left?

38. It takes $21\frac{1}{12}$ days to do a job. If a man works $10\frac{1}{2}$ days at the job; how much is left to do?

39. A man can do a piece of work in $13\frac{7}{8}$ days. A boy can do the same piece of work in $19\frac{1}{2}$ days. How much longer does it take the boy to do the work?

40. A boy owed his friend $\$2\frac{3}{4}$. One day he paid $\$\frac{4}{5}$, and another day he paid $\$\frac{3}{10}$. How much is left to pay?

41. A farmer had $36\frac{3}{4}$ dozen eggs to sell. To one store he sold $13\frac{1}{2}$ dozen; to another store he sold 16 dozen; and the remainder to a third store. How many eggs did the third store buy?

42. A dealer had 16 gallons of oil to sell. He sold $1\frac{1}{2}$ gallons to one customer, $2\frac{3}{4}$ gallons to another, $7\frac{1}{4}$ gallons to another, and the remainder to a fourth customer. How much did he sell to the fourth customer?

43. A tank full of water has two pipes opening from it, one will empty $\frac{1}{4}$ of the water in the tank in one hour and the other $\frac{7}{12}$ of it. What part will both pipes empty in 1 hour? What part remains in the tank? Suppose the two pipes run for 1 hour; the first one filling the tank, and the second emptying it, how much will be left in the tank?

44. Find the distance around Fig. 4 with dimensions as given.

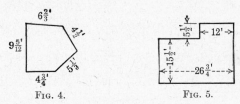

Fig. 4.   Fig. 5.

45. Find the number of feet of molding to extend around the room in Fig. 5 if no allowance is made for waste.

46. The distance from outside to outside between two holes in a steel plate is $6\frac{2}{6}$ inches. If one hole is $1\frac{1}{6}$ inches in diameter and the other is $2\frac{1}{24}$ inches in diameter, find the length of metal between the holes.

Ans. $3\frac{11}{24}$ inches.

MULTIPLICATION OF FRACTIONS

24. Multiplication of a fraction and an integer.

Example 1.—Multiply $\frac{3}{5}$ by 4.

To multiply $\frac{3}{5}$ by 4 is to find a fraction that is 4 times as large as $\frac{3}{5}$. By Art. 16, multiplying the numerator of a fraction multiplies the value of the fraction.

$$\therefore \frac{3}{5} \times 4 = \frac{3 \times 4}{5} = \frac{12}{5} = 2\frac{2}{5} \quad Ans.$$

Example 2.—Multiply 8 by $\frac{2}{3}$.

Since in finding the product of two numbers either may be used for the multiplier without changing the product,

$$\therefore 8 \times \frac{2}{3} = \frac{2}{3} \times 8 = \frac{16}{3} = 5\frac{1}{3} \quad Ans.$$

Example 3.—Multiply $\frac{3}{14}$ by 7.

Here we may use the principle that dividing the denominator multiplies the value of the fraction, or the operation may be thought of as one in cancellation.

$$\frac{3}{14} \times 7 = \frac{3}{14 \div 7} = \frac{3}{2} = 1\frac{1}{2} \quad Ans.$$
$$\text{Or } \frac{3}{14} \times 7 = \frac{3 \times 7}{14} = \frac{3}{2} = 1\frac{1}{2} \quad Ans.$$

Here the 7 and 14 are canceled.

RULE.—*To multiply a fraction by an integer or an integer by a fraction, multiply the numerator or divide the denominator of the fraction by the integer.*

The denominator should be divided when possible because then the result is in lower terms than it would be if the numerator were multiplied.

Thus, in example 3, if the numerator is multiplied, we have $\frac{3}{14} \times 7 = \frac{21}{14}$ instead of $\frac{3}{2}$ which we get when the denominator is divided.

Remark.—When a whole number is multiplied by a whole number the product is larger than the multiplicand; but whenever the multiplier is a proper fraction the product is smaller than the multiplicand. Here we cannot think of multiplication as a shortened addition.

We often write $\frac{2}{3}$ of 6 for $\frac{2}{3} \times 6$. The meaning is the same in each case.

25. Multiplication of a fraction by a fraction.

Example 1.—Multiply $\frac{2}{3}$ by $\frac{5}{7}$.

$\frac{2}{3}$ by $\frac{5}{7}$ is the same as $\frac{5}{7}$ of $\frac{2}{3}$, but $\frac{5}{7}$ of $\frac{2}{3}$ is 5 times $\frac{1}{7}$ of $\frac{2}{3}$ and $\frac{1}{7}$ of $\frac{2}{3}$ has a value $\frac{1}{7}$ as large as $\frac{2}{3}$.

By Art. 16, the value of a fraction is divided when the denominator is multiplied.

$$\therefore \frac{1}{7} \text{ of } \frac{2}{3} = \frac{2}{3 \times 7} = \frac{2}{21}$$

and

$$\frac{5}{7} \text{ of } \frac{2}{3} = 5 \text{ times } \frac{2}{21} = \frac{2 \times 5}{21} = \frac{10}{21}$$

These steps may be combined as follows:

$$\frac{2}{3} \times \frac{5}{7} = \frac{2 \times 5}{3 \times 7} = \frac{10}{21} \quad Ans.$$

Example 2.—Multiply $\frac{14}{18}$ by $\frac{3}{7}$.

$$\frac{14}{18} \times \frac{3}{7} = \frac{\overset{2}{\cancel{14}} \times \cancel{3}}{\underset{\underset{3}{6}}{\cancel{18}} \times \cancel{7}} = \frac{1}{3} \quad Ans.$$

Cancellation should be used when it will shorten the work.

Example 3.—Multiply $\frac{3}{5}$ by $\frac{9}{13}$ by $\frac{26}{27}$.

$$\frac{3}{5} \times \frac{9}{13} \times \frac{26}{27} = \frac{\cancel{3} \times \cancel{9} \times \overset{2}{\cancel{26}}}{5 \times \cancel{13} \times \underset{9}{\cancel{27}}} = \frac{2}{5} \quad Ans.$$

RULE.—*To multiply a fraction by a fraction, multiply the numerators together for the numerator of the product, and the denominators together for the denominator of the product. Cancel when convenient.*

A form like $\frac{2}{3}$ of $\frac{3}{4}$ of $\frac{7}{8}$ is often called a **compound fraction.**

26. Multiplication of mixed numbers and integers.

Example 1.—Multiply $7\frac{3}{5}$ by 6.

$$7\frac{3}{5} \times 6 = \frac{38}{5} \times 6 = \frac{228}{5} = 45\frac{3}{5} \quad Ans.$$

Example 2.—Multiply $8\frac{1}{3}$ by $3\frac{2}{5}$.

$$8\frac{1}{3} \times 3\frac{2}{5} = \frac{2\overset{5}{\cancel{5}}}{3} \times \frac{17}{\cancel{5}} = \frac{85}{3} = 28\frac{1}{3} \quad Ans.$$

RULE.—*To multiply two numbers, one or both of which are mixed numbers, reduce the mixed numbers to improper fractions and multiply as with fractions.*

The work may often be simplified by using the following methods:

Example 3.—Multiply 47 by $16\frac{4}{5}$.

Process

Explanation.—Multiply 47 by 4 and divide by 5, which is the same as multiplying 47 by $\frac{4}{5}$; this gives $37\frac{3}{5}$. Then multiply 47 by 16 in the ordinary way for multiplying whole numbers. Add these three partial products and the entire product is $789\frac{3}{5}$.

$$\begin{array}{r} 47 \\ 16\frac{4}{5} \\ \hline 5)\overline{188} \\ \hline 37\frac{3}{5} \\ 282 \\ 47 \\ \hline 789\frac{3}{5} \end{array}$$

Example 4.—Multiply $25\frac{2}{5}$ by $6\frac{1}{3}$.

Explanation: $\frac{2}{5} \times \frac{1}{3} = \frac{2}{15}$; $25 \times \frac{1}{3} = 8\frac{1}{3}$; $\frac{2}{5} \times 6 = 2\frac{2}{5}$; $25 \times 6 = 150$.

The entire product equals the sum of these partial products.

If several fractions and mixed numbers are to be multiplied together it is usually best to reduce all to fractions for then the work may be shortened by cancellation.

Process

$$\begin{array}{r} 25\frac{2}{5} \\ 6\frac{1}{3} \\ \hline \frac{2}{15} \\ 8\frac{1}{3} \\ 2\frac{2}{5} \\ 150 \\ \hline 160\frac{1}{15}. \end{array}$$

Example 5.—Find the product of $\frac{7}{9} \times 3\frac{2}{3} \times 9 \times 4\frac{2}{11} \times \frac{3}{22}$

$$\frac{7}{9} \times 3\frac{2}{3} \times 9 \times 4\frac{2}{11} \times \frac{3}{22} = \frac{7}{\cancel{9}} \times \frac{\cancel{11}}{\cancel{3}} \times \frac{\cancel{9}}{1} \times \frac{\overset{23}{\cancel{46}}}{\cancel{11}} \times \frac{\cancel{3}}{\underset{11}{\cancel{22}}} = \frac{161}{11} = 14\frac{7}{11}$$

EXERCISES

Find the product of each of the following without using a pencil when possible:

1. $\frac{3}{4} \times 5$.

2. $\frac{2}{5} \times 10$.

3. $\frac{7}{8} \times 3$.

4. $\frac{5}{9} \times 9$.

5. $\frac{7}{20} \times 5$.

6. $\frac{3}{20} \times 8$.

7. $11 \times \frac{2}{3}$.

8. $7 \times \frac{3}{4}$.

9. $12 \times \frac{3}{4}$.

10. $36 \times \frac{7}{9}$.

11. $18 \times \frac{2}{17}$.

12. $7 \times \frac{3}{13}$.

13. $21 \times \frac{5}{7}$.

14. $35 \times \frac{3}{5}$.

15. $66 \times 2\frac{1}{6}$.

16. $55 \times 4\frac{1}{5}$.

17. $63 \times 2\frac{2}{9}$.

18. $\frac{6}{7} \times \frac{7}{6}$.

19. $\frac{2}{3}$ of 9.

20. $\frac{3}{4}$ of 20.

21. $\frac{5}{9}$ of 63.

22. $\frac{9}{10}$ of 110.

23. $\frac{7}{8}$ of 100.

24. $\frac{1}{20}$ of 80.

25. $7\frac{7}{15} \times 75$.

26. $8\frac{2}{3} \times 12$.

27. $5\frac{7}{12} \times 6$.

28. What is 5 times 6 cents? 5 times 6-sevenths? 5 times $\frac{7}{8}$? $5 \times \frac{9}{10}$?

29. What is $\frac{1}{4}$ of \$12? $\frac{1}{4}$ of 8-tenths? $\frac{1}{4}$ of $\frac{8}{11}$? $\frac{1}{4} \times \frac{8}{15}$?

30. A tank is $\frac{5}{6}$ full of gas. If $\frac{1}{8}$ of this is drawn off, what part of the whole tank is drawn off? What part remains in the tank?

31. One man paid \$12,650 for a home and another man paid $\frac{4}{5}$ as much. How much did the second man pay for his home?   *Ans.* \$10,120.

32. A tank holds 300 gallons of gas. If a pipe empties $\frac{1}{4}$ of the gas in an hour, how many gallons will be left in the tank at the end of two hours?   *Ans.* 150.

33. A boy had \$48$\frac{4}{5}$. He spent $\frac{1}{2}$ of this for a suit and $\frac{1}{2}$ of the remainder for a gun. How much did he have left?   *Ans.* \$12$\frac{1}{5}$.

34. The circumference of a circle is about $3\frac{1}{7}$ times the diameter. Find the circumference of a circle if the diameter is 14 feet; if 28 feet; if $\frac{1}{2\frac{1}{2}}$ foot.
    Ans. 44 ft.; 88 ft.; $\frac{1}{7}$ ft.

35. The diagonal of a square is very nearly $1\frac{5}{12}$ the length of one side. Find the diagonal when one side is 24 inches; when 18 inches; when 840 feet.   *Ans.* 34 in.; $25\frac{1}{2}$ in.; 1190 ft.

36. If you have \$250 to spend and spend $\frac{3}{5}$ of it for camping, $\frac{1}{50}$ of it for a hat, and the remainder for traveling, how much did you spend for each?   *Ans.* \$150 camping; \$5 hat; \$95 traveling.

37. A child went to the store with \$7 and 20 cents. He spent $\frac{1}{3}$ of his money for skates, $\frac{3}{8}$ of it for a coat, and $\frac{1}{9}$ of it for a book. How much did he spend for each article? How much did he have left?
    Ans. \$2.40, skates; \$2.70, coat; 80 cents, book; \$1.30 left.

38. $\frac{35}{169} \times 13$.   *Ans.* $2\frac{9}{13}$.

39. $\frac{63}{720} \times 108$.   *Ans.* $9\frac{9}{20}$.

40. $\frac{8080}{2525} \times 625$.   *Ans.* 2000.

41. $32\frac{5}{9} \times 18$.   *Ans.* 586.

42. $618\frac{5}{6} \times 60$.   *Ans.* 37,130.

43. $569\frac{2}{5} \times 15$.   *Ans.* 8541.

44. $11\frac{2}{5} \times 12\frac{2}{5}$.   *Ans.* $141\frac{9}{25}$.

45. $12\frac{2}{3} \times 15\frac{2}{5}$.   *Ans.* $195\frac{1}{15}$.

46. $24\frac{5}{8} \times 40\frac{2}{3}$.   *Ans.* $1001\frac{5}{12}$.

47. $21\frac{5}{9} \times 81\frac{3}{7}$.   *Ans.* $1755\frac{5}{21}$.

48. $16\frac{2}{3} \times 18\frac{3}{4}$.   *Ans.* $312\frac{1}{2}$.

49. $360\frac{7}{12} \times 144\frac{3}{10}$.   *Ans.* $52,032\frac{7}{40}$.

50. Multiply $1\frac{1}{2}$ by $1\frac{1}{2}$, $2\frac{1}{2}$ by $2\frac{1}{2}$, $3\frac{1}{2}$ by $3\frac{1}{2}$, $10\frac{1}{2}$ by $10\frac{1}{2}$.

51. Can you make a rule for finding the product of two factors that are the same and end in $\frac{1}{2}$? See Art. 50 (5).

The product of two factors that are exactly alike is called the *square* of one of them. Thus, the square of $4\frac{1}{2}$ is $4\frac{1}{2} \times 4\frac{1}{2} = 20\frac{1}{4}$.

Find the square of each of the following by your rule: $7\frac{1}{2}$, $9\frac{1}{2}$, $11\frac{1}{2}$, $16\frac{1}{2}$, $12\frac{1}{2}$, $20\frac{1}{2}$, $100\frac{1}{2}$.

52. $\frac{2}{5} \times \frac{5}{6} \times \frac{9}{10}$ = what?   *Ans.* $\frac{3}{10}$.

53. $7\frac{2}{3} \times \frac{6}{7} \times \frac{3}{8} \times \frac{7}{23}$ = what?   *Ans.* $\frac{3}{4}$.

54. $\frac{2}{3} \times \frac{7}{8} \times \frac{4}{5} \times \frac{6}{7}$ = what?   *Ans.* $\frac{2}{5}$.

55. $\frac{11}{12} \times 3\frac{3}{4} \times 5\frac{1}{6} \times \frac{10}{33} \times 7\frac{4}{5}$ = what?   *Ans.* $41\frac{47}{48}$.

56. If butter is worth $24\frac{4}{5}$ cents a pound, what is $20\frac{1}{2}$ pounds worth?
Ans. $508\frac{2}{5}$ cents.

57. If a motor makes 2100 R. P. M., how many revolutions does it make in $\frac{3}{4}$ hour? In $3\frac{10}{21}$ days?
Ans. 94,500 revolutions; 10,512,000 revolutions.

58. Is it cheaper to hire a boy at $35\frac{4}{5}$ cents per hour for $10\frac{5}{8}$ hours to do a piece of work or a man at $95\frac{1}{2}$ cents per hour who can do the work in 4 hours?   *Ans.* Hire the boy, save $13 on 800 such jobs.

59. A company hires 12 men at $1 and $44\frac{1}{2}$ cents per hour, 6 at $1 and $96\frac{2}{3}$ cents per hour, and 10 girls at $90\frac{1}{5}$ cents per hour. They work 8 hours a day for $5\frac{1}{2}$ days a week. What is the weekly pay roll?
Ans. $1679.04.

60. A man drives $8\frac{1}{3}$ hours at an average rate of $38\frac{9}{10}$ miles per hour. If he keeps driving at this rate for $3\frac{1}{2}$ days of $8\frac{1}{3}$ hours per day, what will be the total distance driven?   *Ans.* $1134\frac{7}{12}$ miles.

61. A gang of men mix and place an average of $38\frac{2}{25}$ cubic yards of concrete an hour. How many cubic yards do they place in a day of $7\frac{5}{6}$ hours?   *Ans.* $304\frac{37}{150}$.

62. An alloy, used for bearings in machinery, is $\frac{24}{29}$ copper, $\frac{4}{29}$ tin, and $\frac{1}{29}$ zinc. How many pounds of each in 346 pounds of the alloy?
Ans. $286\frac{10}{29}$; $47\frac{21}{29}$; $11\frac{27}{29}$.

63. An alloy, called antifriction metal, is $\frac{37}{1000}$ copper, $\frac{111}{125}$ tin, and $\frac{3}{40}$ antimony. Find the weight of each metal in a mass of the alloy weighing 1250 pounds.   *Ans.* $46\frac{1}{4}$ lb.; 1110 lb.; $93\frac{3}{4}$ lb.

64. Find the cost of $32\frac{1}{9}$ square yards of floor covering if one square yard costs $2\frac{3}{4}$.   *Ans.* $88\frac{11}{36}$.

65. A boy had $8\frac{11}{20}$. He spent $\frac{5}{8}$ of it for carfare and lost $\frac{1}{3}$ of the remainder. How much did he spend? How much did he lose? How much did he bring home?
Ans. $5\frac{11}{32}$ spent; $1\frac{11}{160}$ lost; $2\frac{11}{8}$ brought home.

66. The velocity of sound in air at 0 degrees centigrade and 76 centimeters pressure is $1086\frac{7}{10}$ feet per second, and the velocity increases

$\frac{1}{546}$ foot per second per degree rise in temperature. Find the velocity of sound in air that is 30 degrees centigrade. The velocity of sound in water is about $4\frac{1}{3}$ times the velocity of sound in air. What is the velocity of sound in water at 30 degrees centigrade?

Ans. $1086\frac{687}{910}$ ft. per second; $4709\frac{19}{70}$ ft. per second.

67. An article costs $$16\frac{13}{20}$ to manufacture. It was found that $\frac{5}{8}$ of the cost was for labor, $\frac{3}{16}$ was for materials, and the remainder for incidentals. What was the amount of each separate cost?

Ans. $$10\frac{13}{32}$, labor cost; $$3\frac{39}{320}$, material cost; $$3\frac{39}{320}$, incidentals.

68. If a city block is $\frac{1}{8}$ mile, how far has a man walked when he has gone 5 blocks east and $11\frac{1}{2}$ blocks north?   *Ans.* $2\frac{1}{16}$ miles.

69. A company employs 165 men at $$2\frac{1}{5}$ per hour, 228 men at $$1\frac{3}{4}$ per hour, 560 men at $$1\frac{1}{20}$ per hour, 105 men at $$\frac{2}{5}$ per hour. What would be the total amount of the pay roll for 1 week of $5\frac{1}{2}$ days of $6\frac{1}{2}$ hours each?   *Ans.* $49,764.

70. Remembering that 6% (6 per cent) means $\frac{6}{100}$, find the value of the following:

(1) 6% of a note of $1200.   *Ans.* $72.

(2) 3% of the cost of a suit that costs $22.   *Ans.* 66 cents.

(3) 20% of a class of 40 students.

(4) 12% of 600 dozen eggs.

(5) 75% of a distance of 132 miles.

(6) $12\frac{1}{2}$% of a gang of 64 men.

(7) $33\frac{1}{3}$% of a tuition fee of $150.

(8) 91% of a weight of 3275 pounds.

DIVISION OF FRACTIONS

27. Division of a fraction by an integer.

Example 1.—Divide $\frac{3}{7}$ by 4.

(1) Since to divide by 4 is to find one of the 4 equal parts and to get $\frac{1}{4}$ of a number is to find one of the 4 equal parts, we have

$$\frac{3}{7} \div 4 = \frac{1}{4} \text{ of } \frac{3}{7} = \frac{3}{28} \quad Ans.$$

(2) Or, using the principle that multiplying the denominator of a fraction divides the value of the fraction, we have

$$\frac{3}{7} \div 4 = \frac{3}{7 \times 4} = \frac{3}{28} \quad Ans.$$

(3) In division of fractions, we can often divide the numerator and thus divide the fraction.

Example 2.—Divide $\frac{925}{11}$ by 25.

$$\frac{925}{11} \div 25 = \frac{925 \div 25}{11} = \frac{37}{11} = 3\frac{4}{11} \quad Ans.$$

This may be written $\frac{925}{11} \div 25 = \frac{925}{11} \times \frac{1}{25} = \frac{37}{11} = 3\frac{4}{11}.$
$$Ans.$$

RULE.—*To divide a fraction by an integer, divide the numerator, or multiply the denominator, of the fraction by the integer; or multiply the fraction by 1 over the integer.*

28. Division by a fraction.

Example 1.—Divide 6 by $\frac{2}{3}$.

(1) If we reduce 6 to thirds, we may divide the numerators, since then the numbers will both be thirds, and so be *like* numbers.

$$6 \div \frac{2}{3} = \frac{18}{3} \div \frac{2}{3} = 18 \text{ thirds} \div 2 \text{ thirds} = 9 \quad Ans.$$

(2) Since there are 3 times $\frac{1}{3}$ in 1, and $\frac{1}{2}$ as many times $\frac{2}{3}$, there are $\frac{1}{2}$ times 3, or $\frac{3}{2}$ times $\frac{2}{3}$ in 1. Now $\frac{3}{2}$ is $\frac{2}{3}$ inverted. Hence we can find how many times the fraction $\frac{2}{3}$ is contained in 1 by inverting the fraction. $\frac{2}{3}$ will be contained 6 times as many times in 6 as it is contained in 1.

$$\therefore \ 6 \div \frac{2}{3} = 6 \times \frac{3}{2} = 9 \quad Ans.$$

Definition.—The **reciprocal** of a number is 1 divided by that number. Thus, $\frac{3}{2}$ is the reciprocal of $\frac{2}{3}$. $\frac{1}{4}$ is the reciprocal of $\frac{4}{1}$ or 4.

Example 2.—Divide $\frac{49}{65}$ by $\frac{14}{39}$.

$$\frac{49}{65} \div \frac{14}{39} = \frac{49}{65} \times \frac{39}{14} = \frac{21}{10} = 2\frac{1}{10} \quad Ans.$$

Example 3.—Divide $4\frac{4}{5}$ by $3\frac{1}{3}$.

First reducing each to improper fractions, we have

$$4\frac{4}{5} \div 3\frac{1}{3} = \frac{24}{5} \div \frac{10}{3} = \frac{24}{5} \times \frac{3}{10} = \frac{36}{25} = 1\frac{11}{25} \quad Ans.$$

RULE.—*To divide a whole number or a fraction by a fraction, invert the divisor and multiply by the dividend. If either or both dividend and divisor are mixed numbers, first change to improper fractions.*

29. Special methods in division.—The work of division may often be simplified by one of the following methods:

Example 1.—Divide $56\frac{2}{3}$ by 5.

Process

Explanation: $56 \div 5 = 11$ with   a   re- $5)56\frac{2}{3}$
mainder of 1. $1\frac{2}{3} \div 5 = \frac{5}{3} \div 5 = \frac{1}{3}$. $11\frac{1}{3}$ *Ans.*

Example 2.—Divide 75 by $3\frac{2}{3}$.

Process

Explanation.—Since multiplying both $3\frac{2}{3})\ 75$
dividend and divisor by the same number $11)225$
does not change the quotient, we can $20\frac{5}{11}$ *Ans.*
multiply both by the denominator in the
divisor, then divide as before.

Example 3.—Divide $125\frac{2}{3}$ by $2\frac{3}{4}$.

Process

Explanation.—The same as in the pre- $2\frac{3}{4})125\frac{2}{3}$
ceding, multiply both by the denominator $11)502\frac{2}{3}$
in the divisor.   Then divide as in Exam-
ple 1. $45\frac{2}{33}\frac{3}{3}$ *Ans.*

EXERCISES

Divide the following, using the pencil only when necessary:

1. $\frac{5}{7} \div 10$.	**10.** $14 \div \frac{7}{8}$.	**18.** $674\frac{2}{3} \div \frac{1}{3}$.
2. $\frac{15}{14} \div 5$.	**11.** $\frac{1}{3} \div \frac{4}{3}$.	**19.** $27\frac{3}{5} \div 9$.
3. $\frac{33}{13} \div 3$.	**12.** $\frac{5}{8} \div \frac{15}{16}$.	**20.** $52\frac{1}{4} \div 4$.
4. $\frac{8}{13} \div 6$.	**13.** $\frac{3}{5} \div \frac{4}{15}$.	**21.** $84\frac{2}{3} \div 7$.
5. $\frac{24}{17} \div 8$.	**14.** $\frac{27}{32} \div \frac{3}{4}$.	**22.** $321\frac{3}{5} \div 3$.
6. $\frac{225}{11} \div 25$.	**15.** $\frac{18}{5} \div \frac{16}{5}$.	**23.** $72\frac{5}{8} \div 5$.
7. $\frac{169}{15} \div 13$.	**16.** $16\frac{1}{2} \div 4$.	**24.** $46\frac{3}{8} \div 3$.
8. $\frac{16}{3} \div 32$.	**17.** $362\frac{4}{5} \div 2$.	**25.** $159\frac{7}{8} \div 4$.
9. $13 \div \frac{1}{3}$.		

26. If the denominator of a fraction is multiplied by 4, how is the unit of the fraction changed?   How is it changed if multiplied by 8?   By 7? Illustrate with the fraction $\frac{28}{5}$.

27. If $\frac{1}{10}$ inch on a map represents 49 miles, how many miles are represented by 3 inches on the map?

28. In the blueprint of a house $\frac{1}{4}$ inch in the print represents 1 foot in the actual house.   Find the dimensions of the rooms that measure as follows: $2\frac{1}{2}$ by $2\frac{1}{2}$ inches, $4\frac{1}{8}$ by $4\frac{5}{8}$ inches, $5\frac{3}{8}$ by 6 inches, $3\frac{1}{16}$ by $4\frac{10}{32}$ inches, respectively, on the blueprint.

29. A boy wants a pair of ski shoes that costs 4\frac{1}{2}$. If he can earn $$\frac{4}{5}$ per day, how long will he need to work before he can buy the shoes? If one day is 8 hours, how many hours does he work?

30. If a golf ball costs $$\frac{3}{5}$, how many can be bought for 7\frac{1}{5}$?

In the following, x is used for the number that is to be found:

31. $\frac{3}{4} \div 8 = x$.

34. $x \div \frac{2}{5} = 5$.

37. $\frac{7}{5} \div 3 = \frac{7}{x}$.

32. $4 \div x = 8$.

35. $\frac{66}{13} \div 11 = \frac{x}{13}$.

38. $\frac{19}{3} \div 6 = \frac{19}{x}$.

33. $3\frac{1}{7} \div x = 22$.

36. $\frac{64}{9} \div \frac{1}{3} = \frac{x}{9}$.

39. $\frac{3}{5} \div x = \frac{5}{6}$.

40. If a boy can complete $\frac{3}{5}$ of his task in 30 minutes, how long will it take him to do $\frac{1}{5}$ of the task? $\frac{1}{2}$ of the task? $\frac{9}{10}$ of the task?

41. If Tom can build $\frac{1}{5}$ of a boat in 1 day and Dick can build $\frac{1}{7}$ of it in 1 day, what part of the boat can they both build in 1 day? How long will it take both boys working together to build the boat?

Ans. $\frac{12}{35}$; $2\frac{11}{12}$.

42. A boy can mow the lawn in 5 hours, and his brother can mow it in 6 hours. If they borrow another mower and both work together, how long will it take to mow the lawn? *Ans.* $2\frac{8}{11}$ hours.

43. On the roof of a factory building is a tank that holds 80 barrels of water and has two pipes opening from it. One of these pipes, when running alone, can empty the tank in 4 hours, and the other, when running alone, can empty it in 16 hours. If both of the pipes are running at the same time, how long will it take to empty the tank? Give two solutions. *Ans.* $3\frac{1}{5}$ hours.

44. Pipe number 1 can empty a tank in 4 hr. and pipe number 2 can empty it in 16 hrs. If both pipes run at the same time, how long will it take to empty the tank? See Exercise 43. *Ans.* $3\frac{1}{5}$ hours.

45. $\frac{625}{18} \div 175$. *Ans.* $\frac{25}{126}$.

46. $711 \div \frac{33}{10}$. *Ans.* $215\frac{5}{11}$.

47. $196 \div \frac{2}{3}$. *Ans.* 294.

48. $300 \div 12\frac{3}{5}$. *Ans.* $23\frac{17}{21}$.

49. $5\frac{11}{13} \div 11\frac{5}{13}$. *Ans.* $\frac{19}{37}$.

50. $13\frac{7}{8} \div 1\frac{11}{100}$. *Ans.* $12\frac{1}{2}$.

51. $23\frac{4}{5} \div 6\frac{7}{8}$. *Ans.* $3\frac{127}{275}$.

52. $5\frac{13}{14} \div 9\frac{26}{28}$. *Ans.* $\frac{83}{139}$.

53. $\frac{169}{225} \div \frac{26}{35}$. *Ans.* $1\frac{1}{90}$.

54. $20\frac{2211}{100} \div \frac{1}{100}$. *Ans.* 4211.

55. $7\frac{2}{5} \div 3\frac{4}{11}$. *Ans.* $2\frac{1}{5}$.

56. $8\frac{4}{33} \div 2\frac{110}{165}$. *Ans.* $3\frac{1}{22}$.

57. $123\frac{3}{10} \div 41\frac{1}{10}$. *Ans.* 3.

58. $910\frac{11}{12} \div 13$. *Ans.* $70\frac{11}{156}$.

In the following five exercises, reduce all to fractions, take reciprocals of each divisor, and cancel:

59. $2\frac{1}{3} \times 3\frac{1}{2} \times \frac{4}{17} \times 2\frac{7}{12} \div 20\frac{2}{3}$.

$$2\frac{1}{3} \times 3\frac{1}{2} \times \frac{4}{17} \times 2\frac{7}{12} \div 20\frac{2}{3} = \frac{7}{\cancel{3}} \times \frac{7}{2} \times \frac{\overset{2}{\cancel{4}}}{17} \times \frac{31}{12} \times \frac{3}{\underset{2}{\cancel{62}}} = \frac{49}{204} \quad Ans.$$

60. $(3\frac{1}{5} \times 5\frac{2}{9}) \div (2\frac{11}{15} \times 10\frac{8}{18})$. *Ans.* $\frac{24}{41}$.

61. $(\frac{15}{17} \times 22\frac{7}{30} \times \frac{34}{667} \times 11\frac{5}{9}) \div (1\frac{2}{3} \times 4\frac{5}{6} \times 7\frac{8}{9} \div 10\frac{11}{12})$.
Ans. $\frac{20436}{10295}$.

62. $(\frac{9}{16} \times \frac{12}{13} \times 14\frac{15}{24} \times 10\frac{26}{31}) \div (\frac{11}{56} \times 10\frac{10}{21} \times \frac{81}{112})$.
Ans. $55\frac{5707}{18755}$.

63. $(9\frac{1}{2} \div 1\frac{9}{26}) \times (12\frac{6}{5} \times 78) \div (2\frac{3}{5} \times \frac{11}{200} \div 1\frac{1}{10})$. *Ans.* 102,960.

64. Find the values of $\frac{7}{4} \div (\frac{2}{3} + \frac{5}{6}) - \frac{1}{4}$. *Ans.* $\frac{11}{12}$.

Parentheses indicate that the inclosed operations must be performed first. For example, in the above, $\frac{2}{3}$ is added to $\frac{5}{6}$ and then $\frac{7}{4}$ is divided by the sum.

65. Find the value of $3\frac{9}{2} + 7\frac{6}{5} - 1\frac{1}{10} + 80\frac{19}{20}$. *Ans.* $95\frac{11}{20}$.

66. Simplify: (a) $\dfrac{5\frac{1}{4}}{7\frac{7}{8}}$. *Ans.* $\frac{2}{3}$. (c) $\dfrac{\frac{2}{3}}{2\frac{2}{3}}$. *Ans.* $\frac{1}{4}$.

  (b) $\dfrac{\frac{17}{50}}{\frac{34}{100}}$. *Ans.* 1. (d) $\dfrac{5\frac{1}{2}}{\frac{11}{10}}$. *Ans.* 5.

67. Multiply $(5\frac{7}{3} \div \frac{11}{12})$ by $\frac{1}{4}$ of $(\frac{3}{4} + \frac{5}{6})$. *Ans.* $\frac{19}{6}$.

68. Find the value of $\dfrac{3\frac{2}{7} \times 8\frac{1}{6}}{4\frac{2}{3} \times 2\frac{1}{16}}$. *Ans.* $2\frac{26}{33}$.

Suggestion.—First, multiply $3\frac{2}{7}$ by $8\frac{1}{6}$; second, $4\frac{2}{3}$ by $2\frac{1}{16}$; then divide the first product by the second.

69. $(31\frac{3}{5} - 10\frac{2}{5} + 17\frac{17}{20}) \div (3\frac{7}{10} + 16\frac{1}{2} - \frac{99}{60}) = ?$ *Ans.* $2\frac{39}{371}$.

70. $(2\frac{2}{3} \div 4\frac{5}{6}) \div (\frac{9}{4} \times \frac{18}{51} \times 2\frac{2}{3}) = ?$ *Ans.* $\frac{68}{261}$.

71. Evaluate $\dfrac{\left(2\frac{5}{8} \div \frac{4}{\frac{5}{10}}\right) \times 2}{2 - \left(\frac{\frac{1}{2}}{4} \div 5\right)}$.

Solution.—The word evaluate means that the indicated operations should be performed and the value of the expression found. At first decide what operations must be performed first, what second, and so on. Then do these operations as simply as possible.

$$\frac{\left(2\frac{5}{8} \div \frac{4}{\frac{5}{10}}\right) \times 2}{2 - \left(\frac{\frac{1}{2}}{4} \div 5\right)} = \frac{(\frac{21}{8} \div 8) \times 2}{2 - (\frac{1}{8} \div 5)} = \frac{\frac{21}{8} \times \frac{1}{8} \times 2}{2 - \frac{1}{40}} = \frac{\frac{21}{32}}{\frac{79}{40}} = \frac{21}{32} \times \frac{40}{79} = \frac{105}{316} \quad Ans.$$

72. Evaluate $\dfrac{(4\frac{1}{3} - 3\frac{1}{6}) \div 2\frac{3}{4}}{\left(3\frac{1}{2} + \frac{1}{3}\right) \div \frac{23}{\frac{1}{6}}}$. *Ans.* $15\dfrac{3}{11}$.

73. Add $\dfrac{3}{4}$ of $\dfrac{5\frac{6}{7}}{\frac{1}{56}}$ to $9 \times \left(7\frac{1}{3} - 3\frac{2}{9}\right)$. *Ans.* 283.

74. Subtract $\frac{7}{8}$ of $\frac{2}{21}$ from $\frac{11}{12}$ of $\frac{3}{5}$. *Ans.* $\frac{7}{15}$.

75. $\frac{2}{3}$ of 4 is $\frac{5}{6}$ of what number? *Ans.* $3\frac{1}{5}$.

76. Find the simplest expression for $\dfrac{22}{3\frac{1}{2}} - \dfrac{3\frac{1}{2}}{2} + \dfrac{9\frac{2}{5}}{1\frac{3}{5}} - 1$. *Ans.* $9\dfrac{23}{56}$.

Perform the operations indicated in the following five exercises:

77. $\dfrac{\frac{2}{3} + \frac{2}{9} + \frac{13}{36} - \frac{11}{12}}{4\frac{1}{4} - 3\frac{1}{3} + 2\frac{1}{2}}$. *Ans.* $\dfrac{4}{41}$.

78. $\dfrac{(5\frac{1}{6} + 6\frac{1}{5}) \div 2\frac{12}{15}}{1\frac{1}{7} \times 2\frac{2}{7} \times 3\frac{27}{28}}$. *Ans.* $\dfrac{16,709}{42,624}$.

79. $5\frac{1}{5} \times \left(\dfrac{12\frac{3}{4} - 5\frac{11}{12}}{12\frac{11}{12} + \frac{3}{4}}\right) \times \dfrac{\frac{14}{15}}{1\frac{1}{5} \times \frac{14}{15}}$. *Ans.* $2\dfrac{1}{6}$.

80. $\dfrac{1}{2\frac{3}{4} + 5\frac{6}{7} - 1} \times \dfrac{(2\frac{2}{3} \div 4\frac{4}{6})}{1 \div 18}$. *Ans.* $1\dfrac{25}{71}$.

81. $\left[\dfrac{4\frac{1}{3}}{(5\frac{1}{4} \times 6\frac{2}{3}) + 1}\right] \times \left(\dfrac{5}{9} \div 7\frac{2}{3}\right) \times \left[\dfrac{6\frac{10}{100} \div 10}{(12 - 10\frac{1}{5}) - 1}\right]$.

Ans. $\dfrac{793}{119,232}$.

In the following four exercises, the letters stand for values as follows: $a = \frac{22}{7}$, $b = 14\frac{2}{7}$, $c = 100$, $d = 1\frac{1}{50}$. Find the values of the fractions expressed by the letters.

82. $\dfrac{(a \div b) + c}{c - d}$. *Ans.* $\dfrac{5011}{4949}$.

84. $\dfrac{c - d - (a + b)}{(c \times d) - a}$. *Ans.* $\dfrac{28,543}{34,600}$.

83. $\dfrac{a(b + c) - d}{a(b + c + d)}$. *Ans.* $\dfrac{877,501}{887,854}$.

85. $\dfrac{(c \times d) \div (7b)}{(a + b) \div b}$. *Ans.* $\dfrac{51}{61}$.

30. Problems in which fractions are used.—So far the work in fractions has been to give the necessary drill so that one may be able to manipulate fractions readily. It is thought that the number of exercises is sufficient for a student who has previously had but little work in fractions, and certainly the student who is only reviewing the subject should not work all the exercises. In either case, the student should now be able to use fractions wherever necessary in solving problems. In the following list of exercises is found a variety of problems in the solution of which fractions are involved.

EXERCISES

1. Two places A and B are 20 miles apart on a river that flows 2 miles an hour. A man who rows 4 miles an hour in still water goes from A to B and back; find the time for the journey.

Solution.—When going downstream the man will travel $4 + 2 = 6$ miles an hour. When going upstream he will travel $4 - 2 = 2$ miles an hour.

$20 \div 6 = 3\frac{1}{3} =$ number of hours to go 20 miles downstream.

$20 \div 2 = 10 =$ number of hours to go 20 miles upstream.

$3\frac{1}{3} + 10 = 13\frac{1}{3}$ hours for the journey.

2. Two places A and B are 24 miles apart on a river that flows 3 miles an hour. A man can row 5 miles an hour in still water. He goes from A to B and back. Find the time for the journey. *Ans.* 15 hr.

3. If a man can do a piece of work in 10 hours, what part of it can he do in 1 hour? in 2 hours? in 5 hours? in $\frac{1}{2}$ hour?

4. If a man can do $\frac{1}{4}$ of a piece of work in 1 hour, in how many hours can he do all the work? $\frac{3}{4}$ of the work?

5. If a man can do $\frac{5}{7}$ of a piece of work in 5 hours, in how many hours can he do all the work? $\frac{3}{7}$ of the work? $\frac{1}{2}$ of the work? $\frac{1}{49}$ of the work?

6. To put an article on the market, the material costs \$12, the labor costs \$45, the advertising costs \$4, and the transportation costs \$3. What part of the total cost is each separate cost?

Ans. $\frac{3}{16}$, materials; $\frac{45}{64}$, labor; $\frac{1}{16}$, advertising; $\frac{3}{64}$, transportation.

7. After driving his car for $22\frac{2}{10}$ months, a man noted that he had gone $19{,}264\frac{2}{10}$ miles. What was the average number of miles driven per month? *Ans.* $867\frac{84}{111}$.

8. How many articles costing \$$\frac{3}{5}$ each can be bought for \$$16\frac{1}{5}$? *Ans.* 27.

9. The height of a book case inside is 6 feet $6\frac{1}{8}$ inches. There are to be inserted six shelves each $\frac{7}{8}$ inch thick and equally spaced. Find the clearance between the shelves. *Ans.* $10\frac{23}{56}$ in.

10. A man drove his car 415 miles in 10 hours 15 minutes. How far can he drive at the same rate in $18\frac{1}{6}$ hours? *Ans.* $735\frac{65}{123}$ mi..

11. A carpenter is to cut nine shelves each 2 feet 8 inches long. There are boards 10, 12, 14, and 16 feet long from which to cut the shelves. Which boards and how many should be chosen so as to cut with the least waste? *Ans.* Use one 10 ft. and one 16 ft.; or one 12 ft. and one 14 ft.

12. Three pipes can empty a reservoir in 6, 5, and 4 hours, respectively. How long will it take them to empty it if running together?

Solution.—Since the first pipe can empty the reservoir in 6 hours, it can empty $\frac{1}{6}$ of the reservoir in 1 hour. Reasoning in the same manner, the second pipe can empty $\frac{1}{5}$ of it in 1 hour, and the third pipe $\frac{1}{4}$ of it in 1 hour. Hence, the three pipes can empty $\frac{1}{6} + \frac{1}{5} + \frac{1}{4} = \frac{37}{60}$ of the reservoir in 1 hour. To empty the whole reservoir, it will take all the pipes together, $1 \div \frac{37}{60} = 1\frac{23}{37}$ hours.

13. In the preceding exercise, how long will it take to empty the reservoir if it is full to begin with, and the first two pipes are emptying out of, and the third emptying into, the reservoir? *Ans.* $8\frac{4}{7}$ hr.

14. Pipes numbered 1, 2, and 3 open from a tank. Pipe 1 can empty the tank in 8 hours; pipe 2 can empty it in 6 hours; and pipe 3 can empty it in 2 hours. How many hours will it take to empty the tank if all three of the pipes are running at the same time? *Ans.* $1\frac{5}{19}$ hr.

15. In the previous exercise the tank is full to begin with and the first and third pipes are emptying out of, and the second emptying into the tank. How long will it take to empty the tank? *Ans.* $2\frac{2}{11}$ hr.

16. A man can paint his garage in 8 hours, and his son can paint it in 12 hours. How long will it take to paint the garage if father and son work together? What part can each do in 1 hour? What part can both working together do in 1 hour?

Ans. $4\frac{4}{5}$ hours both working together, both can do $\frac{5}{24}$ in 1 hr.

17. A father earns enough money in $60\frac{1}{2}$ days to buy a car, and his son earns enough in $88\frac{1}{2}$ days to buy the car. What part of the cost of the car can they earn in 1 day if they work together? If they work together, how long will it take them to earn enough to buy the car?

Ans. $35\frac{557}{596}$ days.

18. The plant property of a company is as follows: land $940,000; building $7,500,000; machinery, tools, and dies $16,200,000; office equipment $50,000. What part of the plant property is the land? What part is the building? What part is machinery, tools, and dies? What part is office equipment? If the total assets of the company are $33,800,000, what part of this total assets is each of the above?

Ans. Land, $\frac{94}{2469}$; building, $\frac{250}{823}$.

19. A contractor is to build a house in 40 days. If 16 men work on the house for 30 days and do $\frac{1}{2}$ of the estimated work, how many men must work for the next 10 days to finish the house on time?

Ans. 48.

20. A contractor agrees to do some grading in 15 days. If 10 men work 12 days and do only $\frac{2}{3}$ of the grading, how many men must work the remaining 3 days to finish the work? *Ans.* 20.

21. A piece of work when forged weighed $214\frac{1}{2}$ pounds. After being turned down, it weighed $156\frac{3}{4}$ pounds. The forging cost $16\frac{1}{2}$ cents per pound, and the metal turned off sold at $3\frac{1}{4}$ cents per pound. Find the net cost of the metal in the finished piece. *Ans.* 33.51\frac{9}{16}$.

22. The following rule is often used to find the weight of round steel and wrought iron: Square the diameter in inches and multiply by $\frac{8}{3}$;

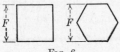

FIG. 6.

the product is the weight in pounds of 1 foot of the bar. (The product of a number multiplied by itself is the square of the number.) Using this rule, find the weights of round bars of steel of the following dimensions:

(1) Diameter $\frac{5}{8}$ inch, length $10\frac{1}{2}$ feet.   *Ans.* $10\frac{15}{16}$ pounds.

(2) Diameter $2\frac{3}{4}$ inches, length $2\frac{1}{8}$ feet.   *Ans.* $42\frac{41}{48}$ lb.

(3) Diameter $6\frac{1}{2}$ inches, length $1\frac{5}{8}$ feet.   *Ans.* $183\frac{1}{12}$ lb.

23. The distance F in Fig. 6 across the flats in a bolthead or nut, either a square or a hexagon, is equal to $1\frac{1}{2}$ times the diameter of the bolt plus $\frac{1}{8}$ inch. As a formula this is

$$F = 1\tfrac{1}{2}D + \tfrac{1}{8}$$

Test the widths across the flats in the following table taken from a manufacturer's catalogue:

Diameter of bolt D	$\frac{1}{4}$	$\frac{5}{16}$	$\frac{3}{8}$	$\frac{7}{16}$	$\frac{5}{8}$	$\frac{3}{4}$	$\frac{7}{8}$	$1\frac{1}{8}$	$1\frac{5}{8}$	$1\frac{3}{4}$	2
Width across flats F	$\frac{1}{2}$	$\frac{19}{32}$	$\frac{11}{16}$	$\frac{25}{32}$	$1\frac{1}{16}$	$1\frac{1}{4}$	$1\frac{7}{16}$	$1\frac{13}{16}$	$2\frac{9}{16}$	$2\frac{3}{4}$	$3\frac{1}{8}$

24. To change from centigrade thermometer reading to Fahrenheit, the following formula is used: $F = \frac{9}{5}C + 32$ degrees, where C is the centigrade reading and F the Fahrenheit.

(a) Find F when $C = 100°$.   *Ans.* 212 deg. F.

(b) Find F when $C = 950\frac{5}{9}°$.   *Ans.* 1743 deg. F.

25. To change a Fahrenheit thermometer reading to centigrade, the following formula is used: $C = \frac{5}{9}(F - 32°)$, where C is the centigrade reading and F the Fahrenheit.

(a) Find C when $F = 81\frac{1}{2}°$.   *Ans.* $27\frac{1}{2}$ deg. C.

(b) Find C when $F = 1760°$.   *Ans.* 960 deg. C.

26. In inspecting steam boilers, the following formula is often used:

$$t = \frac{PRF}{T \times \%}$$

where

t = thickness of plate in inches.

P = steam pressure in pounds per square inch.

R = radius of boiler in inches ($\frac{1}{2}$ of diameter).

F = factor of safety.

T = tensile strength of boiler plate in pounds.

$\%$ = percentage of strength in joints.

Find the thickness of the boiler plate which should be used for a boiler 50 inches in diameter to carry 120 pounds of pressure if the tensile strength is 60,000 pounds. Use 50% as the strength of the joints and a factor of safety of 6.   *Ans.* $\frac{3}{5}$ in.

27. Find the thickness of the boiler plate for a 72-inch boiler to carry a pressure of 90 pounds with a tensile strength of 60,000 pounds. Use 50% as the joint strength and a factor of safety of 6.

Ans. $\frac{5}{8}$ in., approx.

28. The following formula is used in finding the diameter of a steam boiler

$$D = \frac{2tT \times \%}{PF}$$

where

D = diameter of boiler in inches.

t = thickness of plate in inches.

T = tensile strength of boiler plate in pounds.

P = steam pressure in pounds per square inch.

F = factor of safety.

$\%$ = percentage of strength in joints.

Find the diameter for a steam boiler having a $\frac{5}{8}$-inch plate, allowing 50% for strength of joints and a factor of safety of 6, with a tensile strength of 60,000 pounds, and 125 pounds pressure per square inch.

Ans. 50 in.

29. A $\frac{7}{16}$-inch twist drill (Fig. 7) has a speed of 130 R. P. M. when cutting steel. How long will it take to drill through a $\frac{5}{8}$-inch plate if 120 revolutions are required to drill 1 inch?   *Ans.* $\frac{15}{16}$ min.

FIG. 7.

30. A $1\frac{3}{16}$-inch drill makes 66 R. P. M. in iron and has a feed of $\frac{1}{80}$ inch. How long will it take to drill 20 holes through a $\frac{3}{4}$-inch plate if $\frac{1}{2}$ minute is allowed for setting for each hole?   *Ans.* $28\frac{2}{11}$ min.

31. In drilling through mild steel $1\frac{5}{8}$ inches thick, a hole 1 inch in diameter is drilled in $1\frac{3}{4}$ minutes. Find the distance drilled per minute.

Ans. $\frac{13}{14}$ in.

32. A $\frac{5}{16}$-inch drill can make 320 R. P. M. in brass. If 120 turns are made to drill 1 inch, find how many holes can be drilled in a $\frac{5}{8}$-inch plate in 1 hour if one-fourth the time is used in setting the drill. *Ans.* 192.

33. A machinist drills six holes through a piece that is $2\frac{3}{4}$ inches thick. The drill is $1\frac{7}{8}$ inches in diameter and makes 154 R. P. M. with a feed of $\frac{1}{50}$ inch. How many minutes does it take if 3 minutes are used in setting for each hole?   *Ans.* $23\frac{5}{14}$.

34. A hole $6\frac{3}{4}$ inches deep is drilled with a $1\frac{1}{8}$-inch drill making 126 R. P. M. What feed is required to drill the hole in $3\frac{3}{4}$ minutes?

Ans. $\frac{1}{70}$ in.

CHAPTER III

DECIMAL FRACTIONS

31. Fractions that have 10, 100, 1000, etc. for denominators are **decimal fractions.**

Thus, $\frac{53}{100}$, $\frac{3756}{10000}$, $\frac{76}{1000}$, $\frac{4326}{1000}$ are decimal fractions.

In writing a decimal fraction it is convenient to omit the denominator, and indicate what it is by placing a point (.), called a **decimal point,** in the numerator so that there shall be as many figures to the right of this point as there are zeros in the denominator.

Thus, $\frac{53}{100}$ is written 0.53; $\frac{3756}{10000} = 0.3756$; $\frac{76}{1000} = 0.076$; $\frac{4326}{1000} = 4.326$.

In such numbers as 0.53 and 0.3765, the zero is printed at the left of the decimal point for clearness; but it is not necessary and is often omitted. The best practice uses the zero in this way before the decimal point in printed books.

It is to be noted that when there are fewer figures in the numerator than there are zeros in the denominator, zeros are added on the left of the figures to make the required number of decimal places.

From the meaning of the decimal fraction, it is seen that the misplacing of the decimal point changes the meaning greatly. For each place it is moved to the right, the value of the decimal fraction is multiplied by 10; and for each place it is moved to the left, the value is divided by 10.

Thus, 2.75 becomes 27.5 when the point is moved one place to the right, and 0.275 when the point is moved one place to the left. In the first case 2.75 is multiplied by 10, and in the second case it is divided by 10.

It is well to recall the fact that when we have a number such as 3333, where the same figure is used throughout, the values expressed by the threes vary greatly. For every place a three is moved toward the left, its value is increased ten times; and as we pass from left toward the right, each three has one-tenth the value of the one to the left of it. Since the above relations hold when we pass to the right of the place representing units, we have the following relative value of the places:

Thousands	Hundreds	Tens	Units	Decimal point	Tenths	Hundredths	Thousandths	Ten-thousandths	Hundred-thousandths	Millionths	Ten-millionths	Hundred-millionths
0	0	0	0	.	0	0	0	0	0	0	0	0

32. Historical note.—Decimal fractions were invented by *Simon Stevin* of Belgium who lived from 1548 to 1620. He first described them in his *La Disme* published in 1585. He did not use the decimal point but made use of a rather cumbersome notation. The name comes from the Latin *decem* meaning ten. The decimal point was first used by *Pitiscus* in 1612. At the present time the decimal point is printed at or near the top of the figures in books printed in England, as 2·53; and the decimal comma is used instead of the decimal point on the continent, as 2,53.

The invention of decimal fractions is considered one of the great inventions for shortening modern calculations. One would suppose that the invention of decimal fractions would be the natural outgrowth of the Hindu system of writing numbers; but it was more than a thousand years after the Hindu system had been brought to perfection before decimal fractions were invented, and it was more than a hundred years later before decimal fractions came into common use in arithmetics.

33. Reading numbers.—The whole number 23,676 is read twenty-three thousand six hundred seventy-six. It should be noticed that the word "and" is not used in reading a whole number.

A decimal is read like a whole number except that the name of the right-hand place is added.

For example, the number 0.7657 is read, seven thousand six hundred fifty-seven ten-thousandths.

When a whole number and a decimal fraction are written together the word "and" is used between the two parts in reading.

Thus, 73.2658 is read, seventy-three *and* two thousand six hundred fifty-eight ten-thousandths.

Where one person is reading numbers for another to write, it is not customary to proceed in the above manner.

Thus, the number 23.6785 may be read twenty-three, point, sixty-seven, eighty-five. Or we may read it, two, three, point, six, seven, eight, five.

EXERCISES

Read the following, pronouncing the words distinctly, and write in figures. It is of the utmost importance that the student studying alone should not form bad habits in reading numbers and other mathematical expressions. It is well to repeat all new expressions and mathematical terms aloud.

1. Three-tenths.
2. Five-hundredths.
3. Four and two-tenths.
4. Three and three-hundredths.

5. Two hundred forty-five thousandths.
6. Three hundred fifty-six ten-thousandths.
7. Two hundred fifty-six and twenty-three thousandths.
8. One hundred fifty-five millionths.
9. Four hundred fifty-six thousandths.
10. Four hundred and fifty-six thousandths.
11. Three hundred twenty-five and twenty-five ten-thousandths.

Read the following and write in words:

12. 3.24.	**16.** 23.462.	**20.** 1200.3604.
13. 2.03.	**17.** 2003.203.	**21.** 10,101.2301.
14. 17.017.	**18.** 0.4256.	**22.** 5867.0067.
15. 0.347.	**19.** 4200.0056.	**23.** 10,000.0001.

34. Reduction of a common fraction to a decimal fraction.— A decimal fraction differs from a common fraction only in having 1 with a certain number of zeros annexed for the denominator. The common fraction can then be changed to a decimal by reducing it to a fraction having 1 with zeros for a denominator.

It is evident from the method of reducing a common fraction to one with a different denominator, that a common fraction can be changed to a decimal only when its denominator is contained an exact number of times in 10,100,1000, or 10,000, etc.

Thus, $\frac{2}{5} = \frac{4}{10}$ or 0.4, and $\frac{9}{16} = \frac{5625}{10000}$ or 0.5625, but $\frac{2}{7}$ cannot be expressed exactly as a decimal because 7 is not exactly contained in 10, 100, or 1000, etc.

To reduce a common fraction to a decimal proceed as follows:

RULE.—*Annex zeros to the numerator and divide by the denominator. Place the decimal point so as to make as many decimal places in the result as there were zeros annexed.*

Thus, $\frac{7}{8} = 0.875$

$$\begin{array}{l} Process \\ 8)\overline{7.000} \\ \overline{0.875} \end{array}$$

and $\frac{2}{7} = 0.2857+$

$$\begin{array}{l} Process \\ 7)\overline{2.0000} \\ \overline{0.2857+} \end{array}$$

The sign, +, placed after the number indicates that there are still other figures if the division is carried further.

A common fraction in its lowest terms will reduce to an exact decimal only when its denominator contains no other prime factors than 2 and 5.

Thus, $\frac{3}{64}$ reduces to an exact decimal for 64 is made up of $2 \times 2 \times 2 \times 2 \times 2 \times 2$, while $\frac{7}{12}$ cannot be reduced to an exact decimal for its denominator contains the factor 3.

When a common fraction does not reduce to an exact decimal, it will always give what is known as a repeating decimal; that is, certain figures will repeat forever.

Thus, $\frac{1}{3} = 0.3333 \cdots$, where the figure 3 is the repeating part. $\frac{1}{11} = 0.090909 \cdots$, where 09 is the repeating part. $\frac{2}{7} = 0.285714285714 \cdots$, where 285714 is the repeating part.

35. Decimal fraction to common fraction.—To change a decimal fraction to a common fraction proceed as follows.

RULE.—*Replace the decimal point by a denominator having 1 and as many zeros as there are decimal places in the original fraction.* (See Art. 31.)

Thus, $2.375 = \frac{2375}{1000}$, which may be written as a mixed number $2\frac{375}{1000} = 2\frac{3}{8}$.

Many workmen, for instance, those in machine shops, use scales giving the inch divided into decimals as tenths and hundredths; other workmen, as carpenters, use scales where the inch is divided into halves, quarters, eighths, etc. In making computations, the results often appear in a decimal form. These can be used directly by those workmen using decimal scales, but they are not convenient for the carpenter and those using the ordinary carpenter's square for measurements. For this reason it is often necessary to express decimals of an inch to the nearest eighth or sixteenth of an inch.

A decimal of an inch can be reduced to the nearest number of eighths by multiplying the decimal by 8 and pointing off as many decimal places as there are in the original decimal. If the decimal part is 0.5 or more, increase the whole number part by 1; if less than 0.5, it is discarded.

If the decimal is to be reduced to sixteenths or thirty-seconds, use 16 or 32 in the place of 8 and follow the above directions.

The reasonableness of this rule should be apparent to anyone who thinks it through.

Thus, 2.375 is reduced to $2\frac{3}{8}$ by multiplying 0.375 by 8 and pointing off three places.

1.7885 is reduced to $1\frac{13}{16}$ by multiplying 0.7885 by 16, which gives 12.6160 or 13 as the nearest whole number of sixteenths.

EXERCISES

Reduce the following to decimals:

1. $\frac{7}{8}$.   **3.** $\frac{19}{20}$.   **5.** $11\frac{11}{32}$.

2. $\frac{5}{3}$.   **4.** $\frac{762}{625}$.   **6.** $505\frac{606}{2000}$.

Reduce the following to common fractions or mixed numbers in their lowest terms:

7. 0.4040.   **9.** 0.00675.   **11.** 15.0375.

8. 0.72.   **10.** 0.0101.   **12.** 510.0051.

13. Reduce the following decimals of an inch to common fractions in their lowest terms: 0.625; 0.875; 0.734375; 0.00125; 0.453125.

Ans. $\frac{5}{8}$, $\frac{7}{8}$, $\frac{47}{64}$.

14. Express the following in their simplest common fractional form: $3.04\frac{2}{9}$; $0.00\frac{2}{5}$; $0.28\frac{4}{7}$; $0.714\frac{2}{7}$; $0.484\frac{3}{8}$; $0.87\frac{1}{2}$.

Ans. $3\frac{19}{450}$; $\frac{1}{250}$; $\frac{2}{7}$; $\frac{5}{7}$; $\frac{31}{64}$; $\frac{7}{8}$.

Suggestion: $3.04\dfrac{2}{9} = \dfrac{304\frac{2}{9}}{100} = \dfrac{\frac{2738}{9}}{100} = \dfrac{2738}{900} = 3\dfrac{19}{450}$

15. Change the following per cents to their simplest common fractional forms: $87\frac{1}{2}\%$; $133\frac{1}{3}\%$; $\frac{5}{7}\%$; $185\frac{5}{7}\%$; $1.85\frac{5}{7}\%$; $2.21\frac{15}{16}\%$.

Ans. $\frac{7}{8}$; $\frac{4}{3}$; $\frac{1}{140}$; $1\frac{6}{7}$; $\frac{13}{700}$; $\frac{3551}{160000}$.

Suggestion.—Divide each by 100.

16. Tell without trial which of the following common fractions will reduce to exact decimals: $\frac{3}{7}$; $\frac{5}{32}$; $\frac{7}{15}$; $\frac{16}{49}$; $\frac{4}{25}$; $\frac{7}{35}$; $\frac{14}{125}$; $\frac{37}{250}$; $\frac{41}{56}$; $\frac{3}{8}$; $\frac{127}{625}$.

17. Change the following decimals of an inch to the nearest 64ths of an inch: 0.394; 0.709; 1.416; 1.89.   *Ans.* $\frac{25}{64}$; $\frac{45}{64}$; $1\frac{27}{64}$; $1\frac{57}{64}$.

18. Reduce the following measures to the nearest that can be read on a carpenter's square: 3.6258 in., 2.6972 in., 1.4295 in.

Ans. $3\frac{5}{8}$ in.; $2\frac{11}{16}$ in.; $1\frac{7}{16}$ in.

19. Using U. S. standard, the gage and thickness for sheet steel are as follows: No. 00, 0.34375 in.; No. 2, 0.265625 in.; No. 4, 0.234375 in.; No. 7, 0.1875 in.; No. 13, 0.09375 in.; No. 28, 0.015625 in. Find the approximate thickness of each in a common fraction of an inch having 8, 16, 32, or 64 for a denominator.   *Ans.* $\frac{11}{32}$, $\frac{17}{64}$, $\frac{15}{64}$, $\frac{3}{16}$, $\frac{3}{32}$, $\frac{1}{64}$.

20. Reduce the following fractions to decimals and note the repeating part. It may be of interest to note that the repeating part never contains more than one fewer figures than the value of the denominator of the common fraction when in its lowest terms. $\frac{7}{12}$, $\frac{5}{7}$, $\frac{3}{7}$, $\frac{2}{11}$, $\frac{6}{17}$, $\frac{4}{15}$, $\frac{1}{9}$, $\frac{2}{9}$, $\frac{3}{9}$, $\frac{4}{9}$.

36. Addition of decimals. RULE.—*Write the numbers so that the decimal points are under each other. Add as in whole numbers, and place the decimal point in the sum under the other decimal points.*

Example.—Add 36.036; 7.004; 0.00236; 427; 723.0026.

$$
\begin{array}{r}
36.036 \\
7.004 \\
0.00236 \\
427. \\
723.0026 \\
\hline
1193.04496
\end{array}
$$

37. Subtraction of decimals. RULE.—*Write the numbers so that the decimal points are under each other; subtract as in whole numbers, and place the decimal point of the remainder under the other decimal points.*

Example.—Subtract 46.8324 from 437.421.

$$
\begin{array}{r}
437.4210 \\
46.8324 \\
\hline
390.5886
\end{array}
$$

38. Multiplication of decimals. RULE.—*Multiply as in whole numbers, and point off as many decimal places in the product as the sum of the numbers of the places in the factors.*

Example 1	*Example 2*
Multiply 7.32 by 0.032.	Multiply 0.00264 by 0.000314.

$$
\begin{array}{r}
7.32 \\
0.032 \\
\hline
1464 \\
2196 \\
\hline
0.23424
\end{array}
\qquad
\begin{array}{r}
0.00264 \\
0.000314 \\
\hline
1056 \\
264 \\
792 \\
\hline
0.00000082896
\end{array}
$$

Multiplying a whole number or a decimal by 0.1 moves the decimal point one place to the left; by 0.01, two places; by 0.001, three places; etc. If it is necessary, zeros are prefixed to the multiplicand.

Thus, $32.4 \times 0.0001 = 0.00324$.

Multiplying by 10, 100, 1000, etc., moves the decimal point 1, 2, 3, etc., places to the right.

39. Division of decimals. RULE.—*If the number of decimal places in the dividend is less than the number in the divisor, annex zeros to the dividend till there are as many (or more) decimal places as in the divisor. Divide as in whole numbers, and point off as many decimal places in the quotient as there are more decimal places in the dividend than in the divisor.*

Example 1
Divide 0.4375 by 0.125.

```
0.4375|0.125
 375  | 3.5
 ―――――
 625
 625
 ―――――
```

Example 2
Divide 4365 by 0.005.

```
0.005)4365.000
      873,000
```

Dividing by 0.1, 0.01, 0.001, etc., moves the decimal point 1, 2, 3, etc., places to the right. Dividing by 10, 100, 1000, etc., moves the decimal point 1, 2, 3, etc., places to the left.

40. Accuracy of results.—Often we are asked to give a result correct to a certain number of decimal places.

Thus, if in working a problem we have a result as 47.264735, and wish to write it correct to three places, it is 47.265−. Correct to two places, it is 47.26+, correct to one place, 47.3−, correct to five places 47.26474−.

The last place taken is written one larger when the next figure to the right is 5 or more.

The part to the right of the last place taken is thrown away when the first figure of it is less than 5.

In this way we call a half or more of the last unit taken, a whole one of those units, and throw away anything less than a half.

The sign, $+$, is used to show that the accurate result is larger than the one given, that is, that something has been thrown away; and the sign, $-$, is used to show that the accurate result is smaller than the one given, that is, that something has been added.

EXERCISES

Add up and test by adding down:

1.	648.03	2.	897.1	3.	92.928
	17.895		0.989		94.987
	219.921		900.76		60.768
	97005.007		91901.359		19.657
	9.098		9876.		43.542
	100.001		101.109		76.305
	5678.91		77.007		58.143

4. $13\frac{1}{4} + 14\frac{1}{3} + 77\frac{1}{2} + 12.5 + 28.675 + 15\frac{2}{3} + \frac{1}{2} = ?$
Ans. 162.425.

5. $11\frac{1}{9} + 66\frac{2}{3} + 1\frac{2}{9} + 125.125 + 375.375 + 10\frac{1}{2} = ?$ *Ans.* 590.

6. $78.808 + 202.202 + 62\frac{1}{2} + 98\frac{3}{20} + 10\frac{3}{4} + 111.1 = ?$
Ans. 563.510.

7. $1 - 0.69897 = ?$
Ans. 0.30103.

10. $3.1416 - 1.4142 = ?$
Ans. 1.7274.

8. $2 - 1.30103 = ?$
Ans. 0.69897.

11. $1.73205 - 1.44225 = ?$
Ans. 0.28980.

9. $4.641588 - 4.626 = ?$
Ans. 0.015588.

12. $75.7575 - 55.1\frac{1}{8} = ?$
Ans. 20.6375.

13. From one hundred take seven thousandths.   *Ans.* 99.993.

14. From nine million nine take nine hundred and nine thousandths.
Ans. 8,999,108.991.

15. From one hundred and one-tenth take one and ten thousandths.
Ans. 99.09.

16. One quart liquid measure has 57.75 cubic inches, and 1 quart dry measure has 67.200625 cubic inches. How many cubic inches larger is the dry quart than the liquid quart?   *Ans.* 9.450625.

17. $3.62 \times 0.0037 = ?$
Ans. 0.013394.

20. $7.789 \times 4.924 = ?$
Ans. 38.353$+$.

18. $2.53 \times 0.00635 = ?$
Ans. 0.0160655.

21. $2.236 \times 799 = ?$
Ans. 1786.564.

19. $0.00076 \times 0.0015 = ?$
Ans. 0.00000114.

22. $2.967 \times 2.967 = ?$
Ans. 8.803$+$.

23. $8.943 \times 1\frac{2}{3} = ?$ *Ans.* 14.905.

Process: 8.943

        $1\frac{2}{3}$

    $2\ 981 = \frac{1}{3}$ of 8943

    $5\ 962 = \frac{2}{3}$ of 8943

    $8\ 943 = 1 \times 8943$

   $14.905 = 1\frac{2}{3} \times 8.943$

Why would it be best not to reduce $1\frac{2}{3}$ to a decimal before multiplying? The multiplication can be carried out readily as shown here. The process is as if the multiplicand were a whole number.

24. $2.55 \times 4\frac{3}{5} = ?$ *Ans.* 11.73.   **26.** $1\frac{2}{5} \times 1.4142 \times 61 \times 6.5 = ?$

                                            Ans. 785.02242.

25. $0.0506 \times 10\frac{1}{2} = ?$ **27.** $8.4 \times 0.0105 \times 1.0055 = ?$

            Ans. 0.5313.   *Ans.* 0.0887−.

28. $9876.5 \times 0.0011 \times 0.091 = ?$ *Ans.* 0.9886+.

29. $0.6\frac{5}{8} \times 8\frac{5}{8} \times 6.6705 = ?$ *Ans.* 38.1157−.

30. Multiply $5\frac{3}{4}$ thousandths by $5\frac{3}{4}$ hundredths.   *Ans.* 0.00033+.

31. One kilogram equals 2.2046 pounds. How many pounds in 106.5 kilograms?   *Ans.* 234.7899.

32. Multiply each of the following numbers by 0.1; 0.01; 0.001; 0.0001; 10; 100; 1000; 10,000:

         86; 78.125; 0.0021; 25.25.   (See Art. 31.)

33. $33(6.25) \div 8.25 = ?$ **34.** $90.58 \times 2.2046 = ?$

            Ans. 25.   *Ans.* 199.6927−.

35. Divide 43.769 by 4.76 correct to four decimal places.

Explanation.—Since the quotient is to be correct to four places, the dividend must contain four more decimal places than the divisor. Three zeros are added to make this number. Since the fifth decimal figure in the quotient is not less than 5, the answer is 9.1952−.

Process

     43.769000 | 4.76

       4284 | 9.1951

        929

        476

       4530

       4284

       2460

       2380

        800

        476

        324

In the next five exercises, find the result correct to four decimal places

36. $9.375 \div 4.76 = ?$ **39.** $43.45 \div 3.1416 = ?$

       Ans. 1.9695+.   *Ans.* 13.8305.

37. 89.7201 ÷ 3.276 = ?   **40.** 3.1416 ÷ 6.67 = ?

  Ans. 27.3871—.   *Ans.* 0.4710+.

38. 34.675 ÷ 4.375 = ?   **41.** Divide 324.8 by 4000.

  Ans. 7.9257 +.

Explanation.—Cancel the zeros in the divisor. Since this divides the divisor by 1000, the dividend must be divided by 1000, this is done by moving the point three places to the left.

Process

4000)0.3248

  0.0812

Perform the following divisions without a pencil:

42. 5 ÷ 200; 2 ÷ 500; 0.0099 ÷ 11,000; 1.69 ÷ 1300; 2.075 ÷ 5000; 2828 ÷ 0.014.

43. 0.1 ÷ 0.00001; 0.99 ÷ 0.0033; 0.00064 ÷ 1.6; 0.096 ÷ 12,000.

44. Divide 3.1416 × 1.25 × 50 by 0.8 × 2.75 × 3.

Explanation.—The canceling may be done as in whole numbers, paying no attention to the decimal point. When through, point off as many places in the result as the difference between the sum of those above and the sum of those below the line. Thus, in the example there are six places above and three below the line; hence, the result has three decimal places.

Process

$$\frac{3.1416 \times 1.25 \times 50}{0.8 \times 2.75 \times 3} = 29.750$$

Find the value of the following:

45. $\dfrac{37.5 \times 60.6 \times 200}{2.5 \times 303 \times 0.2}$ to units.   *Ans.* 3000.

46. $\dfrac{3.1416 \times 2.2 \times 25 \times 88}{1.25 \times 0.11 \times 40}$ to three places.   *Ans.* 2764.608.

47. $\dfrac{8.2 \times 2.5 \times 10.8 \times 0.96}{41 \times 200 \times 1.2}$ to four places.   *Ans.* 0.0216.

48. $\dfrac{0.7854 \times 60 \times 12.5 \times 5280}{231 \times 0.025 \times 300}$ to two places.   •   *Ans.* 1795.20.

49. $\dfrac{5.8 \times 8.25 \times 10.1 \times 1.732}{60.60 \times 0.25}$ to two places.   *Ans.* 55.25+.

50. For the fiscal year ending Jan. 31, 1939, the consolidated net income of a company was $23,354,363. If the company has 5,588,030 shares of capital stock, what was the net earned per share?

  Ans. $4.179.

51. A company lost $3.375 per share on 265,880 shares of stock. What was the total loss?   *Ans.* $897,345.

52. If carpet is quoted at $4.875 per square yard, what would a rug of 12 square yards cost?   *Ans.* $58.50.

53. A company hires 12 men for 87.5 cents per hour and 9 girls at 62.5 cents per hour. What would be the weekly pay roll if they all work $6\frac{1}{2}$ days of 8 hours each? *Ans.* $838.50.

54. What is the inside diameter of a pipe which is 6.84 inches outside diameter and made of iron $\frac{3}{16}$ inch thick? *Ans.* 6.465 in.

55. A cubic foot of brass is drawn in the form of a circular cylinder of diameter 0.0625 inch. How many miles long is the wire? [The volume of a cylinder is 3.1416 × (the square of its radius) × (its length); 1 mile is 5280 feet.] *Ans.* 8.889+ miles.

56. A pump delivers 16.16 gallons per stroke. What weight of water will it deliver in 120 strokes? (One gallon of water weighs 8.355 pounds.) *Ans.* 16,202.016 lb.

57. In 1 pound of phosphor bronze 0.925 is copper, 0.07 is tin, and 0.005 is phosphorus. How much of each is there in $25\frac{1}{8}$ pounds of phosphor bronze?
Ans. 23.241— lb. of copper; 1.751— lb. of tin; 0.125+ lb. of phosphorus.

58. Add $\frac{5\frac{1}{5}}{7\frac{1}{5}}$ and $\frac{4\frac{1}{4}}{8\frac{1}{8}}$, divide the result by $\left(\frac{8}{65} \div \frac{9}{10}\right)$, and change the result to a decimal. *Ans.* 9.10625.

59. From $\frac{2\,2}{7} \times 1.732$ subtract the product of 0.4343 and $3\frac{1}{3}$, divide the remainder by $\frac{2\,1}{2\,5}$, and change the result to a decimal. *Ans.* 4.756+.

60. Simplify $\dfrac{(\frac{1}{2} \div 3\frac{1}{4}) \times 0.00025}{0.075}$. *Ans.* 0.0005128+.

61. Simplify $\dfrac{(3.71 - 1.908) \times 7.03}{2.2 - \frac{7\,4}{3\,3\,3}}$. *Ans.* 6.405+.

62. Simplify $\dfrac{(201 + 2.25 \times 0.004) \div (1.0337 - 31.09 \times 0.03)}{4.5 \div 960}$.
Ans. 424,573.5—.

63. A child paid 15 cents for $\frac{1}{4}$ pound of cookies. The cookies were equally mixed from one box marked 32 cents per pound and another box marked 28 cents per pound. Explain how the error was made.

64. The length of heat waves varies from 0.810 micron to 314.00 microns. The longest heat wave is how many times as long as the shortest heat wave? *Ans.* 387.6543.

65. A car is going 1.125 miles per hour. How long will it take this car to go $468\frac{3}{4}$ miles? *Ans.* 416.666+ hours.

66. A layer of No. 8 wire, which is 0.162 inch in diameter, is wound on a pipe $24\frac{3}{8}$ inches long. How many turns of wire are wound on the pipe? *Ans.* 150+.

67. What will be the cost of 7.2 miles of railroad track if the rails weigh $42\frac{2}{3}$ pounds per foot and cost $41.75 a ton of 2000 pounds? (1 mile = 5280 feet.) *Ans.* $67,719.17.

68. An iron bar is 10.18 inches long, 3.45 inches wide, and 0.87 inch thick. Find its weight if 1 cubic inch of iron weighs 0.28 pound.

Ans. 8.56— lb.

69. Find the value of the following building material: 27,750 shingles at $4.25 per thousand; 47,256 feet of lumber at $45 per thousand; 126,450 bricks at $7.75 per thousand.   *Ans.* $3224.45.

70. It has been determined by experiment that each square foot of steam radiation will give off to the surrounding air about 3 heat units per hour per degree difference between the air in the room and the steam radiator. If the temperature of the radiator is 212 degrees and that of the room 70 degrees, how many heat units will be given off per hour on 24,000 square feet of radiating surface? How many pounds of coal will it take to make this steam if 1 pound of coal contains 10,000 heat units?

Ans. 10,224,000; 1022.4.

71. Nickel steel will stand a pull of about 90,000 pounds per square inch in cross section. What pull will a bar 1.125 inches wide and 0.875 inch thick withstand?   *Ans.* 88,593+ lb.

72. The composition of white metal as used in the Navy Department is as follows: tin 7.6 parts, copper 2.3 parts, zinc 83.3 parts, antimony 3.8 parts, and lead 30 parts. Find the number of pounds of each in 1270 pounds of white metal.

Ans. Tin, 76; copper, 23; zinc, 833; antimony, 38; lead, 300.

73. The operating budget for Chicago Girl Scouts for 1939 was $40,000. This amount was financed as follows: contributions by friends $\frac{9}{20}$, annual cooky sales $\frac{5}{20}$, scout shops $\frac{3}{20}$, community fund $\frac{3}{20}$. Find the amount of each of the four different financing methods.

Ans. $18,000, friends; $10,000, cookies; $6,000, shops; $6,000, community welfare.

74. A reamer that is 6 inches long is 1.2755 inches in diameter at the small end and 1.4375 inches at the larger end. Find the taper per foot. (The taper per foot means the decrease in diameter per foot of length.)

Ans. 0.324 in.

75. A man has $256 in a closed bank. At different times he was paid $\frac{1}{4}$, $\frac{1}{5}$, $\frac{3}{20}$, $\frac{1}{10}$, and $\frac{1}{20}$ of the total amount. How much was he paid, and how much remains to be paid?   *Ans.* $192 paid; $64 to be paid.

76. For the year 1938 the United States railroads found that 1 pound of coal would pull 8.8 tons of freight 1 mile, and that it took 14.7 pounds of coal to haul 1 passenger-train car 1 mile. At this rate, how many pounds of coal would it take to send an automobile by freight a distance of 425 miles if the automobile weighed 1.76 tons? How many pounds of coal would it take to haul 1 passenger-train car a distance of 340.2 miles (Chicago to Cleveland)?   *Ans.* 85; 5000.94.

77. On Dec. 31, 1938, there was $6,851,199,897 in circulation in the United States. If the total population of the United States was 130,-698,200 on that date, what would be the amount of money in circulation for each man, woman, and child? *Ans.* $52.42.

78. One cubic foot of water weighs 62.5 pounds; find the volume of 1 pound of water; of 23 pounds. *Ans.* 0.016 cu. ft.; 0.368 cu. ft.

79. One cubic foot of ice weighs 57.5 pounds; find the volume of 1 pound of ice; of 49.3 pounds. *Ans.* 0.0174 cu. ft.; 0.857 cu. ft.

80. How many times as heavy as ice is water? How many times as heavy as water is ice? *Ans.* 1.087 — ; 0.92.

81. There are 1,000,000 persons employed in the petroleum industry and their annual earnings are $1,500,000,000. What are the average annual earnings for each person? If this average person pays 0.3 of his earnings for rent, 0.28 of it for food, 0.12 of it for travel, and 0.08 of it for clothing; how much does he pay for each item?
Ans. $1500 each earned; $450, rent; $420, food; $180, travel; $120, cloth.

82. The following round-the-globe records have been set: In 1522, 3 years, 1 month; in 1580, 2 years 9 months; in 1588, 2 years 1 month 21 days; in 1889, 72 days 6 hours 11 minutes; in 1890, 67 days; in 1901, 60 days 13 hours; in 1913, 35 days 21 hours 36 minutes; in 1926, 28 days 14 hours 21 minutes; in 1931, 8 days 15 hours 51 minutes; in 1933, 7 days 18 hours 49 minutes; in 1938, 3 days 19 hours 8 minutes. Reduce all the records to decimals of a year, and find how many times longer it took each of the others as compared with the 1938 record. Use 360 days for a year and 30 days for a month.

83. Using United States standard, the gage and thickness for sheet steel are as follows: No. 00, 0.34375 inch; No. 2, 0.265625 inch; No. 4, 0.234375 inch; No. 7, 0.1875 inch; No. 13, 0.09375 inch; No. 28, 0.015625 inch. If No. 28 is taken as 1, find the thickness of the others. See Exercise 19, page 51.

84. The commission merchants of Chicago receive 150 carloads of Christmas trees each December. If each car holds 1800 trees and the average price per tree is $0.75 delivered to the final buyer, what gross amount will the merchants make if they pay $160,000 for the trees?
Ans. $42,500.

85. A merchant sold 56 topcoats for $24.25 apiece, 38 more at $27.50 apiece, 20 more at $33.75 apiece, and 15 more at $44.25 apiece. What was the total selling price for all the coats? *Ans.* $3741.75.

86. Number 8 (B. & S.) gage sheet steel is 0.1285 inch thick and weighs 5.22 pounds per square foot. (*a*) Find the thickness of a pile of 48 such sheets. (*b*) Find the nearest whole number of sheets to make a pile 1 foot thick.   (*c*) Find the weight of this number of sheets if each sheet has 6.25 square feet.   *Ans.* (*a*) 6.168 in.; (*b*) 93; (*c*) 3034.125 lb.

87. Number 25 (B. & S.) gage sheet copper is 0.0179 inch thick and weighs 0.811 pound per square foot.   Answer the same questions as in Exercise 86.   *Ans.* 1.0024 in.; 670; 2173.5 lb.

88. An iron chain made of $1\frac{3}{8}$-inch round iron has a breaking strain of 88,301 pounds.   If the chain weighs 17.5 pounds per foot, how long would the chain have to be to break of its own weight if suspended from one end?
Ans. 5046 ft.

89. Answer the same question as in Exercise 88 for a chain made of $\frac{5}{16}$-inch round iron, the chain weighing 0.904 pound per foot and breaking under a strain of 4794 pounds.   *Ans.* 5303 ft.

90. The formula for determining the number of threads per inch on machine screws is

$$N = \frac{6.5}{A + 0.02}$$

where
    N = the number of threads per inch.
    A = the diameter of the screw.
Compute the number of threads per inch for machine screws of the following diameters: 0.242; 0.398; 0.450; 0.563; 0.750.   In each case give the answer to the nearest whole number.   *Ans.* 25; 16; 14; 11; 8.

FURTHER APPLICATIONS

41. The remainder of this chapter is concerned with various problems involving computations in decimals.   The student should give his attention to those problems that are of interest to him.   For instance, the exercises that have to do with things electrical may not be understood because of a lack of knowledge of electricity, and should therefore be omitted. Many of the exercises make use of formulas or rules stated in mathematical symbols.   No attempt is made to derive these formulas for their derivation naturally falls in a text on that particular subject.

42. Proportions of machine screw heads. A. S. M. E. standard.—Rules are given here for determining the dimensions of the four standard heads of machine screws.

The proportions are based on and include the diameter of the screw, diameter and thickness of the head, width and depth of the slot, radius for round and fillister heads, and included angle of flat-headed screw. In the exercises for each type of screw all the other dimensions are to be computed when the

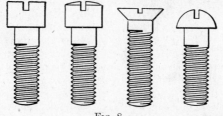

Fɪɢ. 8.

diameter of the body is given. All the dimensions are in inches.

(1) *Oval fillister-head machine screws,* Fig. 9.

A = diameter of body.

$B = 1.64A - 0.009$ = diameter of head and radius of oval.

$C = 0.66A - 0.002$ = height of side.

$D = 0.173A + 0.015$ = width of slot.

$E = \frac{1}{2}F$ = depth of slot.

$F = 0.134B + C$ = height of head.

Fɪɢ. 9.

EXERCISES

Given the values of A, find those of B, C, D, E, and F:

	A	B	C	D	E	F
1.	0.216	0.3452	0.1406	0.052	0.093	0.1868
2.	0.398	0.6437	0.2607	0.084	0.173	0.3469
3.	0.450	0.729	0.295	0.093	0.196	0.3927

Suggestion.—In Exercise 1, $A = 0.216$.

$B = 1.64A - 0.009 = 1.64 \times 0.216 - 0.009 = 0.3452.$
$C = 0.66A - 0.002 = 0.66 \times 0.216 - 0.002 = 0.1406.$

Flat fillister-head machine screws, Fig. 10.

A = diameter of body.

$B = 1.64A - 0.009$ = diameter of head.

$C = 0.66A - 0.002$ = height of head.

$D = 0.173A + 0.015$ = width of slot.

$E = \frac{1}{2}C$ = depth of slot.

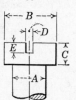

Fɪɢ. 10.

Given the values of A, find those of B, C, D, and E.

	A	B	C	D	E
4.	0.112	0.1747	0.0719	0.034	0.036
5.	0.177	0.2813	0.1148	0.046	0.057
6.	0.320	0.5158	0.2092	0.070	0.105

Flat-head machine screws, Fig. 11

A = diameter of body.

$B = 2A - 0.008$ = diameter of head.

$C = \dfrac{A - 0.008}{1.739}$ = height of head.

$D = 0.173A + 0.015$ = width of slot.

$E = \frac{1}{3}C$ = depth of slot.

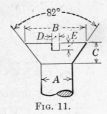
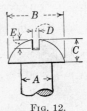

Fig. 11.   Fig. 12.

Given the values of A, find those of B, C, D, and E.

	A	B	C	D	E
7.	0.086	0.164	0.045	0.030	0.015
8.	0.242	0.476	0.135	0.057	0.045
9.	0.372	0.736	0.209	0.079	0.070

Round-head machine screws.   Fig. 12.

A = diameter of body.

$B = 1.85A - 0.005$ = diameter of head.

$C = 0.7A$ = height of head.

$D = 0.173A + 0.015$ = width of slot.

$E = \frac{1}{2}C + 0.01$ = depth of slot.

Given the values of A, find those of B, C, D, and E.

	A	B	C	D	E
10.	0.073	0.130	0.051	0.028	0.035
11.	0.164	0.298	0.115	0.043	0.067
12.	0.398	0.731	0.279	0.084	0.149

43. Computations in electricity.—The meanings of the terms used in electricity such as resistance, current, voltage, watt, etc. are quite generally known.   The student not at all familiar with these terms may omit the following exercises.   No attempt is made here to teach facts of electricity, but the formulas are given in order to give a variety of computations and to establish the meaning and use of simple formulas. These formulas will be dealt with later from the standpoint of algebra.

One should not lose sight of the fact that, in a text on mathematics, the emphasis is always on the mathematics. He should remember that in order to apply mathematics it is necessary not only to know the mathematics, but also to be familiar with the subject to which the mathematics is applied.

EXERCISES

1. The relation between the voltage, current, and resistance in an electric circuit is $I = \dfrac{E}{R}$, where E = voltage measured in volts, I = current measured in amperes, and R = resistance measured in ohms.

How many amperes current will flow through the windings of an electromagnet of 135-ohms resistance when placed across a 110-volt circuit?

Solution: $I = \dfrac{E}{R} = \dfrac{110}{135} = 0.815$ ampere

2. Four resistances connected in series across a 115-volt circuit have resistances respectively of 2.2, 3.7, 6.4, and 5.3 ohms.   Find the number of amperes of current flowing.   *Ans.* 6.534+.

Suggestion.—When resistances are connected in series they are placed one after another so that the total resistance is the sum of the individual resistances.

3. A Daniell cell has a voltage of 1.09 volts.   How many amperes current will this send through a circuit of 170-ohms resistance?

4. A lamp having a resistance of 75.2 ohms is in a 110-volt circuit. How many amperes of current does it use?

5. The power that is developed in an electric machine is expressed in watts or kilowatts.   The power is determined by the formula $P = EI$, where P is the number of watts, E is the number of volts, and I is the number of amperes.

A dynamo furnishes power for the following at 110 volts; 15 electric heaters using 5 amperes each, and 250 incandescent lamps of 0.72 ampere each.   Compute the load on the dynamo in kilowatts.   *Ans.* 28.05.

6. The work, W, done by an electric circuit is equal to the power, P, times the time, T, and is expressed by the formula: $W = PT$, where W is in watt-hours or kilowatt-hours, P is in watts or kilowatts, and T is in hours.   One kilowatt is 1000 watts.

What is the cost to run a 110-volt, 600-watt electric heater for 8 hours at 3 cents a kilowatt-hour? *Ans.* 14.4 cents.

7. What is the cost of lighting a house for 30 days at 5.5 cents a kilowatt-hour if three 40-watt, and five 60-watt lamps are used on an average of 3 hours a day? *Ans.* \$2.08.

8. A family uses a 550-watt toaster 15 minutes each day, five 40-watt and six 60-watt lamps an average of 3 hours a day, and a 660-watt electric iron 6 hours a week.   What is the total cost of 4 weeks if the rate for the first 24 kilowatt-hours is 8 cents a kilowatt-hour; for the second 24 kilowatt-hours is 6 cents; and for the remainder 3 cents?

Watt-hours

Solution.—For toaster, $550 \times \frac{1}{4} \times 28 = 3,850$

For lamps, $(5 \times 40 + 6 \times 60) \times 3 \times 28 = 47,040$

For iron, $660 \times 6 \times 4 = 15,840$

Total watts $= 66,730$

Total kilowatts $= 66.73$

24   kilowatt-hours at 8 cents $= \$1.92$

24   kilowatt-hours at 6 cents $= \$1.44$

18.73 kilowatt-hours at 3 cents $= \$0.56$

Total cost $= \$3.92$ *Ans.*

9. The heat developed in an electric circuit is given by the formula: $H = 0.24Pt$, where $H =$ heat measured in calories, $P =$ power measured in watts, and $t =$ time measured in seconds.   A calorie is the amount of heat required to raise the temperature of one gram of water one degree centigrade.

How much heat is generated in 20 minutes in an electric iron using 660 watts? *Ans.* 190,080 calories.

10. A certain electric corn-popper uses 625 watts.   If it takes 11 minutes to pop a batch of corn, how much heat is generated?   How much does it cost to pop a batch of corn at 3 cents a kilowatt-hour?
Ans. 99,000 calories; $\frac{11}{32}$ cents.

11. The formula for finding the combined or equivalent resistance of several resistances connected in parallel is

$$r = \cfrac{1}{\dfrac{1}{r_1} + \dfrac{1}{r_2} + \dfrac{1}{r_3} + \cdots}$$

where r is the combined resistance and r_1, r_2, r_3, ... are the resistances connected in parallel, all measured in ohms.

Three resistances of 6, 8, and 10 ohms respectively are connected in parallel; find the combined resistance.

Solution: $r = \dfrac{1}{\dfrac{1}{r_1} + \dfrac{1}{r_2} + \dfrac{1}{r_3}} = \dfrac{1}{\dfrac{1}{6} + \dfrac{1}{8} + \dfrac{1}{10}} = \dfrac{1}{\dfrac{47}{120}} = 2.553 +$ ohms. *Ans.*

12. Four lamps having resistances of 75, 75, 80, and 80 ohms respectively are connected in parallel; find the combined resistance.

Ans. 19.35 + ohms.

13. Three lamps each having a resistance of 75 ohms are connected in series, and three other lamps each having a resistance of 80 ohms are connected in series. These two series are connected in parallel; find the combined resistance. When resistances are connected in series, the total resistance is the sum of the several resistances.

Ans. 116.13 − ohms.

THE MICROMETER CALIPER

44. The screw is used in very many mechanical devices. Some of these will be used in illustrative problems in later chapters. The use of the screw in measuring small distances where great accuracy is required, is illustrated in the ordinary *micrometer caliper* shown in Fig. 13.

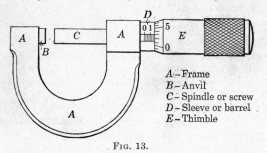

A — Frame
B — Anvil
C — Spindle or screw
D — Sleeve or barrel
E — Thimble

Fig. 13.

The object to be measured is placed between the **anvil** B and the **spindle** C. The spindle has a thread cut 40 to the inch on the part inside the **sleeve** D. The thimble E is outside the sleeve and turns the spindle. It also protects the thread from dust and wear. One complete turn of the thimble changes the opening of the micrometer by $\frac{1}{40} = 0.025$ inch, the same as the pitch of the thread.

The sleeve is graduated on a line along the length of the spindle into divisions of $\frac{1}{40}$ inch each, every fourth of which is marked 1, 2, 3, etc. The numbered marks then represent tenths of an inch.

The thimble has a beveled end that is divided into 25 equal divisions. A turn from one of these to the next evidently moves the spindle $\frac{1}{25}$ of $\frac{1}{40}$ inch or 0.001 inch.

When the end of the thimble is at 0 on the sleeve, the end of the spindle C should just touch B.

As shown in Fig. 13, the thimble has been turned away from the zero point. To determine the complete reading, (1) note the reading on the sleeve as uncovered by the thimble, which here shows 1 numbered division and 3 small divisions; (2) notice that the third division from 0 on the beveled edge of the thimble is on the center line of the spindle. From this we have:

1 numbered division	= 0.100 inch
3 small divisions, 0.025 in. each	= 0.075 inch
3 divisions on thimble	= 0.003 inch
Complete reading	= 0.178 inch

45. The vernier.—The **vernier** is a device, invented by *Pierre Vernier* (1580–1637), by which instruments can be read with a much greater degree of accuracy than is possible by mere mechanical division and subdivision. There are two kinds of verniers, known as the direct and reverse. Only the direct will be described here.

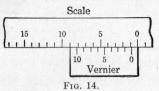

Fig. 14.

The principle is shown in its essentials in Fig. 14, which is a portion of a graduated scale, having below it a sliding scale, which is the vernier. The vernier is so divided that 10 divisions of its scale just equal 9 divisions of the graduated scale. If the 0 mark on the vernier coincides with a division, say the 0 division, as in Fig. 14, of the graduated scale, then the division 1 on the vernier stands at 0.9 on the scale; 2 on the vernier at 1.8 on the scale; and so on for the other divisions.

If the vernier be moved along so that one of its divisions, as 4 in Fig. 15, coincides with a division of the scale, then the division on the vernier just to the right or left of the coinciding division lacks 0.1 of a scale division of coinciding with a scale division. The next division of the vernier to the right or left lacks 0.2 of a scale

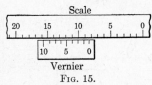

Fig. 15.

division of coinciding with a scale division, and so on. In this case, the 0 point on the vernier is removed 0.4 of a division to the left of a scale division. The reading then in Fig. 15, that is, the distance from the 0 division on the scale to the 0 division on the vernier, is 7.4. If the scale division is tenths of an inch, the reading is 0.74 inch.

If the vernier is moved to the left so that 6 on the vernier coincides with a division on the scale, then 0 on the vernier is 0.6 of a scale division to the left of a scale division.

It is evident that any number of divisions on a scale could be equal to one greater number of divisions on a vernier, and the readings could be made in a similar way. For instance, in instruments for measuring angles, if the scale divisions are to $\frac{1}{2}°$, then a vernier with 30 divisions equaling 29 divisions of the scale will give a reading of $\frac{1}{30}$ of $\frac{1}{2}°$ or $1'$ of angle.

46. Micrometer with vernier.—A micrometer caliper that reads to thousandths of an inch may be made to read to ten-thousandths of an inch by putting a vernier on the sleeve, so that 10 divisions on the vernier correspond to 9 divisions on the thimble. There are eleven parallel lines on the sleeve occupying the same space as ten lines on the thimble. These lines are numbered 0, 1, 2, 3, 4, 5, 6, 7, 8, 9, 0. The difference between one of the ten spaces on the sleeve and one of the nine spaces on the thimble is $\frac{1}{10}$ of a space on the thimble or $\frac{1}{10000}$ inch in the micrometer reading.

In Fig. 16(b), the third line from 0 on the thimble coincides with the first line on the sleeve. The next two lines do not coincide by $\frac{1}{10}$ of a space on the thimble, the next two, marked 5 and 2, are $\frac{2}{10}$ of a space apart, and so on. When the micrometer is opened the thimble is turned to the left and each space

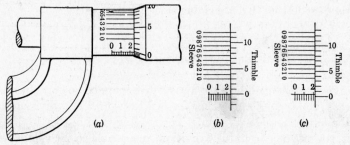

Fig. 16.

on the thimble represents $\frac{1}{1000}$ inch. Therefore, when the thimble is turned so that the lines 5 and 2 coincide, the micrometer is opened $\frac{2}{10}$ of $\frac{1}{1000}$ inch or $\frac{2}{10000}$ inch. If the thimble is turned farther, so that the line 10 coincides with the line 7 on the sleeve as in (c), the micrometer has been opened $\frac{7}{10000}$ inch.

To read a micrometer graduated to ten-thousandths, note the thousandths as usual, then observe the number of divisions on the vernier until a line is noted that coincides with a line on the thimble. If it is the second line, marked 1, add $\frac{1}{10000}$; if the third, marked 2, add $\frac{2}{10000}$, etc. Thus the reading for Fig. 16(c) is

$$0.2000 \text{ inch} + 0.0250 \text{ inch} + 0.0007 \text{ inch} = 0.2257 \text{ inch}.$$

EXERCISES

1. Find the distance the spindle advances when the thimble makes 7 full turns and 17 divisions.   *Ans.* 0.192 in.

2. What is the measurement when the reading on the sleeve is 5 graduations and on the thimble 14?   *Ans.* 0.139 in.

3. The thimble of a micrometer which is fully closed is given 4 full turns and 15 thimble graduations. What is the opening of the micrometer?   *Ans.* 0.115 in.

4. Through how many full turns and graduations must the thimble of a micrometer be turned to open the micrometer 0.178 in.?   0.213 in.? 0.287 in.?

5. What is the setting on a micrometer caliper for each of the following measurements: 0.146 in., 0.348 in., 0.467 in.?

In the following settings of a micrometer caliper with a vernier, *A* is the reading of the numbered graduation on the sleeve, *B* is the reading of the unnumbered graduation on the sleeve, *C* is the thimble reading, and *D* the vernier reading.   Determine the reading of each setting.

6. $A = 1, B = 3, C = 5, D = 6$.   *Ans.* 0.1806 in.

7. $A = 3, B = 1, C = 17, D = 3$.   *Ans.* 0.3423 in.

8. $A = 4, B = 0, C = 15, D = 7$.   *Ans.* 0.4157 in.

9. $A = 2, B = 1, C = 18, D = 8$.   *Ans.* 0.2438 in.

10. What is the setting on a micrometer caliper with a vernier for each of the following measurements: 0.2356 in., 0.1875 in., 0.6643 in., 0.4792 in.?

CHAPTER IV

SHORT METHODS AND CHECKS

47. As a rule the practical man does not use a large number of decimal places in his work. The results of all measurements are at best only an approximation of the truth. The accuracy depends upon the instruments, the method used, and upon the thing measured. All that is necessary is to be sure that the magnitude of the error is small compared with the quantity measured. It might be that in a dimension of several feet, a fraction of an inch would not make much difference; but if the dimension was small, such an error could not be allowed.

A man in practical work uses instruments that are of such accuracy as to secure measurements suitable to his purpose. A carpenter uses his square and may measure accurately to $\frac{1}{8}$ inch. A machinist may use a micrometer and secure measurements correct to 0.001 inch. If he requires measurements accurate to 0.001 inch, it is not necessary for him in a computation to carry his work to 0.00001 inch. A good rule to go by is not to calculate to more than one more decimal place than measurements are made.

48. Contracted multiplication.—When multiplying numbers that are approximate, or when only a certain degree of accuracy is desired in the product, time may be saved by using a contracted form of multiplication.

Thus, if a measurement of 3.265 inch is made, and it is to be multiplied by 3.1416, it is not necessary to multiply in the usual way, as then there would be seven decimal places, while the measurement was accurate to only three places.

If instead of multiplying in the usual manner of multiplying by the right-hand figure of the multiplier first and then proceeding with the other figures toward the left, we begin with the left-hand figure of the multiplier and then proceed with the figures toward the right, we have the following forms:

Form in full	*Contracted form*
3.265	3.265
3.1416	3.1416
9795	9795
3265	3265
13060	1306
3265	32
19590	19
10.2573240	10.2572

It is noted that one more decimal place is retained in the contracted form than is desired.

Here we have assumed that the result is correct to three decimal places, and this is so providing the measurement 3.265 is exact. Suppose, however, that this measurement is simply correct to three decimal places, could we then be sure of three places in the product? To answer the question, suppose the next figure in the measurement were 4, making 3.2654; then the product to three decimals would be 10.258. The question also arises as to the effect of an inaccuracy in 3.1416 upon the product. The following rule may be followed when we wish a desired degree of accuracy in a product obtained from two approximate factors, or in a product obtained from one exact factor and one approximate factor.

RULE.—*Take as many decimal places in an approximate factor as there are whole number digits in the other factor, plus the number of decimal places desired in the product.*

Example 1.—Multiply 1.7320508 by 1.4142136 and obtain a product correct to two decimals.

Solution.—Since both factors are approximate, the rule requires that we use three decimal places in each of the factors. The multiplication carried out in the contracted form is as shown.

This gives 2.45 as the product correct to two decimal places.

If the product was required correct to three decimals, we would use 1.7321 × 1.4142.

$$\begin{array}{r} 1.732 \\ 1.414 \\ \hline 1732 \\ 693 \\ 17 \\ 7 \\ \hline 2.449 \end{array}$$

Example 2.—Multiply the exact number 236 by the approximate number 1.7320508 and obtain a product correct to three decimal places.

Solution.—Here the rule would require six decimal places in the approximate factor, or 1.732051. The multiplication in the contracted form is as shown.

$$\begin{array}{r} 1.732051 \\ 236 \\ \hline 3464102 \\ 519615 \\ 103923 \\ \hline 408.7640 \end{array}$$

49. Contracted division.—A division involving approximate numbers, or exact numbers where an approximate result is desired, may be contracted in a manner analogous to that for multiplication. Suppose it is required to divide 0.04267 by 3.278, and secure an answer correct to four significant figures.

The division in the full and contracted forms is as follows:

```
0.042670000 | 3.278            0.042670 | 3.278
      3278  | 0.013017             3278  | 0.013017
    ───────                      ───────
      9890                         9890
      9834                         9834
    ───────                      ───────
      5600                           56
      3278                           32
    ───────                      ───────
     23220                           24
     22946                           22
    ───────                      ───────
       274                            2
```

Hence the result correct to five decimal places is 0.01302. Here the numbers are assumed to be exact.

EXERCISES

Solve the following by contracted forms:
1. 3.14159 × 3.14159 correct to four decimal places.   *Ans.* 9.8696.
2. 9,376,245 ÷ 3724 correct to the unit's place.   *Ans.* 2518.

3. 100 ÷ 3.14159 correct to 0.01. *Ans.* 31.83.

4. 87,659,734 ÷ 5467 correct to five significant figures.

Ans. 16,034.

5. 45.8636 × 26.4356 correct to five significant figures.

Ans. 1212.4.

If these numbers are approximate, can the product be found correct to two decimal places?

6. 6.234 × 0.05473 correct to four significant figures. *Ans.* 0.3412.

In order that the product shall be correct as stated is it necessary for the factor 6.234 to be exact?

7. 4.326 × 0.003457 correct to five significant figures.

Ans. 0.014955.

Can this product be accurate if either factor is approximate?

8. Find the product of the approximate numbers 2.3764 × 1.71235 correct to as many decimal places as possible.

50. Short methods in multiplication.—One who does much computing will discover various time-saving short cuts. Of course, it is hardly worth while for one who does but little computing to give time to learning contracted methods, for such methods will not be remembered unless used frequently. Numerous short methods in multiplication can be given. A few of the most useful ones are given here. If benefit is to be derived from them, they must be very carefully fixed in mind, and used whenever occasion arises.

(1) *To multiply a number by 5, 50, 500, etc., multiply by 10, 100, 1000, etc., and divide by 2.*

Why will this give the result?

Example: 7856 × 50 = 785,600 ÷ 2 = 392800. *Ans.*

Multiply the following without using the pencil:

76 × 50	432 × 50	5.5 × 5
96 × 5	768 × 500	4.35 × 50
88 × 500	47 × 50	79.2 × 5000

(2) *To multiply by 25, 250, etc., multiply by 100, 1000, etc., and divide by 4.*

Why will this give the result?

Example: 32 × 250 = 32,000 ÷ 4 = 8000. *Ans.*

Multiply the following without using the pencil:

256×25	8956×25	728×250
74.92×250	492×2500	942.3×2500

(3) *To multiply a number by* 125, *multiply by* 1000 *and divide by* 8.

Why will this give the result?

Example:

$$848 \times 125 = 848,000 \div 8 = 106,000 \quad Ans.$$

Multiply the following:

$920 \times 125 \qquad 4.76 \times 125 \qquad 72.88 \times 125 \qquad 55.5 \times 125$

(4) *To multiply a number by* $33\frac{1}{3}$, $16\frac{2}{3}$, $12\frac{1}{2}$, $8\frac{1}{3}$, *or* $6\frac{1}{4}$, *multiply by* 100 *and divide by* 3, 6, 8, 12, *or* 16.

Example:

$$84 \times 8\frac{1}{3} = 8400 \div 12 = 700 \quad Ans.$$

Multiply the following:

$48 \times 33\frac{1}{3}$	$42.6 \times 16\frac{2}{3}$	$32\frac{1}{2} \times 16\frac{2}{3}$	$41\frac{3}{5} \times 8\frac{1}{3}$
$96 \times 12\frac{1}{2}$	$3.97 \times 8\frac{1}{3}$	$33\frac{1}{4} \times 33\frac{1}{3}$	$19\frac{4}{5} \times 6\frac{1}{4}$
$72 \times 6\frac{1}{4}$	$4.76 \times 33\frac{1}{3}$	$98.76 \times 16\frac{2}{3}$	$27\frac{3}{5} \times 12\frac{1}{2}$

This rule can be used easily in multiplying a number by $37\frac{1}{2}$, $62\frac{1}{2}$, $87\frac{1}{2}$, $83\frac{1}{3}$, and other fractional parts of 100 or 1000.

Multiply the following:

$24 \times 62\frac{1}{2}$	$35 \times 333\frac{1}{3}$	$42\frac{2}{5} \times 62\frac{1}{2}$
$32 \times 87\frac{1}{2}$	$476\frac{1}{2} \times 625$	$71\frac{3}{5} \times 37\frac{1}{2}$
$36 \times 83\frac{1}{3}$	$672 \times 62\frac{1}{2}$	$47\frac{3}{5} \times 333\frac{1}{3}$
$64 \times 37\frac{1}{2}$	$272 \times 87\frac{1}{2}$	$36\frac{2}{5} \times 83\frac{1}{3}$

(5) *To multiply a number ending in* $\frac{1}{2}$, *as* $2\frac{1}{2}$, $4\frac{1}{2}$, $11\frac{1}{2}$, *by itself, multiply the whole number by the whole number plus* 1 *and add* $\frac{1}{4}$ *to the product.*

Examples:

$$8\tfrac{1}{2} \times 8\tfrac{1}{2} = 8 \times 9 + \tfrac{1}{4} = 72\tfrac{1}{4} \quad Ans.$$
$$11\tfrac{1}{2} \times 11\tfrac{1}{2} = 11 \times 12 + \tfrac{1}{4} = 132\tfrac{1}{4} \quad Ans.$$

The reason may be shown as follows:

$$3\tfrac{1}{2} \times 3\tfrac{1}{2} = 3 \times 3 + 3 \times \tfrac{1}{2} + \tfrac{1}{2} \times 3 + \tfrac{1}{2} \times \tfrac{1}{2}.$$
But $3 \times \tfrac{1}{2} + \tfrac{1}{2} \times 3 = 1 \times 3$ and $\tfrac{1}{2} \times \tfrac{1}{2} = \tfrac{1}{4}.$
Hence, $3\tfrac{1}{2} \times 3\tfrac{1}{2} = 3 \times 4 + \tfrac{1}{4} = 12\tfrac{1}{4}.$

Multiply the following:

$5\tfrac{1}{2} \times 5\tfrac{1}{2}$	$12\tfrac{1}{2} \times 12\tfrac{1}{2}$	$20\tfrac{1}{2} \times 20\tfrac{1}{2}$	$18\tfrac{1}{2} \times 18\tfrac{1}{2}$
$7\tfrac{1}{2} \times 7\tfrac{1}{2}$	$14\tfrac{1}{2} \times 14\tfrac{1}{2}$	$25\tfrac{1}{2} \times 25\tfrac{1}{2}$	$150\tfrac{1}{2} \times 150\tfrac{1}{2}$
$9\tfrac{1}{2} \times 9\tfrac{1}{2}$	$16\tfrac{1}{2} \times 16\tfrac{1}{2}$	$40\tfrac{1}{2} \times 40\tfrac{1}{2}$	$59\tfrac{1}{2} \times 59\tfrac{1}{2}$

Putting in the decimal form, we have

$$8\tfrac{1}{2} \times 8\tfrac{1}{2} = 8.5 \times 8.5 = 72.25$$

Now removing the decimal point, we have

$$85 \times 85 = 7225$$

Multiply the following:

7.5×7.5	135×135	505×505
12.5×12.5	95×95	615×615
11.5×11.5	155×155	925×925

51. Short methods in division.—By using the inverse operations to those given in the rules for the multiplications in the preceding article, numerous divisions can be readily performed.

(1) *To divide by* $3\tfrac{1}{3}$, *divide by* 10 *and multiply by* 3.

(2) *To divide by* $33\tfrac{1}{3}$, *divide by* 100 *and multiply by* 3.

(3) *To divide by* $333\tfrac{1}{3}$, *divide by* 1000 *and multiply by* 3.

(4) *To divide by* $16\tfrac{2}{3}$, *divide by* 100 *and multiply by* 6.

(5) *To divide by* $12\tfrac{1}{2}$, *divide by* 100 *and multiply by* 8.

(6) *To divide by* $8\tfrac{1}{3}$, *divide by* 100 *and multiply by* 12.

(7) *To divide by* 25, *divide by* 100 *and multiply by* 4.

(8) *To divide by* 125, *divide by* 1000 *and multiply by* 8.

Similar rules can readily be made for dividing by 250, $6\tfrac{1}{4}$, $166\tfrac{2}{3}$, $14\tfrac{2}{7}$, $11\tfrac{1}{9}$, etc.

Examples:
$$84 \div 12\tfrac{1}{2} = (84 \div 100) \times 8 = 6.72$$
$$9 \div 16\tfrac{2}{3} = (9 \div 100) \times 6 = 0.54$$
$$32 \div 125 = (32 \div 1000) \times 8 = 0.256$$
$$450 \div 6\tfrac{1}{4} = (450 \div 100) \times 16 = 72$$
$$23 \div 250 = (23 \div 1000) \times 4 = 0.092$$

The multiplications in such problems can usually be performed without using the pencil.

Divide the following:

$800 \div 12\tfrac{1}{2}$	$492 \div 16\tfrac{2}{3}$	$720 \div 8\tfrac{1}{3}$
$37.6 \div 250$	$923 \div 33\tfrac{1}{3}$	$783 \div 12\tfrac{1}{2}$
$7.62 \div 12\tfrac{1}{2}$	$436 \div 3\tfrac{1}{3}$	$7.29 \div 125$
$297 \div 333\tfrac{1}{3}$	$43.9 \div 250$	$8927 \div 166\tfrac{2}{3}$

52. Checking.—No check can be made that is absolutely certain to detect an error, but there are many very useful devices for checking the accuracy of the work.

(1) *Addition.*—A simple way to check addition is to re-add, taking the figures in some other order. Add first up and then down, is very satisfactory.

(2) *Subtraction.*—An error in a subtraction will generally be detected by adding the remainder to the subtrahend. If this gives the minuend the work is correct.

Example:

$$
\begin{array}{ll}
37249 & \textit{Minuend} \\
18496 & \textit{Subtrahend} \\
\hline
18753 & \textit{Remainder} \\
\hline
37249 & = \textit{subtrahend} + \textit{remainder}
\end{array}
$$

(3) *Multiplication.*—A good way to check multiplication is to interchange the multiplicand and multiplier and multiply again.

A very convenient and quick method is to proceed as follows:

(*a*) Add the digits in the multiplicand. If this sum has more than one digit, add these. Continue till a number of one digit is found.

(b) Add the digits of the multiplier as directed in (a).

(c) Multiply together the numbers obtained in (a) and (b), and add digits till a number of one digit is found.

(d) Add digits of product as directed in (a).

(e) Compare results of (c) and (d). If they are the same the work checks.

Check.—(a) Adding digits in multiplicand, $3 + 4 + 7 + 6 + 8 = 28$, then adding these, $2 + 8 = 10$ and $1 + 0 = 1$.

(b) Adding digits in multiplier, gives 6.

(c) Multiplying results in (a) and (b), gives $1 \times 6 = 6$.

(d) Adding digits in product, gives 6.

(e) The multiplication is checked since the results for (c) and (d) are equal.

Example

```
34768  Multiplicand
  492  Multiplier
─────
69536
312912
139072
────────
17105856  Product
```

(4) *Division.*—Division can be checked by multiplying the divisor by the quotient and then adding the remainder. The result should be the dividend.

A quicker way to check is to add the digits as directed for checking multiplication: (a) the dividend; (b) the divisor; (c) the quotient; (d) the remainder. Multiply the results in (b) and (c), add the result in (d), and then add the digits in this result which should give the same as the result of (a) if the work is correct.

Check

Adding digits:

(a) for dividend gives 9,

(b) for divisor gives 8,

(c) for quotient gives 2,

(d) for remainder gives 2.

$$8 \times 2 + 2 = 18$$

Sum of digits of $18 = 9$, which is the same as the sum in (a) and so checks the work.

Example

```
Dividend 4923567 | 476  Divisor
          476    | 10343  Quotient
         ─────
         1635
         1428
         ─────
          2076
          1904
         ─────
          1727
          1428
         ─────
           299  Remainder
```

The preceding rules apply as well to decimals as to whole numbers, but do not check the position of the decimal point.

EXERCISES

First multiply then divide the following and check as directed in the preceding article:

1. 4,356,785 by 9725.
2. 73,872 by 937.
3. 37,653 by 3647.
4. 30,987 by 4098.
5. 75.859 by 746.

6. 546.89 by 37.94.
7. 1294 by 5.48.
8. 46,378 by 9.0489.
9. 50.05678 by 0.193.
10. 29.29087 by 3.1416.

CHAPTER V

WEIGHTS AND MEASURES

53. Everyone comes in contact with and makes use of the weights and measures in common use in this country, and is more or less familiar with the metric system. The practical man often finds it convenient if not necessary to be able to change a measurement in the common system to an equivalent in the metric system or *vice versa*. Of course, the ideal would be to have but one system of weights and measures for all countries. Then trade could be carried on with the least trouble and all intercourse would be greatly facilitated.

54. Historical note.—*Simon Stevin*, the inventor of decimal fractions, was very enthusiastic not only over decimal fractions, but also over the decimal divisions of weights and measures. He said that he considered it the duty of governments to establish a decimal system of weights and measures. He little knew that two hundred years would elapse before the origin of the metric system; and that now, three centuries and a half later, the two great English-speaking nations would still be using the old system with all its adherent waste in time and labor.

The Constitution of the United States says that Congress shall have power to fix the standards of weights and measures. From a study of weights and measures in our country, however, it is seen that a legal standard, the troy pound, has been established for the use of the mint; but that beyond that, our weights and measures in ordinary use rest on custom only with indirect legislative recognition. It is seen that the metric weights and measures are made legal by direct legislative permission, and that standards of both systems have been equally furnished by the Government to the several states; that the customary system has been adopted by the Treasury Department for use in the custom houses, but that the same department has by formal order adopted the metric standards as "fundamental standards" from which measures of the customary system shall be derived.[1]

The terms "kilowatts," "kilocycles," "milliamperes," and others used commonly in electrical work, are akin to the metric system. Everyone is familiar with the use of the metric system in measuring radio waves.

In fact, it was enacted by Congress in 1894 that the international electrical units based on the metric system "shall be the legal units of electrical measure in the United States."

55. Measure of length. The meter.—The length of the meter was at first determined as one ten-millionth part of the distance from the equator to the north pole. It was afterward found that there had been a slight error in this determination. At present the meter is the length at 0 deg. C. of a certain bar, made of 90 per cent platinum and 10 per cent iridium, called the International Meter, and kept at the International Bureau of Weights and Measures, near Paris.

The two copies of the meter which the United States has are made of the same material. One of these is used as the working standard, and the other is kept for comparison. To ensure still greater accuracy, these are compared at regular intervals with the International Meter.

56. Legal units.—As has been stated the Treasury Department has determined that the meter shall be the "fundamental standard" of length. By the act of July, 1866, Congress fixed the relation,

$$1 \text{ meter} = 39.37 \text{ inches}$$

This is the only legal relation between the two systems, and

[1] See "History of the Standard Weights and Measures of the United States," by Louis A. Fischer. This may be secured from Superintendent of Documents, Government Printing Office, Washington, D. C., for a small sum.

is used in the Office of Standards of Weights and Measures in this country in deriving the inch, foot, yard, etc., from the meter. Determined in this way the customary units are legal.

A comparison of an inch and a centimeter, which is one hundredth of a meter, is shown in Fig. 17.

In the Philippine Islands and Guam the metric system is in general use and is the sole legalized system for these islands.

57. Measure of surface.—There is no fundamental standard of surfaces or areas as there is of the measures of length. But as the measures of areas are based upon the units of length,

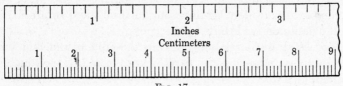

Fig. 17.

and as these are standards, the measures of areas may be so considered.

58. Measures of volume, cubic and capacity measures.— In the United States the fundamental standards of volume are: (1) the cubes of the linear units based on the International Meter; (2) the liter, which is the volume of the mass of one kilogram of pure water at its greatest density; (3) the gallon, which is 231 cubic inches; (4) the bushel, which is 2150.42 cubic inches. The liter here used is almost exactly 1 cubic decimeter, and the inch is derived from the meter according to the relation, 1 meter = 39.37 inches.

59. Measures of mass.—The fundamental standard of mass (weight) in the United States is the International Kilogram, a cylinder of 90 per cent platinum and 10 per cent iridium, preserved at the International Bureau of Weights and Measures, near Paris. As in the case of the meter, one of the two copies of the kilogram possessed by the United States is used as a working standard, and the other is kept under seal and used only to compare with the working standard from time to time.

To ensure still greater accuracy, these are compared at regular intervals with the International Kilogram.

By act of Congress of July 28, 1866, the pound is derived from the kilogram. The relation established at that time was 1 kilogram = 2.2046 pounds avoirdupois. This relation has since been made more nearly accurate and is 1 kilogram = 15,432.35639 grains, which would change the first relation to 1 kilogram = 2.20462234 pounds avoirdupois, or 1 pound avoirdupois = 453.5924277 grams. This value is the one used by the National Bureau of Standards in Washington. It is thus seen that the avoirdupois pounds, ounces, etc., in common use are derived from the kilogram, and so are fixed and definite derived units.

The established relation between the troy pound and the avoirdupois pound is 1 troy pound = $\frac{5760}{7000}$ avoirdupois pound.

When made, the standard kilogram was supposed to be the exact mass of one cubic decimeter or 1 liter of pure water at the temperature of its greatest density. It has been found that this is not exactly true, but the difference is very slight, the kilogram being about 27 parts in 1,000,000 too heavy. This difference is so very small that it could hardly affect any ordinary problem.

60. Terms used.—In the customary system of weights and measures we have about 150 different terms and 50 different numbers, ranging all the way from 2 to 1728, which bear no relation to one another. In the metric system we have only 10 different terms and but a single base, and that is the number 10.

In the metric system, the fundamental unit is the **meter,** the unit of length. From this the unit of capacity, the **liter;** the unit of weight, the **gram;** and the unit of area in measuring land, the **are** are derived. All other units are the decimal subdivisions or multiples of these. These four units are simply related. For all practical purposes 1 cubic decimeter equals 1 liter, 1 liter of water weighs 1 kilogram, and an are is an area 10 meters on a side.

The metric tables are formed by combining the words meter, liter, gram, and are with the six numerical prefixes. These are given with their meanings and abbreviations in the following table. The abbreviations given here are the ones used by our National Bureau of Standards:

meter (m.)—the unit of length.

liter (l.)—the unit of volume, capacity.

gram (g.)—the unit of weight.

are (a.)—the unit of area for land.

milli (m)—which denotes 0.001.

centi (c)—which denotes 0.01.

deci (d)—which denotes 0.1.

deka (dk)—which denotes 10.

hecto (h)—which denotes 100.

kilo (k)—which denotes 1000.

If the foregoing terms are carefully fixed in mind the tables are easily formed.

61. Metric system tables.—In common usage but few terms either in our common system of weights and measures or in the metric system are used. In the following table, the terms most commonly used are printed in bold faced type.

(1) *Measures of length.*

10 **millimeters** (mm.)	= 1 **centimeter** (cm.)	= 0.01 meter
10 **centimeters**	= 1 decimeter (dm.)	= 0.1 meter
10 decimeters	= 1 **meter** (m.)	
10 **meters**	= 1 dekameter (dkm.)	= 10 meters
10 dekameters	= 1 hectometer (hm.)	= 100 meters
10 hectometers	= 1 **kilometer** (km.)	= 1000 meters

(2) *Measures of surface.*—In measuring areas squares determined by the measures of length are used, and we have square centimeters (sq. cm. or cm.^{2}), square meters (sq. m. or m.^{2}), etc. In land measure 100 sq. m. is an are, pronounced är.

(3) *Measures of volume.*—The more common measures of volume are the cubic centimeter (cc. or cm.^{3}), cubic decimeter, and cubic meter.

(4) *Measures of capacity.*—The liter (l.), which is very nearly one cubic decimeter, is the common unit of capacity. It is larger than a liquid quart and smaller than a dry quart. (See Fig. 18.) From this are derived deciliters, dekaliters,

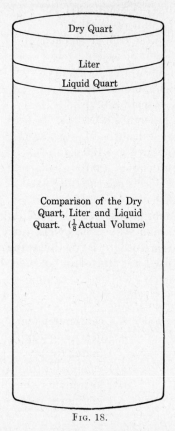

Fig. 18.

hectoliters, kiloliters, etc. The kiloliter is then 1 cu. m., and is commonly used.

(5) *Measures of weight.*—A cubic centimeter of water under certain conditions weighs one gram (g.). The unit of weight commonly used is the kilogram (kg.), which is the weight of a

liter of water, and is very approximately 2.2 pounds. 1000 kg. are a tonneau or a metric ton.

To these may be added the following used in scientific work:

$$1 \text{ mikron } (\mu) = 0.000001 \text{ meter}$$
$$1 \text{ mikrogram } (\gamma) = 0.000001 \text{ gram}$$

62. Tables, common system.—The following tables of the common system of measures are given for reference.

(1) *Measures of time:*

60 seconds (sec.)	= 1 minute (min.)
60 minutes	= 1 hour (hr.)
24 hours	= 1 day (da.)
365 days	= 1 common year (yr.)
366 days	= 1 leap year

(2) *Measures of length:*

12 inches (in. or ″)	= 1 foot (ft. or ′)
3 feet	= 1 yard (yd.)
$5\frac{1}{2}$ yards	= 1 rod (rd.)
320 rods	= 1 mile (mi.)
5280 feet	= 1 mile
1760 yards	= 1 mile

(3) *Measures of area:*

144 square inches (sq. in. or in.²)	
	= 1 square foot (sq. ft. or ft.²)
9 square feet	= 1 square yard (sq. yd. or yd.²)
$30\frac{1}{4}$ square yards	= 1 square rod (sq. rd. or rd.²)
160 square rods	= 1 acre (A.)
640 acres	= 1 square mile (sq. mi.)

(4) *Measures of volume:*

1728 cubic inches (cu. in. or in.³)	
	= 1 cubic foot (cu. ft. or ft.³)
27 cubic feet	= 1 cubic yard (cu. yd. or yd.³)
128 cubic feet	= 1 cord (cd.)

(5) *Liquid measures:*

$$\begin{aligned}
2 \text{ pints (pt.)} &= 1 \text{ quart (qt.)} \\
4 \text{ quarts} &= 1 \text{ gallon (gal.)} \\
31\tfrac{1}{2} \text{ gallons} &= 1 \text{ barrel (bbl.)} \\
231 \text{ cubic inches} &= 1 \text{ gallon}
\end{aligned}$$

(6) *Dry measures:*

$$\begin{aligned}
2 \text{ pints (pt.)} &= 1 \text{ quart (qt.)} \\
8 \text{ quarts} &= 1 \text{ peck (pk.)} \\
4 \text{ pecks} &= 1 \text{ bushel (bu.)} \\
2150.42 \text{ cubic inches} &= 1 \text{ bushel}
\end{aligned}$$

It should be carefully noted that dry and liquid measures are very different. For instance, 4 quarts in liquid measure contain 231 cubic inches, while in dry measure they contain 268.8 cubic inches, approximately.

(7) *Measures of weight (avoirdupois):*

$$\begin{aligned}
7000 \text{ grains (gr.)} &= 1 \text{ pound (lb.)} \\
16 \text{ ounces (oz.)} &= 1 \text{ pound} \\
100 \text{ pounds} &= 1 \text{ hundredweight (cwt.)} \\
2000 \text{ pounds} &= 1 \text{ ton (T.)} \\
2240 \text{ pounds} &= 1 \text{ long ton}
\end{aligned}$$

In practice it is customary to consider 1 cu. ft. of water as 62.5 lb. or 1000 oz.

63. Equivalents.—The following equivalents enable one to change measurements in one system to those in another. The first five should be remembered, the others are for reference.

1 m.	= 39.37 in. (established by law)
1 g.	= 15.432 gr.
1 lb. avoirdupois	= 7000 gr.
1 in.	= 2.54 cm. (approximately)
1 kg.	= 2.2 lb. (approximately)

EQUIVALENTS FOR REFERENCE

Lengths

1 in.	= 2.54001 cm.
1 ft.	= 30.4801 cm.

1 km.	= 3280.83 ft. = 0.62137 mi.
1 mi.	= 1.60935 km.

Areas

1 sq. in.	= 6.45163 cm.^{2}
1 sq. ft.	= 0.0929034 m.^{2}
1 sq. yd.	= 0.836131 m.^{2}
1 cm.^{2}	= 0.155 sq. in.
1 m.^{2}	= 10.76387 sq. ft. = 1.19599 sq. yd.
1 are	= 119.5985 sq. yd.
1 acre	= 40.4687 ares

Volumes, capacities

1 cu. in.	= 16.38716 cc.
1 cu. ft.	= 28.317 liters (l.) or dm.^{3}
1 pt. (liquid)	= 473.179 cc. = 0.473179 l. or dm.^{3}
1 pt. (dry)	= 550.614 cc. = 0.550614 l. or dm.^{3}
1 qt. (liquid)	= 946.358 cc. = 0.946358 l. or dm.^{3}
1 qt. (dry)	= 1101.228 cc. = 1.101228 l. or dm.^{3}
1 cm.^{3}	= 0.0610234 cu. in.
1 l.	= 61.0234 cu. in.
1 l.	= 2.11336 pt. (liquid) = 1.81616 pt. (dry)
1 l.	= 1.05668 qt. (liquid) = 0.90808 qt. (dry)

Weights (mass)

1 grain	= 0.0647989 g.
1 ounce (avoirdupois)	= 28.3495 g.
1 pound (avoirdupois)	= 453.5924277 g. = 0.45359 + kg.
1 ton (short)	= 907.185 kg.
1 gram	= 15.43235639 grains
1 kilogram	= 2.20462 lb. (avoirdupois)
1 metric ton	= 2204.62 lb. (avoirdupois)

64. Simplicity of the metric system.—The metric system was invented for simplicity.

Many look upon the system as difficult because they consider the difficulties of changing from the English to the metric system, or from the metric to the English, as difficulties of the metric system. All such difficulties would disappear if the metric system were in universal use, and considerable time would be saved in our schools that is now devoted to the teaching of our common system of weights and measures.

Practically, where the two systems are in use, one or the other is used almost entirely, and one seldom needs to change from one system to the other. Exercises given in this text that require such changes are to help the student to visualize the relations between the systems. Figure 17 helps to visualize the relation between the inch and centimeter, and Fig. 18 the relation between the liter and the dry and liquid quarts.

The simpleness of the metric system lies in the two facts: first, it is decimal, and therefore fits our decimal notation; second, its units for lengths, surfaces, solids, and weights are all dependent on one unit, the meter.

Ability to handle the metric system easily, depends, in great part, on understanding thoroughly the terms used. It is of first importance then to learn well these terms and their meanings. For instance, the word decimeter should mean, at once, one-tenth of a meter.

Because of the decimal relations between the different terms used, the changing from one unit to another is a very simple matter. In reducing to higher denominations, we divide by 10, 100, 1000, etc., by moving the decimal point to the left.

Thus, to change 3768 cm. to meters, we divide by 100 by removing the decimal point two places to the left, and have

$$3768 \text{ cm.} = 37.68 \text{ m.}$$

In a similar manner 72,468 g. = 72.468 kg., and 8643 l. = 86.43 hl.

It should be noticed that we never write 4 km. 7 hm. 3 dkm. 5 m., but write it 4735 m. The former way of writing it would be similar to writing \$7.265 in the form 7 dollars 2 dimes 6 cents 5 mills.

In reducing to lower denominations, the multiplication is performed by moving the decimal point to the right.

Thus, 25 m. = 250 dm. = 25,000 mm., and 16 kg. = 16,000 g.

65. Relations of the units.—It cannot be impressed upon the mind of the student too strongly that he should understand clearly the relations between the units of different kinds of measure. He must know that a liter is a cubic decimeter, that a kilogram is the weight of a liter of pure water, that an are is a square dekameter, and so on. He should notice that in the surface measures, when using square meters, dekameters, etc., the scale is 100; while in using cubic meters, dekameters, etc., for volumes, the scale is 1000.

Thus, 2 m.^{2} = 200 dm.^{2} = 20,000 cm.^{2}, and 3m.^{3} = 3000 dm.^{3} = 3,000,000 cc. = 3,000,000,000 mm.^{3}

66. Changing from English to metric or from metric to English systems.—The changing from one system to another is simply a matter of multiplication or division.

(1) Thus, to express 17 m. in inches,

$$1 \text{ m.} = 39.37 \text{ in.}$$
$$17 \text{ m.} = 39.37 \text{ in.} \times 17 = 669.29 \text{ in.}$$

(2) Also, to express 2468 lb. in kilograms,

$$2.2 \text{ lb. (approx.)} = 1 \text{ kg.}$$
$$2468 \text{ lb.} = 2468 \div 2.2 = 1121.8 \text{ kg.}$$

Or using the equivalent 1 lb. = 0.45359 kg.,

$$2468 \text{ lb.} = 0.45359 \text{ kg.} \times 2468 = 1119.46 \text{ kg.}$$

The disagreement in the results is on account of 2.2 lb. being a rough approximation.

The United States Bureau of Standards has compiled numerous tables of equivalents for use in the custom houses. By the use of these tables, a conversion from one system to another is made by simply referring to the proper table and reading the result.

EXERCISES

English System

1. Reduce 27 yd. 2 ft. 11 in. to inches.   *Ans.* 1007.
2. Reduce 18 hr. 20 min. 35 sec. to seconds.   *Ans.* 66,035.
3. Reduce 4 T. 7 cwt. 35 lb. 9 oz. to ounces.   *Ans.* 139,769.
4. Reduce 8 bu. 3 pk. 7 qt. 1 pt. to pints.   *Ans.* 575.
5. Reduce 12 A. 35 sq. rd. 6 sq. yd. to square yards.
     Ans. 59,144.75.

6. Reduce 9732 sq. in. to higher denominations.

Ans. 7 sq. yd. 4 sq. ft. 84 sq. in.

7. Multiply 16 cu. yd. 20 cu. ft. 1235 cu. in. by 8.

Ans. 134 cu. yd. 3 cu. ft. 1240 cu. in.

8. How many iron rails each 30 ft. long will be required to lay a railroad track from Chicago to Gary, 26 miles?   *Ans.* 4576.

9. Find the value of a field 240 rd. long and 84.5 rd. wide, at $160 per acre.   *Ans.* $20,280.

10. Reduce 19 pt. to the decimal of a gallon.   *Ans.* 2.375.

11. How many steps does a man take in walking 4 miles 86 rd. if he goes 2 ft. 4.5 in. each step?   *Ans.* 9490+.

12. Find the weight of 1 gal. of water.   *Ans.* 8.355+ lb.

13. If common bricks are $2\frac{1}{8}$ in. thick, find the number of brick in a stack 4 ft. 3 in. high.   *Ans.* 24.

14. In the Indianapolis 1939 automobile race, 500 miles were covered in 4 hr. 20 min. 47.4117 sec. Find the average rate in miles per hour correct to the nearest 0.001 mile.   *Ans.* 115.035−.

15. A wire 6 ft. 8 in. long was suspended with a weight of 250 lb. attached to one end. If the wire was stretched 0.356 in., find the stretch for each foot of wire.   *Ans.* 0.0534 in.

16. One cubic inch of water equals what part of a pint?

Ans. 0.0346+.

17. How long will it take a pump delivering 2.75 gal. per stroke and making 84 strokes per minute to pump 500 bbl. of oil?

Ans. 1 hr. 8 min. 11 sec.

18. How many sacks each containing 2 bu. 2 pk. can be filled from a bin of wheat containing 360 bu.?   *Ans.* 144.

19. What decimal part of a foot is $\frac{1}{32}$ in.?   0.125 in.?   What decimal part of a yard is each?

Ans. 0.002604+; 0.0104+; 0.00087−; 0.00347−.

20. Reduce the following to decimal parts of a foot: 1 in.; 2 in.; $3\frac{1}{2}$ in.; $7\frac{3}{8}$ in.   *Ans.* 0.0833+; 0.1667−; 0.2917−; 0.61458+.

21. Reduce each in Exercise 20 to a decimal part of a yard.

22. Reduce the following to decimal parts of a pound avoirdupois: $\frac{3}{4}$ oz.; $1\frac{1}{2}$ oz.; 3 oz.; $7\frac{1}{2}$ oz.; 13 oz.; $4\frac{1}{2}$ oz.

Ans. 0.046875; 0.09375; 0.1875; etc.

23. Reduce 39.37 in. to a decimal fraction of a rod.   *Ans.* 0.2−.

24. Reduce a pressure of 14.5 lb. per square inch to ounces per square foot.   *Ans.* 33,408.

25. A clock that gains 40 sec. while it runs 8 hr. is correct on Sunday noon. What is the correct time when the clock registers noon one week later?   *Ans.* 46 min. past 11 A.M.

26. A car averages 30 miles per hour. What does it average in feet per second?   *Ans.* 44.

27. If sound travels at the rate of 1090 ft. per second in air, in what time would the report of a gun be heard when fired at a distance of 0.218 mile? *Ans.* 1.056 sec.

28. New York City is 38 ft. above sea level and Niagara Falls is 570 ft. above sea level. The distance between these two cities is 461 miles. What is the average rise in inches for every foot distance between the cities? *Ans.* 0.00262+.

29. A tank holding 7 bbl. has two pipes opening from it; one empties out 2 qt. in 5 sec., and the other 17 gal. per minute. How long will it take to empty the tank if both pipes are open? *Ans.* 9.59− min.

30. A family uses 2 qt. of milk one day and 1 qt. the next. If they get 2 qt. June first and pay 5 cents a pint for it, what will be the milk bill for June? *Ans.* $4.50.

31. A carload of potatoes has a total weight of 55,600 lb. The car alone weighs 15,675 lb. How many bushels of potatoes in the carload if potatoes weigh 60 lb. per bushel? *Ans.* 665.4.

32. If a car averages 88 ft. per second, how many common years would it take to drive to the sun, which is 93,000,000 miles away?
Ans. 176.9406+.

33. Suppose the distance traveled by the earth about the sun to be 596,440,000 miles per year. What is the average hourly distance traveled, taking the year to be $365\frac{1}{4}$ days? Find the average distance per second. *Ans.* 19 miles approx.

34. Find the area in acres of a farm which is represented on paper as a rectangle $3\frac{3}{4}$ in. by $10\frac{1}{2}$ in. on a scale of $\frac{1}{16}$ in. to the rod. *Ans.* 63.

35. The total cost of making a cement walk 300 ft. long, 5 ft. wide, and 6 in. thick, where the cement was hand-mixed, was as follows: Foreman, 8 hr. at $1 per hour; laborers, 120 hr. at a cost of $78.20; cement, $86; gravel, $34.08. Find the total cost per square yard and per square foot. *Ans.* $27\frac{1}{2}$ cents app. per sq. yd.

36. A farmer drew a load of potatoes to market for which he received 76 cents per bushel. If the wagon and load weighed 3710 lb. and the empty wagon weighed 1150 lb., find what he received for the potatoes. Sixty pounds of potatoes make 1 bu. *Ans.* $32.43.

37. How many pounds of charcoal does it take to make 3 tons of gunpowder if the powder is $\frac{1}{10}$ sulphur, $\frac{3}{4}$ saltpeter, and the rest charcoal?
Ans. 900.

38. How many barrels of flour of 196 lb. each does it take to run a bakery 1 week of 7 days if the output is 6000 loaves a day, and there are $9\frac{1}{2}$ oz. of flour in each loaf? *Ans.* 127 bbl. $45\frac{1}{2}$ lb.

39. (1) Find the number of cubic feet in a barrel to the nearest 0.001. (2) Find the number of cubic feet in a bushel to the nearest 0.00001.
Ans. 4.211; 1.24446.

40. A new copper cent weighs 48 gr. How many pounds will $50 in these weigh?   *Ans.* $34\frac{2}{7}$.

41. One of the largest diamonds on the world weighs $3025\frac{3}{4}$ carats. How many pounds avoirdupois is this, correct to the nearest 0.0001? A carat is 3.168 g.   *Ans.* 1.3694.

42. If railroad ties are placed 18 in. apart from center to center, how many miles will 54,320 ties reach?   *Ans.* $15\frac{19}{44}$.

43. How many rails each 30 ft. in length are used in laying two railroad tracks from New York to Chicago, a distance of 870 miles. Find the weight of these rails at 110 lb. per yard.   *Ans.* 612,480; 336,864 tons.

44. Suppose that the distance from the earth to the sun is 91,713,000 miles, and that the sun's light reaches the earth in 8 min. 18 sec. What is the velocity of light per second   *Ans.* 184,163 miles.

45. Work is done when resistance is overcome. It is measured by the product of the force times the distance over which the force acts. As a formula this is $w = f \times s$, where w is the work, f the force, and s the distance. If the force is in pounds and the distance in feet, then the work is in foot-pounds.

A steam crane lifts a block of granite weighing 2 tons 80 ft. Find the work done in foot-pounds.   *Ans.* 320,000.

46. How many foot-pounds of work are necessary to pump 100 bbl. of water to a height of 120 ft.? Use 4.211 cu. ft. in 1 bbl. and 62.5 lb. to 1 cu. ft.   *Ans.* 3,158,250.

47. How many foot-pounds of work are done in lifting an elevator weighing 3 tons to the top of a building 220 ft. high? If the elevator is raised through this height in 2 min., how many foot-pounds of work are done per second? If an engine of one horsepower can do 550 foot-pounds of work per second, an engine of what horsepower will be necessary to lift the elevator to the top in 2 min.?   *Ans.* 20.

EXERCISES

Metric System

1. Express the following, first, in meters and, second, in millimeters: 456 cm.; 1763 dm.; 27 km.

Ans. 4.56 m., 17,630 m., 27,000 m.; 4560 mm., 17,630,000 mm.,

27,000,000 mm.

2. Express the following in square meters: 75 cm.²; 125 mm.², 0.025 dm.²; 0.0029 km.²   *Ans.* 0.0075; 0.000125; 2.5.

3. Radio waves travel at approximately 186,000 miles or 300,000,000 m. per second. Do these agree?   *Ans.* Approximately.

4. A radio station that is broadcasting on a frequency of 720 kilocycles is using what wave length? Use the approximate velocity 300,-000,000 m. a second.   *Ans.* 416.7 m.

5. Express the following in terms of cubic meters: 1756 l.; 467 kl.; 4937 dl.; 1067 dkl.; 735,432 dm.³; 764 dkm.³

Ans. 1.756; 467; 0.4937; 10.67; 735.432; 764,000.

6. Reduce 750 l. to liquid quarts; 326 l. to dry quarts; 75 m. to inches; 576 cm. to feet; 27 m.³ to bushels; 9276 mm.³ to gallons; 12 dm.³ to barrels.

Solution.—From Art. 63 we find 1 l. = 1.05668 qt. (liquid).

$$\therefore\ 750\ l. = 1.05668\ qt. \times 750 = 792.51\ qt.$$

In the fifth part, 27 m.³ to bushels, the change is not so easy from the equivalents given.

$$27\ m.^3 = 27,000\ dm.^3\ or\ l.$$
$$1\ l. = 0.90808\ qt.\ (dry)$$
$$\therefore\ 27,000\ l. = 0.90808\ qt. \times 27,000 = 24,518.16\ qt.$$

Divide this by 32 because 1 bu. = 32 qt.

$$\therefore\ 27\ m.^3 = 766.19\ bu.$$

7. Reduce 456 in. to meters; 43.5 ft. to centimeters; 327 gal. to liters; 92.87 qt. (dry) to liters; 756 bu. to cubic meters.

Ans. 11.58; 1325.88; 1237.84; 102.27; 26.64.

8. No. 16 gage sheet steel is $\frac{1}{16}$ in. thick and weighs 40 oz. per square foot. Find the thickness in millimeters (four decimal places) and the weight per square meter in kilograms (two decimal places).

Solution.—To find the weight in kilograms per square meter, first find the weight of a square meter in ounces, and then change to pounds and to kilograms.

$$1\ m.^2 = 10.76387\ ft.^2$$
$$\therefore\ 1\ m.^2\ weighs\ 40\ oz. \times 10.76387 = 430.5548\ oz. = 26.9097\ lb.$$
$$1\ lb. = 0.45359\ kg.$$
$$\therefore\ 26.9097\ lb. = 0.45359\ kg. \times 26.9097 = 12.20597\ kg.$$

9. No. 24 gage sheet steel is 0.635 mm. thick and weighs 4.882 kg. per square meter. Find thickness in decimals of an inch (three decimal places) and weight per square foot in ounces. *Ans.* 0.025; 16.

10. Find the difference between $3\frac{15}{16}$ in. and 10 cm. *Ans.* 0.0005 in.

11. What is the diameter in inches of the bore of a French "75" gun? This means 75 mm. in diameter. *Ans.* 2.953— in.

12. In international athletic contests the distances are given in the metric system. In ice skating, the time for 1500 m. was 2 min. 20 sec. At this rate find the time for 1 mile. *Ans.* 2 min. 30.2 sec.

13. In describing the making of reinforced concrete the necessary pressure is given as 25 kg. per square centimeter. How many pounds is this per square inch? *Ans.* 355.58+.

14. Find in kilograms the weight of air in a room 10.5 m. by 8.3 m. by 4 m., air being 0.001276 times as heavy as water.   *Ans.* 444.8.

15. Find the weight in kilograms of the mercury in a tube of 1 cm.^{2} cross section and 760 mm. long, mercury being 13.596 times as heavy as water.   *Ans.* 1.0333−.

16. If a map is made on a scale of 1 to 60,000, how many kilometers do 79 mm. on the map represent?   *Ans.* 4.74.

17. If a person in breathing uses 0.25 m.^{3} of air a minute, how long will it take six persons to use the air in a room 6 m. long, 3.5 m. high, and 5.3 m. wide?   *Ans.* 74.2 min.

18. A block of stone weighs 7643 kg.   A cubic decimeter of the stone weighs 2.7 kg.   Find the volume of the block in cubic meters.

Ans. 2.83.

19. Find the weight in kilograms of the water that a tank 2 m. by 3 m. by 6 m. will hold.   *Ans.* 36,000.

20. Find the weight in pounds of the water a tank 6 ft. by 10 ft. by 18 ft. will hold, using 62.5 lb. as the weight of 1 cu. ft. of water.

Ans. 67,500.

21. How many millimeters are there in each of the following: $\frac{1}{8}$ in.; $6\frac{1}{2}$ in.; $4\frac{13}{16}$ in.; $12\frac{7}{8}$ in.?   Check your results by equivalents given in Table IV.

22. Find the capacity in liters of a rectangular tank 2 m. by 9 dm. by 8 dm.   *Ans.* 1440.

23. What is the length of a centigram of wire, 255 mm. of which weigh 0.172 g.?   *Ans.* 14.83 − mm.

24. A liter of mercury weighs 13.596 kg.; how many cubic millimeters of mercury weigh 1 g.?   *Ans.* 73.551.

25. A man's height is 174 cm.   What is his height in feet and inches?
Ans. 5 ft. 8.5+ in.

26. Express the following barometer readings in centimeters: 29.9 in.; 30.0 in.; 30.1 in.; 30.2 in.   *Ans.* 75.946; 76.200; 76.454; 76.708.

27. Express the following in inches to the nearest 0.01; 71.119 cm.; 73.659 cm.; 74.929 cm.   *Ans.* 28.00; 29.00; 29.50.

28. Cast copper being 8.8 times as heavy as an equal volume of water, what is the weight of 5 cm.^{3}?   *Ans.* 44 g.

29. A velocity of 32.2 ft. per second is how many centimeters per second?   *Ans.* 981.5−.

30. A rate of 1 mile in 2 min. 6 sec. is how many kilometers per minute? How many meters per second?   *Ans.* 0.7664− ; 12.77+.

31. A rate of 30 miles per hour is the rate of 1 kilometer in how many minutes?   *Ans.* 1.243−.

32. A pressure of 14.7 lb. per square inch is how many grams per square centimeter?

Solution: $\dfrac{14.7}{6.45163}$ = number of pounds per square centimeter.

$\dfrac{14.7 \times 453.5924}{6.45163} = 1033.5+ =$ number of grams per square centimeter.

Ans.

67. Water pressure.—When water is stored in a tank it exerts pressure against the walls of the tank, whether the walls are horizontal, vertical, or oblique. The force is exerted perpendicular to the wall in all cases. The pressure on a given area is equal to the weight of a column of water of that area in cross section and of height equal to the distance the given area is below the surface of the water. This distance is spoken of as the **head.** Thus, the pressure on a square inch of the wall at a depth of 10 ft. is equal to the weight of a column of water 1 square inch in gross section and 10 feet high.

If 1 cu. ft. of water weighs 62.5 lb., a column 1 ft. high and 1 sq. in. in cross section weighs 0.434 lb.

The following rule may then be used for finding the pressure per square inch at any depth:

Multiply the head of the water in feet by 0.434. The result is the pressure in pounds per square inch.

EXERCISES

1. What is the pressure per square inch on the circular bottom of a tank if the head of water is 45 ft.? What is the total pressure on the bottom of the tank if the area of the bottom is 3.1416 sq. ft.'?

Ans. 19.51 lb.; 8824.7 lb.

2. A closed tank the area of the bottom of which is 6 sq. ft. has a pipe leading upward to a reservoir. If the bottom of the tank is 75 ft. below the surface of the water in the reservoir, find the pressure on the bottom of the tank. *Ans.* 28,123 lb.

3. In the preceding exercise, suppose the tank is 2 ft. by 3 ft. and 8 ft. high. What is the total pressure on one of the larger sides? Here the average pressure per square inch is the pressure at a point halfway between the bottom and the top of the tank. What is the total pressure on the top of the tank? *Ans.* 106,493 lb.; 25,123 lb.

4. A tank 3 ft. long and 2 ft. deep is full of water. What is the total pressure on one side? Does the width of the tank make any difference?

Ans. 375 lb.; no.

5. If it requires 500 lb. to hold a valve 2 sq. in. in area closed at the bottom of a tank, what is the head of water? *Ans.* 576 ft.

CHAPTER VI

PERCENTAGE AND APPLICATIONS

68. A merchant usually thinks of his gain or loss as being a certain *per cent* of the cost. This is a simple and familiar way of stating the *relation* of the gain or loss to the cost; but it does not show the *actual* gain or loss unless the amount of money involved is known. To one who thoroughly understands fractions, percentage offers no new difficulties.

The words per cent mean by the hundred. The symbol % means per cent. Thus, 10% means 10 per cent or $\frac{10}{100}$ or 0.10. A gain of 10% when the cost is \$500 is \$50, the actual gain; while a gain of 10% on \$200 gives an actual gain of \$20.

The following table gives certain per cents with their common fraction and decimal equivalents.

5%	= 0.05	= $\frac{1}{20}$	50%	= 0.50	= $\frac{1}{2}$
10%	= 0.1	= $\frac{1}{10}$	60%	= 0.60	= $\frac{3}{5}$
$12\frac{1}{2}$%	= $0.12\frac{1}{2}$	= $\frac{1}{8}$	$62\frac{1}{2}$%	= $0.62\frac{1}{2}$	= $\frac{5}{8}$
$16\frac{2}{3}$	= $0.16\frac{2}{3}$	= $\frac{1}{6}$	75%	= 0.75	= $\frac{3}{4}$
20%	= 0.20	= $\frac{1}{5}$	80%	= 0.80	= $\frac{4}{5}$
25%	= 0.25	= $\frac{1}{4}$	$83\frac{1}{3}$%	= $0.83\frac{1}{3}$	= $\frac{5}{6}$
$33\frac{1}{3}$%	= $0.33\frac{1}{3}$	= $\frac{1}{3}$	$87\frac{1}{2}$%	= $0.87\frac{1}{2}$	= $\frac{7}{8}$
$37\frac{1}{2}$%	= $0.37\frac{1}{2}$	= $\frac{3}{8}$	90%	= 0.90	= $\frac{9}{10}$
40%	= 0.40	= $\frac{2}{5}$			

To change a fraction, such as $\frac{2}{5}$, to an equivalent form in per cent, reduce it to a fraction having 100 for a denominator. Thus,

$$\frac{2}{5} = \frac{40}{100} = 40\%$$

or

$$\frac{2}{5} = \frac{2}{5} \text{ of } 100\% = 40\%$$

Similarly

$$\frac{7}{8} = \frac{7}{8} \text{ of } 100\% = 87\frac{1}{2}\%$$

A per cent expressed as $\frac{2}{5}\%$, does not mean $\frac{2}{5}$ but $\frac{2}{5}$ of 1%, which is the same as $\frac{2}{5}$ of $\frac{1}{100} = \frac{2}{500} = \frac{1}{250} = 0.004$. In the same way $\frac{3}{8}\% = \frac{3}{8}$ of $\frac{1}{100} = \frac{3}{800} = 0.00375 = 0.375\%$.

It should be carefully noticed that the sign $\%$ does the duty of two decimal places.

Thus, $0.05 = 5\%$, $0.0005 = 0.05\%$, $1.07 = 107\%$, and $4.33\frac{1}{3} = 433\frac{1}{3}\%$.

69. Cases.—The problems of percentage usually occurring are of the following forms:

(1) What is $37\frac{1}{2}\%$ of 720?

(2) 45 is what per cent of 450%?

(3) 85 is $62\frac{1}{2}\%$ of what number?

These three forms can be stated in general terms if the following definitions are given:

The number of which the per cent is taken is the **base.**

The number of per cent taken is called the **rate.**

The part of the base determined by the rate is the **percentage.**

The sum of the base and percentage is the **amount.**

The base minus the percentage is the **difference.**

The three problems now become the cases:

Case I.   *Base* and *rate* given to find *percentage.*

Case II.   *Base* and *percentage* given to find *rate.*

Case III.   *Percentage* and *rate* given to find *base.*

These three cases of percentage correspond to the three cases in multiplication; when any two of the numbers, multiplicand, multiplier, and product, are given, to find the third.

$$\textit{In multiplication} \begin{cases} \textit{multiplicand} \text{ corresponds to} \\ \quad \text{base} \\ \textit{multiplier} \text{ corresponds to } \textit{rate} \\ \textit{product} \text{ corresponds to } \textit{per-} \\ \quad \textit{centage} \end{cases} \textit{in percentage}$$

Case I corresponds to: *multiplicand* and *multiplier* given, to find the *product:*

$$Product = multiplicand \times multiplier$$

Case II corresponds to: *multiplicand* and *product* given, to find the *multiplier:*

$$Multiplier = product \div multiplicand$$

Case III corresponds to: *multiplier* and *product* given to find the *multiplicand:*

$$Multiplicand = product \div multiplier$$

70. Rules and formulas.—In the language of percentage these become:

Case I.   *Percentage = base × rate.*

This may be written as a formula if b stands for base, p for percentage, and r for rate.   The formula is

$$p = b \times r$$

Case II.   *Rate = percentage ÷ base.*   The formula is

$$r = p \div b$$

Case III.   It $= percentage \div rate.$ The formula is

$$b = p \div r$$

71. Solutions.—*Problem* (1) of Art. 69 is solved thus:

By fractions: $37\frac{1}{2}\%$ of $720 = \frac{3}{8}$ of $720 = 270$.   *Ans.*

By formula.—Using the formula $p = b \times r$, gives the same result, for then $p = 720 \times 0.37\frac{1}{2} = 270$.   *Ans.*

Problem (2).   *By fractions.*—45 is what per cent of 450 means 45 is how many hundredths of 450, that is, some number of hundredths of 450 is 45.

Then 45 is $\frac{45}{450} = \frac{1}{10} = \frac{10}{100} = 10\%$ of 450.   *Ans.*

By formula: $r = p \div b$ gives $r = 45 \div 450 = 0.1 = 10\%$.
   Ans.

Problem (3).   *By fractions.*—85 is $62\frac{1}{2}\%$ of what number is the same as 85 is $\frac{5}{8}$ of what number.   It is now a simple problem in fractions and may be reasoned thus:

If 85 is $\frac{5}{8}$ of some number, then 17 is $\frac{1}{8}$ of that number, and 136 is $\frac{8}{8}$ of that number.

Hence, the number = 136.   *Ans.*

By formula: $b = p \div r$ gives $p = 85 \div 0.62\frac{1}{2} = 136$.   *Ans.*

EXERCISES

Do the following exercises orally if possible:

1. What is $\frac{1}{3}$ of 24?   0.33$\frac{1}{3}$ of 24?   33$\frac{1}{3}$% of 24?

2. What is $\frac{2}{3}$ of 45?   0.66$\frac{2}{3}$ of 45?   66$\frac{2}{3}$% of 45?

3. What is $\frac{1}{4}$ of 32?   0.25 of 32?   25% of 32?

4. What is $\frac{3}{4}$ of 16?   0.75 of 16?   75% of 16?

5. What is $\frac{1}{5}$ of 40?   0.20 of 40?   20% of 40?

6. What is $\frac{4}{5}$ of 60?   0.80 of 60?   80% of 60?

7. What is $\frac{1}{8}$ of 64?   0.12$\frac{1}{2}$ of 64?   12$\frac{1}{2}$% of 64?

8. What is $\frac{5}{8}$ of 72?   0.625 of 72?   62.5% of 72?

9. What is $\frac{1}{16}$ of 48?   0.06$\frac{1}{4}$ of 48?   6$\frac{1}{4}$% of 48?

10. What is 25% of 20?   of 48?   of 88?   of 140?

11. What is 33$\frac{1}{3}$% of 45?   of 90?   of 120?   of 360?

12. What is 8% of 8?   of 20?   of 88?   of 800?

13. What is 10% of 8?   of 20?   of 88?   of 800?

14. 4 is what per cent of 8?   of 16?   of 20?

15. 9 is what per cent of 9?   of 18?   of 72?

16. 40 is what per cent of 60?   of 480?   of 800?

17. What per cent is 4 of 74?   7$\frac{1}{2}$ of 24?

18. What per cent is $\frac{2}{5}$ of 6$\frac{1}{2}$?   37$\frac{1}{2}$ of 150?

19. 10% of what number is 4?   8?   15?   90?

20. 33.5% of what number is 6?   16?   25?   96?

21. 62$\frac{1}{2}$% of what number is 5?   20?   60?   500?

22. 66$\frac{2}{3}$% of what number is 2?   20?   80?   6000?

23. 20% from what number leaves 48?

Suggestion: 20% from a number leaves 80% of the number.

24. 10% from what number leaves 9?   *Ans.* 10.

25. 20% from what number leaves 16?   *Ans.* 20.

26. 33$\frac{1}{3}$% from what number leaves 20?   *Ans.* 30.

27. 40 is 20% less than what number?   *Ans.* 50.

28. 20 is 40% less than what number?   *Ans.* 33$\frac{1}{3}$.

29. 40 is 20% more than what number?   *Ans.* 33$\frac{1}{3}$.

30. 20 is 40% more than what number?   *Ans.* 14$\frac{2}{7}$.

31. 37$\frac{1}{2}$ is 87$\frac{1}{2}$% less than what number?   *Ans.* 300.

32. If apples that cost 5 cents per pound were sold 3 lbs. for a quarter, what part of the cost is gained?   What per cent?   *Ans.* $\frac{2}{3}$; 66$\frac{2}{3}$%.

33. Gas was bought for 12 cents per gallon and sold for 16 cents per gallon.   What part of the cost is gained?   What per cent?

Ans. $\frac{1}{3}$, 33$\frac{1}{3}$%.

34. A dealer allowed \$200 for a car and sold it for \$250; find the gain per cent.   *Ans.* 25%.

35. Find the gain per cent in each case if an old car was bought for the following prices: $50, $40, $25, $10, $5, $1; and sold for $50. Find the gain per cent if the car was given to the seller.

36. A pair of shoes cost $8. They were worn 1 year and sold for $1. What was the discount in per cent? *Ans.* $87\frac{1}{2}\%$.

37. My milk bill was $10.20 last month; this month it is $9.80. Find per cent discount. *Ans.* $4-\%$.

38. My gas bill last month was $2.50; this month there was a 20% discount. What was my bill this month? *Ans.* $2.00.

39. The 1937 Dodge sold for $907; the 1938 Dodge sold for $970. Find the per cent increase. *Ans.* $7-\%$.

40. A quantity of wool was bought for $360, and three-fourths of it was then sold for the cost of the whole. What per cent would have been gained if the entire amount had been sold at the same rate?
Ans. $33\frac{1}{3}\%$.

41. A man spent $16\frac{2}{3}\%$ of his salary for board and room. If he spent $12.50 a week for board and room, what was his yearly salary? (52 weeks in a year.) *Ans.* $3900.

APPLICATIONS

72. Relations shown by per cents.—As has been said, the per cent of gain or loss is often more significant than the actual gain or loss. For instance, during the 10-year period from 1920 to 1930 the actual gain in population of Chicago was, in round numbers, 672,000 while that of Los Angeles was 655,000. These figures give no indication of the true rates of increase in the population of the two cities during the period. But, when we consider the population of each city in 1920 and find that the increase in the population of Chicago was 24.87% in the decade while that of Los Angeles was 113.59%, we are able to see very clearly the relative rates of increase in population. As an exercise the reader should solve this problem for the years 1930 to 1940.

Example 1.—The population of Detroit was 993,700 in 1920 and 1,564,000 in 1930. Find the rate of increase for the decade.

Solution: $1,564,400 - 993,700 = 570,700$, which is the actual increase on the base population of 993,700.

∴ $570,700 \div 993,700 = 57.4 + \% = $ the rate of increase.

Example 2.—In a certain machine $\frac{2}{5}$ of the energy supplied to the machine is lost in friction and other resistances. What is the per cent of efficiency? If $\frac{1}{8}$ of the loss of energy is in a certain part of the machine, what per cent of the total loss is in this part?

Discussion.—If in a machine it is known that $\frac{2}{5}$ of the energy expended is wasted in frictional and other resistances, we say that 40% is wasted, meaning that $\frac{40}{100}$ is useless for doing work. This does not state the actual numerical amount of energy wasted; all it tells is that for every 100 units of work expended on the machine, 40 units disappear. Such percentages enable comparisons of different machines to be made. If one machine has an efficiency of 60% and another has an efficiency of 70%, we know that the second is more efficient than the first. If we know that $\frac{1}{8}$ or $12\frac{1}{2}$% of the 40% loss is in a certain part, this gives a percentage of a percentage. The solution of the problem is:

$$\frac{2}{5} = \text{part of the energy lost}$$
$$\frac{3}{5} = 60\% = \text{efficiency of the machine}$$
$$\tfrac{1}{8} \text{ of } \tfrac{2}{5} = \tfrac{1}{20} = 5\% = \text{loss in the particular part of the machine}$$

The **efficiency** of a machine is the relation of the work done by the machine to the work put into the machine, and is usually expressed as a per cent.

$$Efficiency = \frac{output}{input}$$

73. Averages and per cents of error.—The data for practical calculations are in many cases either the result of measuring quantities, or of experimental observations, and in each case are liable to error. To obtain a result which can be relied upon, a number of measurements or observations are taken and the average or mean result calculated.

The average, or mean result, is obtained by adding all the measured results together and dividing the sum by the number of them. This average is accepted as the best approximation to the truth. The error of any particular observation is obtained by finding the difference between it and the average. This error can often be most conveniently expressed as a per cent, and is spoken of as the per cent of error. We always take the correct value, or in this case the average value, as the base.

Example.—In measuring the diameter of a steel rod with a micrometer, the separate measurements are: 0.3562 in., 0.3569 in., 0.3567 in., 0.3570 in., and 0.3565 in. Find the average measurement and the per cent of error in the largest and the smallest measurements.

Solution and discussion: 0.3562 in. + 0.3569 in. + 0.3567 in. + 0.3570 in. + 0.3565 in. = 1.7833 in.

1.7833 in. ÷ 5 = 0.35666 in. = average.

0.3570 in. − 0.35666 in. = 0.00034 in. = error in largest measurement.

Using the formula $r = p \div b$ gives

$r = 0.00034$ in. ÷ 0.35666 in. = $0.00095+$ = 0.095% = per cent of error in largest measurement.

0.35666 in. − 0.3562 in. = 0.00046 in. = error in smallest measurement.

$r = 0.00046$ in. ÷ 0.35666 in. = 0.0013 = 0.13% = per cent of error in the smallest measurement.

It should be emphasized that the per cent of error in any measurement is always found by using the correct measurement as the base and the error as the percentage.

74. List prices and discounts.—The prices of machines and materials, printed in catalogs and price lists, are usually subject to discounts. Often the discount is so large that the list price gives no idea of the actual cost. In preparing an estimate, it is necessary to know what discounts are given from a price list.

Discounts are usually given thus: 60% and 10% off or simply 60 and 10 or perhaps "sixty and ten." This does not mean a discount of 70%, but that a discount of 60% is first made and then a discount of 10% on the remainder.

Thus, if the list price is $3.50 with 60% and 10% off, we find 60% of $3.50, which is $2.10. Then deduct this from $3.50 leaving $1.40.

Now get 10% of $1.40, which is $0.14, and deduct it from $1.40, which leaves $1.26 as the actual cost.

Similarly, we may have discounts of 40%, 10%, and 4%, or 40, 10, and 4 off. These are deducted in turn as with the two discounts.

EXERCISES

1. 48% of 2000 = ? *Ans.* 960.

2. What is $\frac{5}{8}$% of $24.40? *Ans.* 15.25 cents.

3. What is 62.5% of $24.40? *Ans.* $15.25.

4. 30 is $2\frac{1}{2}$% of what number? *Ans.* 1200.

5. What per cent of $70 is $12.50? *Ans.* $17\frac{6}{7}$.

6. 10% of 30 is 3% of what? *Ans.* 100.

7. A man had $256 in a closed bank. If 65% was paid, how much did the man lose? *Ans.* $89.60.

8. There was an 18% reduction in traffic deaths in the United States for 1938, compared with 1937, which was a saving of 7200 lives. What were the traffic fatalities for the year 1938 in the United States?
Ans. 32,800.

9. In addition to the 40,000 motor-vehicle deaths in a single year, there were 1,150,000 nonfatal injuries. What per cent of the total killed and injured was fatal? *Ans.* 3.36+.

10. Accidents of all types claimed 94,100 people in the United States for the year 1938. If 40,000 of these deaths are due to motor vehicles, what per cent of deaths by accidents is this? Of the 130 million people in the United States, what per cent die by accident each year?
Ans. 42.5+.

11. A gas range is priced $103. A reduction of 10% was made for the old stove, and an additional reduction of 6% on the new price was then given for cash. What did the range cost the buyer? *Ans.* $87.14.

12. A United States savings bond increased in value from $18.75 to $19 the first year and from $24.50 to $25 from the $9\frac{1}{2}$ to the 10th year. What was the per cent increase the first year? From the $9\frac{1}{2}$ to the 10th year? *Ans.* $1\frac{1}{3}$; $2\frac{2}{49}$.

13. If the finance cost for 1 year on an unpaid balance of $480 is $28.80, what per cent was charged? *Ans.* 6.

14. A rough casting weighs $45\frac{1}{2}$ lb.; and, after being finished in a lathe, it weighs $43\frac{1}{4}$ lb. The loss in finishing is what per cent of the weight in the rough? *Ans.* 5%, approximately.

15. A steel I beam expands 0.01% of its length when exposed to the sun. Find the increase in the length of an I beam 25 ft. 8 in. long.
Ans. 0.0308 in.

16. The number of hairs on the human head is approximately as follows: Redhead, 88,000; brunette, 102,000; blond, 104,000. What per cent increase has the blond over the redhead? Over the brunette?

Ans. $18\frac{2}{11}$; $1\frac{49}{51}$.

17. A milkman sold milk at 14 cents a quart, which was $233\frac{1}{3}\%$ of the cost; find cost per quart. *Ans.* 6 cents.

Suggestion: $233\frac{1}{3}\% = \frac{7}{3}$. If 14 cents is $\frac{7}{3}$ of the cost, what is the cost?

18. A tradesman marks his goods at 25% above cost and deducts 12% of the amount of a customer's bill for cash. What per cent does he make?

Ans. 10%.

Suggestion.—Suppose the cost is $20. The marked price is 25% above $20, or $25. A deduction of 12% on $25 is $3. Hence the selling price is $25 − $3 = $22. The gain is $22 − $20 = $2. What per cent is $2 of $20? This gives the gain per cent.

19. As cause of death per 100,000 note the following: heart disease, 245; cancer, 108; cerebral hemorrhage 85; pneumonia 82; nephritis, 81. What per cent of deaths is each of the above? What per cent of the total deaths is caused by all five of the above? *Ans.* 0.245; etc.

20. The United States Naval Academy graduated 578 men in June, 1939. Of this total number 52 were dropped from active service as physically unfit. What per cent was dropped? *Ans.* 9−.

21. A firm increases the wages of its employees $12\frac{1}{2}\%$. Find the wages of a man who was getting $3.40 a day. Of a boy who was getting $1.60 a day. A man now receives $6.30 a day; what did he receive before the increase? *Ans.* 3.82\frac{1}{2}$; $1.80; $5.60.

22. An airline company carried 31,233 passengers in May, 1938, and 47,722 in May, 1939. What was the per cent increase? *Ans.* 52.8−.

23. A stock was bought for $13\frac{5}{8}$ and sold three years later for $44.125. What per cent was gained? *Ans.* 224−.

24. The usual allowance made for shrinkage when casting iron pipes is $\frac{1}{8}$ in. per foot. What per cent is this? *Ans.* 1.04+.

25. Water is freezing expands 9% of its volume. How many gallons of water are necessary to make 240 cu. ft. of ice? *Ans.* 1647.

26. The profits of a business this last year were $14,656, and were 28% more than for the previous year. What were the profits the previous year? *Ans.* $11,450.

27. According to tests for career and self-appraisal of high-school students, 105 out of 1000 say they want to become physicians. Of this number, five actually do become physicians. What per cent want to become physicians? What per cent actually do? *Ans.* 10.5; 0.5.

28. An iron meteorite found in 1908 weighed 3275 lb. If 91.63% of its weight was iron, and 7.33% nickel, what was the weight of the iron? Of the nickel? Of other materials?

Ans. 3000.8825 lb. of iron; 240.0575 lb. of nickel.

29. If a man had invested $100 in 1929 at the following peak values, what would his original capital be worth in June, 1939;

Seat on the New York Stock Exchange now 10.1% of 1929 peak.

Farm values now 72.4% of 1929 peak.

Bank account in London now 96.2% of 1929 peak.

Common stock of Homestake Gold Mining now 533.3% of 1929 peak.

U. S. Government Bond now 107.4% of 1929 peak.

Dow-Jones average of 30 industrial stocks now 35.9% of 1929 peak.

30. The per capita income for 1938 averaged $480; for 1937 it was $537. What was the per cent decrease?   *Ans.* 10.6+.

31. The highest per capita income for 1938 was The District of Columbia which was $1065. Among the lowest was Alabama and North Dakota with a per capita income of $225 each for 1938. What per cent increase has the District of Columbia over Alabama?   *Ans.* $373\frac{1}{3}$.

32. The national income for 1938 was $62\frac{1}{2}$ billion dollars. This was a decrease of 10% over 1937. What was the United States national income for 1937? If 80 billion dollars income per year would balance the present United States budget, what per cent increase would this be over the 1938 national income?   *Ans.* $69\frac{4}{9}$ billion dollars; 28%.

33. If a 9 by 12 rug valued at $66.30 was offered for sale at $32.85 plus an additional 20% reduction on the offered price for quick sale, what was the final selling price of the rug? What total per cent reduction was the final selling price over the first price of $66.30?   *Ans.* $26.28; 60.4.

34. A car is priced $824 which includes a federal tax of 3%. What was the price of the car? What was the tax?   *Ans.* $800; $24.

35. The 3% sales tax on a car is $19.95. What is the price of the car including the tax?   *Ans.* $665.

36. A dealer sold two cars at $775 each. On one he lost 25% and on the other he gained 25%. Did he lose or gain on the entire transaction and how much?   *Ans.* $103\frac{1}{3}$ lost.

37. The following measurements of the diameter of a small steel shaft were made with a micrometer: 0.5677, 0.5674, 0.5671, 0.5678 and 0.5673 in. Find the per cent of error in the greatest and in the least measurement.   *Ans.* 1.43; 1.54; 1.67; 1.82; 2.22.

38. When rock is crushed or broken into fragments of nearly uniform size, it increases in bulk and has voids, or interspaces, of from 30 to 55 per cent of the whole volume. Find the number of cubic yards when crushed occupied by 1 cu. yd. of solid rock, if voids are 30%; 35%; 40%; 45%; 55%.

Suggestion.—The volume of the rock, 1 cu. yd., is 30% less than, or 70% of, the bulk of crushed rock. Using formula

$$b = p \div r \text{ gives } b = 1 \div 0.70 = 1.43-$$

39. The best time required for a letter mailed in Chicago and delivered in Washington, D. C., is as follows: straight first class, 22 hr. 45 min.; airmail, 14 hr. 30 min.; and special delivery airmail, 12 hr. 6 min.   By using special delivery airmail, what per cent of time is saved over straight first class?   Over airmail?   *Ans.* 47−; 17−.

40. In estimating the amount to charge per day for the use of a steam roller, a contractor has the following data: first cost of steam roller, $3000; money worth 6%; days actually worked per year, 100; depreciation in value of the machine, $200 per year.   Find the price to be charged per day for use of the roller.   *Ans.* $3.80.

41. The actual cost of removing a cubic yard of rock in excavating a certain canal is $1.10.   What price should be put in the estimate, if 12% is to be allowed for superintending, and 10% on the cost, including superintending, is allowed for profit?   *Ans.* $1.3552.

42. A house depreciates in value each year at the rate of 4% of its value at the beginning of each year, and its value at the end of two years is $6451.20.   Find the original value.   *Ans.* $7000.

43. A house valued at $4000 rents for $27.50 a month.   The repairs on the house each year amount to $40, and the taxes are $17.50.   What interest does the property pay on the investment, no allowance being made for change in the value of the house?   *Ans.* $6\frac{13}{16}$%.

44. In making a certain machine, 750 lb. of iron are used at an average cost of 12 cents per pound.   There are used, in the work on the machine, 20 hr. of time at 60 cents per hour, 7 hr. at 90 cents, and 4 hr. at 30 cents. If 20% is allowed on cost as profit, what is the selling price of the machine? What will it be listed at if sold at 30 and 5 off?

Ans. $131.40; $197.59.

45. A manufacturer sold a suit of clothes to a retailer at a profit of 20% on the cost of making.   The retailer sold the suit to a customer for $72 and made a profit of $33\frac{1}{3}$% on what it cost him.   How much did the suit cost the retailer and what was the cost of making?   *Ans.* $54; $45.

46. A grain dealer in Chicago had his agent in Duluth buy 6500 bu. of wheat at $1.05, 4000 bu. at $1.08, and 7000 bu. at $1.01, paying a commission of $1\frac{3}{4}$% for buying.   The wheat was shipped to Chicago by water and an insurance policy, at $1\frac{1}{4}$% premium, was taken out to cover cost of wheat and commission.   Find the amount of the policy and the premium.   *Ans.* $18,533.76; $231.67.

47. An article is listed at $225, and sells at 40 and 10 off.   How will the 40% discount be changed to offset an increase of 15% in cost of production?   *Ans.* 31%, or better, 30%.

48. The composition of white metal is to be 4 parts by weight of copper, 9 antimony, and 97 tin.   Express these as per cents, and find the weight of each material required to make 2376 lb. of alloy. See Example 6, Art. 80.

Ans. Copper, $3\frac{7}{11}\%$, 86.4 lb.; antimony, $8\frac{2}{11}\%$, 194.4 lb.; tin, $88\frac{2}{11}\%$, 2095.2 lb.

49. A ton of coal from the Rock Island field has 11.57% moisture, and 6.27% of the dry coal is ash. How many pounds of ash in a ton of the coal?   *Ans.* 110.9 −.

50. If 2.346 g. of an ore give 0.362 g. of copper, what per cent of copper does the ore contain?   *Ans.* 15.43%.

51. 2.3656 kg. of ore give 0.7 g. of gold and 2.5 g. of silver, find the per cent of each.   *Ans.* 0.02959 + %; 0.1057%.

52. A merchant buys rubber door mats at $48 per dozen less discounts at 40%, 15%, and 5%. At what price each should he sell them in order that he may make 35%?   *Ans.* $2.62.

53. If the author gets 10% of the selling price of a book, how many books selling at 75 cents each must be sold to pay the author $117.30?

Ans. 1564.

54. In a compound of two substances A and B, their weights are in the ratio of 1.3498 to 1. What is the per cent of each in the compound? (That is, 1.3498 parts of A to 1 part of B.)

Ans. 57.44 + %; 42.56 − %.

55. Two substances A and B form a compound and have a total weight of 3.267 g. If the compound has 24.725% of A and 75.275% of B, find the weight of each substance in the compound.

Ans. 0.8078 g., 2.4592 g.

56. Find the cost of a steam boiler listed at $500 subject to discounts of 40%, 10%, and $7\frac{1}{2}\%$.   *Ans.* $249.75.

57. The recorded measurement of a city block is 528 ft. By chaining carefully the length is 527.75 ft. Find the per cent of error in the recorded length. How wide is a man's lot recorded as 30 ft.?

Ans. 0.047%; 29.99 ft.

58. A sample of nickel steel contained 24.51% of nickel and 0.16% of carbon. How much of nickel and carbon, respectively, in 2240 lb. of nickel steel?   *Ans.* 549.024 lb.; 3.584 lb.

59. If a $3\frac{1}{2}\%$ nickel-steel rail is used to maintain a curve in a streetcar track, it lasts three times as long as carbon steel. How much will be saved per ton when one nickel-steel rail is worn out, if nickel steel costs $56 per long ton and carbon steel $28? It costs $2 a ton for laying, and the old rails are worth $16 per ton; also 20 cents per pound is realized on the nickel.   *Ans.* $15.68.

60. In an experiment to show the loss of pressure for different kinds of valves in water pipes, a globe valve in a 3-in. pipe caused the pressure to fall from 80 lb. to 41 lb. per square inch; while a gate valve caused a loss of pressure of 4 lb. per square inch.   Find (a) the per cent of loss for the globe valve; (b for the gate valve; (c) what per cent the loss through the gate valve is of the loss through the globe valve.

Ans. $48\frac{3}{4}\%$; 5%; 10.26%.

61. In an analysis of the best quality of crucible cast steel, the following was found: carbon 1.2%, silicon 0.112%, phosphorus 0.018%, manganese 0.36%, sulphur 0.02%, iron 98.29%.   Find the number of pounds of each substance if the total weight is 176.5 lb.

Ans. 2.118; 0.1977 −; 0.0318 −; 0.6354; 0.0353; 173.4818.

62. The mean effective pressure on the piston of a steam engine, found from the indicator diagram, was 59.75 lb. per square inch.   The boiler pressure was 87 lb. per square inch.   What per cent of the boiler pressure was the mean effective pressure?   *Ans.* 68.7%.

63. The grade of a railroad track is given in per cent.   A grade of 1% is a rise of 1 ft. in 100 ft.   If a railroad has a constant grade of $1\frac{1}{4}\%$, what is the rise in $3\frac{1}{2}$ miles?   *Ans.* 231 ft.

64. The total rise in a $1\frac{3}{4}\%$ grade is 43.6 ft.   Find the length of the track having this grade.   *Ans.* 2491 ft., approx.

65. A railroad rises 112.7 ft. in $3\frac{1}{2}$ miles.   Find the average grade.

Ans. 0.61 − %.

SIMPLE INTEREST

75. Interest is money that is paid for the use of money.   It is usually reckoned at a certain rate per cent per year.   The base on which the interest is reckoned is called the **principal.** In percentage, the time did not enter, but in reckoning interest the time has to be taken into account.   The interest on a sum of money for 1 *year* at a certain rate is the principal multiplied by the rate; for 2 *years*, it is twice as much; and for any period of time, it is the interest for 1 year multiplied by the time in years.

If p stands for principal, I for interest, r for rate per cent, and t for time in years, the interest is found by the formula

$$I = p \times r \times t$$

The **amount** A is the principal plus the interest.

Many short methods for reckoning interest can be given, but it is not our intention to enter into them here.

Example 1.—Find the interest and amount of $350 for 5 years at 4%.

$$I = p \times r \times t = \$350 \times 0.04 \times 5 = \$70$$
$$A = p + I = \$350 + \$70 = \$420 \quad Ans.$$

Example 2.—Find the interest on $750 for 2 years 7 months at 2%.

Here the time is $\frac{31}{12}$ years, for in getting the time in years we must use 12 months for a year, 30 days for a month, and 360 days for a year.

$$\therefore I = \$750 \times 0.02 \times \tfrac{31}{12} = \$38.75 \quad Ans.$$

It is usually best to use cancellation.

Thus, $\qquad \dfrac{750 \times 2 \times 31}{100 \times 12} = 38.75 \quad Ans.$

Example 3.—Find the interest on $375 for 2 years 5 months 15 days at 2%.

Here the time is $\frac{885}{360}$ years.

$$\therefore I = \$375 \times 0.02 \times \tfrac{885}{360} = \$18.44 \quad Ans.$$

EXERCISES

Find the interest and amount of each of the following:

1. $700 for 3 years at 4%. *Ans.* $84; $784.

2. $14.30 for 2 years 9 months at 2%. *Ans.* $0.7865 interest.

3. $245.60 for 2 years 7 months 21 days at 4%. $25.95 interest.

4. $436.75 for 1 year 2 months 15 days at 5%.

Ans. $26.39 interest.

5. $325.25 for 2 years 9 months 12 days at $3\frac{1}{4}$%.

Ans. $29.42 interest.

6. $87.50 for 3 years 3 months at $3\frac{1}{2}$%. *Ans.* $9.955 interest.

7. $480 for 6 years 3 months at 15%. *Ans.* $450 interest.

8. $18.20 for 9 years 9 months at $5\frac{3}{4}$%. *Ans.* $10.20 interest.

9. A note for $225 at 3% runs for 9 months. What is the amount of the note when due? *Ans.* $230.0625.

10. A note for $390 at $3\frac{1}{2}$% runs for 3 years 6 months. What is the amount due? *Ans.* $437.775.

11. A bought a house from B on a contract for $10,000 and paid $1500 on delivery Apr. 1. The terms of the contract require the payment of $135 on the first of each month, which is to pay the interest on the balance of the principal at 6% for the previous month and the remainder is applied as a payment on the principal. Make a table showing the interest paid, the payment on the principal, and the balance for the first of each month from May 1 to Sept. 1, inclusive.

NOTE: 6% per year = $\frac{1}{2}$% per month. Thus, the interest due on May 1 is

$$I = (\$10{,}000 - \$1500)(0.005)$$
$$I = \$42.50, \text{ etc.}$$

CHAPTER VII

RATIO AND PROPORTION

76. A very common thing to do in dealing with numbers is to compare two numbers as to their size. In division we compare the size of 100 and 500 by dividing 500 by 100, and say that 500 is 5 times as large as 100. In fractions we may think of 100 as $\frac{1}{5}$ of 500. In percentage 100 is found to be 20% of 500. Another way of comparing these numbers as to size is to say that they are in the ratio of 1 to 5, and write it 1:5. In the same manner, we say that 20 and 30 are in the ratio of 2:3. This is a very convenient way of comparing numbers.

77. Ratio.—The **ratio** of one number to another is the quotient of the first number divided by the second.

Thus, the ratio of $6 to $2 is 3, and may be stated in the form $\frac{\$6}{\$2}$ or $6:$2. In either case it is read "the ratio of $6 to $2."

From the idea of a ratio it is evident that we can state a ratio between two magnitudes only when the magnitudes are alike. That is, a ratio cannot be stated between such quantities as dollars and bushels.

The two numbers used in a ratio are called the **terms** of the ratio. The first one is named the **antecedent** and is the dividend; the second is named the **consequent** and is the divisor.

The ratio 2:3 is the **inverse** of the ratio 3:2.

Since a ratio in the form 4:3 is an indicated division or a fraction, the principles applying in division or to a fraction likewise apply to a ratio.

Thus, the ratio 10:15 can be changed to the ratio 2:3 by dividing both terms of the ratio by 5. This is exactly the same as reducing a fraction to its lowest terms.

In stating the relations between the magnitudes of numbers, there are several expressions more or less in common use. The expressions *in the same ratio as, in the same proportion, proportionally,* and *pro rata* all have practically the same meaning.

When it is said that $20 is divided between two men in the ratio of 2 to 3, it is meant that one gets $2 as often as the other gets $3. That is, of each $5, one gets $2 and the other $3. Hence one gets $\frac{2}{5}$ of $20 or $8, and the other gets $\frac{3}{5}$ of $20 or $12.

It should be carefully noted that the statement that one number is 20% of another is the same as stating that the two numbers are in the ratio of 20 to 100. It is then easy to change a comparison of two numbers stated as a per cent to a ratio statement and *vice versa*.

78. The ratio idea in measuring.—The ratio idea enters into all measurements. The **measurement** of any magnitude is the process of finding its *ratio* to another magnitude of the same kind, which is arbitrarily chosen as the unit of measure. The **measure** of the magnitude is this ratio and is an abstract number. For instance, the length of a room is measured by choosing a unit of length, say 1 ft., and finding the ratio between the unit and the length of the room.

In our manner of speaking in English, it is customary, in giving the measure of a magnitude, to use a phrase made up of the number, which is the measure, and the name of the unit chosen. Thus, we say the length of a room is 30 ft., where 30 is the *measure* and the unit is described by the word feet; that is, the measure of the length of the room is the ratio of 30 ft. to 1 ft., and is 30.

EXERCISES

1. Find the value of the following ratios: 10:2; 8:5; 18:2.5; 25 hr.:3 hr.; 9 ft.:2 ft.; 5.5:4.5; 8.8:16.

2. A room is 18 ft. by 12 ft. What is the ratio of its length to its width?

3. Two gear wheels have 90 teeth and 20 teeth, respectively. What is the ratio of the numbers of teeth?

4. One city has a population of 8000 and a second a population of 20,000. What is the ratio of their populations? What part is the first of the second? What per cent? How many times as large as the first is the second? What difference is there in the ideas involved in the questions?

5. Write the inverse ratios of the following: 7:5; 8:2.5; $12:$20; 4.5 yd.:45 yd.

6. Divide 80 apples between two boys in the ratio of 5:3.

Ans. 50 to 30.

7. If a man can fly from Chicago to New York in 3 hr. 55 min. and go by train in 16 hr., what is the ratio of flying time to train time?

Ans. 47 to 192.

8. Fifty-one students entered a class and 33 of them finished the work. What per cent finished? What is the ratio of the number that finished to the whole number? *Ans.* $65 - \%$; 11 to 17.

9. A man and his son earn $60 per week. The ratio of their earnings is 5:1. What does each earn per week? *Ans.* Man, $50; son, $10.

10. Four men owning adjoining lots with frontages of 25, 35, 50, and 75 ft., respectively, on the same street are assessed a total of $1500 for paving. Find the amount each should pay.

11. The efficiency of a machine is the ratio of the output to the input and is usually expressed as a per cent:

$$\text{Efficiency} = \frac{\text{output}}{\text{input}} \quad \text{(see Art. 72)}$$

The input in a motor is 6000 watts and the output 5300 watts. What is the efficiency? When the efficiency is expressed in per cent, it is still a ratio with 100 for the denominator, or the consequent. *Ans.* $88\frac{1}{3}\%$.

12. If the efficiency of a machine is 91% and the input 98 horsepower, what is the output? *Ans.* 89.18 hp.

13. If the efficiency of a motor is 98% and the output 730 watts, what is the input? *Ans.* 745 watts, approx.

14. The output of a machine is 1040 horsepower and the loss 100 horsepower. What is the efficiency? *Ans.* $91.2 + \%$.

15. In a divided electric circuit, the current flowing divides in the same ratio as the ratio of the resistances of the two parts. The two resistances of a divided circuit are 65 and 75 ohms, respectively; and the current is 14 amperes; find the current flowing in each part.

Ans. 6.5 and 7.5 amperes.

PROPORTION

79. A proportion is a statement of equality between two ratios. Thus, 2:3 = 4:6 and 4 men:8 men = $6:$12 are proportions.

The first and last terms of a proportion are called the **extremes.** The second and third terms are called the **means.** In the first proportion above, 2 and 6 are the extremes and 3 and 4 the means.

There are fashions in mathematics as there are in millinery, but the changes are not as frequent. Two and three centuries ago the "Golden Rule," as it was called, was widely used; later, and reaching well into the last century, this was called the "Rule of Three." It was considered the best method for solving a great variety of problems and occupied a consider-able part of arithmetic. In later years this rule was called proportion, and was deemed of importance till some thirty years ago. To-day proportion is given a minor place in our arithmetics, but is still considered convenient in solving certain problems especially in chemistry. It will repay one to become familiar with the methods of proportion as it gives another tool with which to work.

The more modern form for a proportion is the fractional form. Thus, $\frac{2}{3} = \frac{4}{6}$ has exactly the same meaning as $2:3 = 4:6$. Either form may be read "2 is to 3 as 4 is to 6."

80. Principles and methods.—By inspecting several pro-portions the following principles will be evident:

(1) *The product of the means of any proportion is equal to the product of the extremes.*

(2) *The product of the two means divided by either extreme gives the other extreme.*

(3) *The product of the two extremes divided by either mean gives the other mean.*

Example 1.—Find the value of h from the proportion $25:100 = 7:h$.

Solution.—Applying principle (2), $h = \dfrac{100 \times 7}{25} = 28.$ *Ans.*

Example 2.—If 15 tons of coal cost \$63 what will 27 tons cost at the same rate per ton?

Solution.—Since the same relation holds between the cost prices as between the amounts of coal, the ratio of 15 tons to 27 tons must equal the ratio $63 to the cost of 27 tons. Let x stand for the number of dollars 27 tons cost, and we can state the proportion

$$15:27 = 63:x$$
$$\therefore x = \frac{27 \times 63}{15} = 113.40$$

Therefore, 27 tons cost $113.40. *Ans.*

Example 3.—If 25 men can do a piece of work in 30 days, in how many days can 35 men do the same work?

Solution.—It is evident that 35 men can do the work in less time than 25 men; hence the ratio of the number of days is equal to the inverse ratio of the number of men. Using x for the number of days required,

$$35:25 = 30:x$$
$$\therefore x = \frac{25 \times 30}{35} = 21\frac{3}{7}$$

Therefore, 35 men can do the work in $21\frac{3}{7}$ days. *Ans.*

Example 4.—An inclined plane, as shown in Fig. 19, rises 38 ft. in 100 ft., find the height h it will rise in 28 ft.

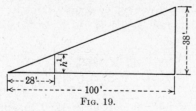

Fig. 19.

Solution.—Here the proportion is

$$100:28 = 38:h$$
$$\therefore h = \frac{28 \times 38}{100} = 10.64$$

Therefore, the rise in 28 ft. is 10.64 ft. *Ans.*

The proportion could as well be stated $100:38 = 28:h$.

Definition.—If the rise of a road bed is h ft. in 100 ft., the **grade** of the road is $\dfrac{h}{100}$, or the ratio of the rise to the horizontal distance. Thus, if a road rises 3 ft. in 100 ft. the grade is $\dfrac{3}{100} = 3\%$.

Example 5.—What is the grade of a road bed that rises 1.2 ft. in a horizontal distance of 40 ft.?

Solution.—Let h stand for the number of feet rise in 100 ft. It is evident that the ratio $\dfrac{h}{100}$ = the ratio $\dfrac{1.2}{40}$. But $\dfrac{1.2}{40} = 0.03$. Therefore, the grade is 0.03 or 3%. *Ans.*

Example 6.—If a bell metal is 25 parts copper to 12 parts tin, what is the weight of each in a bell weighing 1850 lb.?

Solution.—The ratio of the number of parts of each metal to the whole number of parts equals the ratio of the weight of each metal to the whole weight. Use c to stand for the number of pounds of copper and t for the tin. Then we have

$$25:37 = c:1850$$

and

$$12:37 = t:1850$$
$$\therefore c = \frac{25 \times 1850}{37} = 1250$$

and

$$t = \frac{12 \times 1850}{37} = 600$$

Therefore, the weight of copper is 1250 lb. and the weight of tin is 600 lb.

EXERCISES

Find the values of the letters in Exercises 1 to 6.

1. $70:45 = 14:x$.   *Ans.* 9.
2. $3\frac{1}{4}:7\frac{4}{5} = 15:x$.   *Ans.* 36.
3. $h:2.5 = 25:100$.   *Ans.* 0.625.
4. $75:r = 3\frac{1}{8}:\frac{1}{5}$.   *Ans.* 4.8.
5. $65:75 = x:85$.   *Ans.* $73\frac{2}{3}$.
6. $T:1.5 = 1.5:30$.   *Ans.* 0.075.

7. If a boat drifts down stream 40 miles in 12 hr., how far will it drift in 15 hr.? *Ans.* 50 miles.

8. If 5 men can do a piece of work in 40 days, how long will it take 25 men to do it? *Ans.* 8 days.

9. On June 12, 1939, a pilot flew a glider plane across Lake Michigan a total distance of 92 miles in 52 min. He cut loose from the tow plane at 13,000 ft. and descended only 5000 ft. in crossing. At the same rate of descent, how much farther could he have glided? How many more minutes would he have been in the air? *Ans.* 147.2 miles; 83.2 min.

10. A roadbed rises $3\frac{1}{3}$ ft. in a horizontal distance of 300 ft. What is the grade? In how many feet will it rise 1 ft.? *Ans.* $1\frac{1}{9}\%$ grade; 90.

11. If 3 lb. of apples cost 25 cents, find the cost of 60 lb. at the same rate. *Ans.* \$5.

12. If 16 gal. of gas will drive a car 288 miles, at the same rate of using gas, how many gallons will it take to drive the same car from Chicago to Memphis, a distance of 564 miles? *Ans.* $31\frac{1}{3}$ gal.

13. The mixture for a casting has 4 parts of copper, 3 parts lead, and 2 parts tin. How many pounds of each in a casting weighing 96 lb.?
Ans. $42\frac{2}{3}$; 32; $21\frac{1}{3}$.

14. If the upkeep on 62 trucks for a year is \$3100, what would be the upkeep on 48 such trucks for 1 year at the same rate? *Ans.* \$2400.

15. On a certain map $1\frac{1}{2}$ in. represent 50 miles. How many miles are between two cities that are 5 in. apart on the map? *Ans.* $166\frac{2}{3}$.

16. An iron casting weighs 142 lb. and costs \$7.25. At the same rate, what is the cost of a casting weighing 255 lb.? *Ans.* \$13.02.

17. The number of revolutions of two gears in mesh is inversely proportional to the number of teeth in the gears. If the number of teeth in the gear wheels is 15 and 48, respectively, and the R. P. M. of the smaller is 40, find the R. P. M. of the larger. *Ans.* $12\frac{1}{2}$.

18. The volume of a quantity of gas is inversely proportional to the pressure upon it. If the volume of a quantity of gas is 740 cu. ft. under a pressure of 16 lb. per square inch, how many cubic feet will there be when under a pressure of 30 lb. per square inch? *Ans.* $394\frac{2}{3}$.

19. A 10% solution of silver nitrate is formed by dissolving 10 grams of silver nitrate in 100 cc. of water. How many grams of silver nitrate should be used in 745 cc. of water to make a 10% solution?
Ans. $74\frac{1}{2}$.

20. A steel rail in a railroad track expands 0.00000636 in. for every inch of length for each degree increase in temperature. If a steel rail is 32 ft. long, what is the change in length due to a change from a winter temperature of 20 below zero to a summer temperature of 110 degrees above zero? *Ans.* 0.3175 in.

Work the following 4 exercises by proportion:

21. What per cent is 59.1 of 51.3?

Solution.—Let 100% stand for the base; then, using x for the number of per cent required, the proportion is

$$51.3 : 59.1 = 100 : x$$
$$\therefore x = \frac{59.1 \times 100}{51.3} = 115.2$$

Therefore, 59.1 is 115.2% of 51.3.

    22. 36 is what per cent of 80?   *Ans.* 45.

    23. 248 is 21% of what number?   *Ans.* 1180.95+.

    24. If 4% of my money is $2.88, how much money have I?

                                                      Ans. $72.

81. Measuring heights.—There are several methods for determining the height of a standing tree.

(1) One of the simplest is to measure the shadow of the tree and the shadow of a straight pole of known length set upright in the ground. Then if H stands for the height of the tree, h for the height of the pole, S for the length of the shadow of the tree, s for that of the pole, we have the proportion

$$s : S = h : H$$

The two following methods with the figures are given in a bulletin of the Bureau of Forestry, U. S. Department of Agriculture.

(2) A method used when the sun is not shining is to set two poles in a line with the tree as shown in Fig. 20. From a point S on one pole sight across the second pole to the base and to the top of the tree. Let an assistant note the points a and b where the lines of vision cross the second pole and measure the distance between these points, ab, also measure the distance from the sighting point on the first pole to the base of the tree, SB, and to the lowest point on the second pole, Sb. Then the following proportion is true:

$$Sb : SB = ab : AB$$

(3) Another method sometimes used is as follows: The observer walks on level ground to a point A at a convenient distance AD from the foot of the tree. He then lies on his

back as shown in Fig. 21. An assistant notes on an upright staff erected at his feet the exact point C where his line of vision to the top of the tree E crosses the staff. The height

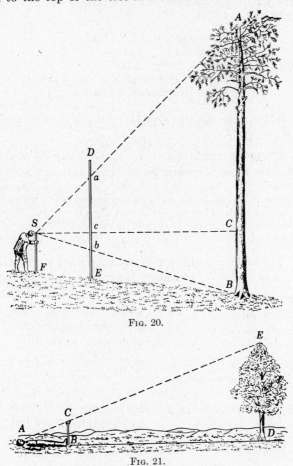

Fig. 20.

Fig. 21.

of the staff BC is measured, and his own height AB from his feet to this eyes, then the following proportion is true:

$$AB:BC = AD:DE$$

EXERCISES

1. Find the height of a tree that casts a shadow 115 ft. long when a pole 8 ft. high casts a shadow of 5 ft.   Use method (1).

Solution: 5:8 = 115:H.

$$\therefore H = \frac{115 \times 8}{5} = 184$$

Therefore, height of tree is 184 ft.   *Ans.*

2. Find the height of a church steeple that casts a shadow 84 ft. long when a pole 11 ft. long casts a shadow of 7 ft. 9 in.

Ans. 119 ft. approx.

3. Find the height of a tree when Sb = 6 ft., SB = 40 ft., and ab = 9 ft.   Use method (2).   *Ans.* 60 ft.

4. Find the height of the tree DE if AB = $5\frac{1}{2}$ ft., BC = 8 ft., and AD = 90 ft.   Use method (3).   *Ans.* 131 ft. approx.

5. Find the height of a tree when AB = 5 ft. 10 in., BC = 10 ft., and AD = 112 ft.   *Ans.* 192 ft.

6. A tree 150 ft. tall stands on horizontal ground 600 ft. from a vertical cliff.   A man whose eyes are $5\frac{1}{2}$ ft. from the ground, standing 200 ft. from the tree, sees the top of the cliff in line with the top of the tree. How high is the cliff?   *Ans.* $583\frac{1}{2}$ ft.

82. The lever.—A stiff bar or rod supported at some pivotal point, about which it can move freely, is called a **lever.**   The

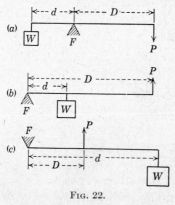

pivotal point is called the **fulcrum.**   The lever enters in one form or another into many mechanical devices.

In Fig. 22, F is the fulcrum, W the weight lifted, P the force that does the lifting, D the distance from the fulcrum to the point of application of the force, and d the distance from the fulcrum to the point where the weight is attached.   In all possible relations of the fulcrum,

Fig. 22.

weight, and force the following proportion holds:

$$P:W = d:D$$

That is, the applied force is to the weight inversely as their distances from the fulcrum. This means that a small force will balance a larger weight only if the weight is nearer the fulcrum than the force.

EXERCISES

1. Given $P = 150$ lb., $D = 12\frac{1}{2}$ ft., $d = 1\frac{1}{2}$ ft., find W.

Ans. 1250 lb.

2. Given $P = 200$ lb., $D = 9\frac{3}{4}$ ft., $W = 775$ lb., find d.

Ans. 2 ft. 6.2 − in.

3. Given $P = 160$ lb., $W = 900$ lb., $d = 1\frac{1}{4}$ ft., find D.

Ans. 7 ft. $\frac{3}{8}$ in.

4. Given $W = 160$ lb., $D = 3\frac{1}{2}$ ft., $d = 8\frac{1}{3}$ ft., find P.

Ans. 381 lb. approx.

5. In a wire cutter the wire is placed $\frac{1}{2}$ in. from the fulcrum and the pressure of the hand is 7 in. from the fulcrum. Find the resistance of the wire if the hand exerts a force of 40 lb. *Ans.* 560 lb.

6. In pulling a nail from a board with a hammer, as shown in Fig. 23, find the resistance of the nail at the start if $P = 50$ lb., $D = 10$ in., and $d = 1\frac{1}{2}$ in. *Ans.* $333\frac{1}{3}$ lb.

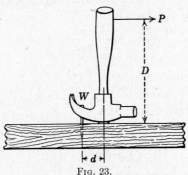

Fig. 23.

7. In the ordinary steelyard (Fig. 24) what must be the weight P to balance a weight W of $17\frac{1}{2}$ lb. if it is $1\frac{1}{4}$ in. from fulcrum to application of W and $8\frac{1}{2}$ in. from application of P to fulcrum?

Ans. 2 lb. 9.2 − oz.

8. If the steelyard is turned over so that the distance from the fulcrum to W is $\frac{1}{2}$ in., what weight W will $1\frac{1}{2}$ lb. at P balance when P is $20\frac{3}{4}$ in. from the fulcrum? *Ans.* $62\frac{1}{4}$ lb.

9. In Fig. 25, what pull at B will balance a pull of 50 lb. at A?

Ans. 130 lb.

83. Hydraulic machines.—A principle known as *Pascal's Law* states that pressure exerted on a liquid in a closed vessel

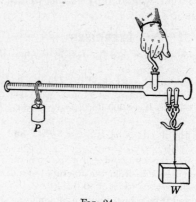

Fig. 24.

is transmitted equally and undiminished in all directions.

In Fig. 26, if the area of a is 1 sq. in., then a pressure of 1 lb. at a gives a pressure of 1 lb. on each square inch of the surface of C. If the area of the top of C is 100 sq. in., then a pressure of 1 lb. at a will lift a weight of 100 lb. at A.

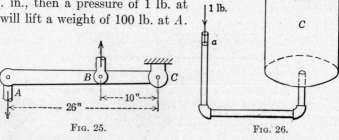

Fig. 25.   Fig. 26.

If a, A, p, and P are the areas and pressures, respectively, then we have the proportion

$$a:A = p:P$$

EXERCISES

1. A pressure of 5 lb. on the cork of a jug filled with water gives how many pounds pressure tending to force out the bottom of the jug? The area of the cork is $1\frac{1}{2}$ sq. in. and the area of the bottom is 245.6 sq. in.

Ans. $818\frac{2}{3}$ lb.

2. A hydraulic lifter used to raise heavy weights, has the pressure applied to a piston having an area of $\frac{1}{2}$ sq. in. by a lever. The distance from the fulcrum to the point attached to the small piston is 4 in. and to the point where a force of 100 lb. is applied in 22 in. Find the weight that can be raised on a piston having an area of 75.6 sq. in.

Solution.—Let x = pressure in pounds applied on small piston
Then $100:x = 4:22$. From which $x = 550$.
And $0.5:75.6 = 550:P$.

$$\therefore P = \frac{550 \times 75.6}{0.5} = 83,160$$

Hence a weight of 83,160 lb. can be raised. *Ans.*

3. A supply pipe for a 14-in. plunger hydraulic elevator piston is $1\frac{1}{4}$ sq. in. in area, and the pressure in the supply pipe is pumped up to 150 lb. per square inch. What is the total pressure on the 14-in. plunger if it has an area of 153.94 sq. in.? *Ans.* 18,473 lb.

DENSITY AND SPECIFIC GRAVITY

84. Density.—Experience tells us that some bodies are heavier than others; that is, of two bodies of the same size, one weighs more than the other. Take a cubic foot of metal and one of wood; suppose the metal weighs 500 lb. and the wood 50 lb., then the metal is ten times as heavy as the wood, or the ratio of their densities is as 10 to 1. We also say that the density of the metal is 500 lb. per cubic foot.

Water has a density of about 62.5 lb. per cubic foot. In the metric system the density of water under standard conditions is one gram per cubic centimeter.

The **density** of a body is its mass per unit volume. For our purpose the mass is the same as the weight. Strictly speaking, the weight of a body near the earth is the force with which the earth attracts the mass of the body.

85. Specific gravity.—The term specific gravity is used for the ratio of the densities of two bodies. Thus, the specific gravity of the metal with reference to the wood is 10, which means that the metal is ten times as heavy as the wood. It should be carefully noticed that the specific gravity of a substance is an abstract number, that is, a number with no name attached.

86. Standards.—For convenience the standard to which other substances are referred, in stating specific gravities, is water for solids and liquids.

The specific gravity of a substance is obtained by finding the weight of a certain volume of it and dividing this weight by the weight of the same volume of the standard. Thus, to find the specific gravity of a stone, it is necessary to find its weight, and the weight of an equal volume of water. The weight of the stone divided by the weight of the water gives the specific gravity of the stone.

To find the specific gravity of a solid that is heavier than water, weigh it in air and then in water. Find the difference between its weight in air and its weight in water. This difference is the buoyant force of the water on the solid and is equal to the weight of the water displaced by the solid; that is, it is the weight of water having the same volume as the solid. Divide the weight of the solid in air by the difference, or the weight of an equal volume of water, and the ratio is the specific gravity of the solid.

The specific gravity of any other body could be found in the same manner. Some difficulty might be found in doing the weighing, but a little ingenuity will devise a plan. Various methods for doing the weighing are discussed in physics.

Water is taken as the standard because of its abundance. All substances can be referred to it, but gases are usually compared with air or hydrogen gas.

If w stands for the weight of the body whose specific gravity is to be found, s the weight of the same volume of the standard, and g for the specific gravity, the rule may be stated as a formula:

$$w \div s = g$$

87. Use.—Tables of the specific gravities of the various substances are given for use in making computations. In Table VII are given the specific gravities of a few of the more common substances.

If it is required to find the weight of a block of iron 2 by 3 by 1 ft. we could find the number of cubic feet in the block which is 6. This times the weight of a cubic foot of water gives the weight of an equal volume of water, or $62.5 \times 6 = 375$ lb. The weight of the water multiplied by the specific gravity of iron gives the weight of the iron, or

$$375 \text{ lb.} \times 7.2 = 2700 \text{ lb.}$$

In terms of the letters already used, since $w \div s = g$,

$$w = s \times g$$

In chemistry and other sciences where the metric system is used, the term *density* is often used instead of specific gravity. This is because density is the weight of the unit volume of a substance, the unit of volume is the cubic centimeter, and the unit of weight is the gram. Then the number of grams of density of a substance is the same as the number that expresses the specific gravity of the substance.

Example 1.—Find the specific gravity of a rock if 1 cu. ft. of it weighs 182 lb.

Solution.—Since water weighs 62.5 lb. per cubic foot the specific gravity of the rock is found thus:

$$182 \text{ lb.} \div 62.5 \text{ lb.} = 2.912$$
$$\therefore \text{ Specific gravity of the rock is 2.912} \quad Ans.$$

Example 2.—How many cubic inches are there in 1 lb. of cork, if its specific gravity is 0.24?

Solution.—Since 1728 cu. in. of water weigh 62.5 lb., 1728 cu. in. of cork weigh 0.24×62.5 lb.

$$\therefore \text{ 1 cu. in. of cork weighs } \frac{0.24 \times 62.5}{1728} \text{ lb.}$$

And

$$1 \div \frac{0.24 \times 62.5}{1728} = \frac{1728}{0.24 \times 62.5} = 115.2$$

∴ There are 115.2 cu. in. in 1 lb. of cork.   *Ans.*

EXERCISES

1. Find the weights of the following: 12 cu. in. of rolled copper; 21 cu. ft. of cast iron; 231 cu. in. of nickel.   (See Table VII.)
Ans. 3.828 lb.; 9450 lb.; 73.458 lb.

2. A body weighs 4 lb. in air and 2.5 lb. in water.   Find its specific gravity.   *Ans.* $2\frac{2}{5}$.

3. What will the body in Exercise 2 weigh in alcohol of specific gravity 0.818?   *Ans.* 2.773 lb.

4. A stone weighs 20 lb. in air and loses 20% of its weight when submerged in water.   Find its specific gravity.   *Ans.* 5.

5. The specific gravity of a machine oil is 0.875.   What would a 5-gal. can of this oil weigh?   Use 7.5 gal. = 1 cu. ft.   *Ans.* $36\frac{11}{24}$ lb.

6. What would 1 bbl. of 31.5 gal., or 4.2 cu. ft., of glycerine weigh if the specific gravity of glycerine is 1.26?   *Ans.* 330.75 lb.

7. A 1000-cc. flask weighs 75 g., and when one half is filled with water and the other with glycerine, it weighs 1205 g.   What is the specific gravity of the glycerine?   *Ans.* 1.26.

8. A body floats half-submerged in alcohol of specific gravity 0.818. What part of its volume would be submerged in water?   *Ans.* 0.409.

9. Given 1 cu. in. of lead and 1 of gold, find the ratio of their weights in air.   What would be the ratio of their weights if both were submerged in water?

10. What is the specific gravity of a substance if 50 cu. in. of it weigh 8 lb. in air?   *Ans.* 4.424+.

11. If the specific gravity of sea water is 1.025 and that of ice 0.92, what fraction of an iceberg floating in the sea is under water?
Ans. 89.75%.

12. If a glass stopper weighs 150 g. in air, 90 g. in water, and 42 g. in sulphuric acid, what is the specific gravity of the acid?   *Ans.* 1.8.

13. A hollow steel ball weighs 1 kg.   What must be its volume so that it will just float in water?   *Ans.* 1000 cc.; 61+ cu. in.

14. Find the number of liters in a vat 2 m. × 75 cm. × 50 cm.   Also find the weight in kg. of the sulphuric acid (s. g. 1.84) required to fill it.
Ans. 750; 1380 kg.

15. Two cubic feet of cast iron immersed in water weigh how much?
Solution.—From Table VII 2 cu. ft. of cast iron weigh in air 2 × 450 lb. = 900 lb.

2 cu. ft. of water weigh 2 × 62.5 lb. = 125 lb.

Weight of iron in water = 900 lb. − 125 lb. = **775** lb.

16. Mercury weighs 13.596 times as much as water at its greatest density. What is the pressure per square centimeter of a column of mercury 76 cm. high? *Ans.* 1033.3 g.

17. A column of mercury how high would cause a pressure per square inch equal to 14.7 lb.? *Ans.* 29.89 in.

18. A tank 1.85 m. long, 1.35 m. wide, and 85 cm. deep is filled with sea water (s. g. 1.025). What is the weight of the water?

Ans. 2175.95 kg.

19. Sandstone of specific gravity 2.5 is crushed. Find the weight of 1 cu. yd. of the crushed stone if the voids are 35%. (See Ex. 38, Art. 74.)

Ans. 2742 lb.

20. Granite of specific gravity 2.8 is crushed. Find the weight of 1 cu. yd. of the crushed rock if voids are 40%. *Ans.* 2835 lb.

21. A casting of iron when immersed in water displaces 2 qt.; find the weight of the casting.

Solution: 2 qt. $= \frac{1}{2}$ gal. $= \frac{231}{2}$ cu. in.

From table, 1 cu. in. of cast iron weighs 0.26 lb.

Hence, the casting weighs $0.26 \times \frac{231}{2} = 30$ lb. *Ans.*

22. An irregular shaped steel forging was found to displace 6.75 qt. of water; find the weight of the forging. (Use sp. gr. of steel = 7.85.)

Ans. 111 lb.

23. A wooden pattern for a casting weighs $2\frac{3}{4}$ lb. An aluminum casting is to be made. Find the weight of the casting if the specific gravity of the wood is 0.52 and that of the aluminum is 2.6.

Solution.—Weight of equal volume of water weighs $2\frac{3}{4} \div 0.52$ lb.

Weight of aluminum $= (2\frac{3}{4} \div 0.52) \times 2.6 = 13\frac{3}{4}$ lb. *Ans.*

CHAPTER VIII

POWERS AND ROOTS

88. Powers.—When we have several numbers multiplied together, as $3 \times 4 \times 6 = 72$, we call the numbers 3, 4, and 6, **factors** and 72 the **product.** If now we make all the factors alike, as $3 \times 3 \times 3 \times 3 = 81$, we call the product by the special name **power.** We say 81 is a power of 3, and 3 is the **base** of the power.

A **power** is a product obtained by using a base a certain number of times as a factor.

If the base is used twice as a factor the power is called the second power; three times as a factor, the third power; and so on for any number of times.

89. Exponent of a power.—Instead of $3 \times 3 \times 3 \times 3$, we may write 3^4. The small figure, placed at the right and above the base, shows how many times the base is to be used as a factor, and is called an **exponent.**

The **exponent** of a **power** is a number placed to the right and above a base to show how many times the base is used as a factor.

It should be noted that the use of the exponent gives us a short concise way of writing a continued product where the factors are all alike.

Exponents were first used during the first half of the seventeenth century and came into quite general use during the following century.

90. Squares, cubes, involution.—The second power of a number is called the **square** of the number, as 3^2.

The third power of a number is called the **cube** of the number, as 5^3.

The higher powers, have no special names. 3^4 is called the **fourth power** of 3, 5^7 the **seventh power** of 5, etc.

Involution is the process of finding the powers of numbers.

EXERCISES

1. Find the square of 6; of 21; of 38; of 606. Find the square of the square of 2; of 5; of 10.

2. Find the cube of 4; of 9. Find the square of the cube of 3.

3. Find the fourth power of 6. Is the fourth power of a number equal to the square of the square of the number? Find the value of 3^4; of $(3^2)^2$.

4. Find values of the following: 792^2, 35^3, 3^4, 2^{16}.

Ans. 627,264; 42,875; 81; 65,536.

91. Roots.—If we take 9 and separate it into the two equal factors 3 and 3, that is, $9 = 3 \times 3$, then one of these factors, 3, is called the **square root** of 9. The process is just the inverse of that by which the power is found. Similarly $64 = 4 \times 4 \times 4$, and we say 4 is the **cube root** of 64.

The **square root** of a number is one of the two equal factors into which a number is divided.

The **cube root** is one of the three equal factors into which a number is divided; the **fourth root** is one of the four equal factors; and so on for the higher roots.

92. Radical sign and index of root.—To indicate a root, we use the sign $\sqrt{\ }$, which is called the **radical sign.** A small figure, called the **index** of the root, is placed in the opening of the radical sign to show what root is to be taken.

Thus, $\sqrt[3]{64}$ indicates the cube root of 64. The small 3 is the index of the root.

Since the square root is the most frequently written root, the index 2 is omitted.

Thus, the square root of 625 is written $\sqrt{625}$ and not $\sqrt[2]{625}$. Higher roots are indicated as $\sqrt[4]{243}$, $\sqrt[7]{128}$.

Evolution is the process of finding a root of a given number.

Often the root of a number can be seen by inspection. For instance, if one is to find the side of a square that contains 36 sq. in., it is readily seen that it must be 6 in. on a side. We say that $\sqrt{36} = 6$. In a like manner, one can determine by inspection that a cube containing 1728 cu. in. is 12 in. on an edge. Usually, however, a root of a number cannot be found by inspection. For instance, the side of a square containing 24 sq. in. cannot be determined readily. It now remains for us to devise methods and processes to find a root of any number.

93. Square root.—The numbers 1, 4, 9, 16, 25, 36, 49, 64, 81, which are the squares of the numbers 1, 2, 3, 4, 5, 6, 7, 8, 9, respectively, should be carefully remembered. It will be noticed that these are the only whole numbers less than 100 of which we can find the square roots. Such numbers as these are called **perfect squares.** As we pass to numbers above 100, the perfect squares become still more scarce.

The square root of 49 is 7, but the square root of 56 cannot be expressed as a whole number, nor can it be expressed as a decimal exactly. We can find it to any desired number of decimal places, and so as accurately as we wish.

The practical man who wishes to find the square root of a number does not care greatly why he goes through a certain process; but it is very important to him that he shall be able to find the root quickly and accurately. In what follows then the attempt is made to tell in as simple a manner as possible *how* to find the square root of a number.

94. Processes for the square root of a perfect square.

Example 1.—Find $\sqrt{522,729}$.

Explanation.—First, separate the number into **periods** of two figures each, beginning at the right, and placing a mark between them. The number of periods thus formed is equal to the number of figures in the root.

Process

```
         52'27'29(723  Root
         49
   142 | 327
       | 284
  1443 | 4329
       | 4329
```

In this number there are three periods, 52, 27, and 29, and there are three figures, 7, 2, and 3, in the root.

Find the largest perfect square which is equal to, or less than, the left-hand period, 52. This perfect square is 49. Write it under 52; and put its square root, 7, at the right as the first figure of the root. Now subtract 49 from 52 and bring down the next period, 27, and unite with the remainder 3, thus obtaining 327.

Take twice 7, the first figure of the root, and write it at the left of 327. Find how many times this, 14, is contained in 32, which is 2, for the second figure of the root. Place this figure 2 in the root, and also at the right of 14, making 142. Now multiply 142 by 2, and write the product, 284, under 327. Subtract 284 from 327 and bring down and unite the next period, 29, with the remainder, 43, thus obtaining 4329.

In the above work 327 is called the **first remainder;** 14, the **trial divisor;** 142, the **true divisor;** and 4329, the **second remainder.**

Next multiply 72 by 2, and write it at the left of 4329 as the second trial divisor. Find how many times 144 is contained in 432, which is 3, for the third figure of the root. Place this figure, 3, in the root and also at the right of 144, making 1443, the second true divisor. Multiply 1443 by 3 and write the product under 4329. This gives no remainder. Therefore, 723 is the exact square root of 522,729, that is, 723 × 723 = 522,729.

Example 2.—Find $\sqrt{6,780,816}$.

Process

Explanation.—First, separate the number into periods of two figures each as in Example 1. As before, we find the greatest square, 4, in the left-hand period, write it under 6 and put

$$
\begin{array}{r}
6'78'08'16(\underline{2604}\ Root \\
4 \\
46\ \overline{)278} \\
276 \\
5204\ \overline{)20816} \\
20816
\end{array}
$$

the square root, 2, of this square for the first figure of the root. Subtract the square, 4, from 6, and bring down the next period, 78, and unite it with the 2, making the first remainder, 278.

Take twice 2 for a trial divisor. Find how many times it is contained in the first remainder, except the right-hand figure; that is, find how many times 4 is contained in 27. The number is 6, which write as the second figure of the root, and also at the right of the trial divisor. This makes 46 the true divisor. Multiply the true divisor by 6, and subtract the product, 276, from the first remainder. Bring down and unite the next period to the difference, making the second remainder, 208.

Multiply the root already found by 2, and get the second trial divisor, 52. Find how many times this is contained in 20, which gives 0 for the next figure of the root. Place this 0 in the root and also at the right of 52, making 520, the second true divisor. Now, since the 0 written in the root is the multiplier, nothing is gained by multiplying the true divisor by it, and subtracting from 208. This part of the process is omitted, and the next period, 16, is united with 208, making 20,816, the third remainder.

The third trial divisor is twice the root, 260, which gives 520. This is contained in 2081, 4 times. Place the 4 as the next figure of the root, and also at the right of 520, making 5204, the third true divisor. Multiply this by 4 and subtract from the third remainder. As the remainder is zero, 2604 is the exact square root of 6,780,816.

95. Square root of a number containing a decimal.

Example.—Find $\sqrt{665.1241}$.

Explanation.—Here the division into periods is made by beginning at the decimal point and going in both directions. The rest of the work is the same as in Examples 1 and 2, Art. 94.

Process

```
      6'65.'12'41  (25.79 Root
      4
 45  |265
     |225
507  |4012
     |3549
5149 |46341
     |46341
```

The student should note that the second trial divisor, 50, is contained 8 times in the first three figures of the second remainder, 4012. However, if 8 were used as the root, it would give a number larger than 4012 when the true divisor was multiplied by it. The relations noted here should help to make clear why we give to the trial divisor its name.

The decimal point in the root is so placed that there are as many whole number *figures* in the root as there are whole number *periods* in the number of which the root is extracted. The position of the decimal point can also be determined so that there are as many decimal places in the root as there are decimal periods in the number of which the root is being extracted.

If the decimal part of the number consists of an odd number of figures a zero is annexed to make a full period at the right. Thus, in pointing off 53.76542 into periods, it is 53'.76'54'20.

96. Roots not exact.—Most numbers are not perfect squares, but the roots may be found to any desired number of decimal places. When extracting the root of a number not a perfect square, one must determine how many decimal places he wishes in the answer, and then annex zeros at the right of the number till there are as many decimal **periods** as there are to be decimal **places** in the root. The root is then extracted in the usual manner. We stop when the desired number of figures is found in the root.

Example.—Find $\sqrt{27}$ to three decimal places in the root.

Process

Explanation.—Since three decimal places are required in the root, annex three periods of zeros at the right of 27. These are the decimal periods. Extract the root as before. Place the decimal point in the root as in example of Art. 95. It will be

$$
\begin{array}{r}
27.'00'00'00(\underline{5.196}\ Root \\
25 \\
101\ |\ \overline{200} \\
|\ 101 \\
1029\ |\ \overline{9900} \\
|\ 9261 \\
10386\ |\ \overline{63900} \\
|\ 62316 \\
\overline{1584}
\end{array}
$$

noticed that there is a remainder; this is disregarded as it affects the next figures only, that is, the fourth and following figures in the decimal part of the root.

97. Root of a common fraction.—If the numerator and the denominator of the fraction are each a perfect square, find the square root of each separately.

Example 1.—Find $\sqrt{\frac{144}{625}}$.

$\sqrt{144} = 12$, and $\sqrt{625} = 25$.

Hence, $\sqrt{\frac{144}{625}} = \frac{12}{25}$. *Ans.*

If the numerator and denominator are not each a perfect square, reduce the fraction to a decimal and then extract the square root as in Art. 95.

Example 2.—Find $\sqrt{\frac{2}{7}}$.

Reducing to a decimal, $\frac{2}{7} = 0.28571428 \cdots$.

$$\sqrt{0.28571428} = 0.5345$$

Hence, $\sqrt{\frac{2}{7}} = 0.5345$ to four decimal places. *Ans.*

It is worth noting here that the square root of $\frac{2}{7}$ may be found by extracting the square root of both numerator and denominator, and then dividing the square root of the numerator by the square root of the denominator. This process would require two extractions of roots and one long division, and so make the work about three times what it is if the fraction is first reduced to a decimal and then the root extracted.

98. Short methods. *Partly division.*—If it is required to extract the square root of a number to, say, five decimal places, making, say, seven figures in the root, the work may be shortened by extracting the root in the usual way till four figures are obtained, and then dividing the last remainder found by the corresponding trial divisor to obtain the last three figures of the root. In general, extract root till more than *half* the required number of figures are found, and then for the other figures of the root divide the remainder by the corresponding trial divisor.

Process

Example 1.—Find $\sqrt{178}$ to five decimal places.

$$1'78.'00'00'00'00(13.34166 \; Root$$

The process may be contracted still further by using contracted division when dividing.

```
    1'78.'00'00'00'00(13.34166 Root
    1
23 | 78
   | 69
263 | 900
    | 789
2664 |11100
     |10656
2668)   444000(166
        2668
        17720
        16008
        17120
        16008
        1112
```

Method by factoring.—When the number of which the square root is to be extracted can be factored into two factors, one of which is a perfect square and the other the number 2, 3, 5, 6, or 7, a very useful short method may be obtained. For this purpose it is necessary to have found the following square roots:

$$\sqrt{2} = 1.4142; \; \sqrt{3} = 1.73205; \; \sqrt{5} = 2.23607;$$
$$\sqrt{6} = 2.4495; \; \sqrt{7} = 2.6457.$$

Of these the most useful are the roots of 2 and 3.

Example 2.—Find the $\sqrt{32}$.

$32 = 16 \times 2$, so we may write

$$\sqrt{32} = \sqrt{16} \times \sqrt{2} = 4 \times 1.4142 = 5.6568 \quad Ans.$$

Example 3.—Find $\sqrt{125}$.

$$\sqrt{125} = \sqrt{25} \times \sqrt{5} = 5 \times 2.236 = 11.180 \quad Ans.$$

99. Reasons for the methods.—It will be noted that, in the examples of the extraction of square root, the *how* is carefully explained but nothing is said about the *why*. A suggestion as to why the steps are taken as given may be found from the consideration of the square of a number consisting of two figures, tens and units. We choose the number 37 and write it as $30 + 7$. Find the square of this as follows:

$$
\begin{array}{r}
30 + 7 \\
30 + 7 \\
\hline
30 \times 7 + 7^2 \\
30^2 + 30 \times 7 \\
\hline
30^2 + 2 \times 30 \times 7 + 7^2
\end{array}
$$

or $\qquad 30^2 + (2 \times 30 + 7)7 = 900 + 67 \times 7 = 1369$

Now extracting the square root of 1369 is the inverse of this process and may be exhibited as follows:

$$
\begin{array}{r}
1369 \ \underline{\lfloor\ 30 + 7 = 37}\ Root \\
30^2 = \ \ 900 \\
\hline
469
\end{array}
$$

Trial divisor,
$2 \times 30 = 60$
True divisor,
$2 \times 30 + 7 = 67$
$(2 \times 30 + 7)7 =$ $\underline{469}$

100. Rule for square root.—After carefully following through the solutions of the preceding examples, the following rule should be understood:

RULE.—(1) *Begin at the decimal point and point off the whole number part and the decimal part into periods of two figures each. If there is an odd number of figures in the whole number part, the left-hand period will have only one figure. If there is an odd number of figures in the decimal part, annex zero so that the right-hand period shall contain two figures.*

(2) *Find the greatest square in the left-hand period and place it under that period. The square root of this greatest square is the first figure of the required root. Subtract the greatest square from the left-hand period and bring down and unite with the remainder the next period of the number. This is the first remainder.*

(3) *Take twice the root already found for a trial divisor, which write at the left of the remainder. Find how many times this trial divisor is contained in the remainder omitting the right-hand figure. This gives the next figure of the root, which place in the root and also at the right of the trial divisor, forming the true divisor. Multiply the true divisor by the figure last placed in the root and write the product under the remainder. Subtract and bring down and unite the next period in the number. This process is repeated for each figure of the root.*

(4) *If at any time the trial divisor will not be contained in the corresponding remainder, place a zero in the root and at the right of the trial divisor, bring down another period, and continue as before.*

(5) *Point off in the root as many decimal figures as there are decimal periods in the number of which the root is extracted.*

101. Cube root.—A process for finding the cube root of a number can readily be devised, and also for any other root desired; but these methods are much more complicated than that for square root. For this reason it is thought best to omit the method by arithmetic for cube root. Any root is found in a very simple manner by logarithms.   (See Art. 353.)

EXERCISES

Find the square root of each of the following:

1. 622,521.   *Ans.* 789.

2. 1,092,025.   *Ans.* 1045.

3. 0.1444.   *Ans.* 0.38.

4. 0.127449.   *Ans.* 0.357.

5. 3481.826049.   *Ans.* 59.007.

6. 3, to four decimals.
             Ans. 1.7320.

7. 553,536.2, to two decimals.   *Ans.* 744.00.
8. 990,025.7, to three decimals.   *Ans.* 995.000.

9. 2, to five decimals.
             Ans. 1.414217.

10. 5, to six decimals.
             Ans. 2.236068.

11. 6, to six decimals.
             Ans. 2.449489.

12. 7, to six decimals.
             Ans. 2.645751.

13. $\frac{36}{169}$.   *Ans.* $\frac{6}{13}$.   14. $\frac{64}{441}$.

15. $\frac{25}{625}$.

16. $\frac{121}{576}$.

17. $\frac{1681}{9801}$.   *Ans.* $\frac{49}{99}$.

18. 27 ÷ 156.25 to four decimals.

Suggestion.—First perform the division, and then extract the root of the quotient.   *Ans.* 0.4157.

19. $\frac{7}{9}$ to four decimal places.   *Ans.* 0.8819.

In each of Exercises 20 to 27, carry the root to five decimal places:

20. 143.   *Ans.* 11.95826.   **24.** 287.   *Ans.* 16.94107.

21. 164.   *Ans.* 12.80624.   **25.** 396.   *Ans.* 19.89975.

22. 92.   *Ans.* 9.59166.   **26.** 416.   *Ans.* 20.39608.

23. 278.   *Ans.* 16.67333.   **27.** 539.   *Ans.* 23.21637.

Find the square roots of the following by short methods:

28. 28.   *Ans.* 5.2915.   **32.** 147.   *Ans.* 12.1244.

29. 72.   *Ans.* 8.485.   **33.** 192.   *Ans.* 13.8564.

30. 288.   *Ans.* 16.971.   **34.** 432.   *Ans.* 20.7846.

31. 75.   *Ans.* 8.6603.   **35.** 4107.   *Ans.* 64.086.

36. Find the side of a square rug whose area is 68 sq. ft.   Give the result to the nearest $\frac{1}{8}$ in.   *Ans.* 8 ft. 3 in.

37. Find to the nearest $\frac{1}{8}$ in. the side of a square table top containing 13.3 sq. ft.   *Ans.* 3 ft. 7$\frac{7}{8}$ in.

38. Cool air enters a room through a square pipe which is attached to, and has the same area of cross section as, a rectangular pipe 38 in. by 17 in.   What is a side of the square pipe to the nearest $\frac{1}{8}$ in.?

Ans. 25$\frac{3}{8}$ in.

39. Two air pipes have square cross sections 10 in. and 12 in. on a side, respectively.   Find the size of a pipe, square in cross section, having the same area as the two pipes.   *Ans.* 15$\frac{5}{8}$ in.

102. Use of table of square roots.—The use of a table of square roots saves much time and labor.   Table IX on page 679 is a table so formed as to give the square root of any number of not more than four significant figures, correct to four figures; that is, the square root of any number formed from any figures from 1 to 9999, with the decimal point in any position, can be found.   It will be found that the last figure of a root when using a number of four figures will occasionally be too large or too small.

The first two figures of a number whose root is to be found are the N column; the third figure, at the top of the page; and the fourth figure, when different from zero, at the top of the right-hand columns. The following will make clear the use of the table.

On page 679, $\sqrt{3.87} = 1.967$.

To find $\sqrt{3.876}$, we add to $\sqrt{3.87}$ the number found in the column headed 6 at the right. In this case the number is 2 and stands for 0.002. This gives $\sqrt{3.876} = 1.969$.

Since, when a number is multiplied by 100, the square root is multiplied by 10; and, when a number is divided by 100, the square root is divided by 10, we have

$$\sqrt{387} = 19.67; \ \sqrt{387.6} = 19.69; \ \sqrt{38700} = 196.7;$$
$$\sqrt{0.0387} = 0.1967; \ \sqrt{0.000387} = 0.01967.$$

For any number with the decimal point placed as here use table on pages 679 and 680. If the decimal point is placed differently, use pages 681 and 682. Thus, on page 681 we find

$$\sqrt{38.7} = 6.221, \text{ and } \sqrt{38.76} = 6.226.$$
Also $\sqrt{3876} = 62.26; \ \sqrt{387600} = 622.6; \ \sqrt{0.3876} = 0.6226$

Stated in another way, pages 679 and 680 give *directly* the square roots of numbers from 1 to 9.999, and pages 681 and 682 give *directly* the square roots of numbers from 10 to 99.99. The square roots of other numbers are found by using the principle, that moving the decimal point two places in the number moves the decimal point one place in the square root.

EXERCISES

By using the table of square roots, find the square roots of the following and check by computing the roots in the ordinary manner:

1. 1.41.	**6.** 48.9.	**11.** 0.1234.	**16.** 2900.
2. 1.414.	**7.** 4567.	**12.** 0.03217.	**17.** 13,240.
3. 141.4.	**8.** 12.12.	**13.** 0.0079.	**18.** 67,340.
4. 45.38.	**9.** 1001.	**14.** 0.0202.	**19.** 60,000.
5. 76.35.	**10.** 1113.	**15.** 0.1909.	**20.** 93,080.

APPLICATIONS

103. Powers and roots of numbers occur in a great variety of problems. These applications will be found frequently as we proceed in the study of mathematics—in evaluating formulas, in various settings in geometry, continually in algebra, and very common in trigonometry.

A simple and interesting application of squares and cubes is in dealing with similar figures; that is, objects that have the same shape. In Fig. 27, are several pairs of figures that have the same shape. The two circles, (a) and (b), are similar; in fact, any two circles are similar. Two squares, as (c) and (d), are always similar. Two rectangles are not necessarily

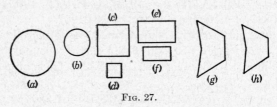

Fig. 27.

similar; but they are similar if the ratio of their widths is the same as the ratio of their lengths. In solids, two spheres are similar. For man, the right hand is similar to the left hand; the right and left sides of most animals are similar. There is something about symmetry that appeals to the eye as beautiful.

The following principles are useful in solving many problems involving symmetry:

(1) *The areas of similar figures are in the same ratio as the squares of their like dimensions.*

(2) *The volumes of similar solids are in the same ratio as the cubes of their like dimensions.*

EXERCISES

1. In Fig. 27, if the diameter of (a) is 6 in. and of (b) is 4 in., how many times as large as (b) is (a)?

Solution.—Area of (a): area of (b) = $6^2 : 4^2 = 36 : 16 = 2\frac{1}{4}$. *Ans.*

2. In Fig. 27, find the ratio of areas of (e) to (f), if the shorter side of (e) is 9 ft. and of (f) 5 ft. *Ans.* 3.24.

3. If a round steel rod $\frac{1}{2}$ in. in diameter, hanging vertically, will support 12,000 lb., what will a rod $\frac{7}{8}$ in. in diameter support?

Ans. 36,750 lb.

4. Given that the electrical resistance is inversely in the same ratio as the areas of the cross sections of the conductors of the same material; find the ratio of the resistances of two copper wires of diameters $\frac{1}{8}$ in. and $\frac{1}{3}$ in., respectively.

Suggestion.—The ratio of the areas of the cross sections is $(\frac{1}{8})^2 : (\frac{1}{3})^2$, and the ratio of the resistances is $(\frac{1}{3})^2 : (\frac{1}{8})^2$. *Ans.* 64:9.

5. Two water pipes are 6 and 2 in. in diameter, respectively. Find the ratio of their carrying capacity. *Ans.* 9:1.

6. The pages of two books are similar in shape. One is $3\frac{1}{2}$ in. wide and the other $3\frac{7}{8}$ in. Six hundred pages of the first will equal how many pages of the second? *Ans.* 489.5.

7. Two steam boilers of the same shape are 12 ft. and 18 ft. long, respectively. Find the ratio of their surfaces. *Ans.* 4:9.

8. How many times as much gold leaf will it take to cover a ball 10 in. in diameter than to cover a ball 6 in. in diameter? *Ans.* $2\frac{7}{9}$.

9. Two balls of steel are respectively 7 in. and 15 in. in diameter. The second is how many times as heavy as the first? *Ans.* 9.84 −.

10. Which is the cheaper, oranges $2\frac{1}{2}$ in. in diameter at 30 cents a dozen or 3-in. oranges at 40 cents a dozen? What should the larger ones sell at to give the same value for the money as the smaller at 30 cents a dozen?

Suggestion.—The price that the 3-in. oranges should sell at is given by the proportion: $(2\frac{1}{2})^3 : 3^3 = 30 : x$.

Ans. The 3-in. oranges; 52 cents a dozen nearly.

11. Two balls of the same material are 10 in. and 3 in. in diameter, respectively. If the smaller ball weighs 9 lb., what is the weight of the larger? *Ans.* $333\frac{1}{3}$ lb.

12. The formula $V = \sqrt{2gh}$ gives the velocity V in feet per second that a body will have after falling from a height h. Find the value of V for a stone that has fallen 400 ft. In the formula $g = 32.2$.

Suggestion.—As in this exercise, the evaluation of a formula often requires the extraction of a square root. The numbers that the letters stand for are put in place of the letters and we have

$$V = \sqrt{2 \times 32.2 \times 400} = \sqrt{25760} = 160.5- \text{ ft.} \quad Ans.$$

13. The effective area of a chimney is given by the formula

$$E = A - 0.06 \sqrt{A}$$

where

E = the effective area.

A = the actual area of the flue.

Find the effective area if $A = 86$ sq. in. If $A = 3.14$ sq. ft.

Ans. 85.44 sq. in.; 3.03 sq. ft.

14. When the pressure of water at the place of discharge is known, the rate of flow is given by the formula

$$V = 12.16 \sqrt{P}$$

where
V = velocity of discharge in feet per second.
P = pressure in pounds per square inch at the place of discharge.

Find the rate of discharge if the pressure as given by a pressure gage is 50 lb. per square inch.   *Ans.* 85.98 ft. per second.

15. As in the last, find the velocity of discharge if the pressure is 200 lb. per square inch.   Compare the result with that of the preceding.
                              Ans. 171.97 ft. per second.

16. The charge E in volts of a condenser in a radio transmitting station is given by the formula $E = 1000 \sqrt{\dfrac{2W}{C}}$, where W is the energy in joules and C is the capacity of the condenser in microfards.   (*a*) if $W = 0.2$ joule and $C = 0.001$ microfarad, find E.   (*b*) If $W = 0.3$ joule and $C = 0.001$ microfarad, find E.   *Ans.* 20,000 volts; 24,495 − volts.

17. The impedance Z in ohms of a radio circuit is given by the formula $Z = \sqrt{R^2 + X^2}$, where R, a resistance, and X, a reactance, are both in ohms.   Given $R = 800$ ohms and $X = 1600$ ohms, find Z.
                              Ans. 1789 − ohms.

PART TWO

Geometry

CHAPTER IX

FUNDAMENTAL IDEAS IN GEOMETRY

104. Many of the facts of geometry are common knowledge. A farmer in dividing his farm into fields, in rowing his crops, and in planning an orchard uses geometry. The mechanic continually makes use of geometric principles. He knows that he cannot turn a five-sided nut with an ordinary wrench. He is familiar with the circle, the square, and various geometric forms as they are encountered in tools and machines. The carpenter uses geometry constantly. Every use to which he puts his square depends upon geometry. The fundamental ideas, upon which the constructions of the engineer and the plans of the architect are based, are geometric. We see geometric forms of utility and beauty on every side, in forms of nature, in buildings and bridges, in landscape gardening and city parks.

In the study of geometry we are concerned with these forms, in classifying and naming them and in applying the facts of geometry in a definite and systematic manner to practical problems that arise in our work.

The word geometry comes from two Greek words meaning earth measurement, and the subject was so called because of its early use in measuring land.

The oldest traces of a systematic knowledge of geometry are found among the Egyptians and Babylonians. This is evidenced in the construction of the pyramids and temples. About the seventh century B.C. the geometry of the Egyptians became known to the Greeks, and there the subject was developed to a very remarkable degree. In fact, the geometry of Euclid, written about 300 B.C., has been used as a text book till the present day with but little change.

In the following pages are discussed some of the facts of geometry and some of their applications to practical problems. The endeavor is to illustrate and make clear the principles and thus lay a broad foundation rather than to follow narrow special lines. Many problems, however, are given. From these the individual student can select those which are best suited to his needs.

There are many terms that, although quite familiar to the student, are used in geometry with such exactness as to require a careful definition or explanation. Point, line, angle, surface, and solid are such terms. Like all simple terms, such as number, space, and time, they are difficult to define; but it is hoped that the explanations given will lead to a reasonable understanding of them.

105. Definitions.—A **material body,** as, for example, a block of wood or an apple, occupies a definite portion of space.

In geometry no attention is given to the *substance* of which the body is composed. It may be *iron, stone, wood,* or *air,* or it may be a *vacuum.* Geometry considers only the *space* occupied by the substance. This space is called a **geometric solid** or simply a **solid.**

If one thinks of a brick and then considers the brick removed and thinks of the space that the brick occupied, he has an illustration of a geometric solid.

A solid has *length, breadth,* and *thickness.*

A boundary face of a solid is called a **surface.**

A surface has *length* and *breadth* but no *thickness.*

The solid shown in Fig. 28 has six faces, the top and bottom, two sides, and two ends.

The boundary of a surface, or that which separates one part of a surface from an adjoining part, is called a **line.**

For instance, in Fig. 28, the edges of the solid, of which there are twelve, are lines; the boundary between Illinois and Indiana is a line; the boundary of a farm is a line.

FIG. 28.

A line has *length* only.

That which separates one part of a line from an adjoining part is called a **point.**

A point has no *length, breadth,* or *thickness.* It has *position* only.

A point is read by naming the letter placed near it. A line is read by naming the letters placed at its ends or by naming the single letter placed upon it. Capital letters are usually

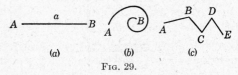

FIG. 29.

used at the ends of a line, whereas a small letter is placed upon a line. In Fig. 29(*a*), the line is read "the line *AB*" or simply "the line *a*."

A **straight line** is a line having the same direction throughout its whole extent. [See Fig. 29(*a*).]

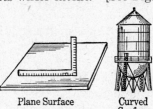

Plane Surface   Curved Surface

FIG. 30.

A **curved line** is a line that is continually changing in direction. [See Fig. 29(*b*).]

A **broken line** is a line made up of connected straight lines. [See Fig. 29(*c*).]

If a surface is such that any two points in it can be connected by a straight line lying wholly in the surface, it is called a **plane surface** or simply a **plane.**

A carpenter determines whether or not the surface of a board is a plane by laying the edge of his square or other straightedge on the surface in different positions and observing if the straightedge touches the surface at all points. (See Fig. 30.)

A **curved surface** is a surface no part of which is a plane surface. Thus, the surface of a circular pipe and the surface of a ball are curved surfaces.

106. Angles.—Two straight lines that meet at a point form an **angle.** (See Fig. 31.) The idea of what an angle is, being a simple one, is hard to define. One should guard against thinking of the point where the two lines meet as the angle. This point is called the **vertex** of the angle.

The two lines are called the **sides** of the angle. The difference in the directions of the two lines forming the angle is the

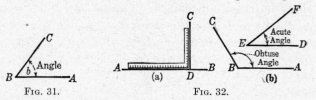

FIG. 31.   FIG. 32.

magnitude, or size, of the angle. For a further discussion of an angle see Art. 359.

An angle is read by naming the letter at the vertex or by naming the letters at the vertex and at the ends of the sides. When read in the latter way, the letter at the vertex must always come between the two others.

Thus, the angle in Fig. 31 is read "the angle b," "the angle ABC," or "the angle at B."

The symbol $\angle$ is used for the word angle. In this way we write $\angle ABC$ for angle ABC and $\angle A$ for angle A.

If one straight line meets another so as to form equal angles, the angles are **right angles.**

In Fig. 32(a), the angles ADC and BDC are each right angles.

If a right angle is divided into 90 equal parts, each part is called a **degree.** It is usually written $1°$.

An **acute angle** is an angle that is less than a right angle. An **obtuse angle** is an angle that is greater than a right angle and less than two right angles. [See Fig. 32(b).]

Two angles whose sum is one right angle, or 90°, are called **complementary angles,** and either one is said to be the **complement** of the other. Two angles whose sum is two right angles, or 180°, are called **supplementary angles,** and either one is said to be the **supplement** of the other. (See Fig. 33.)

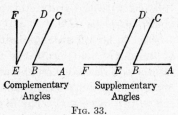

Complementary   Supplementary
Angles   Angles

FIG. 33.

107. Measurement of angles.—A *unit of measure* is necessary in order to measure any magnitude. The degree of angle, which has already been defined as one-ninetieth of a right angle, is a common unit for measuring angles. For more accurate measurements a degree is divided into 60 equal parts called **minutes,** marked (′), and a minute into 60 equal parts called **seconds,** marked (″).

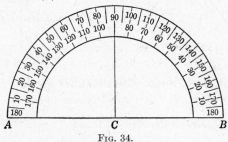

FIG. 34.

The instrument for measuring angles is the **protractor** shown in Fig. 34. It consists of a semicircular scale of convenient size and is divided into degrees and sometimes into half degrees. The divisions of the scale are numbered from 0° to 180°, beginning at each end. The sum of the two readings at any point is 180°. This method of numbering enables one to measure an angle from either end of the protractor, or it enables one to lay off an angle in either a right- or left-hand direction.

108. To measure an angle with a protractor.—Place the protractor on the angle to be measured, so that either half of the side *AB* will fall upon one side of the angle and the point *C* on the vertex. The reading on the scale where the other side of the angle crosses it is the measure of the angle in degrees. In work with the protractor, a hard pencil with a long sharp point should be used.

109. To lay off an angle with a protractor.—Draw one side of the angle, and locate the vertex. Place side *AB* of protractor on side drawn and point *C* on the vertex. Locate reading of value of angle required on scale of protractor, and connect this with the vertex. The degree of accuracy with which an angle can be laid off depends upon the instruments and the one who uses them but largely upon the size of the protractor. It is well then to use a fairly large protractor, one 5 or 6 in. in diameter.

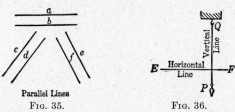

Parallel Lines
FIG. 35.

FIG. 36.

110. Relations of lines.—**Parallel lines** are lines in the same plane and everywhere the same distance apart.

In Fig. 35 are shown pairs of parallel lines.

Two lines that form right angles are said to be **perpendicular** to each other.

In Fig. 32, lines *AB* and *CD* are perpendicular to each other.

A **vertical line** or a **plumb line** is the line along which a string hangs when suspended at one end and weighted at the other.

A **horizontal line** is a line that is perpendicular to a vertical line. (See Fig. 36.)

EXERCISES

Points, Lines, Angles

In the following exercises use a ruler and a hard lead pencil. A protractor is also necessary. Letter all figures.

1. Locate points A, B, and C so that the line ABC is a broken line. Join these three points with three straight lines. Are either of the three angles formed a right angle? An acute angle? An obtuse angle?

2. Draw three curved lines. Does the drawing contain any angles?

3. Locate three points so that the three straight lines connecting them will form one right angle and two acute angles.

4. Locate three points so that the three straight lines connecting them form one obtuse angle and two acute angles.

5. Draw a broken line ACB so that AC is vertical and CB is horizontal. Is AC perpendicular to CB?

6. Draw any broken line ACB so that the angle ACB is a right angle. If either of the lines AC or CB is vertical, is the other horizontal?

7. Use a protractor, and lay off the following angles: 30°, 45°, 60°, 120°, 135°, 180°, 125° 30′, 210°, 310°. Which are acute angles? Which are obtuse angles? Pick out two angles whose sum is a right angle. Pick out two angles whose difference is a right angle. Pick out two complementary angles. Pick out two supplementary angles.

8. Draw the following: two acute angles, two obtuse angles, three angles larger than two right angles. Use a protractor, and measure each of the angles that you have drawn.

9. A man driving east turns so as to drive northeast. Through what angle does he turn? *Ans.* 45°.

10. A man driving due north turns and drives due west. Through what angle does he turn? *Ans.* 90°.

SURFACES

111. Polygons.—A **polygon** is a plane surface bounded by any number of straight lines. Any one of these lines is called a **side**. The point where two sides meet is called a **vertex**. The distance measured around the polygon, or the sum of the lengths of the sides, is called the **perimeter** of the polygon.

A **triangle** is a polygon having three sides.

A **quadrilateral** is a polygon having four sides.

A **pentagon** is a polygon having five sides.

A **hexagon** is a polygon having six sides.

An **octagon** is a polygon having eight sides.

A **regular polygon** is one whose sides are all equal and whose angles are all equal.

A **diagonal** is a line joining any two vertices not adjacent in a polygon.

The triangle is very common in bridge structures and frame works; four-sided figures are common in buildings; the pentagon is not common, it is found in the fittings for fire plugs as

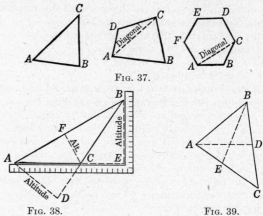

FIG. 37.

FIG. 38.   FIG. 39.

then they cannot be opened with an ordinary wrench; hexagonal forms are found frequently in nuts and bolt heads and in tile.   All these forms are of frequent occurrence in architecture.

It may be of interest to note that the words triangle and quadrilateral are derived from the Latin language whereas pentagon, hexagon, octagon, and the words for polygons of a larger number of sides are derived from the Greek.

112. Triangles.—A line drawn from any vertex of a triangle perpendicular to the opposite side and ending in it is called an **altitude** of the triangle.   Since a triangle has three vertices, each triangle has three altitudes.   The altitude may meet the opposite side, as *CF* in triangle *ABC*, Fig. 38; or the opposite side may have to be extended to meet it, as *AD* and *BE*, Fig. 38.

A line drawn from any vertex of a triangle to the center of the opposite side is called a **median.** It is evident that in any triangle there are three medians. In Fig. 39, AD is a median and bisects the side BC.

A line drawn through the vertex of an angle and dividing the angle into two equal parts is called the **bisector** of the angle. The bisector of an angle of a triangle is often taken as the length of the bisector of an angle of the triangle from the vertex to the opposite side. BE in Fig. 39 is the bisector of the angle ABC of the triangle. It is evident that there are three bisectors of the angles in any triangle.

The sum of the three angles of any triangle is 180°, *or two right angles.*

That this is so can be shown by measuring the angles of a triangle with a protractor and finding the sum:

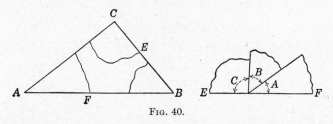

Fig. 40.

That the sum of the angles is 180° can also be shown by drawing any triangle, then tearing off the corners and placing as shown in Fig. 40. The sides will form a straight line EF.

If one angle of a triangle is a right angle, the sum of the two other angles is 90°, or a right angle. They are, therefore, complementary angles and must be acute angles. Such a triangle is called a **right triangle.**

113. Equal triangles.—Two triangles are equal when one may be made to fit the other exactly. There are several sets of conditions that will make two triangles equal.

(1) *If the two angles and the side between them in one triangle are equal, respectively, to two angles and the side between them in another triangle, the triangles are equal.*

In Fig. 41 are two such triangles. Evidently, if one is placed upon the other, they will fit exactly.

(2) *If two sides and the angle between them in one triangle are equal, respectively, to two sides and the angle between them in another triangle, the triangles are equal.*

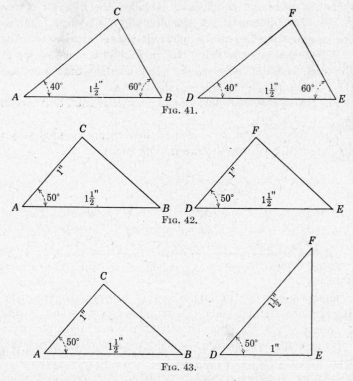

FIG. 41.

FIG. 42.

FIG. 43.

In Fig. 42 are two such triangles. Can they be fitted together exactly? Suppose that the two triangles are as shown in Fig. 43. Can these be fitted together exactly?

(3) *If the three sides of one triangle are equal, respectively, to the three sides of another triangle, the triangles are equal.*

Draw two such triangles, and show that they can be fitted together exactly.

Since two equal triangles can be fitted together exactly, it follows that for each angle in one of two equal triangles there is a *corresponding* equal angle in the other and that for each side in one of two equal triangles there is a *corresponding* equal side in the other.   These are called **corresponding angles** and **corresponding sides.**

114. Quadrilaterals.—A **parallelogram** is a quadrilateral whose opposite sides are parallel.   [See Fig. 44(*a*).]

A **rectangle** is a parallelogram whose angles are right angles. [See Fig. 44(*b*).]

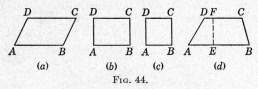

Fig. 44.

A **square** is a rectangle whose sides are all equal.   [See Fig. 44(*c*).]

A **trapezoid** is a quadrilateral with only two sides parallel. The parallel sides are called the **bases.**   The **altitude** is the distance between the two bases.

Figure 44(*d*) is a trapezoid; *AB* and *DC* are the bases, and *EF* is the altitude.

These particular quadrilaterals together with the triangle are the most important forms of areas occurring in practical applications of geometry.

A diagonal divides a parallelogram into two equal triangles. This is true because of (3), Art. 113.   It follows that *the opposite angles of a parallelogram are equal.*

EXERCISES

A. Polygons (Triangles)

1. Draw a triangle with two acute angles; with three acute angles; with one obtuse angle.   Can a triangle have two obtuse angles?

2. Draw two triangles, one with three acute angles, and one with one obtuse angle.   Draw the three altitudes in each triangle.

3. Draw two triangles as in Exercise 2. Draw the three medians in each triangle.

4. Draw two triangles as in Exercise 2. Draw the three bisectors of the angles in each triangle.

5. Draw two triangles with the three angles of one equal to the three angles of the other but the three sides of one not equal, respectively, to the three sides of the other.

6. Draw two triangles with the three sides of one equal to the three sides of the other, respectively. What can be said about the three angles of these two triangles?

7. Can a triangle have two right angles? Two angles each $89\frac{1}{2}°$?

8. Will a framework of three sticks, fastened with one nail at each joint as shown in Fig. 45, hold its shape? Upon what principle of geometry does this depend?

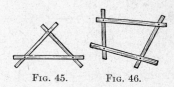

Fig. 45.   Fig. 46.

9. Why is the triangle the form seen in the framework of bridges and other rigid structures?

10. From your experience do you judge the framework of four sticks, nailed with one nail at each joint as shown in Fig. 46, to be rigid? If not, where could a fifth stick be nailed to make it rigid?

11. Draw a diagonal of a quadrilateral; and by considering the two triangles formed, show that the sum of all the angles of a quadrilateral is four right angles.

12. Draw all the diagonals possible from one vertex of a hexagon. How many triangles are formed? What is the sum of all the angles of a hexagon? If all the angles are equal, what is the value of each angle?

Ans. 720°; 120°.

EXERCISES

B. Polygons (*Quadrilaterals*)

1. Draw the following regular polygons: one of three sides; one of four sides; one of five sides; one of six sides; one of eight sides.

2. Draw the diagonals of each polygon in Exercise 1. How many diagonals has each? How many triangles were formed in each case?

3. What are the vertices of each polygon of Exercise 1? What are the perimeters?

4. Draw a rectangle; a square; a parallelogram; a trapezoid; a quadrilateral that is not any of these. Draw the altitude of each. What exception is there?

5. Are all the triangles equal that were formed in each particular drawing of Exercise 2?

6. Draw a parallelogram with one side 3 units and its adjacent side 5 units. What is its perimeter?

7. Draw a parallelogram with its adjacent sides $4x + 2$ and $3x - 1$ units, respectively. Find each side if the perimeter is 44 units. (See Part III.) *Ans.* 14; 8.

8. Draw a regular hexagon with sides 3 units long. Find its diagonals. Find the sum of all its angles. *Ans.* 6; 720°.

9. What is the sum of all the interior angles of each drawing in Exercise 1? [If n = the number of sides, then the number of degrees in all of the interior angles = $(n - 2)180$.]

Ans. 180°; 360°; 540°; 720°; 1080°.

10. Draw a trapezoid with its parallel sides 4 and 6 units long, respectively. If its other two sides are each equal to 2 units, what is its altitude? Show that its acute angles are each 60° and its obtuse angles each 120°.

CHAPTER X

AREAS OF POLYGONS

115. Areas of plane surfaces can often be divided into rectangles and triangles; and in this way, the areas of such surfaces can be found by finding areas of rectangles and triangles. The fundamental idea of a unit of area is that it is a square whose sides are each one linear unit; that is, a square foot is the area of a square 1 ft. on a side and a square centimeter is a square 1 cm. on a side.

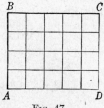

Fig. 47.

116. The rectangle.—How to find the area of a rectangle is illustrated in Fig. 47. Suppose that this represents a rectangle whose length AD is 5 ft. and width AB is 4 ft. The rectangle is divided into small squares 1 ft. on a side, and so each represents 1 sq. ft. Since there are four rows of squares each containing 5 sq. ft., there are 4×5 sq. ft. $= 20$ sq. ft. in the rectangle. What is said will also be true if the lengths of the sides are fractional. This leads to the following:

RULE.—*The area of a rectangle is equal to the product of its length and its width.*

The length and the width of the rectangle must be in the same unit before taking their product. The product is then square units of the same kind as the linear unit. Thus, if the unit of length is the foot, the product will be square feet.

117. The parallelogram.—A parallelogram and a rectangle, each having the same base and altitude, are equal in area. This is illustrated in Fig. 48. $ABCD$ is the rectangle, and $ABEF$ is the parallelogram. The altitude BC is the same for each, and they have the same base, AB. Since the part BCE

156

of the parallelogram may be cut off and fitted on *ADF*, it is evident that the parallelogram is just equal to the rectangle. Therefore, we have the following:

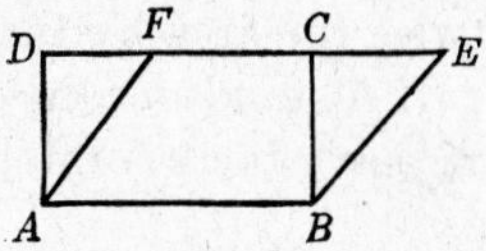

RULE.—*The area of a parallelogram is equal to the product of its base and its altitude.*

FIG. 48.

118. Formulas.—A rule stated in letters and signs is called a **formula.** It is a shorthand way of stating a rule.

If *A* is used as an abbreviation for area, *b* for base, and *a* for altitude, the rule for the area of a rectangle or a parallelogram is given in the following formula:

[1]
$$A = ab$$

The form *ab* means altitude times base.

Since the altitude times the base equals the area, by using well-known principles of division we have for the rectangle or parallelogram the following:

RULE.—(1) *The altitude equals the area divided by the base.* (2) *The base equals the area divided by the altitude.*

These rules written as formulas are

[2] $$a = A \div b$$
[3] $$b = A \div a$$

119. The triangle.—If a triangle and a parallelogram have the same base and have their altitudes equal, the triangle has half the area of the parallelogram.

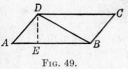
FIG. 49.

This is illustrated in Fig. 49. ABCD is the parallelogram. The diagonal *BD* divides it into two triangles *ABD* and *BCD*, which are equal by (3) of Art. 113.

From this and the rule for the area of a parallelogram, it is clear that the following is true:

RULE.—*The area of any triangle is equal to one-half of its base times its altitude.*

If the area and either base or altitude of a triangle are given, the other dimension (altitude or base) is found by dividing twice the area by the given dimension.

If A stands for the area, a for the altitude, and b for the base, we have these formulas for the triangle:

[4] $A = \frac{1}{2}ab$

[5] $a = 2A \div b$

[6] $b = 2A \div a$

EXERCISES

Areas

1. Compute the areas of the following figures using the dimensions as given.   What about the perimeters?

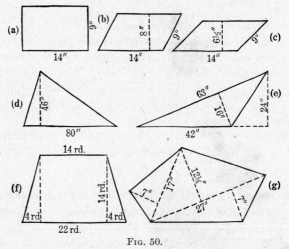

Fig. 50.

Ans. (*a*) 126 sq. in.; (*b*) 112 sq. in.; (*c*) 91 sq. in.; (*d*) 12 sq. ft. 112 sq. in.; (*e*) $3\frac{1}{2}$ sq. ft.; (*f*) 252 sq. rd.; (*g*) $319\frac{3}{8}$ sq. in.

2. The sides of a parallelogram are 3 and 4 ft.   Find its perimeter. Can its area be found?

3. Draw two triangles, and find their areas by drawing the three altitudes of each and measuring the sides and altitudes.

4. What measurements are necessary in order that the area of a parallelogram may be found?

5. Why does a median of a triangle divide the triangle into two triangles that are equal in area?

6. A parallelogram has sides 10, 10, 20, and 20 ft.; find its perimeter. A rectangle has the same sides; find its area. *Ans.* 60 ft.; 200 sq. ft.

7. The two diagonals of a parallelogram bisect each other and divide the parallelogram into four triangles. Are these triangles equal in area? Show why.

8. Find the area of the following squares:

(1) One side 3 ft. 6 in.

(2) One side 6 ft. 3 in.

(3) One side 6 ft. *a* in. *Ans.* $\left(6 + \dfrac{a}{12}\right)^2$ sq. ft.

(4) One side *a* ft. *b* in.

(5) One side $\sqrt{3}$ ft.

9. Find the side of a square whose area is 200 sq. ft. Express the result in feet to the nearest $\frac{1}{8}$ in. *Ans.* 14 ft. 1$\frac{3}{4}$ in.

Draw the following four rectangles:

10. Given $a = 10$ ft. and $b = 5$ ft. 3 in.; find A in square feet.
  Ans. 52.5.

11. Given $a = 4.6$ ft. and $b = 6.4$ ft.; find A in square feet.
  Ans. 29.44.

12. Given $A = 6.25$ sq. in. and $a = 2.5$ in.; find b. *Ans.* 2.5 in.

13. Given $A = 160$ acres and $b = 40$ rods; find a. *Ans.* 640 rods.

Draw the following triangles:

14. Given $a = 2$ ft. 6 in. and $b = 6$ ft. 2 in.; find A in square feet. How many such triangles? *Ans.* $7\frac{17}{24}$.

15. Given $a = \sqrt{20}$ in. and $b = \sqrt{5}$ in.; find A in square inches.
  Ans. 5.

16. Given $A = 200$ sq. cm. and $b = 2.5$ cm.; find a. *Ans.* 160 cm.

17. Given $A = 116$ sq. ft. and $a = 116$ in.; find b. *Ans.* 24 ft.

120. Area of a triangle when the three sides only are given.

It is sometimes necessary to find the area of a triangle when all that is known is the lengths of the three sides. The formula or rule for doing this will now be given, but no attempt will be made to derive the formula. The formula given is known as **Hero's Formula** because Hero, who lived in Alexandria and was

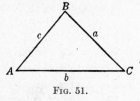

Fig. 51.

one of the great mathematicians of his time, used it in surveying in the second century B.C.

If a, b, and c stands for the three sides of a triangle, and if s stands for one-half the sum of a, b, and c, then the area A of the triangle is given by the formula

[7] $$A = \sqrt{s(s - a)(s - b)(s - c)}$$

This formula cannot well be derived here, but it is found in geometry. The area of the triangle can also be found by constructing it to scale, as explained later. The altitude can then be measured and the area be found by taking one-half the product of the base and the altitude.

Since a formula is a rule stated in symbols, the preceding formula may be stated as the following rule for the area of a tri-angle when the three sides only are given:

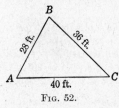

Fig. 52.

RULE —*Find half the sum of the three sides. Subtract each side from this half sum. Take the continued product of the half sum and the three differences. The square root of this product is the area of the triangle.*

This rule can be illustrated best by an example.

Example.—Find the area of a triangle with sides 40, 28, and 36 ft.

Solution:

$a = 40, b = 28, c = 36$

$s = \frac{1}{2}(40 + 28 + 36) = 52$

$s - a = 52 - 40 = 12$

$s - b = 52 - 28 = 24$

$s - c = 52 - 36 = 16$

$A = \sqrt{52 \times 12 \times 24 \times 16} = \sqrt{239,616} = 489.506-$

∴ Area = 489.506− sq. ft. *Ans.*

With very ordinary instruments this triangle can be constructed to scale and measured and the area found to within half a square foot of the computed area.

121. Area of trapezoid.—A diagonal of a trapezoid divides it into two triangles that have the same altitude and have as bases the two bases of the trapezoid. Thus, in the trapezoid of Fig. 53, the diagonal AD divides the trapezoid into two triangles ACD and ADE. The area of $ACD = \frac{1}{2}$ of $AC \times a$ and area of $ADE = \frac{1}{2}$ of $ED \times a'$. But $a = a'$; hence, the sum of the areas of the two triangles $= \frac{1}{2}(AC + ED) \times a.$

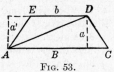

Fig. 53.

Now the area of the trapezoid can evidently be found by finding the sum of the areas of the two triangles into which it is divided, or what amounts to the same thing, by the following:

RULE.—*The area of a trapezoid equals one-half the sum of the two bases times the altitude.*

If B and b stand for the two bases and a for the altitude of the trapezoid, the formula is

[8]　　　　　　　　$A = \frac{1}{2}(B + b) \times a$

Example.—Find the area of a trapezoid whose lower base is 20 rods, upper base 14 rods, and altitude 9 rods.

Solution.—By formula [8], $A = \frac{1}{2}(B + b)a$. Putting the numbers of the example in place of the letters of the formula,

$$A = \frac{1}{2}(20 + 14) \times 9 = 153$$
$$\therefore \text{ Area} = 153 \text{ sq. rods } \quad Ans.$$

EXERCISES

Polygons (Applications)

1. Draw the following parallelograms. Find the parts not given.

(1) Base 12.5 in., altitude 25 in., area ————. *Ans.* 312.5 sq. in.

(2) Base ————, altitude 42 ft., area 462 sq. ft.　　*Ans.* 11 ft.

(3) Base 44 ft. 4 in., altitude ————, area 696.6 sq. ft.
Ans. 15.7+ ft.

(4) Base ————, altitude 72 ft. 8 in., area 2162 sq. ft.
Ans. 29.75+ ft.

2. At 10 cents per square foot, find the cost of a lot 150 ft. long and 35 ft. wide.　　*Ans.* \$525.

3. At \$80 per acre, find the cost of a farm 160 rods long and 80 rods wide.　　*Ans.* \$6400.

4. A rectangle is 105 cm. long and 0.1 m. wide. Find its area in square meters.　　*Ans.* 0.105.

5. The top of a table is a rectangle 4.5 by 6.5 ft. Find its area.

Ans. 29.25 sq. ft.

6. A rug is a rectangle 9 by 12 ft. Find its price at $4 per square yard. *Ans.* $48.

7. A box 6 in. long, 4 in. wide, and 3 in. deep has six rectangular faces. Find the area of the surface of the box. *Ans.* 108 sq. in.

8. A metal wardrobe is 61 in. high, 18 in. deep, and 20 in. wide. Find the area of the surface of the wardrobe. *Ans.* 5356 sq. in.

9. A wardrobe is 61 by 24 by 18 in. Find the area of its surface.

Ans. 5988 sq. in.

10. A utility cabinet is to be painted inside and outside. It has four shelf spaces. If it is 50 by 24 by 11 in., what is the total surface in square feet to be painted? Disregard thickness of surface and shelves.

Ans. 9640 sq. in.

11. How many bricks each 9 by $4\frac{1}{2}$ by $1\frac{3}{4}$ in. will it take to pave a court 16 by 126 ft. if the bricks are laid flat? If laid on edge?

Ans. 7168; 18,432.

12. How many paving blocks each 4 by 4 by 10 in., placed on their sides, will it take to pave an alley 600 ft. long and 12 ft. 6 in. wide?

Ans. 27,000.

13. What will be the expense of painting the walls and ceiling of a room 12 ft. 6 in. by 16 ft. and 10 ft. 4 in. high at 30 cents per square yard?

Ans. $26.30.

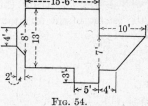
Fig. 54.

14. Find the cost of sodding a lawn 31 ft. wide and 52 ft. long, at 36 cents per square yard. *Ans.* $64.48.

15. Find the number of square feet in the floor of the room shown in Fig. 54.

Ans. 277.5.

Suggestion.—Divide into rectangles and trapezoids.

16. At 30 cents per square foot, find the cost of building a cement walk 6 ft. wide, on two sides of a corner lot 33 by 100 ft. *Ans.* $250.20.

17. Find the area of a trapezoid whose bases are 17 and 11 in., respectively, and whose altitude is 26 in. *Ans.* 364 sq. in.

18. A roof of a house is 20 ft. long, 18 ft. wide at one end, and 10 ft. wide at the other. Find its area. *Ans.* 280 sq. ft.

19. The gable of a house is 36 ft. long at the bottom, 10 ft. long at the top, and 12 ft. wide. Find its area. *Ans.* 276 sq. ft.

20. Find the area of a board 14 ft. long and 18 in. wide at one end and 12 in. at the other. *Ans.* 17.5 sq. ft.

21. Find the area in acres of a farm that is represented on paper as a rectangle $3\frac{3}{4}$ by $10\frac{1}{2}$ in. on a scale of $\frac{1}{16}$ in. to the rod. *Ans.* 63 acres.

22. Find the area of Fig. 55(*a*).　　　　　　*Ans.* 23.592 sq. in.
23. Find the area of Fig. 55(*b*).　　　　　　*Ans.* 6.02 sq. in.
24. Find the area of Fig. 55(*c*).　　　　　　*Ans.* 8.625 sq. in.

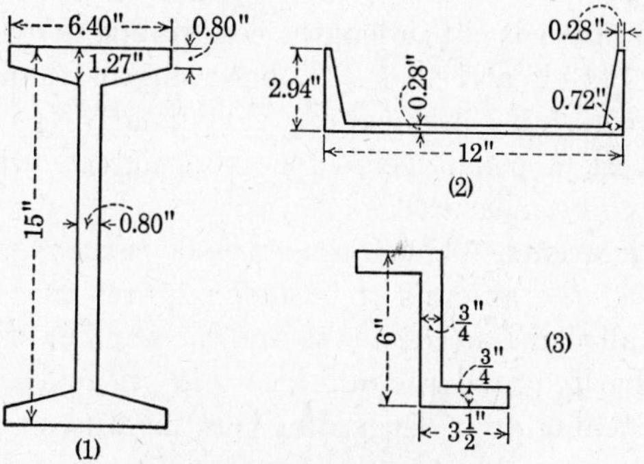

Fig. 55.

25. Find the area of the footing for a column with a load of 168,000 lb. if the safe bearing load of the soil is 4000 lb. per square foot.

Ans. 42 sq. ft.

LUMBER AND SHINGLES

122. Measuring lumber.—Lumber is measured in board measure. Timber used in framework is counted as lumber. Lumber and timber are sold by the 1000-ft. board measure. This is sometimes written 1000 ft. B.M., but more often it is indicated by the single letter M.

One **board foot** is 12 in. square and 1 in. thick and so contains one-twelfth of a cubic foot. The number of board feet in a stick of timber is the number of cubic feet times 12. The following rule may be used to find the number of board feet in a stick of timber:

RULE.—*Take the product of the end dimensions in inches; divide by 12; and multiply the quotient by the length in feet.*

The student should make clear to himself the correctness of this rule.

Example.—Find the number of board feet in a stick of timber 6 by 8 in. and 14 ft. long.

Solution: $\dfrac{6 \times 8}{12} \times 14 = 56$ ft. B.M.　*Ans.*

Lumber less than 1 in. is counted as if 1 in. thick in buying and selling.   In widths, a fraction of $\frac{1}{2}$ in. or more is counted as 1 in.

Usually lumber is cut in lengths containing an even number of feet, as 12, 14, and 16 ft.   Longer lengths than these are usually special, but classifications vary greatly.

Timberwork is usually paid for at an agreed price per M, the timber to be measured in the work.

123. Estimations.—There are various rules regarding the estimating of the amount of lumber required in a structure. In general, all that is necessary to find the number of board feet in the lumber required and add a certain per cent for waste in cutting, matching, etc.   Regarding this, the student can consult a handbook specially prepared for those in this line of work.

124. Shingles.—Shingles are 16, 18, or 24 in. in length, are counted as 4 in. wide, and are put up in bunches of 250.   The part of the shingle that is exposed when laid is said to be "laid to the weather."   The part so exposed varies from 4 to $7\frac{1}{2}$ in. on roofs and up to 12 in. on side walls.   So a single shingle covers a space 4 in. wide and from 4 to 12 in. long.

In laying shingles, the estimating is often made by the *square*, an area 10 by 10 ft., or containing 100 sq. ft.

The following table allows for waste and gives the number of square feet covered by a thousand shingles and also the number of shingles required to cover a square when laid at various distances to the weather.

Inches to the weather	Area covered by 1000 shingles, sq. ft.	No. to cover a square
4	100	1000
$4\frac{1}{4}$	110	910
$4\frac{1}{2}$	120	833
5	133	752
$5\frac{1}{2}$	145	690
6	157	637

See a handbook or a lumber dealer for extension of this table.

In stating the number of shingles, give the number so that only whole bunches will be required. Thus, do not give a number as 5650 but as 5750.

EXERCISES

Lumber and Shingles

1. A man builds, with boards 1 in. thick, a tight board fence around his garden, which is 150 by 36 ft. The fence is 6 ft. high and nailed at top and bottom to pieces of 2- by 6-in. material. If there is no waste, find the number of feet of lumber used. *Ans.* 2,976.

2. A man builds a walk 4 ft. wide and 160 ft. long with planks 2 in. thick laid crosswise on three pieces of 4- by 4-in. timbers, running lengthwise of the walk. Find the cost of the lumber at $48 per M.

Ans. $92.16.

3. Find the amount of lumber to floor a room 30 by 40 ft. with strips 3 in. wide, allowing one-sixth for matching and 15% for waste.

4. Find how many shingles it will take to shingle a roof 36 by 40 ft. if shingles are laid $4\frac{1}{2}$ in. to the weather. (Use the table of Art. 124.)

Solution: $\dfrac{36 \times 40}{100} = 14.4 =$ number of squares.

$833 \times 14.4 = 11,995 =$ number of shingles requires. *Ans.*

$\therefore$ 12,000 shingles must be bought.

5. How many board feet in 26 pieces 2 by 4 in. by 14 ft. long and in 20 pieces 3 by 10 in. by 16 ft. long? *Ans.* 1043.

6. What will it cost, at $48 per M, to cover the floor of a barn 32 by 42 ft. with 2-in. plank? *Ans.* $129.02.

7. How many board feet are there in 3 sticks of timber 12 by 14 in. and 22 ft. long? *Ans.* 924.

8. Find the total cost of shingling the two sides of a roof each 18 by 40 ft. Redwood shingles at $6.75 per thousand are used, and the laying, nails, etc., cost $2.90 per square. Shingles are to be laid 5 in. to the weather. (Use the table in Art. 124.) *Ans.* $114.85.

9. What does the following cost at 25 cents per foot:

> 1 piece $\frac{7}{8}$ by 6 in. by 10 ft.
> 1 piece $\frac{5}{8}$ by 8 in. by 12 ft.
> 1 piece $\frac{7}{8}$ by 18 in. by 4 ft.
> 2 pieces $\frac{1}{4}$ by 6 in. by 8 ft.? *Ans.* $6.75.

10. Find the cost of the following bill of lumber if the quarter-sawed is $90 per M and the common sawed is $65 per M:

2 pieces 1½ by 2½ in. by 12 ft. quartersawed
2 pieces ⅜ by 8 in. by 12 ft. quartersawed
1 piece ¾ by 2½ in. by 12 ft. quartersawed
1 piece ¾ by 2 in. by 12 ft. quartersawed
5 pieces ¾ by 3 in. by 12 ft. quartersawed
1 piece ⅞ by 10 in. by 12 ft. quartersawed
1 piece ½ by 10 in. by 6 ft. common sawed
6 pieces ½ by 6 in. by 12 ft. common sawed
4 pieces 8⁄4 by 6 in. by 12 ft. common sawed.

Ans. $9.18.

11. In Fig. 56, find the area of one end. Find the area of the roof. The rafters are placed 16 in. from center to center. Find the number of

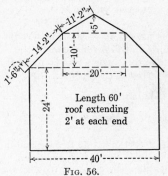

board feet in the rafters if made of 2 by 6 in. material. (Use 12-ft. material for short rafters.) Find the number of feet of lumber to cover ends, sides, and roof. Find how many shingles it will take for the roof if laid 4½ in. to the weather.

Ans. 1310 sq. ft.; 3434⅔ sq. ft.; 2744;
8935; 28,750 approx.

12. A shipbuilder gave $300 for a standing oak tree to make a long ship timber. The cost of felling, hewing, and hauling was $275. If the timber was 18 in. square and 98 ft. long, find the number of board feet in it and the cost per thousand feet.

Length 60'
roof extending
2' at each end

Fig. 56.

Ans. 2646; $217.31.

13. Find the number of board feet in the following list of framing timber for a house:

Girders..................	5 pieces 6 by	8 in. by 20 ft.
Sills....................	16 pieces 6 by	6 in. by 16 ft.
First-floor beams.........	45 pieces 3 by 10 in. by 28 ft.
Second-floor beams.......	45 pieces 3 by	8 in. by 28 ft.
Ribbons................	16 pieces 1 by	8 in. by 20 ft.
Plates..................	32 pieces 2 by	4 in. by 16 ft.
Outside-wall studs........	156 pieces 2 by	4 in. by 20 ft.
Inside-wall studs.........	200 pieces 2 by	4 in. by 12 ft.
Rafter studs.............	90 pieces 2 by	8 in. by 24 ft.
Collar beams...........	45 pieces 2 by	6 in. by 16 ft.

Ans. 14,673.

CHAPTER XI

TRIANGLES

THE RIGHT TRIANGLE

125. A right triangle is a triangle having one right angle. The side opposite the right angle is called the **hypotenuse,** and the sides about the right angle are called **base** and **altitude,** the base being the side upon which the triangle is supposed to rest.

The right triangle is of great importance, as it is of very common occurrence in applying mathematics. The solution of the right triangle depends upon the following relation established in geometry:

The square formed on the hypotenuse is equal to the sum of the squares formed on the two other sides.

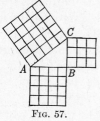

FIG. 57.

This may be illustrated as in Fig. 57. AC is the hypotenuse and is 5 units in length. AB is the base, 4 units long. BC is the altitude, 3 units long. Here it is easily seen that the square on AC is equal to the sum of the squares on AB and BC. Hence, $\overline{AC^2} = \overline{AB^2} + \overline{BC^2}$; or in general, if c stands for the hypotenuse, b for the base, and a for the altitude, then $c^2 = a^2 + b^2$. From this are derived the three following formulas, by which any side can be found if the two others are known.

[9] $$c = \sqrt{a^2 + b^2}$$
[10] $$a = \sqrt{c^2 - b^2}$$
[11] $$b = \sqrt{c^2 - a^2}$$

Example.—Find the hypotenuse of a right triangle whose base is 14 ft. and altitude 16 ft.

Solution.—Using formula [9], $c = \sqrt{a^2 + b^2}$.

$$\therefore c = \sqrt{16^2 + 14^2} = \sqrt{452} = 21.26 + \text{ ft.} \quad Ans.$$

126. Historical note.—This relation between the hypotenuse and the two other sides of a right triangle is, perhaps, the most noted theorem in geometry. It is known as the **Pythagorean Proposition** because it is said to have been first proved by Pythagoras, a famous Greek mathematician who lived about 500 B.C.

The proposition in a special form was known and used by the Egyptians as early as 2000 B.C. The Chinese also made use of the same relations at a very early date.

It may interest the student to discover various groups of three whole numbers that can be the three sides of a right triangle. The following are a few: 3, 4, and 5; 6, 8, and 10; 5, 12, and 13; 7, 24, and 25.

Such groups that can be the three sides of a right triangle can be found from the formulas $2n$, $n^2 - 1$, and $n^2 + 1$, by letting n be any integer larger than 1. For instance, if $n = 2$, $2n = 4$, $n^2 - 1 = 3$, and $n^2 + 1 = 5$; and we have seen that 3, 4, and 5 units may be the lengths of the sides of a right triangle. Again, if $n = 4$, we have 8, 15, and 17, which can be the sides of a right triangle, for $8^2 + 15^2 = 17^2$.

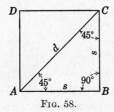

Fig. 58.

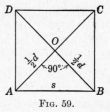

Fig. 59.

127. The square and its diagonals.—A diagonal of a square divides it into two equal right triangles which have two equal sides and whose acute angles are each 45°, as shown in Fig. 58.

If s is a side and d a diagonal, then

$$d^2 = s^2 + s^2 = 2s^2$$
$$\therefore \ d = \sqrt{2s^2} = s\sqrt{2}$$

Similarly, in Fig. 59, we find that $s = \frac{1}{2}d\sqrt{2}$.

These two formulas are stated in the following rules:

(1) *The diagonal of a square equals a side of the square multiplied by $\sqrt{2}$.*

(2) *The side of a square equals one-half the diagonal multiplied by $\sqrt{2}$.*

The number of decimal places used in $\sqrt{2}$ will depend upon the degree of accuracy desired. Pipe fitters usually use $\sqrt{2} = 1.41$. It is often necessary to take three or more decimal places. $\sqrt{2} = 1.4142136$ to seven decimal places.

These rules are well worth remembering. In one form or another they are widely used by pipe fitters, mechanics, carpenters, and others, as will be mentioned in several of the exercises that follow.

EXERCISES

The following four exercises refer to the right triangle in Fig. 60.

1. $a = 12$, $b = 16$; find c and area.   *Ans.* 20; 96 square units.

2. $b = 40$, $c = 50$; find a and area.   *Ans.* 30; 600 square units.

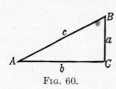

Fig. 60.

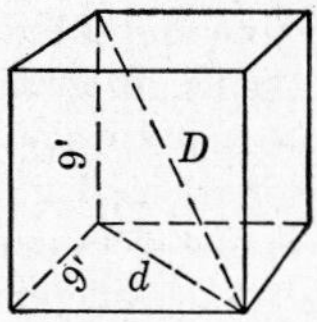

Fig. 61.

3. Area = 4 acres, $b = 20$ rods; find a and c.

Ans. 64+ rods; 67+ rods.

4. Area = 81 sq. ft., $a = 6$ yd.; find b and c.

Ans. 3 yd.; 6.7+ yd.

5. Find the length of the diagonal of a rug 9 by 12 ft.   *Ans.* 15 ft.

6. A lot is a square with its diagonal 60 yd.; find its edges.

Ans. 42.43− yd.

7. Find the diagonal of a cube 9 ft. on an edge.

Suggestion.—In Fig. 61, the line marked D is called the diagonal of the cube. First find d and then D.

$$d = \sqrt{9^2 + 9^2} = \sqrt{162}$$
$$D = \sqrt{162 + 9^2} = \sqrt{243}$$
$$= \sqrt{81 \times 3} = 9\sqrt{3} \text{ ft.} \quad Ans.$$

8. If the edge of a cube is 1 ft., find its diagonal.   *Ans.* 1.732 ft.

9. If the total area of a cube is 12 sq. ft., find its diagonal.

Ans. 2.449 ft.

10. If the diagonal of a cube is 3 $\sqrt{3}$ ft., find its total area.

Ans. 54 sq. ft.

11. A man swims at right angles to the bank of a stream at the rate of 3.5 miles per hour. If the current is 7.5 miles per hour, find the rate at which the man is moving. *Ans.* 8.28− miles per hour.

Suggestion.—The combined effect of the current and swimming will cause the man to move on the hypotenuse of a right triangle.

12. A man rows at right angle to the banks of a river. If the river is 1 mile wide and flows at the rate of 4 miles per hour, how long will it take the man to row across if his rate of rowing is 3 miles per hour in still water? How many miles will he have rowed when he has crossed?

Ans. $\frac{1}{3}$ hr.; $\frac{5}{3}$ miles.

13. A steamer goes due north at the rate of 15 miles per hour, and another due west at 18 miles per hour. If both start from the same place, how far apart will they be in 6 hr.? *Ans.* 140.58+ miles.

14. The diagonal of a rectangle is 130, and the altitude is 32. Find the area. *Ans.* 4032 square units.

15. What is the length of the longest line that can be drawn within a rectangular box 12 by 4 by 3 ft.? *Ans.* 13 ft.

16. The hypotenuse of a right triangle, with base and altitude equal, is 12 ft. Find the length of the base and altitude. *Ans.* 8.485+ ft.

17. The base of a triangle is 20 ft., and the altitude is 18 ft. What is the side of a square having the same area? *Ans.* 13.416+ ft.

18. The area of a rectangular lawn is 5525 sq. m., and the length of one of its sides is 8.5 decameters. Find the length of its diagonal in meters to three decimal places.

Ans. 107.005−.

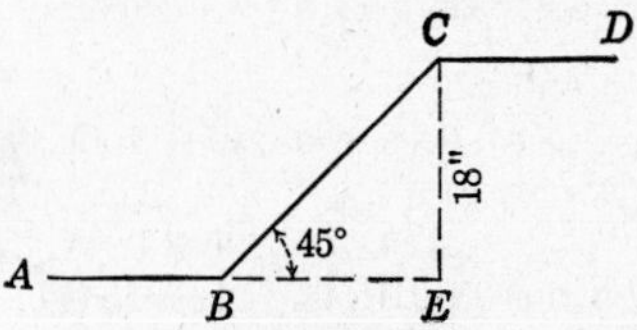

19. Find the length of the diagonals of the following rooms:

FIG. 62.

(1) 20 by 16 by 12 ft.

Ans. 28.28+ ft.

(2) *a* by *b* by *c* feet.

(3) 2*a* by 2*b* by 2*c* feet.

20. Find the cost at $30 per M of roof boards on a third-pitch roof of a barn 45 by 65 ft. if projections at ends and eaves are 2 ft. (A third-pitch roof has a length from the plate to the ridge equal to one-third the width of the building.) *Ans.* $120.23.

21. In fitting a steam pipe to the form *ABCD* (Fig. 62), making a bend of 45°, the fitter takes $BC = CE + \frac{5}{12}CE$. What is the error if *CE* = 18 in.? What is the correct length of *CB*, and what is the per cent of error by the fitter's method?

Ans. 0.0442− in.; 25.4558+ in.; 0.17+ %.

This is a pipe fitter's form of rule (1) of Art. **127**. For $CE + \frac{5}{12}CE$ $= (1 + \frac{5}{12})CE = CE \times 1.416 \ldots$, which is approximately $CE \times \sqrt{2}$.

22. In cutting a rafter for a half-pitch roof, a carpenter makes the length of the rafter AB equal 1 ft. 5 in. for every foot that there is in AC (Fig. 63). If $AC = 8$ ft., find AB by this rule. What is the per cent of error by this method?

Ans. 11 ft. 4 in.; 0.17+ %.

Note that the rule used here by the carpenter is the same as that of the preceding exercise used by the pipe fitter.

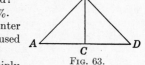

Fig. 63.

23. To find the diagonal of a square, multiply the side by 10, take away 1% of this product, and divide the remainder by **7**. Test the accuracy of this "rule of thumb."

Solution.—Take a square with a side of, say, 25 in.,

$$
\begin{aligned}
10 \times 25 &= 250 \\
1\% \text{ of } 250 &= \underline{2.5} \\
\text{Remainder} &= 247.5 \\
247.5 \div 7 &= 35.357+ \text{ in.} = \text{diagonal by rule}
\end{aligned}
$$

By the formula for the hypotenuse, the diagonal $= \sqrt{25^2 + 25^2} = 35.355+$ in.

Hence, error $= 35.357$ in. $- 35.355$ in. $= 0.002$ in., and $0.002 \div 35.355 = 0.006- \% =$ per cent of error.

It is evident that this rule is very accurate and is also easy of application.

24. What is the distance across the corners of a square nut (Fig. 64) that is $3\frac{3}{8}$ in. on a side? Use rule (1) of Art. **127**. *Ans.* 4.773− in.

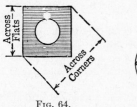

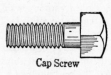

Cap Screw

Fig. 64.　　　　Fig. 65.　　　　Fig. 66.

25. What must be the diameter of round stock so that a square bolt head $1\frac{3}{4}$ in. on a side may be milled from it? Use rule (1) of Art. **127**.

Ans. 2.475− in.

26. Find the distance across the flats of the square head of a cap screw that may be milled from round stock $1\frac{1}{8}$ in. in diameter. Use rule (2) of Art. **127**. *Ans.* 0.7955− in.

27. Figure 67 shows a "scissors" roof truss with the lengths AB = BC = AC = 30 ft., CD = CF = 16 ft., and CG = CE = 8 ft. Find the length of NC and FG.

Ans. 25 ft. $11\frac{3}{4}$ in.; 13 ft. $10\frac{1}{4}$ in.

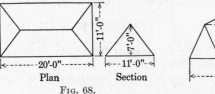

Fig. 67.

28. A smokestack is held in position by three guy wires that reach the ground 49 ft. from the foot of the stack. Find the length of a guy wire if they are fastened to the stack 70 ft. from the ground.

Ans. 85.4+ ft.

29. The center of an engine shaft is 9 ft. below and 3 ft. to the left of the center of a line shaft. Find the distance between the centers of the two shafts.

Ans. 9 ft. $5\frac{7}{8}$ in.

30. The dimensional sketch in Fig. 68 shows plan and section of a roof. It has to be boarded. What will be the number of feet of boards required? *Ans.* 356.

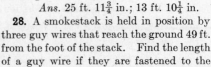

Plan   Section

Fig. 68.

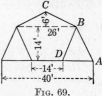

Fig. 69.

31. In the gambrel roof shown in section in Fig. 69, find AB, DB, and BC, each to the nearest $\frac{1}{4}$ in. *Ans.* 15 ft. $7\frac{3}{4}$ in.

32. The base of a right triangle is 30 ft., and the hypotenuse is 6 ft. longer than the altitude; find the altitude. *Ans.* 72 ft.

33. The hypotenuse of a right triangle is 24 ft., and the base is 8 ft. longer than the altitude; find the base and altitude.

Ans. 20.49+ ft.; 12.49+ ft.

34. The area of a right triangle is 30 sq. ft., and the altitude is 7 ft. longer than the base; find the hypotenuse. *Ans.* 13 ft.

35. The perimeter of a rectangle is 28 in., and a diagonal is 10 in.; find the sides. *Ans.* 6 and 8 in.

SIMILAR TRIANGLES

128. Triangles that have the same shape are said to be similar.

In Fig. 70 (1), ABC and ADE are similar. In (2) ABC and $A'B'C'$ are similar.

Draw two triangles as in (1), and measure the sides a, b, c and a', b', c'. Then determine the ratios $a:b$, $a:c$, $b:c$, $a':b'$, $a':c'$, and $b':c'$. Follow the same directions for the triangles in (2). Now compare the values of the ratios, and notice whether or not they are equal.

The results of the foregoing should lead to the following: $a:b = a':b'$; $a:c = a':c'$; and $b:c = b':c'$.

Two triangles that have the angles of one equal, respectively, to the angles of the other are similar.

The sides about the equal angles in the similar triangles are called **corresponding sides**.

Thus, c and c' are corresponding sides. Other corresponding sides are a and a' and b and b'.

From the proportions given above, we arrive at the following principle:

Corresponding sides of similar triangles form a proportion.

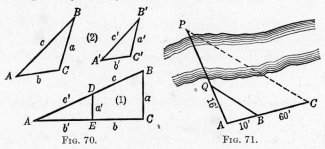

FIG. 70.   FIG. 71.

Example.—Find the distance between the points P and Q on opposite banks of a stream, Fig. 71, where P is inaccessible.

Solution.—As shown in the figure, measure distances $AQ = 16$ ft., $AB = 10$ ft., and $BC = 60$ ft. Because triangles AQB and APC are made similar, we have the proportion

$$AB:AQ = AC:AP$$
$$\therefore \ 10 \text{ ft.}:16 \text{ ft.} = 70 \text{ ft.}:AP$$
$$\therefore \ AP = \frac{16 \times 70}{10} = 112 \text{ ft.}$$
$$\therefore \ PQ = 112 \text{ ft.} - 16 \text{ ft.} = 96 \text{ ft.} \quad \textit{Ans.}$$

129. Tapers.—The man in the machine shop often finds it necessary to determine the **taper per foot** of a piece that is to be turned, in order that he may set his lathe properly. By the **taper per foot** is meant the **decrease** in **diameter** if the piece is 1 ft. long.

In Fig. 72(*a*), the taper is evidently $4\frac{1}{2}$ in. $-$ 3 in. $= 1\frac{1}{2}$ in per foot. In (*b*) the taper is $2\frac{1}{2}$ in. $-$ 2 in. $= \frac{1}{2}$ in. in 4 in. Hence the taper per foot is three times as much, or $1\frac{1}{2}$ in.

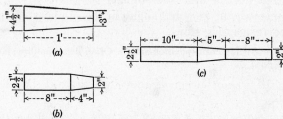

Fɪɢ. 72.

If *l* stands for the length of tapered part in feet, *t* for the taper in inches in this part, and *T* for the taper in inches per foot, then the following proportion is true by similar triangles:

[12] $$1:1 = t:T$$

The taper for the total length of the piece is evidently the taper per foot times the length in feet.

Example.—In Fig. 72(*c*), what is the taper per foot? What would be the taper for total length of piece?

Solution.—Substituting in formula [12], $\frac{5}{12}:1 = \frac{1}{2}:T$.

$$\therefore T = 1 \times \frac{1}{2} \div \frac{5}{12} = 1\frac{1}{5} \text{ in.} \quad Ans.$$

$1\frac{1}{5}$ in. $\times \frac{23}{12} = 2.3$ in. $=$ the taper if it were tapered the full length.

130. Turning.—In turning a piece in a lathe the taper is sometimes made by shifting the tailstock of the lathe. Since, when the piece is revolved, the same cut is made on all sides, it is necessary to set the tailstock over one-half of what the taper would be if the piece were tapered the full length. Thus, a piece 1 ft. long with a taper $1\frac{1}{4}$ in. per foot requires the tail-stock to be set over $\frac{1}{2}$ of $1\frac{1}{4}$ in. $= \frac{5}{8}$ in.

If $D =$ the large diameter and d the small diameter of the tapered portion, L the total length of the piece, and l the length of the tapered portion, then the offset x of the tailstock is determined by the following formula:

[**13**]
$$x = \frac{D - d}{2} \times \frac{L}{l}$$

Example.—A shaft 3 ft. long is to have a taper turned on one end 10 in. long, the large end of the taper being 4 in. in diameter and the small end $3\frac{1}{2}$ in. Find the distance to offset the tailstock.

Solution:
$$x = \frac{4 - 3\frac{1}{2}}{2} \times \frac{36}{10} = 0.9 \text{ in.} \quad Ans.$$

EXERCISES

1. The following tapers per inch are what tapers per foot: 0.0013 in.; 0.0260 in.; 0.0473 in.; 0.0758 in.

2. If the barrel of a gun is 30 in. long, 1.5 in. in diameter at the small end, and 2 in. in diameter at the large end, what is its taper per foot?
Ans. $\frac{1}{5}$ in.

Taper Pin   Taper $\frac{1}{4}$ in. Per Foot

Taper Pin Reamer   Taper $\frac{1}{4}$ in. Per Foot
Fig. 73.

3. How much will the tailstock need to be offset to give a taper of $1\frac{1}{8}$ in. per foot if the work is 1 ft. in length? If 8 in. in length?
Ans. $\frac{9}{16}$ in.; $\frac{3}{8}$ in.

4. The standard pipe thread taper is $\frac{3}{4}$ in. per foot. How much is this per inch?
Ans. $\frac{1}{16}$ in.

5. Find the taper per foot to be used in turning a pulley with a 14-in. face crowned $\frac{3}{16}$ in.
Ans. 0.32 + in.

6. If the crowning of a pulley is one-twenty-fourth of the width of the face, find the taper per foot to be used in turning a pulley with a 10-in. face.
Ans. 1 in.

7. A taper-pin reamer has a taper of $\frac{1}{4}$ in. per foot. If the diameter of the small end is 0.398 in. and the length of the flutes is $5\frac{1}{4}$ in., find the diameter of the large end of the flutes. *Ans.* 0.5074 in.

8. A taper reamer has a taper of $\frac{5}{8}$ in. per foot, and the flutes are $3\frac{1}{2}$ in. long. If it is $\frac{3}{4}$ in. in diameter at the large end, find the diameter at the small end. *Ans.* 0.568— in.

9. Find the taper per foot of a taper reamer that has a diameter of $1\frac{1}{16}$ in. at the large end of the flutes, and $\frac{32}{64}$ in. at the small end, if the flutes are $2\frac{3}{4}$ in. long. *Ans.* $\frac{3}{4}$ in.

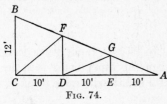

FIG. 74.

10. A taper reamer has a taper of $\frac{3}{4}$ in. per foot. If the diameter of the large end is $1\frac{3}{16}$ in., find the diameter of the small end, the flutes being $3\frac{3}{4}$ in. long. *Ans.* $\frac{61}{64}$ in.

11. In Fig. 74, the timbers CB, DF, and EG are perpendicular to CA. From the given dimensions find the lengths of DF, EG, CF, DG, and AB.
Ans. $EG = 4$ ft.; $DG = 10.770$ ft.; $AB = 32.311$ ft.

Suggestion: $CA:CB = DA:DF$
Or
$$30:12 = 20:DF$$
$$\therefore DF = \frac{12 \times 20}{30} = 8 \text{ ft.}$$
$$CF = \sqrt{10^2 \times 8^2} = \sqrt{164} = 12.806+ \text{ ft.}$$

12. How much should the tailstock be offset to turn a taper on a piece of work 10 in. long if the tapered portion is $4\frac{1}{8}$ in. long and measures 1.275 in. in diameter at the large end and 0.845 in. at the small end?
Ans. 0.521+ in.

13. In Fig. 75, the distance BC across the lake is to be found. The following measurements were taken: $AB = 200$ yd., $AD = 80$ yd., and $DE = 60$ yd. Find BC. Is it necessary to make right-angled triangles? *Ans.* 150 yd.; no.

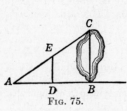

FIG. 75.

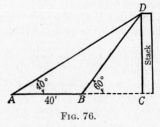

FIG. 76.

14. Show how to find the height of a smokestack CD of Fig. 76, when the foot of the stack cannot be reached.

Suggestion.—On a level place measure from *A* to *B* in a line with *C*, and measure angles *BAD* and *CBD*. Suppose that the line *AB* is 40 ft. and the angles are 40° and 60°, respectively. Construct a figure to scale on paper, and measure the line that corresponds to the smokestack.

15. The *grade* of a road is expressed in per cent. Thus, a rise of 1 ft. in a *horizontal* distance of 100 ft. is a 1% grade; likewise a rise of 5 ft. in 100 ft. is a 5% grade. What is the horizontal distance in miles to give a rise of 4652 ft. on a 6% grade? What is the distance traveled in ascending this grade? *Ans.* 15 miles; 15.03 miles.

THE STEEL SQUARE

131. One of the most useful instruments known to man is the ordinary **steel square** or **carpenter's square** shown in Fig. 77. It is made in various sizes but the most common size is with the longer arm, called the **body, blade,** or **stock,** 24 in. in length and 2 in. in width and the shorter arm, called the **tongue,** 16 or 18 in. in length and 1½ in. in width.

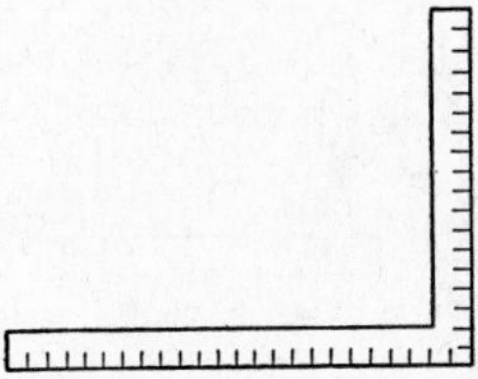

Many books, having in some cases five or six hundred pages, have been

Fig. 77.

written on the uses of the steel square. Here we wish to call attention only to the fact that the principles involved in using the steel square are mainly those involved in the solution of the right triangle and in similar triangles. One who understands the right triangle can devise many uses for the steel square and can readily see the principles underlying the various uses of this instrument given in the treatises on the steel square.

Upon the ordinary steel square are found many figures, telling lengths of braces, board measures, etc. No attempt will be made here to explain these.

Example.—By use of a steel square, find the length of the hypotenuse of a right triangle that has a base of 8 in. and an altitude of 7 in.

Solution.—Measure the line drawn from the 8-in. mark on the blade to the 7-in. mark on the tongue. This measures about $10\frac{5}{8}$ in., which is near enough for most practical purposes. By the right-triangle method the hypotenuse = $\sqrt{8^2 + 7^2}$ = $10.63+$ in.   (See Fig. 78.)

This method can readily be applied to find the lengths of braces supporting two pieces that are perpendicular to each other, to find rafter lengths, lengths of the parts of a trestle, etc.

132. Rafters and roofs.—The **run** of a rafter is the distance measured on the horizontal from its lower end to a point under its upper end.   The **rise** is the distance of the upper end above the lower end.   In Fig. 79, AC is the run and CB the rise.

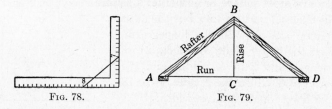

FIG. 78.   FIG. 79.

The slant of a roof is usually told by stating the relation of the *rise* to the *run*.   It is often given by stating the **rise per foot of run,** as 6 in. to 1 ft.   Another way is to state what is known as the **pitch** of the roof.   A roof is said to be **half pitch, quarter pitch, full pitch,** etc., when the rise is $\frac{1}{2}$, $\frac{1}{4}$, 1, etc., times the full width of the building as represented in Fig. 79, where AD is the width of the building.

The relation between rise and pitch is shown by the following table:

12 ft. run to 4 ft. rise is $\frac{1}{6}$ pitch.
12 ft. run to 6 ft. rise is $\frac{1}{4}$ pitch.
12 ft. run to 8 ft. rise is $\frac{1}{3}$ pitch.
12 ft. run to 10 ft. rise is $\frac{5}{12}$ pitch.
12 ft. run to 12 ft. rise is $\frac{1}{2}$ pitch.
12 ft. run to 15 ft. rise is $\frac{5}{8}$ pitch.
12 ft. run to 18 ft. rise is $\frac{3}{4}$ pitch.
12 ft. run to 24 ft. rise is full pitch.

133. Uses of the square.—The **bevel** or **slant** on the end of a race or rafter, necessary to make it fit the part that it rests gainst, can easily be marked by the square.

Example 1.—Required to cut the lower end of a rafter that is to rest on the plate if the rise of the rafter is 8 ft. and the un 12 ft.

Discussion.—Place the square as shown in Fig. 80, and mark along the lower edge. This gives he proper slant. Marking along he tongue gives the slant for the pper end of the rafter.

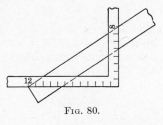

In placing the square on the tick it is necessary only to take he distances on the blade and ongue in the same ratio as the

Fig. 80.

atio of the run to the rise. In this case we could as well have aken 24 and 16 in. or 9 and 6 in.

Example 2.—Required to cut a rafter for a V-shaped roof n a building 12 ft. wide if the rise of the rafter is to be 4 ft. The rafter is to be made of a piece of 2 by 4 in., and half its vidth is to project 18 in. beyond the plate.

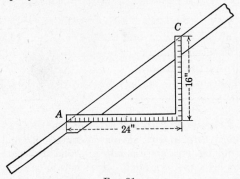

Fig. 81.

Discussion.—Determine the slant for the plate end as lescribed in Example 1. Then place the square as shown in Fig. 81 so as to give a run of 24 in. to a rise of 16 in. The square is replaced with point *A* on *C*, and this repeated often as necessary to give a run of half the width of the buil ing. In this case, it is necessary to place the square thr times. In the last position, a mark along the tongue giv the slant of the upper end of the rafter and determines t length of the rafter. Any rafter can be cut in this way.

EXERCISES

1. Use a carpenter's square, and show how to determine the length o brace for a run of 6 ft. 6 in. and a rise of 4 ft. 6 in. Show how to c bevels on ends.

2. Show how to make the slants for the legs of the sawhorse shown Fig. 82. Compute the length of legs. *Ans.* $29\frac{3}{4}$ in.

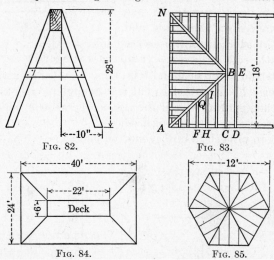

FIG. 82.   FIG. 83.

FIG. 84.   FIG. 85.

3. In Fig. 83 is a plan of one end of a roof on a house 18 ft. in wid and 28 ft. long. *CB*, *DE*, etc., are *common* rafters; *AB* and *NB* are h rafters; and *FQ*, *HI*, etc., are *jack* rafters. Find the lengths to cut t several rafters if the roof is $\frac{1}{3}$ pitch. Show how to determine the slan at both ends of each. The rafters do not extend beyond the plates ar are placed 1 ft. 6 in. from center to center.

4. Find lengths of the common, hip, and jack rafters for the roof which Fig. 84 is the plan. It is $\frac{1}{2}$ pitch; rafters are 1 ft. 6 in. from cent to center and extend 2 ft. beyond the plates.

5. Figure 85 is a plan of the roof of a hexagonal tower. Find lengths of the rafters that end at the plates. Full pitch and rafters 1 ft. 6 in. between centers. Width of tower is 12 ft.

6. Figure 86 represents the plan of a roof of a house 20 ft. square, with a flat circular portion 8 ft. in diameter. If the circle is one-third the width of the building above the plates and the rafters 2 ft. between centers on the plates, find the length of each rafter and show how to cut slants.

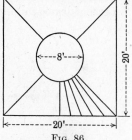

Fig. 86.

ISOSCELES AND EQUILATERAL TRIANGLES

134. Two other forms of triangles of common occurrence are *isosceles* and *equilateral triangles*.

A triangle that has two equal sides is called an **isosceles triangle**.

A triangle that has all its sides equal is called an **equilateral triangle**. Of course, an equilateral triangle is also isosceles, and whatever can be said of an isosceles triangle, in general, may apply to an equilateral triangle.

The following facts are proved in geometry. The student should satisfy himself that they are true by constructing the figures and measuring the parts.

135. The isosceles triangle.—In Fig. 87 the isosceles triangle *ABC* has equal sides *AC* and *BC*.

Fig. 87.

The angles *A* and *B* opposite the equal sides are equal.

The line *CD* drawn bisecting the vertex angle *C* is perpendicular to and bisects the base *AB*. That is, *AD = DB*. It also divides the isosceles triangle into two equal right triangles, *BDC* and *ADC*.

The line *CD* is then the *bisector* of the angle *C* and also a *median* and an *altitude* of the triangle.

The diagonal of a square divides the square into two equal right isosceles triangles. In these isosceles triangles each of

the equal angles is 45°.   This triangle is often called the 45°
right triangle.   Rules (1) and (2) of Art. 127 apply to the 45°
right triangle.

136. The equilateral triangle.—In Fig. 88, triangle *ABC* has
its three sides equal and is an equilateral triangle.

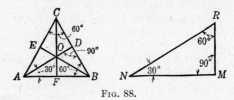

Fig. 88.

The angles opposite the equal sides are equal, and therefore
each angle equals 60° because the sum of three angles of any
triangle is 180°.

The line drawn from the vertex *A* and bisecting the angle is
perpendicular to and bisects the opposite side *BC*.   It also
divides the equilateral triangle into two equal right triangles,
ABD and *ADC*.

Furthermore, each of the lines *BE* and *CF* divides the triangle in the same manner that it is divided by *AD*.

Each of these lines then is a *bisector* of an angle and also a
median and an *altitude* of the equilateral triangle.

The point *O* where these three lines meet is called the
center of the equilateral triangle.   It is one-third the distance
from one side to the opposite vertex.   That is, $DO = \frac{1}{3}DA$,
$FO = \frac{1}{3}FC$, and $EO = \frac{1}{3}EB$.

It follows then that $AO = 2DO$, $BO = 2EO$, and $CO = 2FO$.

Either of the triangles formed when an equilateral triangle
is divided into two triangles by an altitude is a right triangle
having acute angles of 30° and 60°.   This triangle is very
important in practical work and is often called the 30–60°
right triangle.   It is readily seen that in such a right triangle, the hypotenuse is twice the shortest side; that is,
$NR = 2MR$, because *MR* is one-half a side of the equilateral
triangle of which triangle *NMR* is a part.

137. Altitude and area of equilateral triangle.—The altitude of an equilateral triangle can readily be found when a side is known.

Let s = one side, and let h = the altitude.

Then

$$h = \sqrt{s^2 - (\tfrac{1}{2}s)^2} = \sqrt{\tfrac{3}{4}s^2} = \tfrac{1}{2}s\sqrt{3}$$

$$\therefore \mathbf{h} = \tfrac{1}{2}\mathbf{s}\sqrt{3} = \tfrac{1}{2}\mathbf{s} \times \mathbf{1.732}$$

For greater accuracy use $\sqrt{3} = 1.73205$.

Stated in words this formula is: *An altitude of an equilateral triangle equals one-half of a side times* $\sqrt{3}$.

Solving this formula for s,

$$\mathbf{s = 2h \div \sqrt{3}}$$

Stated in words this formula is: *A side of an equilateral triangle equals twice the altitude divided by* $\sqrt{3}$.

An easier formula to use in numerical work is the following in which a multiplication instead of a division by the $\sqrt{3}$ is made.

$$\mathbf{s = \tfrac{2}{3}h\sqrt{3}}$$

Since the area A is one-half the base times the altitude,

$$A = \tfrac{1}{2}s \cdot h = \tfrac{1}{2}s \cdot \tfrac{1}{2}s\sqrt{3}$$

$$\therefore \mathbf{A} = (\tfrac{1}{2}\mathbf{s})^2\sqrt{3} = (\tfrac{1}{2}\mathbf{s})^2 \times \mathbf{1.732}, \text{ or } \mathbf{A} = \tfrac{1}{4}\mathbf{s}^2\sqrt{3}$$

Stated in words the first formula is: *The area of an equilateral triangle equals the square of one-half a side times* $\sqrt{3}$.

Example.—Find the altitude and area of an equilateral triangle whose sides are 8 in.

Solution: $h = \tfrac{1}{2}s \times 1.732 = 4 \times 1.732 = 6.928$ in. *Ans.*

$A = (\tfrac{1}{2}s)^2 \times 1.73205 = 4^2 \times 1.73205 = 27.713$ sq. in. *Ans.*

138. The regular hexagon.—Another form often used in practice is the *regular hexagon*, that is, a hexagon in which all the sides are equal and all the angles equal. From geometry we learn the following facts which will appear true from a careful consideration of Fig. 89. The diagonals, drawn as shown, divide the hexagon into six equal equilateral triangles. The distance from the center O to any vertex is the same as the

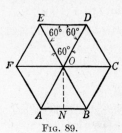

FIG. 89.

length of a side. The *area* of the regular hexagon is equal to six times the area of an equilateral triangle with sides equal to the sides of the hexagon. The altitude NO may be found by solving the right triangle ANO or may be found by taking AN times $\sqrt{3}$.

If s is one side, h the altitude NO, and A the area of the hexagon, the following formulas can be derived, which apply to any regular hexagon:

$$h = \tfrac{1}{2}s\sqrt{3}, \text{ or } 2h = s\sqrt{3}$$
$$s = 2h \div \sqrt{3} \text{ or } s = \tfrac{2}{3}h\sqrt{3}$$
$$A = 6(\tfrac{1}{2}s)^2\sqrt{3}, \text{ or } A = \tfrac{3}{2}s^2\sqrt{3}$$

EXERCISES

Draw the following isosceles triangles, and find the parts indicated:

1. Equal sides are 8 ft. and the base is 7 ft.; find the altitude.

Ans. 7.2— ft.

2. Equal sides are 36 in. and the altitude is 33 in.; find the base.

Ans. 28.77+ in.

3. Equilateral triangle sides are 48 ft.; find the altitude.

Ans. 41.57— ft.

4. Equilateral triangle altitude is 12 ft.; find the sides.

Ans. 13.86— ft.

5. In Fig. 89, given $AB = 36$ ft.; find ON.   *Ans.* 31.18— ft.

6. Equilateral triangle sides are 3 ft.; find the area.

Ans. 3.9— sq. ft.

7. In an isosceles triangle the equal sides are 1.5 ft. and the base is 1 ft.; find the area.   *Ans.* 0.707 sq. ft.

8. Compute the area of Fig. 89 if AB is 10 ft.   *Ans.* 259.8 sq .ft.

9. The area of an equilateral triangle is 21.217 sq. ft.; find the length of one side.

Solution.—In Art. 137, it is stated that the area of an equilateral triangle equals the square of one-half a side times $\sqrt{3}$.

Or

$$A = (\tfrac{1}{2}s)^2 \times 1.732$$

Then

$$\tfrac{1}{2}s = \sqrt{A \div 1.732}$$

But A is given equal to 21.217.

$$\therefore \tfrac{1}{2}s = \sqrt{21.217 \div 1.732} = \sqrt{12.25} = 3.5$$

Or

$$s = 2 \times 3.5 = 7 \text{ ft.} \quad Ans.$$

10. The area of an equilateral triangle is 108.996 sq. in.; find its sides and its altitude. *Ans.* 15.866 in.; 13.74 in.

11. Find the length of the steam pipe $ABCD$ (Fig. 90) if $AD = 6$ ft., $CE = 16$ in., and angle $EBC = 30°$. *Ans.* 76.29— in.

12. The hypotenuse of a right triangle is 5 ft., and one side is 4 ft. Show that the equilateral triangle made on the hypotenuse is equal to the sum of the equilateral triangles made on the other two sides.

Suggestion.—Find the areas of the three triangles, and show that the sum of the areas of the two smaller triangles equals the largest triangle. Use the formula $A = (\tfrac{1}{2}s)^2 \times 1.732$.

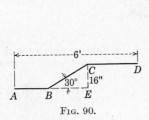

Fig. 90.

Isosceles right triangle   30°-60° Right triangle

Fig. 91.

13. Two very convenient forms of triangles used by draftsmen are right triangles made of celluloid or rubber, one a right isosceles triangle having the acute angles each 45° and one having acute angles of 30° and 60°. If one of the equal sides of the isosceles right triangle is 6 in., find the hypotenuse. *Ans.* 8.485 in.

14. If the shortest side of the 30°-60°-right triangle is 4 in., find the other sides. *Ans.* 6.928 in. and 8 in.

15. Using the draftsman's triangles, show how to construct the following angles: 15°, 75°, 105°, 120°, 135°, 150°.

16. A hexagonal nut for a $1\frac{1}{16}$-in. screw is $1\frac{1}{4}$ in. across the flats. Find the diagonal, or the distance across the corners, of such a nut. *Ans.* 1.443 in.

Suggestion.—The distance across the corners is twice a side of the hexagon.   Find one side by the formula $s = \frac{2}{3}h \sqrt{3}$ of Art. 137.   Note that $h =$ one-half the distance across the flats.

17. What is the distance across the corners of a hexagonal nut that is $\frac{3}{4}$ in. on a side?   What is the distance across the flats of the same nut?

Ans. 1.5 in.; 1.299 in.

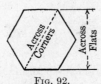

Fig. 92.

Fig. 93.

Suggestion.—To find the distance across the flats use the formula $h = \frac{1}{2}s \sqrt{3}$ of Art. 138, and note that $2h$ is the distance across the flats.

18. Show that the distance across the corners of a hexagonal nut is approximately 1.15 times the distance across the flats.

Suggestion.—It is readily seen that the distance across the corners is twice the side of an equilateral triangle whose altitude is one-half the distance across the flats.

By Art. 138, $s = 2h \div \sqrt{3}$.

$\qquad \therefore 2s = 4h \div \sqrt{3} = 2h \times 1.15$

But $\qquad 2s =$ distance across corners.

and $\qquad 2h =$ distance across flats.

19. In a standard hexagonal bolt nut the distance across the flats is given by the formula $F = 1.5D + \frac{1}{8}$, where F is the distance across the flats and D the diameter of the body of the bolt.

Find the distance across the flats and across the corners on a hexagonal nut for a bolt $1\frac{3}{4}$ in. in diameter.   *Ans.* 2.75 in.; 3.1754 in.

20. To what diameter should a piece of stock be turned so that it may be milled to a hexagon and be $1\frac{3}{4}$ in. across the flats?

Ans. 2.0207 in.

Suggestion.—Note that the diameter of the stock is the distance across the corners of the hexagon.

21. To what size should a piece of stock be turned so that it may have full corners when milled down to a square 2 in. across the flats? So that it may be milled down to a hexagon 2 in. across the flats?

Ans. 2.828+ in.; 2.309+ in.

SCREWS AND SCREW THREADS

139. Screws are commonly used for fastening together wooden or metal parts.   For convenience in entering wood

wood screw is tapered, whereas a machine screw is the same diameter throughout and is often fitted with a nut.

The thread of a screw is formed by cutting a spiral groove round the body of the screw. Screw threads used for fastening are made by means of dies and taps. A die is a tool used to make external threads on the body of a screw or bolt, and a tap is a tool for making an internal thread as in a nut.

The threads on parts used in machines and for communicating motion are made by a cutting process by using a lathe and a single-pointed cutting tool of the proper size. The grooves and threads formed are of various sizes and several shapes depending on the size of the screw and the purposes for which the screw, bolt, or other device is to be used.

140. Pitch and lead of screw threads.—The **pitch** of a screw thread is the distance from, say, the center of the top of one thread to the center of the top of the next.

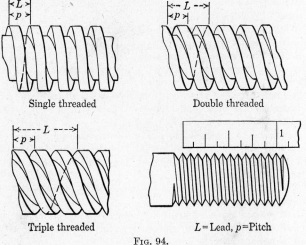

Single threaded   Double threaded

Triple threaded $L =$ Lead, $p =$ Pitch

Fig. 94.

The **lead** of a screw thread is the distance that the screw will move forward in a nut for each complete turn of the screw.

In a **single-threaded screw** there is only one groove cut spirally any number of times around the body of the screw;

in a **double-threaded screw** there are two grooves running side by side spirally around the screw; and a **triple-threaded screw** has three grooves running around the screw.

For a single-threaded screw, the pitch and the lead are equal, but for a double-threaded screw, the lead is twice the pitch, and for a triple-threaded screw, the lead is three times the pitch.

The meaning and relations of *pitch* and *lead* will be made clear by reference to Fig. 94. The pitch can be easily determined by placing a scale on the screw as shown in Fig. 94 and counting the number of threads for 1 in. If the screw is single-threaded, this is the number of times that the screw must be turned around to advance 1 in. This is often called the pitch. Thus, a 10-pitch single-threaded screw requires 10 turns to advance 1 in.

EXERCISES

1. What is the lead of a single-threaded screw that advances $\frac{1}{2}$ in. in 8 turns? What is the pitch?

2. What is the lead in a double-threaded screw that has 18 threads to an inch? What is the pitch?

3. A jackscrew is single-threaded and has 3 threads to an inch. How far does it advance in $\frac{1}{3}$ of a turn? How many turns will advance it 6 in.?

4. A single-threaded screw with 40 threads to an inch will advance how far in $\frac{1}{25}$ of a turn? In $1\frac{1}{5}$ turns? In $17\frac{1}{2}$ turns? In how many turns will it advance $\frac{778}{1000}$ inch?

5. According to the Franklin Institute standards for the dimensions of bolts and nuts, a $\frac{5}{8}$-in. bolt has 11 threads per inch. What is the pitch? The lead if single-threaded? How many full turns of the nut will it take to advance the bolt $2\frac{1}{4}$ in.?

6. A $4\frac{1}{4}$-in. bolt has $2\frac{7}{8}$ threads per inch. What is the pitch? What is the lead if triple-threaded? *Ans.* $\frac{8}{23}$ in.; $1\frac{1}{23}$ in.

7. In a special threaded screw for a screw-power stump puller, the screw is double-threaded with a pitch of $\frac{11}{16}$ in. How many turns of the nut are required to lift the stump $4\frac{1}{3}$ ft.? *Ans.* $37\frac{9}{11}$ in.

8. How many turns must be made with a triple-threaded screw having $4\frac{3}{4}$ threads to the inch to have it advance a distance of 3 in.?

9. The lead screw on the table of a milling machine has a double thread with a pitch of $\frac{1}{4}$ in. How many inches per minute is the feed if the lead screw is making 4 R. P. M.?

141. Screw threads.—In the United States several different kinds of screw threads are in use. Here we will consider: first, the *sharp V thread*, or *common V thread;* and second, the *United States standard screw thread*. Other kinds will be considered on page 592. Computations connected with screw threads may have to do with finding the depth of the thread so that the strength of the bolts may be found. In this computation the equilateral triangle is involved.

142. Sharp V thread.—The **sharp V thread,** or **common V thread,** is a thread having its sides at an angle of 60° to each other and perfectly sharp at the top and bottom. The cross section of the sharp V thread is then an equilateral triangle

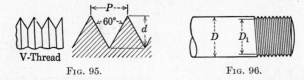

FIG. 95.   FIG. 96.

with the pitch as one side, as shown in Fig. 95, and the depth, as the altitude of the triangle.

The objections urged against this thread are (1) that the top, being so sharp, is injured by the slightest accident and (2) that in the use of taps and dies the fine sharp edge is quickly lost, thus causing constant variation in fitting.

The common V thread with a pitch of 1 in. has a depth equal to the altitude of an equilateral triangle 1 in. on a side. Hence, its depth = $\frac{1}{2}\sqrt{3} = 0.866$ in. The root diameter equals the diameter of the bolt less twice the depth of the thread. We have then the following formulas:

$$p = \frac{1}{N}$$

$$d = 0.866p = \frac{0.866}{N}$$

[14] $$\mathbf{D_1 = D - 2d = D - \frac{1.732}{N}}$$

where

p = the pitch.
d = the depth of thread.
N = the number of threads to the inch.
D = the diameter of bolt.
D_1 = the root diameter.

143. United States standard thread.—The **United States standard screw thread** (U. S. S.) shown in Fig. 97, has its sides also at an angle of 60° to each other but has its top cut off to the extent of one-eighth of its depth and the same amount filled in at its bottom, thus making the depth three-fourths that of the common V thread of the same pitch. The distance f on the flat is one-eighth of its pitch.

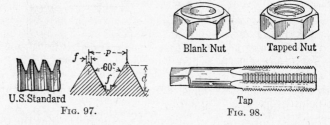

Blank Nut Tapped Nut

U.S.Standard
Fig. 97.

Tap
Fig. 98.

This thread is not so easily injured; the taps and dies retain their size longer; and bolts and screws having this thread are stronger and have a better appearance.

For the U. S. S. screw thread we have the following formulas:

$$p = \frac{1}{N}$$

$$d = \frac{3}{4} \times 0.866p = 0.6495p = \frac{0.6495}{N}$$

[15] $$D_1 = D - 2d = D - \frac{1.299}{N}$$

The blank nut for a bolt is drilled with a tap drill the same size as the root diameter of the screw or bolt or very nearly that size.

Table V can be used in computations connected with screw threads.

144. Metric threads.—A metric thread is alike in form to the U. S. S. thread, but the dimensions are in millimeters. There are two standard metric threads, the International Standard thread and the French Standard thread. These two threads differ but very slightly.

Because of the different units of measure used, a nut with a metric thread will not fit a bolt with a U. S. S. thread and a separate set of dies are necessary for cutting each kind of thread.

EXERCISES

1. Find the depths of common V threads of the following number of threads to an inch: 10, 20, 5, 8, 40, 13.
Ans. 0.0866 in.; 0.0433 in.; 0.1732 in.; 0.1083 in.; 0.0217 in.; 0.0666 in.

Suggestion.—Use formula $d = \dfrac{0.866}{N}$ of Art. 142.

2. Find the depths of U. S. S. threads of same pitches as in Exercise 1.
Ans. 0.0649 in.; 0.0325 in.; 0.1299 in.; 0.0812 in.; 0.0162 in.; 0.0500 in.

3. Find the root diameter of a screw of outer diameter $\frac{1}{2}$ in. and 14 sharp V threads to the inch. Use formula [14].   *Ans.* 0.3763 in.

4. Show that the depth of any sharp V thread in inches is $\frac{1}{2}\sqrt{3}$ divided by the number of threads per inch, or, what is the same thing, 0.866 divided by the number of threads per inch.

5. Check the depth of the sharp V thread for five of the sizes given in Table V.

6. Find the size of tap drill for a $\frac{9}{16}$-in., 12-pitch, sharp V-thread nut.
Ans. 0.4182 in.

7. What is the tap drill size of a $\frac{9}{16}$-in., 20-pitch, common double-threaded nut?   *Ans.* 0.4759 in.

8. Find the depth of the U. S. S. screw thread when there are 15 threads to the inch; 16 threads.   *Ans.* 0.0433 in.; 0.0406 in.

9. Show that the depth in inches of any U. S. S. in $\frac{3}{8}\sqrt{3} = 0.6495$ divided by the number of threads per inch.

10. Using the diameter of the screw, check the depth of the U. S. S. thread for five of the sizes given in Table V.

11. Using the formula, find the root diameter of the following U. S. S. threads: $\frac{5}{8}$ in.-11, 1 in.-8, $1\frac{3}{4}$ in.-5.   *Ans.* 0.507 in.; 0.838 in.; 1.490 in.

12. Find the depth of a metric thread of pitch 1.25 mm. This is for a screw 8 or 9 mm in diameter by the International Standard.
Ans. 0.812 mm.

13. A screw 14 mm in diameter has a metric thread of pitch 2 mm. Find the root diameter. Use the formula for U. S. S. thread.
Ans. 11.402 mm.

CHAPTER XII

THE CIRCLE

145. The importance of a geometrical form in the study of practical mathematics is determined, to a great extent, by the frequency of its occurrence in the applications. The circle occurs often, perhaps more frequently than any other geometric form in applied mathematics. Wires, tanks, pipes, steam boilers, pillars, etc., involve the circle. In the present chapter will be considered the more useful facts about the circle and some of their applications. Again, the student is recommended to select those parts most closely connected with his work or interests for his most careful study.

146. Definitions.—A **circle** is a plane figure bounded by a curved line every point of which is the same distance from another point, called the center.

The curved line is called the **circumference.**

In the study of mathematics, when one is not giving so much attention to the applications, it is better to define the circle as the *curved line* that is here called the circumference. No confusion will arise if it is used in this sense.

A line drawn through the center and terminating in the circumference is called a **diameter.** The diameter divides the circle into two equal parts called **semicircles.**

A line drawn from the center to the circumference is called a **radius.**

Any part of the circumference is called an **arc.**

In Fig. 99, *BC* and *DmE* are arcs.

If the arc equals $\frac{1}{360}$ of the circumference, it is 1° of arc. There are then 360° of arc in one circumference.

The straight line joining the ends of an arc is called a **chord.**

In Fig. 99, *DE* is a chord.

The chord is said to **subtend** its arc.

The chord *DE* subtends the arc *DmE*.

The area bounded by an arc and a chord is called a **segment.**

In Fig. 99, the area *DmE* is a segment.

The area bounded by two radii and an arc is called a **sector.**

In Fig. 99, the area *BOC* is a sector.

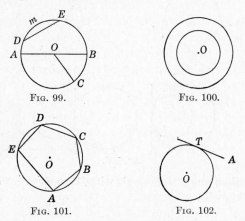

FIG. 99.   FIG. 100.

FIG. 101.   FIG. 102.

Circles are said to be **concentric** when they have a common center as in Fig. 100.

A polygon is **inscribed in** a circle when it is inside the circle and has its vertices on the circumference.   The circle is then **circumscribed about the polygon.**

The polygon *ABCDE* in Fig. 101 is inscribed in the circle *O*.

A line is **tangent** to a circumference when it touches but does not cut through the circumference.

In Fig. 102, *AT* is tangent to the circle *O* at the point *T*.

The point *T* where it touches the circle is called the **point of tangency.**

A polygon is **circumscribed about** a circle, or the circle **i** **inscribed in** a polygon, when the sides of the polygon are a tangent to the circle.

In Fig. 103, the polygon *ABCDE* is circumscribed about the circle *C*

A **central angle** is an angle with its vertex at the center *c* the circle.

In Fig. 104, angle *AOB* is a central angle.

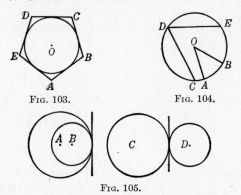

FIG. 103.   FIG. 104.

FIG. 105.

An **inscribed angle** is an angle with its vertex on the circum ference of the circle.

In Fig. 104, angle *CDE* is an inscribed angle.

An inscribed or a central angle is said to **intercept** the ar between its sides.

The sides of the angle *AOB* intercept the arc *AB*, and the sides of th angle *CDE* intercept the arc *CE*.

Two circles that are tangent to the same straight line at th same point are **tangent circles**.

When both circles are on the same side of the common tar gent, they are tangent **internally**. When they are on opposit sides of the common tangent, they are tangent **externally**.

In Fig. 105, circles *A* and *B* are tangent internally and circles *C* and *.* are tangent externally.

147. Properties of the circle.—In geometry are proved a very large number of facts about circles and their relations to straight lines, angles, and polygons. Here a few of these facts are given and are called properties. The truth of these should be readily seen by the student; he should become familiar with these facts and satisfy himself that they are true by actual drawings and measurements.

(1) *In the same circle or in equal circles, chords that are the same distance from the center are equal.*

(2) *A radius, drawn to the center of a chord, is perpendicular to the chord and bisects the arc that the chord subtends.*

FIG. 106.   FIG. 107.

In Fig. 106, the radius *OC* is drawn through the center of the chord *AB*. It is perpendicular to *AB* and makes arc *AC* = arc *CB*. This appears true by measuring the parts in the drawing.

(3) *The angle at the center, which intercepts an arc, is double the inscribed angle that intercepts the same arc.*

In Fig. 107, the central angle *AOC* = 60° and the inscribed angle *ABC* is measured and found to equal 30°.

The student should draw several such figures and measure the angles with a protractor.

(4) *The central angle has as many degrees in it as there are in the arc that its sides intercept; and it is said that the central angle is measured by the arc that its sides intercept.*

This is so because there are four right angles, or 360°, in the angles at the center and the circumference also contains 360°.

One should be careful not to think of a degree of angle and a degree of arc as the same thing. It is only when the vertex of an angle is at the center of a circle that there are the same *number* of degrees of one kind as there are of the other.

(5) *The inscribed angle has one-half as many degrees as the arc its sides intercept; and hence, the inscribed angle is measured by one-half the arc its sides intercept.*

FIG. 108.

(6) *A radius drawn to the point of contact of a tangent is perpendicular to the tangent.*

In Fig. 108, *OP* is drawn to the point of contact of the tangent *AB*. The angles can be measured and found to be right angles. Hence, the radius is perpendicular to the tangent.

(7) *If two circles are tangent to each other, the straight line joining their centers passes through the point of tangency.*

EXERCISES

1. Draw circles with 2-in. radii. In these circles draw the following:
(1) A radius. (2) A diameter. (3) A tangent.
(4) A chord 2 in. long. (5) A central angle of 90°.
(6) An inscribed angle of 90°.
(7) A chord subtending an arc of 120°. Of 45°.
(8) An inscribed square. A circumscribed square.
(9) An inscribed triangle. A circumscribed triangle.
(10) An inscribed hexagon. A circumscribed hexagon.
(11) An inscribed angle of 60°. How many degrees are there in the two arcs thus formed?
(12) A central angle of 60°. How many degrees are there in the two arcs thus formed?

2. In a circle of radius 3 in., draw a radius and four lines perpendicular to this radius so that the four lines divide the radius into three equal parts. Indicate a diameter, a chord, and a tangent in this drawing. Find the length of the chords formed.

3. Draw two concentric circles of radii 2 in. and 1 in. Draw tangents to the smaller circle. Are the chords thus formed all of equal length?

4. Draw two circles that are tangent externally. If one of these circles has a radius of 2 in. and the other 1 in., what conclusions may be deduced? Make the drawing with the circles tangent internally, and discuss.

LINES CONNECTED WITH SEGMENT

148. In practical work it is often necessary to find the radius of the circle when we know the chord *AB* and the height of the segment *DC* of Fig. 109. If *r* stands for the radius of the circle, *h* for the height of the segment, and *w* for the length of the

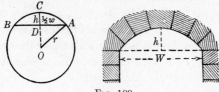

chord, we have the following formulas for finding *r*, *h*, and *w*:

$$[16] \qquad r = \frac{(\tfrac{1}{2}w)^2 + h^2}{2h}$$

$$[17] \qquad h = r - \sqrt{r^2 - (\tfrac{1}{2}w)^2}$$

$$[18] \qquad w = 2\sqrt{h(2r - h)}$$

For the derivation of formula [16] the student is referred to Exercise 49, page 407. It can also readily be obtained from formula [17] by algebra.

Formula [17] is readily found as follows: Since *ODA* is a right triangle,

$$h = r - OD, \text{ and } OD = \sqrt{r^2 - (\tfrac{1}{2}w)^2}$$
$$\therefore h = r - \sqrt{r^2 - (\tfrac{1}{2}w)^2}$$

Formula [18] can be derived from formula [17] by algebra.

Example.—If the chord of the segment of a circle is 5 ft. 6 in. and the height of the segment is 10 in., find the radius of the circle.

Solution.—From formula [16], $r = \dfrac{33^2 + 10^2}{2 \times 10} = 59.45$.

$$\therefore \text{ radius} = 59.45 \text{ in.} \quad Ans.$$

The method given in this article for finding the radius of the circle when the length of the chord and the height of the segment are known is used by street-car trackmen as follows: A straightedge 10 ft. long is laid against the rail on the inside of the curve.   The distance from the center of the straightedge to the rail is measured.   This is the height of the segment, or, as it is usually called, the "middle ordinate."   The radius can now be found by formula [**16**].

For the use of the practical man, tables are arranged that give the radius corresponding to any "middle ordinate" for the 10-ft. chord.   These tables are found in handbooks.

EXERCISES

1. In the arch of the doorway of Fig. 109, w = 6 ft. and h = $1\frac{1}{2}$ ft. Find the radius of the arc.   *Ans.* 3 ft. 9 in.

2. Find the height of a segment cut off from a circle 8 ft. in diameter by a 3-ft. chord.   Give result to nearest $\frac{1}{8}$ inch.   *Ans.* $3\frac{1}{2}$ in.

3. In a circle 6 ft. in radius a segment has a height of 3 ft.; find the length of the chord.   Give result to nearest $\frac{1}{8}$ inch.   *Ans.* 10 ft. $4\frac{5}{8}$ in.

4. In a circle of radius 5 ft., there is a chord 6 ft. 6 in. in length.   Find the height of the segment.   *Ans.* 1 ft. $2\frac{3}{8}$ in.

FIG. 110.

5. A segment of a circle cut off by a chord 4 ft. 6 in. in length has a height of 1 ft. 10 in.   Find the radius of the circle.   *Ans.* 2 ft. 3.57— in.

6. Find the radius of a circle in which a chord of 10 ft. has a middle ordinate of 3 in.

Ans. 50 ft. $1\frac{1}{2}$ in.

7. In Fig. 110, W, W is a wall with a round corner, of dimensions as given from A to B, on which a molding, gutter, or cornice is to be placed.   Find the radius of the circle of which arc ANB is a part.   *Ans.* 3 ft. $\frac{1}{2}$ in.

MEASUREMENT OF CIRCLE

149. Relations between the diameter, radius, and circumference.—If the diameter and the circumference of a circle be measured, and the length of the circumference be divided by the length of the diameter the result will be nearly $3\frac{1}{7}$.   This value is the ratio of the circumference to the diameter of a circle and cannot be expressed exactly in figures.   In mathematics the ratio is represented by the Greek letter π (pi), the exact numerical value of which cannot be expressed.   The value to four decimal places is 3.1416.

Because of this relation, if the diameter, the radius, or the circumference is known, the two others can be found.

Rule.—*The* **radius** *equals one-half the diameter, or the diameter equals twice the radius.*

The **circumference** *equals the diameter times* 3.1416 *approx.*

The **diameter** *equals the circumference divided by* 3.1416 *approx.*

If r stands for the radius, d for the diameter, and C for the circumference, the rules are stated in the following formulas:

[19] $$C = \pi d$$
[20] $$d = C \div \pi$$
[21] $$C = 2\pi r$$
[22] $$2r = C \div \pi$$

150. Area of the circle.—The method of finding the area of a circle when the radius, diameter, or circumference is given is established in geometry. The following will show the reasonableness of the rules.

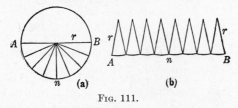

Fig. 111.

In Fig. 111, suppose that the half of the circle AnB is cut as indicated from the center nearly to the circumference and then spread out as in (b). The length AnB of (b) is the half circumference. Let the other half of the circle be cut in the same manner and fitted into the first half. It is evident that if we make the number of the cuts large, the figure formed will be approximately a rectangle whose length is equal to one-half the circumference and whose width is equal to the radius. We then have the following:

Rule.—*To find the area of a circle, multiply one-half the circumference by the radius.*

This may be put in either of the following forms which are usually more convenient to use.

RULE.—*The area of a circle equals π times the square of the radius; or the area of a circle equals one-fourth of π times the square of the diameter.*

If A stands for the area, C for the circumference, d for the diameter, and r for the radius, these rules are stated in the following formulas:

[23] $$A = \tfrac{1}{2}Cr$$
[24] $$A = \pi r^2 = 3.1416 \times r^2$$
[25] $$A = \tfrac{1}{4}\pi d^2 = 0.7854 \times d^2$$

From formula [24], if the area of the circle is given, the radius equals the square root of the quotient when the area is divided by π. Or, in a formula,

[26] $$r = \sqrt{A \div \pi}$$

From formula [25], we get by algebra

[27] $$d = \sqrt{A \div \tfrac{1}{4}\pi} = \sqrt{A \div 0.7854}$$

Example.—Find the radius of a circle whose area is 28 sq. ft.
Solution.—Using formula [26] and putting in the numbers,

$$r = \sqrt{28 \div 3.1416} = \sqrt{8.9126} = 2.985$$
$$\therefore \text{ Radius} = 2.985 \text{ ft.} \quad Ans.$$

151. Historical note.—Down through the centuries from ancient times many efforts have been made to find an exact numerical value for π and thus to find the area of a circle. The people of Babylon and the early Hebrews (I Kings vii: 23) used 3 as the value of π. Perhaps the earliest known attempt to find the area of a circle accurately was made by Ahmes of Egypt about 1700 B.C. His method gave a value for π that, in our notation, equals 3.1604.

Archimedes (287–212 B.C.) found that π must be between $3\tfrac{1}{7}$ and $3\tfrac{10}{71}$.

Ludolph van Ceulen of Holland (1540–1610) computed π to 35 decimal places and devoted 15 years to the computation.

Others who computed π were Sharp in 1705 to 72 places, Machin in 1706 to 100 places, Rutherford in 1841 to 208 places and in 1853 to 440 places, and Shanks in 1873 to 707 places.

In 1761, Lambert proved that π cannot be expressed as a common fraction or a decimal. The following is the value of π to 42 decimal places:

$$\pi = 3.141592653589793238462643383279502884197169$$

152. Area of a ring.—In the ring, which is the area between the circumferences of two concentric circles, the area can be found by subtracting the area of the small circle from the area of the large circle.

If A and a, R and r stand for the areas and the radii, respectively, of the two circles, and A_r for the area of the ring, then

[28] $\mathbf{A}_r = \mathbf{A} - \mathbf{a} = \pi\mathbf{R}^2 - \pi\mathbf{r}^2 = \pi(\mathbf{R}^2 - \mathbf{r}^2) = \pi(\mathbf{R} + \mathbf{r})(\mathbf{R} - \mathbf{r})$

This last is a very convenient formula to use. It may be stated in words as follows:

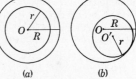

Rule.—*To find the area of a ring, multiply the product of the sum and the difference of the two radii by* π.

Example.—Find the area of a ring of inner diameter 8 in. and outer diameter 12 in.

(a)   (b)

Fig. 112.

Solution.—Using formula [28] and putting in the numbers,

$$A_r = 3.1416(6 + 4)(6 - 4)$$
$$= 3.1416 \times 10 \times 2 = 62.832$$
$$\therefore \text{Area} = 62.832 \text{ sq. in. } Ans.$$

It should be noted that the rule holds even though the circles are not concentric; that is, the circles may be as in Fig. 112(b).

EXERCISES

Choose a suitable unit, say 1 ft. $= \frac{1}{10}$ in., etc., and draw a sketch of the following circular window openings, in which d is a diameter, C is a circumference, and A is an area (find the parts indicated; estimate them first, then compute them):

1. Given $d = 2$ ft.; find C and A.　*Ans.* 6.283+ ft.; 3.1416— sq. ft.

2. Given $d = 3$ ft.; find C and A.　*Ans.* 9.425— ft.; 7.0686— sq. ft.

3. Given $d = 4$ ft.; find C and A.　*Ans.* 12.566+ ft.; 12.566+ sq. ft.

4. Given $d = 20$ ft.; find C and A.　*Ans.* 62.83+ ft.; 314.16— sq. ft.

5. Given $d = 12$ ft.; find C and A.

Ans. 37.699+ ft.; 113.097+ sq. ft.

Note.—There are many handbooks in which C and A may be read directly.

6. Given $C = 31.41593$ ft.; find d and draw the circle.　Find A.

Ans. 10 ft.; 78.54— sq. ft.

7. Given $C = 113.0973$ ft.; find d and draw the circle.　Find A.

Ans. 36 ft.; 1017.88— sq. ft.

8. Given $A = 201.0619$ sq. ft.; find d and draw the circle.　Find C.

Ans. 16 ft.; 50.265+ ft.

9. Given $A = 3.141593$ sq. ft.; find d and draw the circle.　Find C.

Ans. 2 ft.; 6.283+ ft.

10. Find the area of the cross section of a 1-in. rod.

Ans. 0.7854— sq. in.

By the **cross section** is meant the area of the end of the rod when cut square off.

11. Find the area of the ring in the cross section of a pipe with outer diameter of 4 in. and inner diameter of 2 in.　*Ans.* 9.424+ sq. in.

12. Find the area of the ring in the cross section of a water main if its outer diameter is 18 in. and the iron in the pipe is 1 in. thick.

Ans. 53.4+ sq. in.

The angle at the center of a circle made by two radii is as follows:
Hint.—Use

$$\frac{\text{Intercepted arc}}{\text{Circumference}} = \frac{\text{angle at center}}{360}$$

13. Angle of 15°, radius of 10 in.; find the intercepted arc.

14. Angle of 30°, $r = 10$ in.; find the intercepted arc.

15. Angle of 45°, intercepted arc $= \pi$ feet; find r.

16. Angle of 270°, intercepted arc $= 3\pi$ ft.; find r.

17. In a circle of 6-in. radius, the sides of an angle of 30° at the center intercept what length of arc? What length of arc is intercepted by the sides of an inscribed angle of 90°?　*Ans.* 3.1416 in.; 18.8496 in.

18. The diameter of the safety valve in a boiler is 3 in. Find the total pressure tending to raise the valve when the pressure of the steam is 120 lb. per square inch.　*Ans.* 848.23 lb.

19. If the diameter of a piston is 30 in., find the total pressure on the piston when the pressure of steam is 100 lb. per square inch.

Ans. 70,686 lb

20. A circular sheet of steel 2 ft. in diameter increases in diameter by $\frac{1}{200}$ when the temperature is increased by a certain amount. (*a*) Find the increase in the area of the sheet. (*b*) Find the per cent of increase in area. *Ans.* 0.0315 sq. ft.; 1%.

21. A 6-in. water pipe can carry how many times as much as a 1-in. pipe?

Solution: Area of 6-in. pipe $= 0.7854 \times 6^2$ in.²

Area of 1-in. pipe $= 0.7854 \times 1^2$ in.²

$$\frac{\text{Area of 6-in. pipe}}{\text{Area of 1-in. pipe}} = \frac{0.7854 \times 6^2}{0.7854 \times 1^2} = \frac{6^2}{1^2} = 36 \quad Ans.$$

The quotient or the ratio of the areas of two circles can always be found by dividing the square of one diameter by the square of the other. The radii may be used instead of the diameters.

The foregoing is simply the principle that similar areas are in the same ratio as the squares of their like dimensions, applied to circles.

22. Find the ratio of the cross-sectional areas in the following wires: (See Exercise 21.)

(1) A 1-in. wire and a 0.5-in. wire.

(2) A $\frac{1}{8}$ in. wire and a $\frac{1}{2}$-in. wire.

(3) A $\frac{1}{16}$-in. wire and a 1-in. wire.

(4) An *s*-in. wire and an *S*-in. wire.

23. How many 3-in. steam pipes could open off an 18-in. steam pipe?
Ans. 36.

24. How many No. 20 B. & S. copper wires will have the same cross-sectional area as one No. 00? (See Table VI.) *Ans.* 130.3—.

25. In a steel plate 3 by $2\frac{1}{2}$ ft. are 26 round holes, each $1\frac{3}{4}$ in. in diameter. Find the area of steel remaining. *Ans.* 1,017.46 sq. ft.

26. If the drive wheels of a locomotive are 66 in. in diameter, find the number of R. P. M. to go 40 miles per hour.

Solution: $\dfrac{40 \times 5280 \times 12}{60 \times 66 \times 3.1416} = 203.7 \quad Ans.$

It is usual to work such problems as this by cancellation. Above the line are the numbers that give the inches in 40 miles. Below the line is 60, which we divide by to get the number of inches that the train goes in 1 min.; and 66×3.1416, which is the number of inches in the circumference of the wheel.

27. The circumference of a drive wheel of a locomotive is 16 ft. If a train is to hold a speed of 60 miles per hour, and if there is no slipping, how many R. P. M. must the wheel make? *Ans.* 330.

28. A locomotive wheel 5 ft. in diameter made 10,000 revolutions in a distance of 24 miles. What distance was lost due to the slipping of the wheel? *Ans.* 5.75 miles.

29. There are 32 hoops weighing 3 lb. per linear foot on a tank 15 ft. in diameter.   Find the weight of the iron hoops.   *Ans.* 4,524 lb.

30. The side of a square is 20 in.   Find the following:

(1) The circumference and the area of the inscribed circle.

Ans. 20π in.; 100π sq. in.

(2) The circumference and the area of the circumscribed circle.

Ans. $20\pi \sqrt{2}$ in.; 200π sq. in.

(3) The area of the ring formed by the two circles in (1) and (2).

Ans. 100π sq. in.

31. What is the waste in cutting the largest possible circular plate from a piece of sheet steel 17 by 20 in.?   *Ans.* 113.02 sq. in.

32. The minute hand of a tower clock is 6 ft. long.   What distance will the extremity move over in 36 min.?   *Ans.* 22 ft. 7.4+ in.

33. The area of a square is 49 sq. ft.   Find the length of the circumference and the area of the circle inscribed in this square.

Ans. 21.99+ ft.; 38.48+ sq. ft.

34. Find the size of the largest square timber which can be cut from a log 24 in. in diameter.   *Ans.* 16.97+ in.

35. Using 4000 miles as radius of earth, find length in feet of 1 sec. of arc on the equator.   *Ans.* 102.4− ft.

Note: 1° = 60 min. (60′) and 1 min. of arc = 60 sec. (60″) of arc.

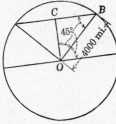

36. Using 4000 miles as radius of earth, find the length in miles of arc of 1′ (*a*) on the parallel of 45° north; (*b*) on the parallel of 60° north.   *Ans.* 0.823− miles; 0.582− miles.

Suggestion.—For the parallel of 45° north, *CB* is the radius.   But *CB = OC* since the triangle *OCB* is a right triangle with two equal angles.   The relations are as shown in Fig. 113.

37. A 10-in. pipe is to be branched off into two equal pipes.   What must be the diameter of each of these pipes if the two pipes shall equal the area of the 10-in. pipe?   *Ans.* 7.07+ in.

Fig. 113.

38. Show that the following rule is correct for finding the length of an arc of a circle: Multiply the diameter of the circle by the number of degrees in the arc and by 0.0087266.

39. If an automobile wheel has a diameter of 32 in., how many R. P. M. will the wheel make when the automobile is going 60 miles per hour?

Ans. 630+.

40. Find the length in feet of the arc of contact of a belt with a pulley if the pulley is 3 ft. 6 in. in diameter and the arc of contact is 210°.

Ans. 6 ft. 5 in.

41. As in the preceding, find the length of the arc of contact if it is 120° and the diameter of the pulley is 16 in. *Ans.* $16\frac{3}{4}$ in.

AREAS OF SECTOR AND SEGMENT

153. Area of a sector.—The area of a sector of a circle is equal to that fractional part of the area of the whole circle that the angle of the sector is of 360°. Thus, if the angle of the sector is 90°, the area of the sector is $\frac{90}{360}$ of the area of the circle.

Fig. 114.

Example.—Find the area of a sector of 60° in a circle of radius 10 in.

Solution.—In Fig. 114, the sector AOB has an angle of 60°. Its area equals $\frac{60}{360} \times \pi r^2$. If the radius is 10 in., the area of the sector is

$$A = \tfrac{1}{6} \times 3.1416 \times 10^2 = 52.36 \text{ sq. in.} \quad Ans.$$

If θ (the Greek letter theta) stands for the number of degrees in the angle of the sector, and the other letters the same as before, the area of the sector is given by the formula

$$[29(a)] \qquad \mathbf{A} = \frac{\theta}{360} \times \pi \mathbf{r}^2$$

By the same reasoning as was used in Art. 150, the area of a sector is found to be one-half the arc length times the radius of the circle, or

$$[29(b)] \qquad \mathbf{A} = \tfrac{1}{2}\mathbf{arc} \cdot \mathbf{r}$$

154. Area of a segment.—In Fig. 114, it is evident that the area of the segment ABD equals the area of the sector AOB minus the area of the triangle AOB. Since it requires a knowledge of trigonometry to find the area of a triangle when we have only two sides and an angle or to find the area of a sector when the angle is unknown, we cannot usually find the area of a segment by geometry. (See page 603.)

If the angle and the lines in the segment are measured, the area of (1) the sector and (2) the triangle can be found. The difference between these areas is the area of the segment.

Example 1.—Find the area of a segment in a circle of radius $11\frac{1}{4}$ in. and subtending an angle at the center of 105°.

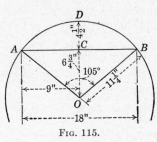

Solution.—The dimensions are as shown in Fig. 115, where the parts are constructed accurately to scale and measured.

The area of sector $OADB = \frac{105}{360}$ of the area of the circle.

∴ Area of sector $= \frac{105}{360} \times 3.1416 \times (11\frac{1}{4})^2 = 115.97$ sq. in.

Fig. 115.

Area of triangle $OAB = \frac{1}{2} \times 18 \times 6\frac{3}{4} = 60.75$ sq. in.

Area of segment = area of sector − area of triangle =
115.97 sq. in. − 60.75 sq. in. = 55.22 sq. in.   *Ans.*

Many approximate rules are given to find the area of a segment. Perhaps the following are as good as any.

[30(a)] $$A = \frac{2}{3}\,hw + \frac{h^3}{2w}$$

[30(b)] $$A = \frac{4}{3}\,h^2\,\sqrt{\frac{2r}{h} - 0.608}$$

In these formulas A is the area of the segment, h the height, and w the width, while r is the radius of the circle to which the segment belongs.

If the height of the segment is less than one-tenth the radius of the circle, formula [30(a)] may be shortened to $A = \frac{2}{3}hw$.

Steam engineers often wish to find the area of a segment when the height is large compared with the radius, say, two-thirds

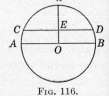

Fig. 116.

of the radius. They then proceed as follows: In Fig. 116, let it be required to find the area of the segment CnD. Find the area of the half circle AnB and then the area of the part

ACDB considered as a rectangle. The area of the segment is roughly the difference between these.

Example 2.—Find the area of the segment whose chord is 10 ft. and height 1.5 ft.

Solution.—By formula [**30(a)**],

$$A = \frac{2}{3} \times 1.5 \times 10 + \frac{1.5^3}{2 \times 10} = 10.17 - \text{ sq. ft.}$$

By formula [**30(b)**], first finding r by formula [**16**],

$$r = \frac{5^2 + 1.5^2}{2 \times 1.5} = 9.083$$

$$A = \frac{4}{3} \times 1.5^2 \sqrt{\frac{2 \times 9.083}{1.5} - 0.608} = 10.175 \text{ sq. ft.}$$

EXERCISES

Find the areas of the following sectors of circles (draw the figure; estimate the area; then compute it):

1. Radius = 5 in.; angle of sector = 30°.   *Ans.* $\frac{25\pi}{12}$ sq. in.

2. Radius = 10 in.; angle of sector = 120°.   *Ans.* $\frac{100\pi}{3}$ sq. in.

3. Radius = 20 in.; angle of sector = 225°.   *Ans.* 250π sq. in.

4. Radius = 43.17 ft.; arc of sector = 49.79 ft.

         Ans. 1074.72 sq. ft.

5. Radius = 100 m.; arc of sector = 100 m.   *Ans.* 5000 sq. m.

Find the areas of the following segments of circles:

6. Chord = 20 in.; height = 3 in.   *Ans.* $40\frac{27}{40}$ sq. in.

7. Chord = 21 in., height = 1 in. Use formula [**30(a)**] and also its shortened form.   *Ans.* $14\frac{1}{40}$ sq. in.

8. In Exercises 6 and 7, find r first, then use formula [**30(b)**] to find the areas of the segments.

9. A segment of a circle has a radius of 10 ft. and a height of 9 ft. Find its area by method as indicated by Fig. 116.   *Ans.* 137 sq. ft.

10. In formula [**30(a)**], take the segment as half the circle. What approximate value does this give for π? In formula [**30(b)**], what value does this give for π?   *Ans.* 3.1666; 3.144.

THE ELLIPSE

155. The **ellipse** is a curved line such that the sum of the distances of any point in it from two fixed points is constant, that is, always the same.

In Fig. 117, F and F' are the two fixed points and are called the **foci** (singular, **focus**). The point O is the **center** of the ellipse. NA is the **major axis,** and MB is the **minor axis.** OA and OB are the **semiaxes.**

The curved line is so traced that any point P has the distances $PF + PF'$ equal to the distances $P'F + P'F'$, drawn

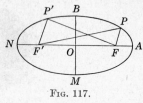

Fig. 117.

from any other point in the curved line. This suggests the following method for drawing an ellipse: Take a string equal in length to the major axis of the ellipse desired. On a drawing board, fasten the ends of the string at F and F' as shown in Fig. 117. Place a pencil point P in the string and move it about, keeping the string taut. Then the point P will trace the ellipse.

The ellipse is closely related to the circle. If a circular pipe is cut on a slant, the section is a true ellipse. It is for this reason that sheet-metal workers often have to consider an ellipse.

156. Uses of the ellipse.—The ellipse is involved in many practical considerations, as well as being frequently used in mathematics and its applications.

It was believed by the ancient Greeks that the sun was the center of the universe in which we live. Kepler (1571–1630) stated that the orbits of the planets are ellipses. Newton (1642–1727) showed that the law of gravitation determines the orbits to be ellipses.

In architecture, because of the beauty of its form, the elliptic arch is frequently used. Some noted structures were built in the form of an ellipse, for example, the Colosseum at Rome.

In bridge structures, many of the most noted stone-arch bridges of the world are elliptical.

In machinery, elliptical gears are often used where changeable rates of motion are desired, as in shapers, planers, and slotters where the cutting speed is less than the return motion.

In the study of electricity and mechanics, the ellipse is frequently used.

157. Area of ellipse.—We know that the area of a circle is given by the formula $A = \pi r^2$, which may be written $A = \pi rr$. Now, if a circle is flattened somewhat, it may take the form of an ellipse, and the semiaxes, OA and OB of Fig. 117, will be lengthened and shortened radii. If a stands for AO and b for OB, it can be proved that the area of the ellipse can be found by replacing rr in the formula for the area of the circle by ab. This gives the following formula for the area of an ellipse:

[31] $$A = \pi ab$$

Example.—Find the area of an ellipse whose two axes are 30 and 26 ft., respectively.

Solution.—Using formula [31] and putting in the values,

$$A = 3.1416 \times 15 \times 13 = 612.612 \text{ sq. ft.} \quad Ans.$$

158. Circumference of ellipse.—Although the area of an ellipse is easily found when the major and minor axes are given, the circumference, or perimeter, of the ellipse is determined with difficulty. Various approximate formulas are given for finding the circumference of an ellipse. If the ellipse is very nearly the shape of a circle, that is, if the major and minor axes are nearly equal, then

[32(a)] $$P = \pi(a + b)$$

where

P = the perimeter or circumference.

a = the semimajor axis.

b = the semiminor axis.

When the ellipse differs considerably from a circle, that is, when there is considerable difference between the major and minor axes, either of the following rules may be used to good advantage:

[32(b)] $$P = \pi[\tfrac{3}{2}(a + b) - \sqrt{ab}]$$
[32(c)] $$P = \pi \sqrt{2(a^2 + b^2)}$$

The exact formula derived by the methods of higher mathematics may be stated in the following form:

$$P = 2\pi a(1 - \tfrac{1}{4}e^2 - \tfrac{3}{64}e^4 - \tfrac{5}{256}e^6 - \tfrac{175}{16384}e^8 - \cdots)$$

where $e = \dfrac{\sqrt{a^2 - b^2}}{a}$. This formula is not given with the intention that it should be used, as the computation required is considerable.

The result obtained by using formula [**32(a)**] is too small, and the result from formula [**32(c)**] is too large. It is fortunate, however, that the mean, or average, of these results is very approximately correct; in fact, the error is then only about $\tfrac{5}{16384}e^3(2\pi a)$.

Example.—Find the circumference of an ellipse whose major axis is 18 in. and whose minor axis is 6 in.

Solution.—Here $a = 9$ and $b = 3$.

By [**32(a)**], $P = 3.1416(9+3) = 37.699$ in.   *Ans.*
By [**32(b)**], $P = 3.1416[\tfrac{3}{2}(9+3) - \sqrt{9 \times 3}] = 40.225$ in.   *Ans.*
By [**32(c)**], $P = 3.1416\sqrt{2(9^2 + 3^2)} = 42.148$ in.   *Ans.*

Formula [**32(b)**] is the best to use when the two axes are not very nearly equal.

Note that the mean of the result obtained from formulas [**32(a)**] and [**32(c)**] is 39.974 in., which closely approximates that obtained from formula [**32(b)**].

EXERCISES

1. A garden is an ellipse with longest diameter 22 ft. and shortest diameter 18 ft.   Find the area of the garden.   *Ans.* 99π sq. ft.

2. An elliptic pipe has major and minor axis 16 and 10 in., respectively. Find the diameter of a circular pipe that has the same area of cross section.   *Ans.* 12.648 in.

3. A horizontal steam pipe 8 in. in diameter is to pass through a half-pitch roof.   If the direction of the pipe is perpendicular to the sides of the building, show how the carpenter is to make out the hole to be cut in the roof.

Suggestion.—The hole will be an ellipse with minor axis 8 in. and major axis $8\sqrt{2}$ in. by the formula of Art. 127 for the diagonal of a square.

4. A 10-in. smoke pipe is cut off on an angle of 45°. Use the mean of formulas [**32(a)**] and [**32(b)**] to find the circumference of the section.

Ans. 38+ in.

5. The Colosseum at Rome is in the form of an ellipse with a major axis of 620 ft. and a minor axis of 510 ft. Find its area and its circumference. Use formulas [**31**] and [**32(a)**].

GENERAL EXERCISES

NOTE.—Some of the problems in these exercises may be omitted until Part III is studied. However, the better students should be able to solve them at this stage of their development.

1. A device used in air conditioning a building consists of two circular pipes joined and continued as a rectangular pipe.

(1) If the circular pipes are 11 and 14 in. in diameter, respectively, and the rectangular pipe is 14 in. wide, what is the length of the cross section of the rectangular pipe. *Ans.* 17.75 in.

(2) If R and r are the radii of the circular pipes and a and b are the width and length of the rectangular pipe, derive a formula connecting R, r, a, and b. Solve this formula for b, and test the result obtained in (1).

$$Ans. \ \frac{\pi(R^2 + r^2)}{a}.$$

2. Two pipes of radii R and r, respectively, are connected to an oil tank.

(1) If the small pipe has a diameter of 1 in. and will empty 2 bbl. of oil in 15 min., how many barrels will the large pipe empty in 24 hr. if it has a diameter of 8 in.? (Make no allowance for friction.)

Ans. 12,288.

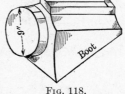

FIG. 118.

(2) If the small pipe will empty b bbl. in t min., how many barrels will the large pipe empty in T hr.? Derive a formula. Check the result obtained in (1).

3. A hot-air pipe 9 in. in diameter passes into a boot as shown in Fig. 118, and a rectangular pipe of same capacity passes upward from the boot. If the rectangular pipe is 4 in. wide, find its length in cross section.

$$Ans. \ \frac{\pi(4\frac{1}{2})^2}{4}.$$

Derive a formula for this exercise if the hot-air pipe has a radius of r in. and the rectangular pipe is w in. wide. Check the results for the particular values given by substituting in the formula.

$$Ans. \ \frac{\pi r^2}{w}.$$

4. At the center of one side of a barn 40 ft. on a side, a horse is tied by a rope 70 ft. in length. Find the area that he can graze over in square rods. *Ans.* 43.27 + square rods.

5. Prove that the area of a circle with the hypotenuse of a right triangle as diameter is equal to the sum of the areas of the two circles having the base and altitude, respectively, as diameters.

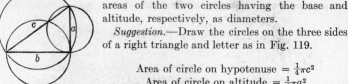

Suggestion.—Draw the circles on the three sides of a right triangle and letter as in Fig. 119.

Area of circle on hypotenuse = $\frac{1}{4}\pi c^2$
Area of circle on altitude = $\frac{1}{4}\pi a^2$
Area of circle on base = $\frac{1}{4}\pi b^2$

Fig. 119.

By Pythagorean proposition,

$$c^2 = a^2 + b^2$$

Multiplying by $\frac{1}{4}\pi$,

$$\frac{1}{4}\pi c^2 = \frac{1}{4}\pi a^2 + \frac{1}{4}\pi b^2 \quad Ans.$$

6. Show by means of the carpenter's square how to find the diameter of a circle having the same area as the sum of the areas of two given circles.

Discussion.—Suppose that we take two circles 6 and 8 in. in diameter, respectively. Lay off on one arm of the carpenter's square, as shown in

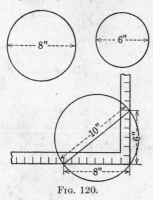

Fig. 120, the diameter of the 6 in. circle and on the other arm the diameter of the 8-in. circle. The line joining the ends of these, or the hypotenuse of the right triangle, is the diameter of the circle having the same area as the sum of the areas of the two given circles, as was proved in Exercise 5.

7. Given two joining pipes 12 and 8

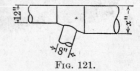

Fig. 120.

Fig. 121.

in. in diameter, respectively. Find the diameter x of the continuation. (See Fig. 121.) *Ans.* $14\frac{3}{8}$ in.

If the joining pipes have radii of R and r, respectively, derive a formula for x as a function of R and r. *Ans.* $\sqrt{R^2 + r^2}$.

8. Show by means of the carpenter's square how to find the diameter of a circle having the same area as the sum of the areas of any number of given circles.

9. If an arc of a circle is equal in length to the radius, what is the value of the central angle that it measures?

Suggestion.—Circumference $= 2\pi r$. An arc of length r is $\dfrac{r}{2\pi r}$ or $\dfrac{1}{2\pi}$ part of the circumference.

The central angle that this arc measures is the same fractional part of $360°$. Hence, the central angle is

$$\frac{1}{2\pi} \times 360° = \frac{180°}{\pi} = 180° \div 3.14159 = 57.2958° \quad Ans.$$

It will be found later that this angle is 1 radian.

10. A regular hexagon, the perimeter of which is 42 ft., is inscribed in a circle. Find the area of the circle. *Ans.* 153.9 sq. ft.

11. The maximum circumferential velocity of cast-iron flywheels is 80 ft. per second. Find the maximum number of R. P. M. for a cast-iron flywheel 8 ft. in diameter. *Ans.* 191 approx.

12. An emery wheel may have a circumferential velocity of 5500 ft. per minute. Find the number of revolutions per second that an emery wheel 9 in. in diameter may make. *Ans.* 39 approx.

13. The peripheral speed of a grindstone of strong grain should not exceed 47 ft. per second. Find the number R. P. M. that a grindstone 3 ft. in diameter may turn. *Ans.* 299 approx.

14. Four of the largest possible equal-sized pipes are enclosed in a box of square cross section 18 in. on an edge. What part of the space do the pipes occupy? *Ans.* 0.7854.

15. Find size of the box to enclose five 6-in. pipes, placed as in Fig. 122, and find the part that the area of the pipes is of the area of the box.

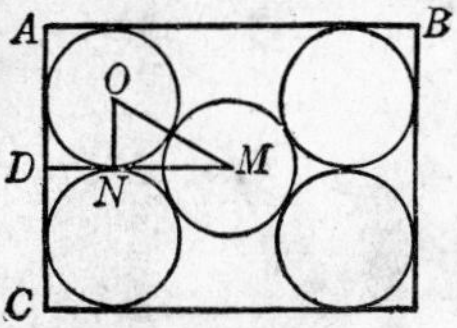

Solution: $AC = 12$ in.

$$AB = 2DM$$
$$DM = DN + NM$$

but

$$DN = 3 \text{ in.}$$

and

Fig. 122.

$$NM = \sqrt{OM^2 - ON^2} = \sqrt{6^2 - 3^2} = \sqrt{27} = 5.196 \text{ in.}$$
$$\therefore DM = 3 \text{ in.} + 5.196 \text{ in.} = 8.196 \text{ in.}$$
$$\therefore AB = 2 \times 8.196 \text{ in.} = 16.392 \text{ in.}$$
$$\therefore \text{area} = 12 \times 16.392 = 196.704 \text{ in.}^2 \quad Ans.$$

Area of 5 circles $= 5 \times 0.7854 \times 6^2 = 141.372$ in.²
Part occupied by pipes $= 141.372 \div 196.704 = 0.7187 +. \quad Ans.$

16. Three circles are enclosed in an equilateral triangle. If the circles are 10 in. in radius, find the sides of the triangle. *Ans.* 54.64 in.

Suggestion.—The circles are as shown in Fig. 123. The triangle

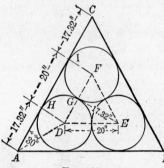

FIG. 123.

DEG = triangle DAH. Hence AH = GE = $10 \times \sqrt{3}$ = 17.32 in.; HI = the diameter of one of the circles = 20 in.; and $IC = AH =$ 17.32 in.

17. The strength of a hemp rope is determined by the formula

$$W = 1420A$$

where

W = the strength in pounds.

A = the area, in square inches, of the cross section of the rope.

Determine the diameter of a hemp rope to support a weight of 2400 lb. *Ans.* $1\frac{1}{2}$ in. approx.

18. Find the diameter of a single pipe having the same carrying capacity as three pipes of diameters $1\frac{1}{2}$, $2\frac{1}{2}$, and $3\frac{1}{2}$ in., respectively.

Ans. $4\frac{9}{16}$ in.

19. Find the value of x in Fig. 124 *Ans.* 0.2071.

Suggestion: $x = OC$

$$\therefore (x + \tfrac{1}{2})^2 = (\tfrac{1}{2})^2 + (\tfrac{1}{2})^2$$

20. Find the value of x in Fig. 125. *Ans.* $\frac{3}{16}$.

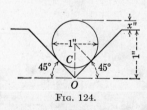

FIG. 124.

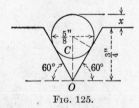

FIG. 125.

21. Find the radius of the circle in Fig. 126. All the angles are right angles. *Ans.* 1.55+ in.

Suggestion.—Draw right triangle AOB, and note that $OB = r$, $AO = r - 1$, and $AB = 3 - r$.

22. What is the per cent of error in taking $4 \times CA$ in Fig. 127 as the circumference of circle O? *Ans.* 0.66− % too large.

23. In the same circle, what is the per cent of error in taking $4(DE + \frac{1}{2}AB)$ as the circumference? *Ans.* 0.65− % too small.

24. If statements in Exercises 22 and 23 gave the exact length of the circumference, what would be the value of π in each case?

Ans. 3.1623−; 3.1213+.

25. Make a construction as shown in Fig. 128. *AB* is approximately the quadrant of the circle. Find the per cent that it differs from the correct value. *Ans.* 0.4+ % too large.

26. Justify the following rule used by sheet-metal workers, or show the per cent of error if it is not correct: Divide the radius *AO*, Fig. 129,

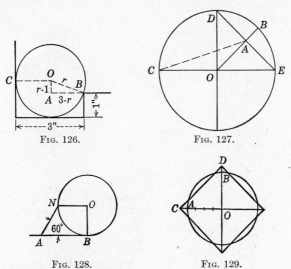

Fig. 126.

Fig. 127.

Fig. 128.

Fig. 129.

into four equal parts, and place one of these parts from *A* to *C* and another from *B* to *D*, the ends of two perpendicular diameters. Connect *C* and *D*, which gives the side of the square of the same area as the circle.

Ans. 0.5+ % too small.

27. The stem of a 4-in. safety valve, Fig. 130, is $2\frac{3}{4}$ in. from the fulcrum. Suppose that the valve will blow when the gage reads 7 lb. without any weight on the lever (that is, 7 lb. per square inch on the valve overcomes weight of valve and lever); at what pressure would it blow with a weight of 75 lb. 32 in. from the fulcrum? *Ans.* 76.4+ lb. per square inch.

28. What weight of ball would be required to allow the valve in Exercise 27 to blow off at 80 lb.? *Ans.* 78.8+ lb.

29. If the original weight of 75 lb. is used, at what distance from the fulcrum should it be placed to allow the valve to blow off at 80 lb.?

Ans. 33.6+ in.

30. The following is an approximate formula for determining the number of inscribed tangent circles as in Fig. 131:

$$N = 0.907 \left(\frac{D}{d} - 0.94\right)^2 + 3.7$$

where

N = the number.

D = the diameter of the enclosing circle.

d = the diameter of the inscribed circles.

Apply the preceding formula, and find how many wires $\frac{1}{2}$ in. in diameter can be placed inside a 5-in. pipe.   *Ans.* 78.

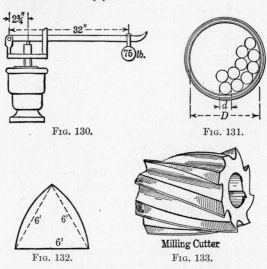

Fig. 130.

Fig. 131.

Fig. 132.

Milling Cutter

Fig. 133.

31. How many steel balls 0.4 in. in diameter can rest at the bottom of a closed pipe $2\frac{1}{2}$ in. in diameter?   *Ans.* 29.

32. From the formula of Exercise 30 the following can be derived:

$$D = d \left(0.94 + \sqrt{\frac{N - 3.7}{0.907}}\right)$$

Derive the formula.   Use the formula to find the size of a pipe or conduit required to hold 50 wires 0.075 in. in diameter.   *Ans.* 0.606 in.

33. The Gothic arch is formed by two arcs each one-sixth of a circle. The center of each circle is at the extremity of the width of the arch; that is, the radius equals the width.   Find the area of such an arch of radius 6 ft.   (See Fig. 132.)   *Ans.* 22.11 sq. ft.

34. Each of four steam engines is supplied by a 6-in. steam pipe. These open off from a single steam pipe. Find the diameter of the larger pipe so that it may have the same capacity as the four 6-in. pipes.

Ans. 12 in.

35. A milling cutter $4\frac{1}{2}$ in. in diameter is cutting soft steel at the rate of 45 ft. per minute. Find the number of R. P. M. *Ans.* 38 approx.

36. How many turns per second must a drill $\frac{1}{2}$ in. in diameter make so that the outer edge of the lip will have a cutting speed of 35 ft. per minute? *Ans.* 4.5 approx.

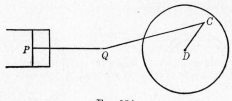

Fig. 134.

37. The distance between the center of the crankpin C, Fig. 134, and the center of the flywheel at D is 20 in. What is the length of the stroke of the piston? If the flywheel makes 144 R. P. M., find the average speed of the piston in feet per minute.

38. The "piston speed" in a Corliss engine should be 600 ft. per minute. How many R. P. M. should be made by an engine having a 20-in. stroke? By an engine having a 36-in. stroke?

39. Which would occupy the greater portion of the square shown in Fig. 135 the four small circles or the large circle?

40. The drivers on a locomotive are making 210 R. P. M. and are 76 in. diameter. Find the speed of the locomotive in miles per hour if 2% is allowed for slipping. *Ans.* 46.53 miles per hour.

Fig. 135.

41. In a Corliss engine the high-pressure cylinder is 22 in. in diameter. What must be the diameter of the low-pressure cylinder in order that it may have double the area of the high-pressure cylinder?

Ans. 31.1+ in.

42. If the total pressure on the piston of a brake cylinder is 8100 lb., what is the diameter of the cylinder if the pressure is 60 lb. per square inch? *Ans.* 13.1+ in.

43. A machine screw $\frac{5}{8}$ in. in diameter has 12 sharp V threads to the inch. Find the root diameter. Find the tensile strength at 50,000 lb. per square inch. Give answer to the nearest 100 lb. *Ans.* 9100 lb.

44. What should be the area of the opening of a cold-air box for a hot-air furnace in order to supply seven hot-air pipes 9 in. in diameter and one pipe 14 in. in diameter if the area of the cold-air opening is three-fourths the area of the hot-air pipes?   *Ans.* 449.4 sq. in.

45. A cylinder of a double-acting engine is 26 in. in diameter, and the length of the stroke is 30 in.   Compute the pressure on the piston if the piston rod is $3\frac{1}{2}$ in. in diameter and the steam pressure in the cylinder is 150 lb. per square inch.   (Use formula [**28**].)

46. In practice, piston rings, Fig. 136, for a steam engine are turned so that they are $1\frac{1}{2}\%$ larger in diameter than the diameter of the cylinder barrel.   They then have a piece cut out and are sprung into place.   Find

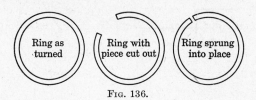

Fig. 136.

the diameter of the ring for a cylinder 24 in. in diameter.   Find the length of the piece to be cut out if when sprung into place it has a clearance of $\frac{1}{16}$ in. between ends.   Give dimensions to the nearest $\frac{1}{32}$ in.
Ans. $24\frac{3}{8}$ in.; $1\frac{3}{16}$ in.

47. Find the speed of a belt running over a pulley having a diameter of 22 in. and making 320 R. P. M., if 2% is allowed for slipping.
Ans. 1806 ft. per minute.

48. If the greatest and least diameters of an elliptical manhole are 2 ft. 7 in. and 2 ft. 3 in., respectively, find its area.   Find its perimeter using formulas [**32(b)**] and [**32(c)**].
Ans. 4.565 sq. ft.; 91.2 in.; 91.3 in.

49. Given an elliptical pipe of longest and shortest axes 16 and 10 in. respectively, find the diameter of the circular pipe having the same area of cross section.   *Ans.* $12\frac{5}{8}$ in.

50. What is the horsepower of a single-acting steam engine with an 18-in. stroke and a 10-in. piston, making 150 R. P. M. with an average steam pressure of 40 lb. per square inch.

Solution: $H = \dfrac{PLAN}{33,000}$

$A = \frac{1}{4}\pi \times 10^2 = 78.54,\ L = 1\frac{1}{2},\ N = 150,\ P = 40$

$$H = \frac{40 \times 3 \times 78.54 \times 150}{2 \times 33,000} = 21.42$$

REGULAR POLYGONS AND CIRCLES

159. It is often necessary to determine the dimensions of a regular polygon inscribed in or circumscribed about a given circle or to determine the size of a circle that can be inscribed in or circumscribed about a given polygon.

Such problems are readily solved by trigonometry, and some of them may be solved by geometry. In either case, though, the computation may be long and tedious. For this reason handbooks give rules by which the computations can be readily made. In the table on page 220 are classified certain facts about the **regular polygons** named. These facts can readily be applied to polygons of any size.

(1) **To find the area of a polygon when the length of one side is given.**—*Multiply the square of the side by a number given in column* (3).

This rule is an application of the principle that similar areas are in the same ratio as the squares of their like dimensions. Show that this is the case.

Example.—Find the area of a regular pentagon having sides of 7 in.

Area = $7^2 \times 1.7204774$ sq. in. = 84.30339 sq. in. *Ans.*

(2) **To find the side of a polygon when its area is given.**— *Divide the area of the polygon by a number from column* (3). *The square root of the quotient is the required side of the polygon.*

Example.—The area of an octagon is 4376 sq. ft.; find a side of the polygon.

Side = $\sqrt{4376 \div 4.828}$ = 30.106 ft. *Ans.*

(3) **To find the radius of the circumscribing circle when a side of the polygon is given.**—*Multiply the length of a side by a number chosen from column* (5).

This can be used to good advantage in drawing a regular polygon of a given side.

Example.—Construct a regular decagon having sides of $2\frac{1}{2}$ in.

No. of sides	Name of polygon	Area when side = 1	Radius of circumscribed circle		Radius of inscribed circle when side = 1	Length of sides when radius of circumscribed circle = 1	Angle at center	Angle between adjacent sides
			When perpendicular from center = 1	When side = 1				
(1)	(2)	(3)	(4)	(5)	(6)	(7)	(8)	(9)
3	Triangle	0.4330127	2.	0.5773	0.2887	1.732	120°	60°
4	Square	1.	1.414	0.7071	0.5	1.4142	90°	90°
5	Pentagon	1.7204774	1.238	0.8506	0.6882	1.1756	72°	108°
6	Hexagon	2.5980762	1.156	1.	0.866	1.	60°	120°
7	Heptagon	3.6339124	1.11	1.1524	1.0383	0.8677	51° 26′	128° 34$\frac{2}{7}$′
8	Octagon	4.8284271	1.083	1.3066	1.2071	0.7653	45°	135°
9	Nonagon	6.1818242	1.064	1.4619	1.3737	0.684	40°	140°
10	Decagon	7.6942088	1.051	1.618	1.5388	0.618	36°	144°
12	Dodecagon	11.1961524	1.037	1.9319	1.866	0.5176	30°	150°

Radius of circumscribing circle = $2\frac{1}{2} \times 1.618$ in. = 4.045 in. With the compasses construct a circle of this radius. Then with the dividers open $2\frac{1}{2}$ in., step around the circle, which should be divided into 10 parts. Connect these points successively, and the construction is complete.

(4) **To find the radius of the inscribed circle when a side of the polygon is given.**—*Multiply the length of a side by a number chosen from column* (6).

(5) **To find the length of the side of a polygon that can be inscribed in a circle of given radius.**—*Multiply the given radius by a number chosen from column* (7).

Example.—Construct a regular heptagon in a circle of 3-in. radius.

A side of the polygon = 3×0.8677 in. = 2.6 in.

With the dividers open 2.6 in., step around the circle, which should be divided into 7 equal parts. Connect these points successively, and the construction is complete.

EXERCISES

This set of exercises may be solved by applying the table on page 220. (Trigonometry offers an elegant method here.)

1. A round drive shaft is D in. in diameter. The end of this round shaft is to be cut so that it forms a regular polygon of side S in. If the regular polygon is

  (1) A triangle and $D = 4$ in.; find S.   *Ans.* 3.464 in.
  (2) A square and $D = 4$ in.; find S.
  (3) A hexagon and $D = 4$ in.; find S.
  (4) An octagon and $D = 4$ in.; find S.

2. Table tops are regular polygons of side S. Circular covers are to be made for these tables. Find the radius R of these covers if the table tops are

  (1) Triangular and $S = 20$ in.   *Ans.* 11.546 in.
  (2) Square and $S = 30$ in.
  (3) Hexagonal and $S = 40$ in.
  (4) Octagonal and $S = 60$ in.

3. Find the diameter of the bearings that can be made on the following regular polygonal shafts:

  (1) Triangular shaft of side 1 in.; of side s in.   *Ans.* 0.5773 in.
  (2) Hexagonal shaft of side 1 in.; of side s in.

(3) Decagonal shaft of side 1 in.; of side s in.

(4) Dodecagonal shaft of side 1 in.; of side s in.

4. The design in a floor consists of two concentric circles with a square inscribed in each. If the large circle has a radius of 6 ft. and the smaller 4 ft., find the ratio of the areas of the two squares. What about the ratio of the area of the two circles?

5. The area of a regular hexagon inscribed in a circle is $24 \sqrt{3}$. Find the area of the circle and the length of the circumference.

Ans. 50.266−; 25.133−.

6. A square end 0.875 in. on a side must be milled on a shaft. What is the diameter to which the shaft should be turned? *Ans.* 1.237+ in.

7. A pipe 10 in. in diameter is connected to a hexagonal pipe of the same area in cross section. Find the edge of the hexagon of the cross section of the hexagonal pipe. *Ans.* 5.50− in.

TURNING AND DRILLING

160. Rules.—The **cutting speed** of a tool is the rate at which it passes over the surface being cut. This applies to a lathe tool in turning a piece of work, such as a car axle, or to a drill used in making holes in a metal of any kind.

The rate at which the tool can cut the metal without injuring the tool depends upon the material in the tool, as well as upon the kind of work being turned.

Since cutting speeds are usually given in feet per minute, the rate at which a tool is cutting can be found by the following:

RULE.—*Multiply the circumference of the piece or of the drill in feet by the number of R. P. M. This gives the cutting speed in feet per minute.*

This applies to work turned in a lathe or to the drill in a drill press.

It follows from the foregoing that the number of revolutions, allowable per minute, is found by the following:

RULE.—*Divide the cutting speed in feet per minute by the circumference of the work in feet. This gives the number of revolutions per minute.*

161. Feed.—The **feed** of a tool is the sideways motion given to the cutting tool. It is expressed in one of the following ways:

(1) The feed is the part of an inch that the tool advances along the work for each revolution or stroke, as a feed of $\frac{1}{16}$ in.

(2) The feed is the number of revolutions or strokes necessary to advance the tool 1 in., as a feed of 20 turns to the inch.

(3) The feed is the number of inches that the tool advances in 1 min., as the feed is $\frac{3}{4}$ in. per minute.

Thus, in turning a car axle, the shaving may be $\frac{1}{4}$ in. wide, which means that the tool must advance that distance along the axle for every revolution of the axle. That is, it will take four turns of the axle to cover 1 in. of its length with the turning tool.

162. Cutting speeds.—Cutting speeds for carbon steel tools should be about 30 ft. per minute in steel, 35 ft. per minute in cast iron, and 60 to 100 ft. per minute in brass.

The general rule is to run high-speed steel tools, in steel, about double and in iron about three times the speed of the carbon-steel tool.

The maximum speed given to any tool must be governed by the density and toughness of the material being cut and by the way in which the tool "holds up."

The feed of a drill should be from 0.004 to 0.01 in. per revolution.

EXERCISES

In lathe work let the following letters denote the numbers that are of interest:

d = the diameter of the rotating piece in inches.

n = the number of R. P. M.

t = the number of minutes to turn the piece.

f_1 = the feed expressed as the part of 1 in. that the tool advances along the work for each revolution or stroke.

f_2 = the feed expressed as the number of revolutions or strokes necessary to advance the tool 1 in.

f_3 = the feed expressed as the number of inches the tool advances in 1 min.

In the following four exercises find the value of all the foregoing letters whenever possible:

1. A piece of steel 10 ft. long and $3\frac{3}{4}$ in. in diameter is being turned at 30 R. P. M., and $f_1 = 3$ in.

$Ans.\ d = 3\frac{3}{4};\ n = 30;\ t = \frac{4}{3};\ f_1 = 3;\ f_2 = \frac{1}{3};\ f_3 = 90.$

2. An iron shaft 2 in. in diameter and 30 in. long is turning at a cutting speed of 25 ft. per minute and a feed of $\frac{1}{40}$ in.

$$Ans. \ d = 2; n = \frac{150}{\pi}; t = 8\pi; f_1 = \frac{1}{40}; f_2 = 40; f_3 = \frac{15}{4\pi}.$$

3. A brass rod is 2 in. in diameter, and the cutting speed 100 ft. per minute. The rod is 10 ft. long.

4. The speed of a lathe tool is 60 R. P. M., and the tool moves along the work 7.5 in. in 1 min.

5. Find the R. P. M. for a lathe to rough a cast bushing $4\frac{1}{8}$ in. in diameter, using a high-speed-steel tool cutting at 190 ft. per minute.

Ans. 176 approx.

6. In the previous exercise, how long does it take to rough a bushing $6\frac{1}{4}$ in. in length if the feed is $\frac{3}{32}$ in.?

7. In turning a locomotive wheel 78 in. in diameter, what is the proper number of R. P. M. in order that the cutting speed may be 10 ft. per minute? *Ans.* 0.49.

8. In turning a tool-steel arbor, a carbon-steel turning tool is used. The cutting speed is 18 ft. per minute. How many R. P. M. should the work make if the arbor is 3 in. in diameter? *Ans.* 23 approx.

9. A $\frac{3}{4}$-in. drill, cutting cast iron, may cut at the rate of 40 ft. per minute. How many R. P. M. can it make? *Ans.* 204 approx.

10. How long will it take to turn off one layer from the surface of a car wheel 4 in. thick and 30 in. in diameter if the cutting speed is 15 ft. per minute and the feed $\frac{1}{8}$ in.? *Ans.* $16\frac{3}{4}$ min.

11. How long would it require to make one cut over the surface of a tool-steel arbor 2 in. in diameter and 10 in. in length if the cutting speed is 18 ft. per minute and the feed of the cutting tool $\frac{1}{16}$ in. per revolution of the work? *Ans.* 4.65 + min.

12. In Kent's "Mechanical Engineer's Hand-book" are given the following formulas for finding results in cutting-speed problems:

Let

d = the diameter of the rotating piece in inches.

n = the number of R. P. M.

S = the cutting speed in feet per minute.

Then

$$S = \frac{\pi dn}{12} = 0.2618n$$

$$n = \frac{S}{0.2618d} = \frac{3.82S}{d}$$

$$d = \frac{3.82S}{n}$$

Show that these are true, and apply them to the preceding exercises.

13. Give to the nearest $\frac{1}{16}$ in. the length of a $\frac{3}{4}$-in. steel rod that is turned per minute if the cutting speed is 36 ft. per minute and the feed 25. *Ans.* $7\frac{5}{16}$ in.

14. In turning a car wheel 3 ft. in diameter, the highest rate of speed allowable for the cutter is 40 ft. per minute. How many revolutions per hour can the wheel make? *Ans.* 254.6.

15. A car axle may be turned with the cutter moving 9 ft. per minute. If the axle is $4\frac{1}{2}$ in. in diameter, how many R. P. M. can it make?

Ans. 7.64.

BELT PULLEYS AND GEAR WHEELS

163. The relations of size and speed of driving and driven gear wheels are the same as those of belt pulleys. In calculating for gears we use the diameter of the pitch circle or the number of teeth as may be necessary.

A mechanic should be able to determine quickly and accurately the speed of any shaft or machine and to find the size of a pulley in order that a shaft or machine may run at a desired speed. He should master the principles underlying the rules and formulas used as well as know how to use them. It is well, then, for the student to work many problems on pulley speeds before special formulas are taken up. This will help him to master the principles and will make him independent of the formulas. It will also put him into position to derive the formulas.

For a complete discussion of questions connected with belts and belting see any mechanical engineer's handbook.

In the study of pulleys or gears the diameter and the R. P. M. of both the driving (power) shaft and the driven (tool) shaft are of fundamental importance. This power may be conveyed from the power shaft to the tool shaft by belts, by gears, or by chains.

It should be understood that the R. P. M. of the tool may be changed either by changing the R. P. M. of the driving shaft (as speeding up the engine in a car) or by changing the ratio of the diameters of the pulleys on the power shaft and the tool shaft (as shifting gears in a car).

EXERCISES

1. A driving shaft makes 840 R. P. M. and has a pulley 6 in. in diameter. If the speed is to be reduced to 320 R. P. M. but the belt speed or tool speed is to remain unchanged, what size pulley should be used to replace the one on the driving shaft?

Solution.—If the 6-in. pulley makes 840 R. P. M., a point on the belt moves $6 \times 3.1416 \times 840$ in. per minute. Then in order to make 320 R. P. M., the pulley must be $\dfrac{6 \times 3.1416 \times 840}{320}$ in. in circumference and,

hence, $= \dfrac{6 \times 3.1416 \times 840}{320 \times 3.1416} = 15\dfrac{3}{4}$ in. in diameter.

2. The armature shaft of a dynamo must make 1700 R. P. M., and it has a pulley 4 in. in diameter. The armature shaft is to be belted to a driving shaft that makes 500 R. P. M. What must be the diameter of the pulley on the driving shaft?   *Ans.* $13\frac{3}{5}$ in.

3. A shaft has upon it two pulleys, each 8 in. in diameter. The speed of the shaft is 400 R. P. M. What must be the size of the pulleys of two machines if, when belted to the shaft, one of them has a speed of 300 R. P. M. and the other 900?   *Ans.* $10\frac{2}{3}$ in.; $3\frac{5}{9}$ in.

4. The pulley on the headstock of a lathe is 3 in. in diameter. This is belted to an 8-in. pulley on a shaft that makes 420 R. P. M. At what rate will a block of wood placed in the chuck revolve?
Ans. 1120 R. P. M.

5. In two connected belt pulleys, or gear wheels, if D is the diameter of the driving wheel, d the diameter of the driven wheel, R the number of

Fig. 137.

R. P. M. of driver, and r the number of R. P. M. of driven; find r in terms of D, d, and R. ·

Discussion.—In Fig. 137, (A) is the driving pulley and (B) is the driven pulley. It is evident that since the belt does not slip, a point on the circumference of (B) must move as far in a minute as a point on the circumference of (A).

Since (A) makes R R. P. M., a point on its circumference will move $R\pi D$ units per minute. Similarly a point on the circumference of (B) will move $r\pi d$ units per minute.

$$\therefore R\pi D = r\pi d$$

or

$$RD = rd, \text{ and } r = \frac{RD}{d} \quad Ans.$$

6. In any system of pulleys or gears, the general rule holds that the product of the diameters or numbers of teeth of the driving wheels and the numbers of R. P. M. of the first driver must be equal to the product of the diameters or the numbers of teeth of the driven wheels and the number of R. P. M. of the last driven wheel. As a formula this may be stated

$$r = \frac{R \times D \times D' \times D'' \times D''' \times \cdots}{d \times d' \times d'' \times d''' \times \cdots}$$

where

D, D', D'', etc. = the diameters of the driving pulleys.

d, d', d'', etc. = the diameters of the driven pulleys.

R = the R. P. M. of the first driver.

r = the R. P. M. of the last driven pulley.

Show why this is true.

7. The number of revolutions that the governor of a steam engine is intended to run is given by the builder. If the speed of the governor is 120 R. P. M., size of governor pulley 8 in., and the desired speed of the engine 90 R. P. M., find the diameter of the pulley to be put on the engine shaft to run the governor pulley.

Ans. $12\frac{2}{3}$ in.

8. An endless knife runs on pulleys 48 in. in diameter, as shown in Fig. 138, at a rate of 180 R. P. M. If the pulleys are decreased 18 in. in diameter, how many R. P. M. will they have to make to keep the knife traveling at the original speed? *Ans.* 288.

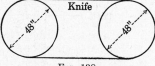

FIG. 138.

9. Apply the formula of Exercise 6 to the following: A train of wheels consists of four wheels each 12 in. in diameter of pitch circle and three pinions 4, 4, and 3 in. in diameter, respectively. The large wheels are the drivers, and the first makes 36 R. P. M. Required, the speed of the last wheel. *Ans.* 1296 R. P. M.

10. In the train of the preceding exercise, what is the speed of the first large wheel if the pinions are the drivers, the 3-in. pinion being the first driver and making 36 R. P. M.? *Ans.* 1 R. P. M.

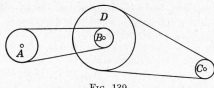

FIG. 139.

11. Pulleys are arranged as in Fig. 139. Pulley A makes 192 R. P. M., is the driver, and is 14 in. in diameter. Pulley B is 8 in. in diameter.

Pulley C is 6 in. in diameter and is to make a required 1400 R. P. M. Find the diameter to make the pulley D, fastened to the same shaft as B, in order that C may have the desired number of R. P. M.   *Ans.* 25 in.

12. Find the number of R. P. M. of the last gear shown in Fig. 140, if the gear having 84 teeth makes 36 R. P. M.   *Ans.* 1134.

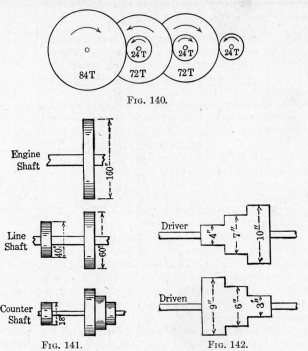

Fig. 140.

Fig. 141.   Fig. 142.

13. In Fig. 141 if a 160-in. pulley on the engine shaft drives a 60-in. pulley on the line shaft, and a 40-in. pulley on the line shaft drives an 18-in. pulley on the countershaft, find the number of R. P. M. of the countershaft if the engine shaft runs at 80 R. P. M.   *Ans.* 474 approx.

14. The driver of the cone pulleys shown in Fig. 142 has 1200 R. P. M. Find the three speeds of the driven pulleys.

Ans. $533\frac{1}{3}$; 1400; 4000 R. P. M.

15. In a set of cone pulleys, the driving cone has pulleys of diameters 11, 9, 7, and 5 in.; and the driven cone, pulleys of diameters 5, 7, 9, and 11 in. If the driving shaft makes 425 R. P. M., find the rates of the driven cone as the belt is slipped from step to step.

16. Figure 143 is a sketch of a hoisting machine. If the handles are turned 20 R. P. M., find the rate at which a weight will be raised in feet per minute. The numbers are the number of teeth in the gear wheels.

Ans. 2.4+ ft.

17. An 18-in. emery wheel has a cutting speed of 4200 ft. per minute. The wheel is driven by a 4-in. pulley on the same shaft as the emery wheel and takes a belt from a 10-in. pulley. Find the R. P. M. of the 10-in. pulley. *Ans.* $356\frac{1}{2}$ approx.

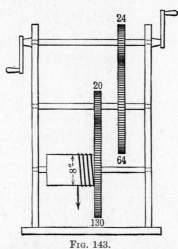

Fig. 143.

18. A flywheel 20 ft. in diameter and making 60 R. P. M. drives a countershaft by means of a pulley 4 ft. in diameter. What size pulley must be used on the countershaft to give 400 R. P. M. to a pulley 2 ft. in diameter? *Ans.* 2 ft. 8 in. in diameter.

19. A 16-in. pulley is fixed to a line shaft turning at 160 R. P. M. and is belted to a 12-in. pulley on a countershaft. A grindstone on a shaft with a 20-in. pulley is to be run at 75 R. P. M. from the countershaft. Find the size of the pulley to be placed on the countershaft.

Ans. $7\frac{1}{16}$ in. in diameter.

THE MIL

164. The circular mil.—In most cases, electrical conductors have a circular cross section. We know that the area of a circle is found by the formula $A = \frac{1}{4}\pi d^2$, which brings in the inconvenient factor $\frac{1}{4}\pi$, or 0.7854. In order to avoid this factor, a new unit has been adopted for commercial work This unit is the **circular mil** (abbreviation C. M.), which is the area of a circle 1 **mil,** or 0.001 in., in diameter.

If A is the area in circular mils of any circle and d the diameter in mils, then, since a circle 1 mil in diameter has an area of 1 C. M., we have the proportion

$$\frac{1}{A} = \frac{1^2}{d^2}$$

for the areas of the circles are in the same ratio as the square of the diameters. This proportion gives

$$A = d^2$$

This stated in words is the following:

RULE.—*The area of a circle in circular mils is the square of the diameter in mils, or thousandths of an inch.*

Thus, a 0000 gage B. & S. wire is 0.46 in. = 460 mils in diameter and hence has an area of $460^2 = 211,600$ C. M.

If the area in circular mils is given, the diameter in mils can evidently be found by taking the square root of the area, or

$$d = \sqrt{A}$$

165. The square mil.—The **square mil** is sometimes used and is the area of a square 1 mil on a side. Since the area of a circle is $0.7854d^2$, it is seen that 0.7854 square mil = 1 C. M.

EXERCISES 56

1. Find the number of circular mils in the area of B. & S. gage wire Nos. 40, 20, and 10. (See Table VI.)

Ans. 9.88+; 1021.5+; 10,383−.

2. How many square mils in a bar $\frac{1}{2}$ by $\frac{3}{8}$ in. in cross section?

Ans. 187,500.

3. How many circular mils are equal to 20,000 square mils?

Ans. 25,464.8−.

4. Find the diameter in mils and in inches of a circular rod having a cross section of 237,600 C. M. *Ans.* 487.4+ mils; 0.4874+ in.

5. In ordinary practice, trolley wire is 0 or 00 B. & S. hard-drawn copper wire. What is the area of the cross section of each in circular mils? *Ans.* 105,535− C. M. or 133,076+ C. M.

CHAPTER XIII

CONSTRUCTIONS AND GRAPHICAL METHODS

VARIOUS USEFUL CONSTRUCTIONS

166. To divide a line of any length into a given number of equal parts.—In Fig. 144, let AB be the line that it is required to divide into seven equal parts. Draw a line AC, making

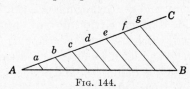

Fig. 144.

any convenient angle with AB. Take a convenient length, as a half-inch, and beginning at A mark seven of these lengths on AC. This determines the points a, b, c, d, e, f, and g. Draw a line from g to B, and draw lines parallel to gB through f, d, c, b, and a. These lines divide AB into seven equal parts.

It is readily seen that this method can be used to divide any line into any number of equal parts.

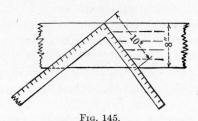

Fig. 145.

Example.—The carpenter makes use of this construction when he uses his steel square, as shown in Fig. 145, to divide a board of any width into any number of equal strips. Here

231

an 8-in. board is to be divided into five equal strips. A number of inches divisible by 5, as 10 in., is taken on the square, and the square is placed as shown. A mark is made on the

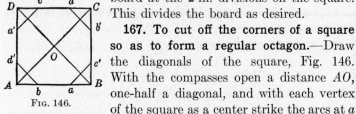

FIG. 146.

board at the 2-in. divisions on the square. This divides the board as desired.

167. To cut off the corners of a square so as to form a regular octagon.—Draw the diagonals of the square, Fig. 146. With the compasses open a distance AO, one-half a diagonal, and with each vertex of the square as a center strike the arcs at a and a', b and b', c and c', d and d'. Connect these points as shown in the figure, and get the regular octagon $bac'b'dca'd'$.

167a. To divide a given circle into any number of equal parts by concentric circles.—Let the largest circle of Fig. 147 be the given circle, and let it be desired to divide it into four equal parts. Draw the radius OA, and divide it into the same number of equal parts. Draw a semicircle on this radius as a diameter.

Erect perpendiculars to OA at each division point a, b, and c, and let them intersect the circumference of the semicircle at a', b', and c', respectively. Using Oc', Ob', and Oa' as radii and O as a center, draw the three concentric circles. These circles divide the original circle as desired.

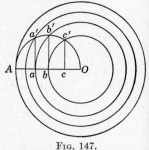

FIG. 147.

168. To inscribe regular polygons.—(See Art. 159.) (1) *To lay out a square in a circle.*—Draw two perpendicular diameters as shown in Fig. 148, and connect their successive extremities. This gives the inscribed square $ACBD$.

(2) *To lay out a pentagon in a circle.*—Draw two perpendicular diameters AB and CD, Fig. 149, bisect AO at E. With E as a center and ED as a radius, draw the arc DF. The length DF is equal to the side of the inscribed pentagon.

(3) *To lay out a hexagon in a circle.*—The radius of the circle is equal to the side of the inscribed hexagon.

(4) *To lay out an equilateral triangle in a circle.*—Connect the alternate vertices of the hexagon as shown in Fig. 150.

(5) *To lay out a regular heptagon in a circle.*—Make a construction as shown in Fig. 151, and AB is very nearly the side of the inscribed regular heptagon.

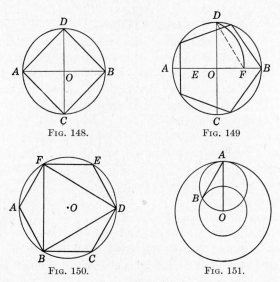

Fig. 148. Fig. 149

Fig. 150. Fig. 151.

(6) *To lay out a regular octagon in a circle.*—Bisect the arcs of the inscribed square.

(7) *To lay out a regular decagon in a circle.*—Bisect the arcs of the inscribed regular pentagon.

169. To draw the arc of a segment when the chord and the height of the segment are given.—This method is to be used when it is not convenient to find the radius and use it. In Fig. 152, AB is the chord and FC is the height. Draw AC, AD perpendicular to AC, CD parallel to FA, AE perpendicular to AF, and divide AF, DC, and AE into the same number of equal parts. Letter them as in the figure. Draw

da, eb, fc, C1, C2, and C3.   The points of intersection of these
are points on the arc.   The more equal parts the lines are
divided into the more points of the arc will be determined.

**170. To find the radius of a circle when only a part of the
circumference is known.**—It often happens that one has a
part only of a wheel or pulley from which he must determine
the size of a new wheel or pulley.   The method by bisecting

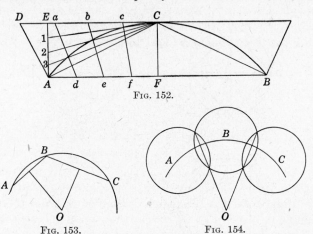

Fig. 152.

Fig. 153.

Fig. 154.

the arcs is shown in Fig. 153.   Let *ABC* be the arc given.
Draw two chords *AB* and *BC* of any convenient lengths.
Draw perpendicular bisectors of these.   They will intersect
at a point *O*, which is the center of the circle of which the given
arc is a part.

What amounts to the same thing and is more quickly done
is shown in Fig. 154.   Draw three equal intersecting circles
with their centers on the arc; then the lines drawn through
the intersecting points as shown meet at the center of the
circle of which the given arc is a part.

AREAS, GRAPHICAL METHODS

171. Drawing to scale.—If we wish to draw to scale the
floor of a room 10 by 20 ft., we may conveniently represent

1 ft. in the dimensions of the room by $\frac{1}{8}$ in. in the drawing. Whatever dimension is measured in the drawing and given in eighths of an inch can be interpreted as feet when applied to the floor. The map of a country may be drawn on a scale of 50 miles to an inch or any other convenient scale.

172. To draw a triangle to scale.—(1) *To construct a triangle having given two sides and the angle between these sides.*—Let the side $AB = 10$ ft., and $AC = 8$ ft., and the angle A between these sides be $47° 45'$. Choose a convenient scale, say, $\frac{1}{8}$ in. for 1 ft. Draw line AB, Fig. 155, in length $\frac{10}{8}$ in.; lay off

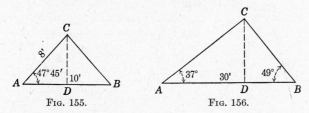

FIG. 155.   FIG. 156.

angle $BAC = 47° 45'$; make AC $\frac{3}{8}$ in.; and draw CB. Then the triangle ACB is the required representation of the given triangle.

If it is required to find the area of the triangle, the measured length of the altitude DC in eighths of an inch times one-half of the base AB in the same unit would give the area of the triangle in square feet.

(2) *To construct a triangle when given two angles and the side between these angles.*—Let the side $AB = 30$ ft., the angle $A = 37°$, and the angle $B = 49°$. Choose a scale, say, $\frac{1}{16}$ in. for 1 ft. Draw line AB, Fig. 156, in length $\frac{30}{16}$ in.; lay off angle $A = 37°$ and $B = 49°$, and extend the sides of these angles till they meet. Then the triangle ACB is the required triangle represented on a scale of $\frac{1}{16}$ in. to 1 ft. The area of this triangle can easily be found by measuring the altitude DC and applying the rule for the area of a triangle.

(3) *To construct a triangle when the three sides are given.*—Let $AB = 60$ rods, $AC = 70$ rods, and $BC = 80$ rods. Choose a

scale of, say, 40 rods to the inch.   Then 60 rods is represented by $1\frac{1}{2}$ in., 70 rods by $1\frac{3}{4}$ in., and 80 rods by 2 in.   Draw AB, Fig. 157, in length $1\frac{1}{2}$ in.   With the compasses and a radius of $1\frac{3}{4}$ in. draw an arc with A as center.   With B as center and radius 2 in., draw an arc to intersect this at C.   Draw the lines AC and BC.   Then triangle ABC is the required triangle.

In a similar manner other shaped figures may be constructed to scale.   In many cases these drawings may be divided into triangles, squares, and rectangles, which may be measured and so the entire area of the figure be found.

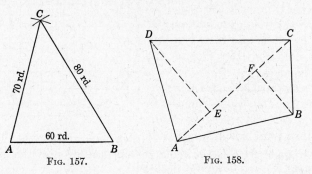

Fig. 157.   Fig. 158.

Example.—A piece of ground in the form of a quadrilateral is represented by Fig. 158 to a scale of 40 rods to an inch. The area can be found by drawing the diagonal AC and the altitudes of the triangles ACD and ABC.   The sum of the areas of these triangles equals the area of the quadrilateral $ABCD$.

173. Areas found by the use of squared paper.—It is often convenient to find the area of an irregular figure by drawing it on squared paper (paper accurately ruled into small squares). The figure will usually be drawn to a scale that uses the side of one of the small squares as a unit.

The method is most nearly accurate on irregular figures and is liable to considerable error when the boundary has long straight lines, nearly parallel to the lines forming the squares.

As an illustration of the method, find the area of the circle in Fig. 159, if the circle is drawn on a scale of 1 in. to a side of the squares.

First, determine how many squares are wholly within the circle.

Second, count as whole squares the squares that are half or more than half within the circle, and neglect those squares which are less than half within the circle.

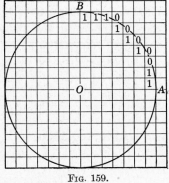

Fɪɢ. 159.

Here it is most convenient to count the squares in one quarter of the circle and then multiply by 4 to get the area of the whole circle.

From the figure, it is seen that there are 30 whole squares in the quarter of the circle *AOB.* Counting the squares marked 1 gives 8 partial squares to be taken as whole squares. The squares marked 0 are not counted.

30 + 8 = 38 squares for the quarter circle.

38 × 4 = 152 squares for the circle.

Therefore, the area of the circle is 152 sq. in.

By formula [24], area = 3.1416 × 7² = 154− sq. in.

174. Other methods for approximating areas.—(1) The planimeter is an instrument for estimating areas. There are several forms of this device; but as instructions for its use are given with each instrument, it will not be described here.

(2) The area, when very irregular, can often be estimated quite accurately by cutting full size or to scale out of cardboard or sheet tin. Weigh on accurate scales the piece of tin or cardboard; also weigh a square unit of the same material. Divide the weight of the piece by the weight of the square unit. The quotient is the number of square units in the figure. A

specially prepared paper made in uniform weight for this purpose is now on the market.

EXERCISES

1. The edges of a square table top are 30 in. Draw a diagram, and show how to form a table that has a regular octagonal top. Let 0.1 in. be 1 in. on the drawing.

2. A triangle has its sides in the ratio 3:4:5. Measure its angles. Add the angles opposite 3 and 4. How does this sum compare with the angle opposite 5?

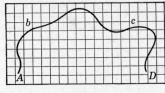

Fig. 160.   Fig. 161.

3. The three sides of a triangle are 4, 11.1, and 14.5 in. Determine graphically the length of the three altitudes. What is the area of the triangle? Check the area by three results. Also check by the formula for the area when the three sides are known.

4. The angles of a triangle are in the ratio 1:2:3. Draw one such triangle. What is special about this triangle?

5. The angles of a triangle are 48°, 78°, and 54°. Find the length of the side opposite the angle 78° if the side opposite 48° is 32 ft.

6. The two sides AB and BC of a triangle are 44.7 and 96.8 ft., respectively, the angle ABC being 32°. Find (1) the length of the perpendicular drawn from A to BC; (2) the area of the triangle ABC; (3) the angles at A and C.

Ans. 23.69 ft.; 1147 sq. ft. 22° and 126°.

7. Find the area of $AbcD$, Fig. 160, which is on a scale of 1 in. to the side of a square, by counting the squares.

8. Find the area of the ellipse in Fig. 161, which is on a scale of 4 rods to the side of a square, by counting squares. Find the area by formula [**32**], and compare results.

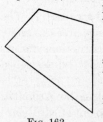

Fig. 162.

9. The quadrilateral in Fig. 162 is on a scale of 16 rods to the inch. Find its area by dividing into triangles.

10. Draw a triangle on a scale of $\frac{1}{8}$ in. to the foot, having sides of 17, 19, and 23 ft., respectively. Draw any altitude of the triangle; measure it;

and compute the area of the triangle. Check by drawing the other altitudes and computing the area again.

11. Draw the following to scale, using $\frac{1}{16}$ in. to the rod; then find the area in acres. Start at a point A; go east 20 rods to B, north 10 rods to C, east 10 rods to D, north 40 rods to E, west 40 rods to F, south 20 rods to G, east 20 rods to H, and then to A. *Ans.* $9\frac{1}{16}$ acres.

12. Find the area of the following plot of ground: Start at A; go east 10 ft. to B, north 20 ft. to C, northeast 14.14 ft. to D, north 10 ft. to E, west 20 ft. to F, and south to A. *Ans.* 550 sq. ft.

175. Simpson's Rule.—The area of the space included between a curve and a straight line can easily be found approximately by the use of *Simpson's Rule* which may be stated as

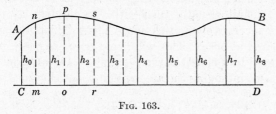

FIG. 163.

follows: Let AB, in Fig. 163, be the curve and CD the straight line. Divide the length CD into an *even* number of equal parts, say 8, of length a, and erect the ordinates h_0, h_1, h_2, . . . , h_8. Then the area of the figure $CDBA$ will be given by the formula:

Area
$$= \tfrac{1}{3}a(h_0 + 4h_1 + 2h_2 + 4h_3 + 2h_4 + 4h_5 + 2h_6 + 4h_7 + h_8)$$

It is to be noticed that the coefficients of the ordinates are alternately 4 and 2, excepting the first and the last. The greater the number of divisions made the more nearly accurate, in general, will be the result.

In words this rule may be stated thus: *Divide the base CD into an **even** number of equal parts, and measure the ordinate at each point of division. Add together the first and last ordinates, twice the sum of the other even ordinates, and four times* *the sum of the odd ordinates; multiply the sum by one-third the distance between consecutive ordinates. The result is the area inclosed (approximately).*

176. The average ordinate rule.—For approximate results the area between a curve and a straight line, base line, may be found as follows:

RULE.—*Divide the base line into any number of equal parts, at the center of each of these parts draw ordinates. Take the average length of these ordinates and multiply by the length of the base line. The result is the area inclosed (approximately).*

In Fig. 163, *mn, op, rs,* etc., are the ordinates.

A convenient way for adding the ordinates is to draw a line of indefinite length, then with the dividers lay off the ordinates successively on this line. The total length can then be measured at once. This will avoid errors to some extent.

177. Area in a closed curve.—Either of the methods given may be used in finding the area within a closed curve. Thus,

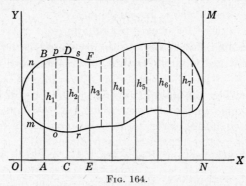

FIG. 164.

in Fig. 164, draw the two parallel tangents *OY* and *NM*, and draw *OX* perpendicular to these. Divide *ON* into any number of equal parts (an even number for Simpson's Rule), and draw the ordinates *AB, CD,* etc. Call the several widths of the figure on these ordinates h_1, h_2, h_3, etc. These widths can be used in Simpson's Rule to find the area within the closed curve.

The widths mn, op, rs, etc., can be used in the average ordinate rule to find the area.

It should be noted that h_0 and h_8 for this figure are each 0.

178. The steam indicator diagram.—As a useful application of the discussion in the preceding articles, we will consider the steam indicator diagram.[*]

The steam indicator is a mechanical device to attach to a steam engine to make a graphical representation of the steam pressure acting on the piston throughout the stroke. Knowing the pressure, the indicated horsepower of the engine can be calculated from the formula

$$H = \frac{PLAN}{33000}$$

where

H = the indicated horsepower.

P = the mean effective pressure in pounds per square inch.

L = the length of stroke in feet.

A = the area of piston in square inches.

N = the number of strokes per minute.

The **indicated horsepower** is the power developed by the steam on the piston of the engine, without any deduction for friction.

The **effective horsepower** is the actual available horsepower delivered to the belt or gearing and is always less than the indicated horsepower, because the engine itself absorbs some power by the friction of its moving parts.

The indicator diagram may be given as Fig. 165. The width of a rectangle the same in length as this and of the same area would represent the **mean effective pressure** per square inch on the piston during the stroke.

The diagram is always to a certain scale, which is known from the indicator. For instance, the scale might be 60 lb. per inch in diagram. The mean effective pressure is then 60 lb. multiplied by the average width of the indicator diagram.

[*] For a full discussion of the steam indicator the student is referred to Peabody, "Manual of the Steam Engine Indicator."

The average width of the diagram may be found by dividing the area by the length.   The area can be found by Simpson's Rule or by the average ordinate rule.

A convenient method for locating the ordinates is to place a common ruler as in Fig. 166, and locate 10 ordinates, the

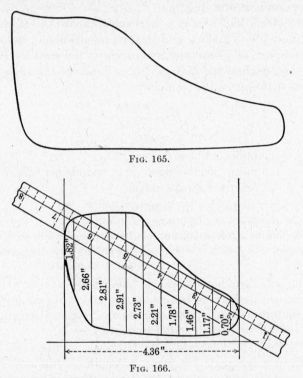

FIG. 165.

FIG. 166.

two end ordinates being half as far from either end as the distance between the other ordinates.

The average length of these ordinates multiplied by the scale, taken from the indicator, gives the mean effective pressure.

Example.—Taking the indicator diagram in Fig. 166, find the mean effective pressure of the steam if the scale is 30 lb.

to the inch. Find the horsepower of the engine if the diameter of the piston is 18 in., length of stroke $2\frac{1}{2}$ ft., and number of revolutions 110 per minute. (The number of strokes of the piston is twice the number of revolutions.)

Solution.—Adding together the ten ordinates, we have $1.82 + 2.66 + 2.81 + 2.91 + 2.73 + 2.21 + 1.78 + 1.46 + 1.17 + 0.70 = 20.25$. Since there are 10 ordinates, the mean is $20.25 \div 10 = 2.025$. Multiplying by the scale, we have $2.025 \times 30 = 60.75 =$ pounds pressure per square inch, the answer to the first part.

Area of piston $= 3.1416 \times 9^2 = 254.47$ in.^{2}

Formula for the horsepower is $H = \dfrac{PLAN}{33000}$.

$$P = 60.75, L = 2.5, A = 254.47$$
$$\therefore H = \frac{60.75 \times 2.5 \times 254.47 \times 220}{33000} = 257.65 \quad Ans.$$

EXERCISES

1. An indicator diagram has a length of 2 in. The ten ordinates, beginning at the left, are 0.70, 0.90, 0.97, 0.85, 0.67, 0.52, 0.42, 0.35, 0.23 and 0.07 in. Draw a diagram that these ordinates will satisfy. If the indicator scale is 120 lb. to the inch, find the mean effective pressure.

2. Find the indicated horsepower of an engine having the indicator diagram of Exercise 1 if length of stroke is 3 ft., diameter of piston 23 in., and number of strokes 100 per minute.

3. Draw a semcircle 2 in. in radius. Divide the diameter into four parts, and find the area by Simpson's Rule. Divide the diameter into 10 parts, and find the area by the same rule. Find the area by the formula. Compare the three results and state your conclusions.

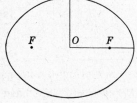

4. Find the area of the ellipse in Fig. 167 by Simpson's Rule. Find the area by the formula $A = \pi ab$, and compare the two results.

Fig. 167.

5. Secure an actual indicator diagram, and find the area both by Simpson's Rule and by the average ordinate rule, using 10 divisions. Compare the results.

6. Find the area of the indicator diagram of Fig. 165 both by Simpson's Rule and by the average ordinate rule, using 10 divisions. Compare the results.

CHAPTER XIV

PRISMS

179. In this and the four following chapters will be considered some of the solids most commonly observed in nature and very frequently used in buildings, bridges, machines and other structures in architecture, engineering, and the arts. We shall deal chiefly with the areas and volumes of these solids. It is necessary at the outset to give certain definitions in order that these solids may be accurately described.

180. Definitions.—Two planes are said to be parallel when they will not meet however far they may be extended. That is, they are everywhere the same distance apart.

A line is parallel to a plane when it will not meet the plane however far it may be extended.

A line is perpendicular to a plane when it is perpendicular to every line of the plane that passes through its foot.

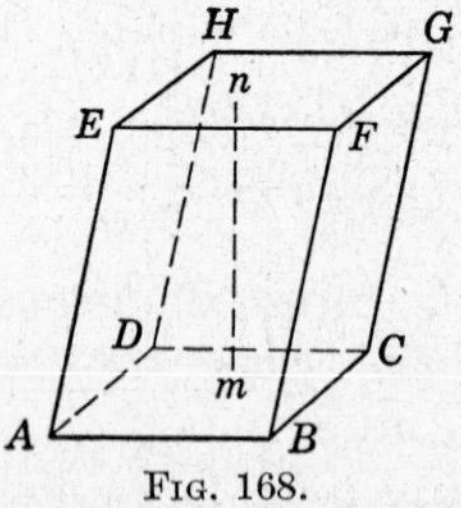

A **prism** is a solid whose ends, or **bases,** are parallel polygons, and whose sides, or **faces,** are parallelograms.

Figure 168 is a prism. The bases *ABCD* and *EFGH* are parallel polygons. The faces *AEFB*, *BFGC*, etc., are parallelograms. The lines *AB*, *BC*, etc., and *EF*, *FG*, etc., are **base edges.** The lines *AE*, *BF*, etc., are **lateral edges.**

Fig. 168.

If the lateral edges are perpendicular to the bases of the prism, the prism is a **right prism.**

If the lateral edges are not perpendicular to the bases, the prism is an **oblique prism.**

244

In an oblique prism, the faces are parallelograms; but in a right prism, they are rectangles.

A prism is called triangular, square, rectangular, hexagonal, etc., according as its bases are triangles, squares, rectangles, hexagons, etc. Figure 169 is a right triangular prism.

A **cross section** of a prism is a section that is perpendicular to the edges of the prism. In Fig. 169, *MNO* or either base is a cross section.

The sum of the edges of the base is the **perimeter** of the base.

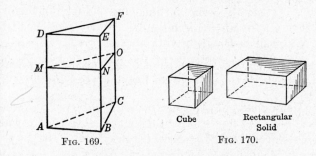

FIG. 169.

Cube

Rectangular Solid

FIG. 170.

The **altitude** of a prism is the perpendicular line between the two bases, as *mn*, Fig. 168. In a right prism, the altitude is the same length as an edge. In an oblique prism, this is not true.

A right prism that has rectangles for bases is called a **rectangular solid.** The **cube** is a rectangular solid all of whose six faces are squares.

181. Surfaces.—The right prisms are the forms of prisms that are met with usually in practical work. They are the ones considered here.

The **lateral area** of a right prism is the area of its faces, not including the two bases. Since the faces are rectangles, their areas can be easily found. As the area of each face is the product of its base by its altitude, the sum of the areas of the faces, or the lateral area of the prism, is given by the following:

RULE.—*The lateral area of a right prism equals the perimeter of the base times the altitude.*

The total area of the prism equals the lateral area plus the area of the two bases.

Since the cube has six equal square faces, the total area is six times the square of an edge.

If S stands for lateral area, T for total area, A for area of each base, p for perimeter of the base, h for altitude, and a for an edge, the rules are stated in the following formulas:

[33] $S = ph$

[34] $T = ph + 2A$

[35] $T = 6a^2$, for the cube

[36] $p = S \div h$

[37] $h = S \div p$

Example.—Find the total area of a right triangular prism, of altitude 20 ft., if the edges of the base are, respectively, 2, 3, and 4 ft.

Solution: $p = 2 + 3 + 4 = 9$

By formula [7], $A = \sqrt{s(s - a)(s - b)(s - c)}$

But $s = \frac{1}{2}(2 + 3 + 4) = 4\frac{1}{2}$

$s - a = 4\frac{1}{2} - 2 = 2\frac{1}{2}$

$s - b = 4\frac{1}{2} - 3 = 1\frac{1}{2}$

$s - c = 4\frac{1}{2} - 4 = \frac{1}{2}$

$\therefore A = \sqrt{4.5 \times 2.5 \times 1.5 \times 0.5} = \sqrt{8.4375} = 2.9047$

By formula [34], $T = ph + 2A$

$\therefore T = 9 \times 20 + 2 \times 2.9047 = 185.81 -$ sq. ft.   *Ans.*

182. Volumes.—In Fig. 171, there are as many cubic inches on the base $ABCD$ as there are square inches in its area; and since there are as many layers of cubic inches in the rectangular solid as there are inches in the altitude AE, the total number of cubic inches in the solid is found by multiplying the number of square inches in the base by the number of linear inches in the altitude. Any right prism can be taken in the same manner as the rectangular solid; hence the following:

RULE.—*The volume of a right prism equals the area of the base times the altitude.*

If the prism is a rectangular solid this rule becomes:

RULE.—*The volume of a rectangular solid equals the continued product of the length, breadth, and height.*

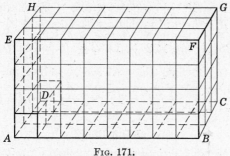

FIG. 171.

If V stands for volume, and the other letters are as before, we have these formulas:

[38] $V = Ah$, for any prism
[39] $V = a^3$, for the cube
[40] $h = V \div A$
[41] $A = V \div h$

Example 1.—One of the concrete pillars to hold up a floor in a concrete building has a cross section that is a regular hexagon. The dimensions are as shown in Fig. 172. Find its weight if concrete weighs 138 lb. per cubic foot.

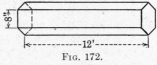

FIG. 172.

Solution.—The volume is found by formula [38] $V = Ah$, where h is 12 ft. and A the area of a hexagon with one side 8 in.

By Art. 138, $A = 6 \times 4^2 \times 1.732$ sq. in. $= \dfrac{6 \times 4^2 \times 1.732}{144}$ sq. ft.

$$\therefore V = \frac{12 \times 6 \times 4^2 \times 1.732}{144} \text{ cu. ft.}$$

Weight $= \dfrac{12 \times 6 \times 4^2 \times 1.732 \times 138}{144} = 1912$ lb.   *Ans.*

Example 2.—How deep is a cistern in the form of a hexagonal prism to hold 100 bbl. if the base is 4 ft. on an edge?

Solution.—By formula [**40**], $h = V \div A$.

$$V = 100 \text{ bbl.} = 100 \times 31\tfrac{1}{2} \times 231 \text{ cu. in.}$$
$$A = \text{area of hexagon with edge of 4 ft.}$$

By Art. 138, $A = 6 \times 2^2 \times 1.732 = 41.568$ sq. ft.

$$41.568 \text{ sq. ft.} = 41.568 \times 144 \text{ sq. in.}$$

$$\therefore h = \frac{100 \times 31\tfrac{1}{2} \times 231}{41.558 \times 144} = 121.563 \text{ in.} = 10 \text{ ft. } 1\tfrac{1}{2} \text{ in.} \quad Ans$$

EXERCISES

1. The following grained-metal wardrobes are rectangular solids. Find the volume and price per cubic foot of each.

(1) 61 by 18 by 20 in.; price complete, $4.28.
    Ans. 12.71− cu. ft.; $0.3367−.

(2) 61 by 18 by 24 in.; price complete, $5.28.
    Ans. 15.25 cu. ft.; $0.3462−.

(3) 61 by 24 by 20 in.; price complete, $6.29.
    Ans. 16.94+ cu. ft.; $0.3713+.

2. Find the price per cubic foot of the following utility cabinets:

(1) 50 by 24 by 11 in.; price complete, $3.84.   *Ans.* $0.50+.

(2) 53 by 24 by 12 in.; price complete, $4.79.

(3) 64 by 26 by 12 in.; price complete, $5.95.

3. A radio cabinet is 41 by 27 by 14 in. Find its total outside area. Find its area if it has no back.   *Ans.* 4118 sq. in.; 3011 sq. in.

4. A schoolroom is 40 by 24 by 12 ft. If there are 36 students in the room, how many cubic feet of air space has each?   *Ans.* 320.

5. Two different soap-flakes containers, which are rectangular solids 9 by $3\tfrac{1}{4}$ by $6\tfrac{1}{4}$ in. and $8\tfrac{3}{8}$ by $3\tfrac{1}{8}$ by $6\tfrac{5}{8}$ in., are sold at the same price. Which is the better buy if value depends only on volume?
    Ans. The former.

6. A rectangular solid container $6\tfrac{1}{2}$ by $2\tfrac{1}{2}$ by $3\tfrac{1}{2}$ in. is filled with granulated cane sugar, net weight 2 lb. Find the weight of 1 cu. in. of this sugar. How many $\tfrac{1}{2}$ in. cubes of this sugar will weight 1 lb.?
    Ans. 0.56+ oz.; $227\tfrac{1}{2}$.

7. A common brick is 2 by 4 by 8 in. Find the number of bricks in a pile $8\tfrac{1}{2}$ by 4 by 10 ft. (Use cancellation.)   *Ans.* 9180.

8. How many rectangular solids 3 by 4 by 9 in. will fill a box 4 by 6 by 8 ft.?   *Ans.* 3072.

9. One hundred and eighty square feet of zinc is required for lining the bottom and sides of a cubical vessel. How many cubic feet of water will it hold? *Ans.* 216.

10. A boxcar that is $36\frac{2}{3}$ ft. long and $8\frac{1}{6}$ ft. wide, inside measurements, can be filled with wheat to a height of $5\frac{1}{2}$ ft. Find how many bushels of wheat it will hold if $\frac{5}{4}$ cu. ft. are 1 bu. *Ans.* 1318 approx.

11. A mineral-oil bottle is a rectangular solid with inside measurements 5.5 by 3 by 2 in. It is marked 1 pt. By a closer inspection it is noted that the bottom curves inward. If there are 231 cu. in. to a gallon, how many cubic inches of oil are displaced by this curved bottom? *Ans.* $4\frac{1}{8}$.

12. A swimming tank is 40 ft. long by 20 ft. wide. It is 3 ft. deep at one end and slopes uniformly to a depth of 10 ft. at the other end. How many gallons does it hold when full if 7.5 gal. equals 1 cu. ft.?

Ans. $693\frac{1}{3}$.

Note.—Volume $= [(40)(20)(3) + \frac{1}{2}(40)(20)7]$ cu. ft. Why?

13. How many cubic yards of soil will it take to fill in a lot 50 by 100 ft. if it is to be raised 3 ft. in the rear end and gradually sloped to the front where it is to be $1\frac{1}{2}$ ft. deep? *Ans.* $416\frac{2}{3}$.

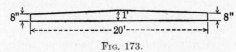

Fig. 173.

Suggestion.—The vertical cross section the long way of the lot is a trapezoid having parallel sides of lengths 3 and $1\frac{1}{2}$ ft., respectively, and an altitude of 100 ft. Use formula [**8**].

14. Find the number of cubic yards of crushed rock to make a road 1 mile in length and of cross section as shown in Fig. 173.

Solution.—The area of the vertical cross section can be found by considering it as two trapezoids each having parallel sides of 8 in. and 1 ft., respectively, and altitudes of 10 ft.

Area of cross section $= (\frac{2}{3} + 1)10 = 16\frac{2}{3}$ sq. ft.

No. of cu. ft. of rock $= 5280 \times 16\frac{2}{3} = 88,000$.

No. of cu. yd. of rock $= 88,000 \div 27 = 3259\frac{7}{27}$.

Ans.

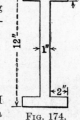

Fig. 174.

15. One cubic inch of steel weighs 0.29 lb. An I beam has a cross section as shown in Fig. 174 and a length of 22 ft. Find its weight. *Ans.* $1531+$ lb.

16. Find the weight of steel beams 10 ft. in length and of the cross sections given in Fig. 55, page 163. *Ans.* 821 lb.; 209.5 lb.; 300.2 lb.

17. What length must be cut from a bar of steel $\frac{1}{2}$ by $1\frac{1}{4}$ in. in cross section in order to make 1 cu. ft.? *Ans.* 230.4 ft.

18. The base of a right prism is a triangle whose sides are 12, 15, and 17 ft. and whose altitude is $8\frac{1}{2}$ ft. Find the lateral area.

Ans. 374 sq. ft.

19. Find the volume of the aforementioned prism.

Ans. 745.872− cu. ft.

Suggestion.—Use formula [7] to find the area of the base.

20. The cost of digging a ditch, including all expenses and profits, is estimated at 27 cents per cubic yard. Find the cost of digging a ditch 15 miles long, 10 ft. wide at the bottom, 20 ft. at the top, and 6 ft. deep.

Ans. \$71,280.

21. A river is 76 ft. wide and 12 ft. deep and flows at the rate of $3\frac{1}{2}$ miles per hour. How many cubic feet of water per minute passes a given point on the river? *Ans.* 280,896.

Suggestion.—The flow per minute is the volume of a prism of water of the cross section of the river and in length equal to the distance the water flows per minute.

22. An iron casting shrinks about $\frac{1}{8}$ in. per linear foot in cooling down to 70 deg. F. What is the shrinkage per cubic foot?

Ans. 53.44− cu. in.

Suggestion.—The shrinkage per cubic foot is the difference between a cubic foot and the volume of a cube $11\frac{7}{8}$ in. on an edge.

23. A fall of $\frac{7}{8}$ in. of rain is how many barrels per square rod?

Ans. $4\frac{5}{7}$.

24. A flow of 300 gal. per second will supply water for how deep a stream if the stream is 4 ft. broad and flows 5 miles per hour?

Suggestion.—The computation in the form of cancellation is

$$\frac{300 \times 231 \times 60 \times 60}{4 \times 5 \times 5280 \times 12 \times 12} = 16\frac{13}{32} \quad Ans.$$

25. If a glass rod 1 in. long at 0 deg. C. is increased to 1.000008 in. at 1 deg. C., find the increase in volume of 1 cu. in. of glass when heated from 0 to 1 deg. C. *Ans.* 0.000024+ cu. in.

Suggestion.—Use the formula

$$(a + b)^3 = a^3 + 3a^2b + 3ab^2 + b^3$$

where $a = 1$ and $b = 0.000008$, and disregard the last two terms, since they are very small because of b^2 and b^3.

26. Find the volume of a cube whose diagonal is 8 in.

Ans. 98.534+ cu. in.

Suggestion.—Let a represent one edge.
Then

$$\text{Diagonal} = \sqrt{a^2 + a^2 + a^2} = a\sqrt{3}$$
$$\therefore a\sqrt{3} = 8$$

27. There are as many square feet in the surface of a cube as there are cubic feet in its volume. Find its edge. *Ans.* 6 ft.

STONEWORK

183. A full description of stonework cannot be given here. For such the student is referred to a trade handbook.

Stonework where the stones are broken with the hammer only is called **rubblework.** If the stones are laid in courses, it is called **coursed rubble.** When the stones showing in the outside face of the wall are squared, the work is designated as **ashlar.** If all the stones of a course are of the same height, the work is called **coursed ashlar.** When the stones are of different heights, it is called **broken ashlar.** Ashlar work is both hammer-dressed and chisel-dressed. Any stonework where any other tool than the hammer is used for dressing is called **cutwork.**

184. Estimating cost of stonework.—In estimating the cost of stonework, the custom varies greatly; we find it varying even among the contractors of the same city. Cutwork is often measured by the number of square feet in the face of the wall.

Rubblework is almost universally measured by the perch, but the perch used varies greatly. The legal perch of $24\frac{3}{4}$ cu. ft. is seldom used by stonemasons. The perch of $16\frac{1}{2}$ cu. ft. is the one most used. That of 25 or of 22 cu. ft. is sometimes used.

Stonework on railroads is usually measured by the cubic yard.

Openings, as a rule, are not deducted if containing less than 70 sq. ft.

EXERCISES

1. Find the cost of laying a hammer-dressed ashlar wall, 45 ft. long, 6 ft. high, and 2 ft. thick, at $4.75 per perch, using the 22-cu. ft. perch.
Ans. $116.59.

2. Find the cost of making a rubblework wall at $5.25 per perch, including all the material, under a building 25 by 60 ft., the wall to be 30 in. thick and 8 ft. high. Use the $16\frac{1}{2}$-cu. ft. perch.
Ans. $1018.18.

3. Find the cost of laying the stonework in two abutments for a bridge, each abutment to be 8 ft. high, $3\frac{1}{2}$ ft. thick, 20 ft. long at the bottom, and 15 ft. at the top. (The shape is a trapezoid.) The price for laying is $2.75 per cubic yard. *Ans.* $99.82.

4. Find the cost of building a sandstone rubblework wall for a basement 36 by 47 ft., 8 ft. high, and the wall 18 in. thick. (Use outside measurements and make no allowances for openings.) The stone costs $2.40 per perch (25 cu. ft.), and the labor of laying, including lime and sand, is $2.25 per perch.

BRICKWORK

185. Brick.—The size of brick varies. In the United States, there is no legal standard. The common brick is approximately given as 8 by 4 by 2 in. In the New England States, they average about $7\frac{3}{4}$ by $3\frac{3}{4}$ by $2\frac{1}{4}$ in. In most of the western states, the common brick averages about $8\frac{1}{2}$ by $4\frac{1}{8}$ by $2\frac{1}{2}$. The brick from the same lot may vary as much as $\frac{3}{16}$ in., depending upon the degree to which they are burned. The hard-burned brick are the smaller.

Walls made from these brick are about 9, 13, 18, and 22 in. in thickness, that is, 1, $1\frac{1}{2}$, 2 and $2\frac{1}{2}$ brick.

Pressed brick are usually larger than common brick; the prevailing size is $8\frac{3}{8}$ by $4\frac{1}{8}$ by $2\frac{3}{8}$ in.

186. Estimating number, and cost of brickwork.—This cannot be discussed in full here. The student is referred to an architect's and builder's handbook for the details. Plain walls are quite universally figured at 15 brick to the square foot, *outside measure,* of 8- or 9-in. wall; $22\frac{1}{2}$ brick per square foot of 12- or 13-in. wall; 30 brick per square foot of 16-, 17-, or 18-in. wall; and $7\frac{1}{2}$ brick for each additional 4 or $4\frac{1}{2}$ in. in thickness of wall. These figures are used without regard to the size of the brick, the effect of the latter being taken into account in fixing the price per thousand. No deduction is made for openings of less than 80 sq. ft.; and when deductions are made for larger openings, the width is measured 2 ft. less than the actual width. Hollow walls are measured as if solid. For chimney breasts, pilasters, detached chimneys, and other forms the student is referred to a builder's handbook.

Example.—Find the cost of brickwork in the walls of a house 26 by 34 ft., no cross walls, the basement walls to be 13 in. thick; the first-story walls, 13 in. thick; second-story walls, 9 in. thick; height of basement walls to top of first floor joists, 9 ft.; from first-floor joists to top of second-floor joists, 10 ft. 6 in.; from second-floor joists to plate, 9 ft. (The chimneys, openings, and pressed brickwork are not considered, as the method of estimating has not been given.) The cost of brick and laying, including lime, sand, scaffolding, etc., is $20 per thousand.

Solution.—Basement and first story walls:

Girth of house = 2 × 26 ft. + 2 × 34 ft. = 120 ft.

Height of wall = 9 ft. + 10 ft. 6 in. = $19\frac{1}{2}$ ft.

Thickness of wall is 13 in.; and hence, $22\frac{1}{2}$ brick are counted per square foot. Hence the number of brick required is

$$120 \times 19\tfrac{1}{2} \times 22\tfrac{1}{2} = 52,650$$

Similarly for the second story,

$$120 \times 9 \times 15 = 16,200$$
$$\therefore \text{ Total number of brick } = 52,650 + 16,200 = 68,850$$
$$\therefore \text{ Cost } = \$20 \times 68.850 = \$1377.00 \quad Ans.$$

EXERCISES

1. Find the cost of $16.50 per thousand to cover brick, material, and labor to build a brick wall on the front and one side of a corner lot 50 by 100 ft.; the wall to be $6\frac{1}{2}$ ft. high and a brick and a half thick, allowance being made for one opening 12 ft. in length (count it 2 ft. less.)

Ans. $337.84.

2. The following is about the cost of furnishing and laying 1500 bricks, or 1 day's work.

> 1500 bricks at $9 per M
> Lime putty at $1.90
> 1 day's work for mason at $12.75
> 1 day's work for helper at $5.40

Using this as a basis for estimating, find the cost of building the walls of an apartment house 25 by 54 ft., 41 ft. high in front and 36 ft. high in the rear. The walls are to be 13 in. thick with no allowances for openings.

3. Find the cost of common brick in the pier with a cross section as shown in Fig. 175, and a height of 12 ft. 6 in. at $9 per thousand.   Count 20 brick to 1 cu. ft. *Ans.* $31.05.

Fig. 175.

4. How many enamel brick 4 by 8 in. are required to face a wall 30 ft. long and 12 ft. high, deducting for two windows 4 by 8 ft. and one door 3 ft. 4 in. by 10 ft.? *Ans.* 1182.

CHAPTER XV

CYLINDERS

187. The cylinder is of very common occurrence. We see it in wire and pipes, in tanks and other containers, in pillars, and in various parts of machines. It is often necessary to find the area of the surface and the volume of a cylinder. As will be seen, the rules in making computations in connection with a cylinder are very similar to the rules applying to the prism.

188. Definitions.—A **right circular cylinder,** or a **cylinder of revolution,** is a solid formed by revolving a rectangle about one of its sides as an axis. As shown in Fig. 176, the rectangle $OABO'$ is revolved about OO' as an axis to form the cylinder as drawn.

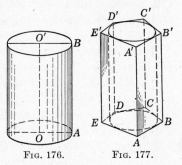

From this definition, the two bases are circles and the lateral surface is a curved surface. The **axis** of the cylinder is the line OO' joining the centers of the bases. It is perpendicular

FIG. 176. FIG. 177.

to the bases; and hence, it is equal to the **altitude** of the cylinder, which is the perpendicular distance between the two bases. The **cross section** of a cylinder is a section perpendicular to the axis.

A cylinder is **inscribed in** a prism when its bases are inscribed in the bases of the prism. (See Fig. 177.) The prism is then **circumscribed about** the cylinder. A cylinder is **circumscribed about** a prism, or the prism is **inscribed in** the cylinder, when the bases of the prism are inscribed in the bases of the cylinder.

Of course, there are right cylinders that do not have circular bases. For instance, a cylinder may have an ellipse for a base. Cylinders may be oblique as shown in Fig. 178, but these are not dealt with here.

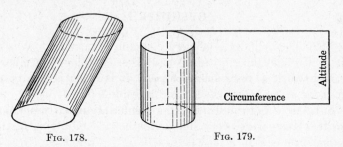

FIG. 178.   FIG. 179.

189. Area and volume.—If the lateral surface of a right cylinder could be peeled off and spread out as shown in Fig. 179, it would form a rectangle of width equal to the altitude of the cylinder and of length equal to the circumference of the base of the cylinder. From this we get the following:

RULE.—*The area of the lateral surface of a right cylinder equals the circumference of the base times the altitude.*

The total area equals the lateral area plus the area of the two bases.

Note that in the foregoing rule the base of the cylinder does not have to be a circle but it must be a *right* cylinder.

From a consideration similar to that for the prism, Art. 182, the volume of the cylinder is obtained by the following:

RULE.—*The volume of a cylinder equals the area of the base times the altitude.*

The similarity of the cylinder and the prism is seen if the cylinder is thought of as a prism having a great number of sides to the base.

The preceding rule holds when the cylinder is not circular.

Since the altitude times the area of the base gives the volume, the altitude equals the volume divided by the area of the base. Also the area of the base equals the volume divided by the altitude.

If S stands for lateral area, V for volume, A for area of base, and h for altitude, the rules given are stated in the following formulas:

[42] $\qquad$ $S = Ch = \pi dh = 2\pi rh$

[43] $\qquad$ $V = Ah = \pi r^2 h = \frac{1}{4}\pi d^2 h$

[44] $\qquad$ $h = V \div A = V \div \pi r^2$

[45] $\qquad$ $A = V \div h$

Example 1.—Find the lateral area and the volume of a right cylinder whose radius is 3 ft. and altitude 8 ft.

Solution.—By formula [**42**], $S = 2 \times 3.1416 \times 3 \times 8 = 150.8$ sq. ft. *Ans.*

By formula [**43**], $V = 3.1416 \times 3^2 \times 8 = 226.2$ cu. ft.

$\qquad\qquad\qquad\qquad\qquad\qquad\qquad\qquad\qquad$ *Ans.*

Example 2.—Find the effective heating surface of a boiler of diameter 5 ft. and length 16 ft., with 54 tubes $3\frac{1}{2}$ in. in diameter, assuming that the effective heating surface of the shell is one-half the total surface.

Solution.—By formula [**42**], effective heating surface of the shell $= \frac{1}{2}(\pi dh + 2 \times \frac{1}{4}\pi d^2)$

$\qquad\qquad = \frac{1}{2}(3.1416 \times 5 \times 16 + 2 \times 0.7854 \times 5^2)$

$\qquad\qquad = 145.299$ sq. ft.

Effective heating surface of 54 tubes

$$= \frac{3\frac{1}{2} \times 3.1416 \times 54 \times 16}{12} = 791.683 \text{ sq. ft.}$$

$\therefore$ Total heating surface $= 145.299 + 791.683 = 937$ sq. ft. approx. *Ans.*

Example 3.—What is the weight of a cylindrical shaft of marble 3 ft. in circumference and 9 ft. high?

Solution: $\qquad r = \frac{1}{2}(3 \div 3.1416) = 0.47746$

By formula [**43**], $V = \pi r^2 h = 3.1416 \times 0.47746^2 \times 9 = 6.4457$ cu. ft.

Weight = 2.7 × 62.5 × 6.4457 = 1087 lb.   *Ans.*

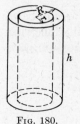

Fig. 180.

Since 62.5 lb. = weight of 1 cu. ft. of water, and 2.7 = specific gravity of marble.

190. The hollow cylinder.—The volume of a hollow cylinder, Fig. 180, may be found by subtracting the volume of the cylindrical hollow from the volume of the whole cylinder. If R is the radius of the cylinder, and r the radius of the hollow, then the volume of the hollow cylinder is as follows:

$$[46] \quad V = \pi R^2 h - \pi r^2 h = \pi h(R^2 - r^2) = \pi h(R + r)(R - r)$$

Example 1.—Find the number of cubic inches of copper in a hollow cylinder 7 in. long, 6 in. in inner diameter, and 8 in. in outer diameter.

Solution.—By formula [46]

$$V = \pi h(R + r)(R - r)$$
$$\therefore V = 3.1416 \times 7(4 + 3)(4 - 3) = 153.938 \text{ cu. in.} \quad Ans.$$

EXERCISES

NOTE.—Some of the following exercises can be more easily solved after Part III has been studied.

1. A boy was asked to measure two cylindrical coffee cans. He reported as follows:

(1) For the half-pound can: altitude, $2\frac{3}{4}$ in.; diameter, $3\frac{7}{8}$ in.

(2) For the pound can: altitude, $3\frac{3}{8}$ in.; diameter, $4\frac{7}{8}$ in.

Could these measurements be accepted as approximately correct?
Ans. $V_1 = 0.515 V_2$ approx.

2. A rectangular piece of sheet iron containing 625 sq. in. is bent to form a cylinder 9 in. in diameter. Find (1) the height and (2) the volume of this cylinder. *Ans.* 22.1 in.; 1406 cu. in.

3. Compare the lateral areas of the cans in Exercise 1.
Ans. $S_1 = 0.65 S_2$ approx.

4. A cubic foot of copper was drawn into a wire $\frac{1}{16}$ in. in diameter. Guess the length of this wire in miles, and then find its length. (5280 ft. = 1 mile.) *Ans.* 8.889 + miles.

5. Compare the total area of the cubic foot of copper with the lateral area of the wire in Exercise 4. *Ans.* 1:128.

6. A copper rod 1 in. in diameter and 8 in. long is drawn into a wire of uniform diameter and 200 ft. long. Find the diameter of the wire.

Ans. 0.0577 in.

7. Compare the lateral areas of the rod and the wire in Exercise 6.

Ans. 1:17.32 approx.

8. If r, d, h, A, S, and V have the meaning given in Art. 189:

(1) Given $h = 16$ in. and $A = 48$ sq. in.; find r, S, and V.

(2) Given $A = 160$ sq. ft. and $V = 4800$ cu. ft.; find d and S.

9. If V, R, r, and h have the meaning given in Art. 190:

(1) Given $R = 5$ in., $r = 4$ in., and $h = 10$ in.; find V.

(2) Given $V = \pi r^2 h$; find the ratio of R to r.

Interpret by a drawing. *Ans.* 282.74 cu. in.; $R = r\sqrt{2}$.

10. Using 4.211 cu. ft. to a barrel, find the number of barrels in the following cylindrical tanks:

(1) $h = 20$ ft. and $r = 15$ ft. *Ans.* 3357.3.

(2) $h = 9$ ft. and $r = 4$ ft. *Ans.* 107.4.

11. A baking-powder can with $d = 2\frac{1}{4}$ in. and $h = 3\frac{5}{8}$ in. is marked 6 oz. How much would 1 qt. of this powder weigh? Use 231 cu. in. = 1 gal. *Ans.* 24 oz. approx.

12. A cubic foot of glass is made into a hollow tube with $R = \frac{3}{16}$ in. and $r = \frac{1}{8}$ in. Find the length of this tube. Compare with Exercise 4.

Ans. 0.4445− miles.

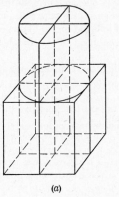 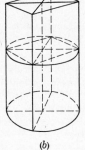

(a)   (b)

Fig. 181.

13. A container has as a bottom part a cube with its edges 2 in., and the top part is a cylinder with its diameter and height each 2 in. Find the volume and total area of this container. [See Fig. 181(a).]

Ans. $8 + 2\pi$ cu. in.; $24 + 4\pi$ sq. in.

14. A container has as a bottom part a right circular cylinder with $d = h$. Its top part is a cube with the diagonals of the base the same as the diameter of the cylinder. Find the volume and total area of this container. [See Fig. 181(*b*).] Let $d = h = 2$ in.

Ans. $2\pi + 2\sqrt{2}$ cu. in.; $6\pi + 8$ sq. in.

15. A can is 2 ft. in diameter and 2 ft. high. A second can is 1.9 ft. in diameter and holds the same as the first can; find its height. Compare the total area of the two cans. *Ans.* 2.216 ft.; $T_1 : T_2 = 6 : 6.015$.

NOTE.—It is known that for a given volume a cylindrical can has the least total area when its diameter equals its height.

16. The external diameter of a hollow cast-iron shaft is 18 in., and its internal diameter is 10 in. Calculate its weight if the length is 20 ft. and cast iron weighs 0.26 lb. per cubic inch. *Ans.* 10,980 lb. approx.

17. Water is flowing at the rate of 10 miles per hour through a pipe 16 in. in diameter into a rectangular reservoir 197 yd. long and 87 yd. wide. Calculate the time in which the surface will be raised 3 in.

Ans. 31.38 min.

Suggestion.—Ten miles per hour is $\dfrac{10 \times 5280}{60} = 880$ ft. per minute. Now find the number of cubic feet of water that will flow through the 16-in. pipe in 1 min. Then find the number of cubic feet required to fill the reservoir 3 in. The quotient found by dividing the required number of cubic feet by the flow per minute is the time in minutes.

18. In a table giving weights and sizes of square nuts for bolts, a nut 2 in. square and $1\frac{1}{4}$ in. thick with a hole $1\frac{1}{16}$ in. in diameter has a given weight of 1.042 lb. Use wrought iron and find this weight. (See Table VII.)

19. Find the length of steel wire in a coil if its diameter is 0.025 in. and its weight is 50 lb. (Use 1 cu. in. weighs 0.29 lb.)

Ans. 29,270 ft. approx.

20. Find the weight of a cylinder of lead 1 ft. long and 1 in. in diameter, considering 1 cu. in. of lead to weigh 0.412 lb. *Ans.* 3.883 lb.

21. Find the weight of 1200 ft. of lead pipe with inside diameter $\frac{7}{16}$ in. and outer diameter $\frac{7}{8}$ in. *Ans.* 2676 lb.

22. Down the middle of a four-lane highway there is a safety guard made of concrete. A cross section of the guard has as a base a trapezoid and as a top a semicircle. If the lower base of the trapezoid is 18 in., if the upper base, which is also the diameter of the semicircle, is 6 in., and if the distance between the bases is 12 in., how many cubic yards in a mile of the guard? *Ans.* 214.75 +.

23. A cylindrical gasoline tank 9 ft. long and 5 ft. in diameter is to have only its radius changed so that the volume will be doubled; find the new radius. *Ans.* 3.535 ft.

24. If in Exercise 23 only the length of the tank is changed in order to double its volume, find this new length. *Ans.* 18 ft.

25. If in Exercise 23 the length and radius are changed the same amount in order to double the volume, find, approximately, the change. (See Chap. XXX.) *Ans.* 0.87 ft.

26. In a table giving size, etc., of wrought-iron washers, a washer $3\frac{1}{2}$ in. in diameter with a whole $1\frac{1}{2}$ in. in diameter is $\frac{5}{32}$ in. thick. Find the number of these in a keg of 200 lb. *Ans.* 582.

27. Find the per cent of error in the following rule which applies to round bars, (1) for wrought iron, (2) for cast iron. Multiply the square of the diameter in inches by the length in feet and that product by 2.6. The product will be the weight in pounds approximately. (See Table VII.)

Ans. 1.5− % too small; 6.1+ % too large.

28. A conduit made of concrete has a cross section as shown in Fig. 182. How many cubic yards of concrete are used in making 500 yd. of this conduit?

Ans. 1113.4.

FIG. 182.

29. In a table giving weights and areas in cross section of steel bars, a round steel bar $\frac{3}{8}$ in. in diameter has its area given as 0.1104 sq. in. and weight 0.376 lb. per linear foot. Verify these results if steel weighs 489.6 lb. per cubic foot.

30. A cylindrical water tank holds 10 bbl. It has a radius of 3 ft. Find its height. (See Exercise 10.) *Ans.* $17\frac{7}{8}$ in.

31. Water is being pumped through a 6-in. pipe. If the flow is 3 ft. per second, how many barrels are being pumped per hour?

Ans. 503.6.

32. A right circular cylinder has $d = h = 10$ ft. In order to double the lateral area, find the equal amount to be added to h and d. (See Chap. XXX.) *Ans.* 4.14 ft.

33. Discuss the solution of Exercise 32 if an amount is added to d and the same amount subtracted from h, instead of added to h.

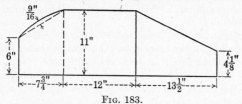

FIG. 183.

34. A water tank in a Pullman car has a vertical cross section as shown in Fig. 183 and a length of 52 in. Find its capacity in gallons.

Ans. 68.3.

Suggestion.—Consider the part bounded by the straight line and the curve as a segment of a circle. To find its area use $A = \frac{2}{3}wh$ from formula [**30(a)**].

35. The rain that falls on a house 22 by 36 ft. is conducted to a cylindrical cistern 8 ft. in diameter. How great a fall of rain would it take to fill the cistern to a depth of $7\frac{1}{2}$ ft.?   *Ans.* 5.7+ in.

36. To test the flow of water through a $\frac{1}{4}$-in. circular nozzle, a flow of 60 gal. was recorded in 10 min. Find the rate in feet per second of the flow of the water if the stream is supposed to be as large as the nozzle.

Ans. 39.3 ft. per second.

37. Find the tensile strength of 0000 B. & S. gage copper wire. (See Tables VIII and VI).   *Ans.* 5000 lb. approx.

By tense force is meant a pulling force. The problem asks how great a weight the wire will hold when hanging vertically.

38. Calculate the size of a square wrought-iron bar to stand a pull of 43,000 lb. (See Table VIII.)   *Ans.* 0.927 in. square.

39. What should be the diameter of a round cast-iron bar that is subjected to a tension of 30,000 lb. if the pull on each square inch of cross section is 2400 lb.?   *Ans.* 3.989 in.

40. Find the pull per square inch necessary to break a rod $2\frac{1}{2}$ in. in diameter that breaks with a load of 270,000 lb.

Ans. 55,000 lb. approx.

41. If a wrought-iron bar 2 in. by $1\frac{1}{4}$ in. in cross section breaks under a load of 125,000 lb., what load will break a wrought-iron rod $2\frac{1}{2}$ in. in diameter?   *Ans.* 245,400 lb. approx.

42. A cylinder in which $d = 9$ in. is cut parallel to its axis and developed into a rectangle with area equal to 625 sq. in. Find the height of the cylinder. Compare with Exercise 2.   *Ans.* 22.1 in.

43. A rectangle x by y is bent to form two different cylinders. First x is used as a height, and then y is used as a height. Find the ratio of the volumes of these two cylinders.   *Ans.* $y:x$.

44. A cast-iron bar has an elliptical cross section with axes 6 and 4 in. Find the pull per square inch of cross section under a total tensile load of 125,000 lb.   *Ans.* 6631 lb.

45. A wrought-iron cylindrical rod 2000 ft. long and $1\frac{1}{2}$ in. in diameter is suspended vertically from its upper end. What is the total pull at this end and the pull per square inch of cross section?

Ans. 11,875 lb.; 6720 lb.

46. Find the length of a wrought-iron bar supported vertically at its upper end that will just break under its own weight.

Ans. 15,000 ft. approx.

47. At 27 cents per pound, find the cost of the copper in a sheet-copper, cylindrical tank 3 ft. high and $1\frac{1}{2}$ ft. in diameter, open at the top and weighing 12 lb. per square foot.   *Ans.* $51.53.

48. A rectangular block of wood with dimensions a, b, and c has a circular hole d in. in diameter bored through it perpendicular to the faces with dimensions a and b. Write a formula for the volume V remaining.

$$Ans. \ V = abc - \pi cd^2.$$

49. A rectangular block of wood with dimensions a, b, and c has each of its four edges of length b rounded in the form of a quarter of a circle of radius r. Find the volume V of the remaining block.

$$Ans. \ V = abc - 4br^2 \left(1 - \frac{\pi}{4}\right).$$

50. A cylinder to cool lard is 4 ft. in diameter and 9 ft. long and makes 4 R. P. M. The hot lard covers the surface $\frac{1}{8}$ in. deep. How many pounds of lard will it cool in 1 hr. if the specific gravity of lard is 0.9? Assume an entire change of lard passes over the cylinder during each revolution. *Ans.* 15,900 approx.

51. If a tank 5 ft. in diameter and 10 ft. deep holds 10,000 lb. of lard, what will be the depth of a tank of 2000 lb. capacity if its diameter is 3 ft.? If this tank has a jacket around it on the bottom and sides 3 in. from the surface of the tank as in Fig. 184, how many gallons of water will the space between the jacket and tank hold?

Ans. 5 ft. $6\frac{11}{16}$ in.; 124 approx.

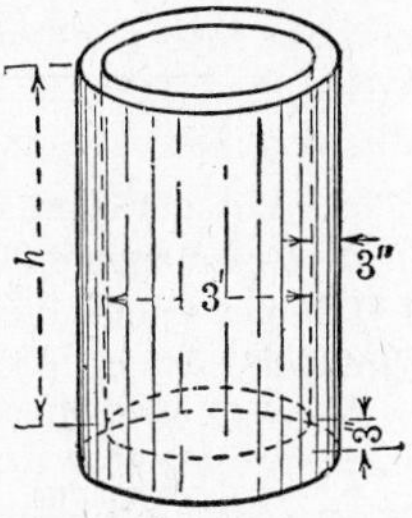

52. Find the volume of a wash boiler if the bottom is in the form of a rectangle with a semicircle at each end. The rectangle is 10 by 14 in., and the semicircles are on the smaller dimensions. The depth of the boiler is 16 in.

Ans. 15.14 − gal.

53. Find the height of a 10-gal. wash boiler whose base is 10 in. wide with semicircular ends, the length of the straight part of the sides being $9\frac{1}{4}$ in. *Ans.* $13\frac{1}{2}$ in.

Fig. 184.

54. A certain handbook gives the following "rules of thumb" for finding the volume in gallons of a cylindrical tank:

(1) V (in gallons) = (diameter in feet)^2 × $5\frac{7}{8}$ × (height in feet).

(2) V (in gallons) = diameter in feet)^2 × $\frac{1}{2}$ of height in inches less 2% of same.

Find the per cent of error for each rule.

Ans. (1) 0.003 + % too small; (2) 0.08 + % too large.

Remark.—Rule (2) is a quick rule to apply if the 2% is disregarded. This rule is in common use by many estimators.

55. In making the pattern of a teakettle with an elliptical bottom to hold 6 qt., it is decided to have the bottom an ellipse with axes 10 and 7 in. Find the height. *Ans.* 6.30 + in.

56. How long a piece of copper will it take to make the body of the above teakettle? Use formula [**32**(b)]. *Ans.* $26\frac{7}{16}$ in.

57. Find the amount of sheet metal in an elliptical tank whose base has axes of 42 and 32 in. and whose height is 40 in. The tank is to have a bottom but no top. Find the number of gallons the tank will hold. Use formula [**32(c)**].   *Ans.* 39.9 sq. ft.

58. In drilling in soft steel, a $1\frac{9}{16}$-in. twist drill makes 37 R. P. M. with a feed of $\frac{1}{80}$ in. Find the number of cubic inches cut away in $3\frac{1}{2}$ min.   *Ans.* 3.1+.

59. A $\frac{3}{16}$-in. twist drill makes 310 R. P. M. with a feed of $\frac{1}{125}$ in. Find the volume cut away in $3\frac{1}{2}$ min.   *Ans.* 0.24− cu. in.

60. Find the number of pounds of cast iron turned off per hour in the following (consider the cutting as if on a plane):

	Speed per minute, feet	Depth of cut, inches	Breadth of cut, inches
(1)	37.90	0.125	0.015
(2)	25.82	0.015	0.125
(3)	25.27	0.048	0.048

Ans. 13.3; 9.06; 10.9.

61. A steam-chest cover is 42 by 24 in. How many steel studs $1\frac{1}{4}$ in. in diameter should be used to hold the cover if the steam pressure is 160 lb. per square inch? The diameter of the bolts at the bottom of the thread is 1.065 in. Allow a stress of 11,000 lb. per square inch.

Solution: $42 \times 24 \times 160$ lb. = 161,280 lb. total pressure

$$161{,}280 \div 11{,}000 = 14.662 \text{ sq. in.} = \text{area in cross section of all bolts}$$
$$0.7854 \times 1.065^2 = 0.89082 + \text{sq. in.} = \text{area of one bolt}$$
$$14.662 \div 0.89082 = 16.5-$$

Therefore number of bolts is 18 to be even.

62. The flanges at the joining of two ends of flanged steam pipes 9 in.

Fig. 185.

in inside diameter are bolted together by 12 bolts $\frac{3}{4}$ in. in diameter. If the pressure in the pipes is 200 lb. per square inch, find what each bolt must hold. How much is this per square inch cross section of the bolts? Suppose that bolts have 10-pitch U.S.S. thread. This makes the root diameter 0.620 in. (See Fig. 185.)

Ans. 1060.3 lb.; 3512 lb.

63. As in the last exercise, if the steam pipe is 18 in. in diameter, and allowing the same pull per square inch of cross section of each bolt, find the number of bolts $1\frac{1}{8}$ in. in diameter at a joint of the pipe. (A $1\frac{1}{8}$ in. bolt with 7-pitch U.S.S. thread is 0.940 in. in diameter at root of thread.)

Ans. 22.

64. The following rule is often used to find the heating surface of any number of tubes in a steam boiler: Multiply the number of tubes by the diameter of one tube in inches, and multiply this product by its length in feet and then by 0.2618. The final product is the number of square feet of heating surface. Using this rule, what is the heating surface of 66 three-inch tubes each 18 ft. long? Does the rule give the correct result?

Ans. 933 sq. ft.; yes.

65. To find the water capacity of a horizontal tubular boiler, find two-thirds the volume of the shell and subtract from this the volume of all the tubes. Find the water capacity of a horizontal tubular boiler $18\frac{1}{2}$ ft. long and 66 in. in diameter with 72 three-inch tubes.

Ans. 227.6+ cu. ft.

66. The steam capacity of a horizontal boiler is often reckoned as one-third the volume of the shell. Find the steam capacity of a horizontal boiler 18 ft. long and 78 in. in diameter. *Ans.* 199 cu. ft.

67. Use the following rule and find the heating surface of a boiler 12 ft. long and 5 ft. in diameter, having 52 two and one-half-inch tubes.

Ans. 518.7 to 556.7 sq. ft.

Rule.—In finding the heating surface in a horizontal boiler, it is customary to take one-half to two-thirds of the lateral area of the shell and add to this the lateral area of the tubes and one-half to two-thirds the area of the ends of the boiler and then subtract from this total sum the areas of both ends of the tubes.

68. A steam boiler is 72 in. in diameter and 18 ft. long and contains 70 tubes 4 in. in diameter. Find the heating surface, using one-half in the rule. *Ans.* 1505 sq. ft.

69. Find the steam capacity of a boiler 4 ft. in diameter and 16 ft. long if the height of the segment occupied by the steam is 18 in. Is this more or less, and by how much, than one-third the total capacity of the boiler shell? *Ans.* 68.9 cu. ft.; 1.9 cu. ft. more.

Suggestion.—Use formula [**30(a)**] for the area of the segment and formula [**18**] for the width of the segment.

70. The cylinder of a pump is 6 in. in diameter, the length of stroke, 8 in.; and the number of strokes per minute, 160. Find the flow in gallons per minute if the pump is double acting, that is, pumps the cylinder full each stroke. *Ans.* 156.7 − gal.

71. When the piston of a hand pump is 3 in. in diameter, and the supply of water is drawn from a depth of 25 ft., what pressure is required on the handle 24 in. from the fulcrum when the piston rod is attached $3\frac{1}{4}$ in. from the fulcrum? *Ans.* 10.39 − lb.

72. The Cleveland Twist Drill Company records a test in which a $1\frac{1}{4}$-in. "Paragon" high-speed drill removed 70.56 cu. in. of cast iron per minute. The penetration per minute was $57\frac{1}{2}$ in.; the feed, $\frac{1}{10}$ in.; and the drill made 575 R. P. M. Do these numbers agree?

73. What will be the weight of a cast-iron pipe 10 ft. long, 2 ft. in outer diameter, and 1 in. thick? (Use 0.26 lb. per cubic inch.)

Ans. 2254 lb.

74. A tank car with a cylindrical tank 8 ft. in diameter and 34 ft. long will hold how many gallons? What weight of oil will it hold if the specific gravity of oil is 0.94? *Ans.* 12,784 gal.; 100,400 lb.

75. Find the height of a cylindrical tank having a diameter of 30 in. and holding 4 bbl. *Ans.* $41\frac{3}{16}$ in.

76. If a bar $1\frac{1}{2}$ in. in diameter weighs 6.01 lb. per foot of length, what is the weight per foot of a bar $1\frac{1}{2}$ in. square and of the same material?

Ans. 7.65 + lb.

77. Find the weight of a hollow hexagonal bar, Fig. 186, 16 ft. long and weighing 0.28 lb. per cubic inch. The cross section is a regular hexagon $1\frac{1}{4}$ in. on a side, with a circle $1\frac{1}{4}$ in. in diameter at the center.

Ans. $152\frac{1}{4}$ lb.

78. A cylindrical tank 22 ft. long and 6 ft. in diameter rests on its side in a horizontal position. Find the number of gallons of oil that it will

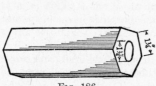

Fig. 186.

Fig. 187.

hold when the depth of the oil is 8 in.; when 1 ft. 6 in.; when 2 ft. 6 in. Use formula [**30(b)**] for finding the area of the segment.

Ans. 282.5 gal.; 909.3 gal.

79. The segment in Fig. 187 is a counterbalance $5\frac{1}{2}$ in. thick. Find its weight if made of cast iron weighing 0.26 lb. per cubic inch.

Solution.—Area of segment AnB = area of sector $AOBn$ − area of triangle AOB.

Area of sector $AOBn = \frac{1}{6} \times 84^2 \times 0.7854 = 923.63$ sq. in.

Area of triangle $AOB = \frac{1}{2} \times 42 \times 21 \times \sqrt{3} = 763.81$ sq. in.

Area of segment AnB = 923.63 sq. in. − 763.81 sq. in. = 159.82 sq. in.

Volume of counterbalance = $5\frac{1}{2} \times 159.82$ cu. in. = 879.0 cu. in.

Weight of counterbalance = 879.0×0.26 lb. = 228.5 lb.   *Ans.*

80. Because the body of a bolt is greater in diameter than the threaded part, when the bolt is under strain, the two parts will not stretch uniformly. For this reason the bolt is most liable to break where the threaded part joins the other part. To overcome this a hole is sometimes drilled from the center of the head to the beginning of the threaded part. This hole is made of such size that the cross-sectional area of the body is the same as that at the root of the thread.

Find the diameter of the hole to be drilled in the following bolts in accordance with the preceding:

(1) Diameter of bolt $\frac{3}{4}$ in. with 10 U.S.S. threads to 1 in.

Ans. 0.442 in.

(2) Diameter of bolt $1\frac{7}{8}$ in. with 5 U.S.S. threads to 1 in.

Ans. 0.952 in.

81. In computing the safe working pressure for a steam boiler, a factor of safety of 5 is used. That is, the safe working pressure is one-fifth of the bursting pressure. The bursting pressure in pounds per square inch is given by the formula

$$P = \frac{Ttk}{r}$$

where

P = the bursting pressure in pounds per square inch.

T = the tensile strength of boiler plate per square inch.

t = the thickness of boiler plate in inches.

r = the radius of boiler in inches.

k = a constant depending upon the riveting and is 0.56 for single riveted boilers, 0.70 for double-riveted boilers, and 0.8 for triple-riveted boilers.

Derive the formula.

Suggestion.—The tensions in the section of the shell at the extremities of any diameter AB of Fig. 188 are equal to the pressure on one-half of the shell and perpendicular to this diameter. This pressure is the same as would be on a rectangle of width equal to the diameter and of length equal to the length of the boiler.

82. Find the bursting and the safe working pressure for a double-riveted boiler 66 in. in diameter made of plate $\frac{5}{16}$ in. thick, if tensile strength is 50,000 lb. per square inch. *Ans.* 331.4 lb.; 66.3 lb.

83. What would be the bursting pressure in pounds per square inch of a wrought-iron pipe having an inside diameter of 3 in. and a shell $\frac{1}{8}$ in. thick? Use a tensile strength of 40,000 lb. per square inch. *Ans.* $3333\frac{1}{3}$ lb.

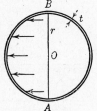

Fig. 188.

84. Holes are punched in sheets of metal by means of great pressure applied by a punch press. The pressure is usually reckoned at 60,000 lb. per square inch of surface cut over. For example, a hole 2 in. in circumference punched in a ½-in. plate would require a pressure of $2 \times \frac{1}{2} \times 60,000$ lb., that is, the area of the cylindrical surface sheared off times 60,000 lb.

Find the pressure necessary to punch a hole, having a diameter of ½ in.,

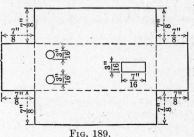

Fig. 189.

through a steel plate ⅛ in. thick.
Ans. 11,781 lb.

85. Find the pressure necessary to punch at one blow a round hole ¾ in. in diameter and a rectangular hole ¾ by ¼ in. through a steel plate ½ in. thick.

Ans. 130,686 lb.

86. Find the blow necessary to punch out the box shown in Fig. 189. The dimensions are as given, and the thickness of the sheet steel is $\frac{1}{32}$ in.   *Ans.* 17,678 lb.

87. Many small metal articles in common use are punched out of sheet metal and pressed into shape. The blank is usually cut so as to have the same area as the area of the finished article. For example, the blank for a cylindrical box, having a diameter of 1 in. and a depth of 2 in., Fig. 190, would have an area equal to the combined area of the sides and bottom of the box. Find the area and diameter of the blank for this box.

Solution.—Area = $3.1416 \times (\frac{1}{2})^2 + 3.1416 \times 1 \times 2 = 7.0686$ sq. in.

Diameter of blank =
$\sqrt{7.0686 \div 0.7854} = 3$ in.

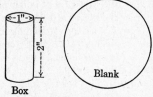

Box

Blank

Fig. 190.

In shallow articles, as pail covers, the diameter of the blank is often found by adding twice the depth to the diameter of the top.

88. Find the diameter of the blank for a pail cover whose diameter is 8 in. and depth ¾ in. Work by both methods suggested above, and compare results.

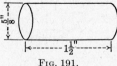

Fig. 191.

89. An aluminum cap for a paste bottle has the dimensions given in Fig. 191. Find the diameter of the blank from which it was pressed.   *Ans.* 2.04 in.

90. A shoe-blacking box has a diameter of 3 in. and a depth of 1 in. Find the diameter of the blank from which it was pressed.   *Ans.* 4.58 in.

91. The height of a right circular cylinder is 6 in., and the entire area is 100 sq. in. Find the radius of the base.   *Ans.* 1.99 + in.

CHAPTER XVI

PYRAMIDS, CONES, AND FRUSTUMS

191. Pyramid.—A **pyramid** is a solid whose base is a polygon and whose sides are triangles with their vertices at a common point, called the **vertex** or **apex** of the pyramid. A pyramid is triangular, square, hexagonal, etc., according as its base is a triangle, square, hexagon, etc.

A **right pyramid,** or a **regular pyramid,** is a pyramid whose base is a regular polygon and the sides or faces equal isosceles triangles.

At the left in Fig. 192 is a regular pyramid with a square base.

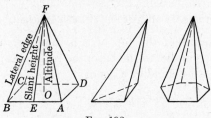

Fig. 192.

In a regular pyramid the **axis,** or the line drawn from the vertex to the center of the base, is perpendicular to the base. This line is the **altitude** of the pyramid.

In Fig. 192 *OF* is the altitude.

The **slant height** of a right pyramid is the line drawn from the vertex to the center of one edge of the base.

EF of Fig. 192 is the slant height.

A **lateral edge** is the line in which two faces meet.

BF of Fig. 192 is a lateral edge.

192. Cone.—A **circular cone** is a solid whose base is a circle and whose lateral surface tapers uniformly to a point, called the **vertex** or **apex**. The axis of the cone is a straight line drawn from the vertex to the center of the base.

A **right circular cone** is a cone whose base is a circle and

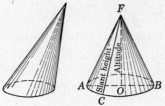

whose axis is perpendicular to the base.

In Fig. 193, *F-ABC* is a right circular cone.

This might also be defined as a solid formed by a right triangle revolved about one of its

Fig. 193.

legs as an axis. It may be called a **cone of revolution.**

The **altitude** of a cone is the perpendicular line from the vertex to the base. The **slant height** is a straight line drawn from the vertex to the circumference of the base.

In Fig. 193, *OF* is the altitude and *CF* a slant height.

193. Frustum.—If the top of a pyramid or a cone is cut off by a plane parallel to the base, the remaining part is called a **frustum** of a pyramid or a cone.

In Fig. 194, (*a*) and (*b*) are frustums.

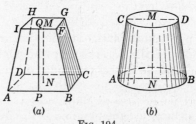

(*a*)   (*b*)

Fig. 194.

The **altitude** of a frustum is the length of the perpendicular between the bases, as *NM* of Fig. 194. The **slant height** of the frustum of a right pyramid is the shortest line between the perimeters of the two bases, and for the frustum of a right circular cone it is any straight line between the perimeters of the bases. It is perpendicular to the edge of each base in the frustum of a right pyramid and is, therefore, the altitude of the trapezoids that form the faces of the frustum.

In Fig. 194(*a*), *PQ* is the slant height.

194. Areas.—The **lateral area** of a right pyramid is found by taking the sum of the areas of the triangles forming the faces of the pyramid. Since the altitudes of these triangles are each the slant height of the pyramid, they are equal. Because the base of a right pyramid is a regular polygon, the bases of the triangles are equal. We then have the following:

RULE.—*The lateral area of a right pyramid or cone equals the perimeter of the base times one-half the slant height.*

The total area equals the lateral area plus the area of the base.

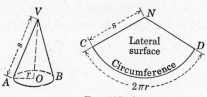

FIG. 195.

That the rules are true for the surface of a cone will be evident if one considers the cone as a pyramid whose base is a polygon with a very large number of sides. Or, perhaps, a better way is to think of the lateral surface of a cone as peeled off and flattened into the sector of a circle as shown in Fig. 195. The slant height of the cone will be the *radius* of the sector, and the circumference of the base of the cone the *arc* of the sector. Then by formula [**29(b)**] we have the rule for the lateral area.

Since the faces of the frustum of a pyramid are trapezoids, we have, by use of formula [**8**], the following:

RULE.—*The lateral area of the frustum of a right pyramid or cone equals one-half the sum of the perimeters of the two bases times the slant height.*

The total area equals the lateral area plus the areas of the two bases.

That these rules apply to the cone as well as to the pyramid may be seen by thinking of the cone as a pyramid with a very great number of sides to the base.

Using S for lateral area, T for total area, h for altitude, s for slant height, p for perimeter (P and p for frustum), A for area of base (B and b for frustum), the rules may be written as the formulas:

[47] $S = \frac{1}{2}ps$, for pyramid or cone

[48] $T = \frac{1}{2}ps + A$, for pyramid or cone

[49] $S = \frac{1}{2}(P + p)s$, for frustum

[50] $T = \frac{1}{2}(P + p)s + B + b$, for frustum

Example 1.—A regular pyramid has a slant height of 10 in. and an equilateral triangle 6 in. on a side for its base. Find its lateral area.

Solution.—Here $s = 10$ in., and $p = 3 \times 6$ in. $= 18$ in.

Substituting in formula [47], $S = \frac{1}{2} \times 18 \times 10 = 90$ sq. in.

Ans.

Example 2.—Find the total area of the frustum of a right cone if the slant height is 8 in. and the radii of the bases are respectively 5 and 3 in.

Solution.—Here $s = 8$ in., $P = 2\pi \times 5$ in., $p = 2\pi \times 3$ in., $B = \pi \times 5^2$ sq. in., and $b = \pi \times 3^2$ sq. in.

By formula [50], $T = \frac{1}{2}(2\pi \times 5 + 2\pi \times 3)8 + \pi \times 5^2 + \pi \times 3^2 = 307.9$ sq. in.   *Ans.*

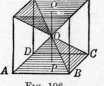

Fig. 196.

195. Volumes.—A particular case of the volume of a pyramid is seen as follows: The cube of Fig. 196 is divided into six equal pyramids with their vertices at the center of the cube. The volume of the cube equals the area $ABCD$ times the altitude PQ.

Now the volume of one of the six pyramids, as O-$ABCD$, equals one-sixth of the volume of the cube and, hence, equals the area of the base $ABCD$ times one-third of PO.

The student should form a cube from a large potato and then, with a knife having a narrow blade, cut the six pyramids mentioned here.

The volume of a pyramid or cone is equal to one-third the volume of a prism or cylinder of the same base and altitude. This means that if a prism or cylinder is cut away so as to form a pyramid or cone, exactly two-thirds of the original is cut away.

RULE.—*The volume of a pyramid or a cone equals the area of the base times one-third the altitude.*

This may be written as the formula

[51] $$V = \tfrac{1}{3}Ah$$

The volume of the frustum of a pyramid or cone is best stated in the following formula:

[52] $$V = \tfrac{1}{3}h(B + b + \sqrt{B \times b})$$

The volume of a frustum of a cone is usually more easily found by

[53] $$V = \tfrac{1}{3}\pi h(R^2 + r^2 + Rr)$$

or

[54] $$V = \tfrac{1}{12}\pi h(D^2 + d^2 + Dd)$$

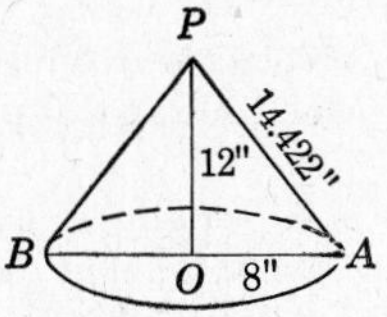

FIG. 197.

where

R and D = the radius and diameter of the lower base.

r and d = the radius and diameter of the upper base.

Example.—Find the volume and the lateral area of a right cone of a diameter of 16 in. and an altitude of 12 in.

Solution: $A = \pi r^2 = 3.1416 \times 8^2 = 201.0624$ sq. in.

$$V = \tfrac{1}{3}Ah = \tfrac{1}{3} \times 201.0624 \times 12 = 804.25 \text{ cu. in.}$$
Ans.

$$s = \sqrt{12^2 + 8^2} = 14.422 \text{ in.}$$

since the altitude, radius, and slant height form a right triangle *AOP* of Fig. 197.

$$S = \tfrac{1}{2}ps = \pi rs = 3.1416 \times 8 \times 14.422 = 362.465 \text{ sq. in.}$$
Ans.

EXERCISES

1. Two monuments weigh the same (have the same volume). One is a cube with edges 6 ft., and the other is a right pyramid with a 6-ft. square base. Find the altitude, the slant height, and a lateral edge of the pyramid. *Ans.* 18 ft.; 18.248 ft.; 18.493 ft.

2. Two monuments weigh the same. One is a right circular cylinder with diameter and height each 6 ft., and the other is a right circular cone with diameter of 6 ft. Find the altitude and the slant height of the cone. (See Exercise 1.) *Ans.* 18 ft.; 18.248 ft.

3. Cut out three semicircular pieces of paper with radii 1, 2, and 3 in., respectively. Form three cones. Compare the three as to their altitudes, their slant heights, and their lateral areas.

4. A student in industrial design was given a circular cylinder and was required to form a circular cone with the same base and altitude as that of the cylinder. Compare the weights of the finished piece and the original piece. *Ans.* 1 to 3.

5. A regular hexagonal pyramid has an altitude of 12 in., and each edge of the base is 9 in. Planes parallel to the base divide the altitude into three equal parts. Find the ratio of the volumes of the three solids formed. Find the slant height of each.
Ans. 1:7:19; slant height of each is 5 in.

6. Solve Exercise 5 if a right circular cone is used instead of the regular hexagonal pyramid. (Let altitude = 12 in., radius = 9 in.)
Ans. Same as Exercise 5.

7. A right triangle with legs 3 and 4 in. long and hypotenuse 5 in long is revolved about each leg and also about the hypotenuse; find the lateral area and the volume of each solid formed.
Ans. $S_1 = 15\pi$, $S_2 = 20\pi$, $S_3 = 16.8\pi$, $V_1 = 12\pi$, $V_2 = 16\pi$, $V_3 = 9.6\pi$.

NOTE.—If in a right triangle a line is drawn from the right angle perpendicular to the hypotenuse, it divides the triangle into two similar right triangles and each is similar to the original right triangle.

In a right circular cone,
r = the radius of base.
p = the circumference of base.
h = the altitude.
s = the slant height.
S = the lateral area.
T = the total area.
V = the volume.

Solve the following (draw the cone in each case, estimating the parts to be found before finding them):

8. Given $h = 8$ in., $r = 6$ in.; find S, T, and V.
Ans. 60π sq. in.; 96π sq. in.; 96π cu. in.

9. Given $p = 12\pi$ in., $h = 8$ in.; find s, S, T, and V.

Ans. Same as Exercise 8.

10. Given $s = \sqrt{2}$ in., $p = 2\pi$ in.; find r, h, S, T, and V.

Ans. $r = h = 1$ in.; $S = \pi\sqrt{2}$ sq. in.; $T = \pi(1 + \sqrt{2})$ sq. in.;

$$V = \frac{\pi}{3} \text{ cu. in.}$$

11. Given $S = 256$ sq. in., $s = 16$ in.; find r and h.

Ans. 9.027 in.; 13.210+ in.

Suggestion.—Use formula [47] to find p, and then find r.

12. Given $V = 400$ cu. in., $r = 8$ in.; find h. *Ans.* 5.97— in.

13. Given $T = 500$ sq. in., $r = 5$ in.; find s and h.

Ans. 26.83 in.; 26.36 in.

14. A pail is marked 1 gal. It is 6 in. in diameter at the bottom and 8 in. in diameter at the top. These pails are open at the top. Find the number of square inches of tin required to make 100 of them.

Ans. 16,110 sq. in. approx.

15. The Pyramid of Cheops has a square base, 720 ft. on a side, and an altitude of 480 ft. Find its volume in cubic yards. *Ans.* 3,272,000.

Note.—Exercises 16 to 21 may be omitted until Part III is studied.

16. Use formula [51], and derive a formula for finding the altitude of a cone in terms of its volume and radius. *Ans.* $h = \dfrac{3V}{\pi r^2}$.

17. Solve formula [50] for s.

18. Solve formula [53] for r.

19. A buoy has the shape formed by revolving a right triangle (with legs a and b, and hypotenuse c) about its hypotenuse c. Find S and V as functions of a, b, and c. See the note under Exercise 7.

$$Ans. \ S = \frac{\pi ab(a + b)}{c}; \ V = \frac{\pi a^2 b^2}{3c}.$$

20. The bottom of an oilcan is a right circular cylinder; the top is a right circular cone. Find S and T for this can as functions of the diameter D, altitude H of the bottom, and altitude h of the top.

Ans. $S = \dfrac{\pi D}{4}(4H + \sqrt{4h^2 + D^2}); \ T = \dfrac{\pi D}{4}(4H + D + \sqrt{4h^2 + D^2}).$

21. If in Exercise 20 the radius of the cone is three-fourths its height, it is known that for the least amount of material to make a can with a given volume then $H = h$. Make these substitutions, and simplify the formulas derived in Exercise 20.

22. Find the diameter of a blank to make the pressed basin shown in Fig. 198. The depth is 2 in.; the bottom has a diameter of 5 in.; the top, an inside diameter of 6 in.; and the rim is $\frac{1}{2}$ in. wide.

Fig. 198.

Suggestion.—The blank must have an area equal to the total area of the basin. The area of the rim is a ring between two concentric circles. The slant height is the hypotenuse of a right triangle whose base is $\frac{1}{2}$ in. and whose altitude is 2 in.

23. A cone 12 in. in altitude and with circular base 8 in. in diameter

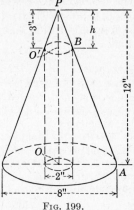

Fig. 199.

has a hole 2 in. in diameter bored through the center from apex to base. Find the volume of the part remaining.

Ans. 169.65— cu. in.

Suggestion.—The part cut away, as shown in Fig. 199, consists of a cylinder 9 in. in altitude and a cone 3 in. in altitude. The height of the small cone can be found from the similar triangles AOP and $BO'P$ in which the porportion

$$AO:BO' = OP:O'P$$

or

$$4:1 = 12:O'P$$

$$\therefore O'P = 3$$

24. It is known that the dimensions of the right circular cylinder of greatest volume inscribed in a given right circular cone have the altitude of the cylinder equal to one-third of that of the cone. Find the volume of the largest right circular cylinder that can be inscribed in a right circular cone with $d = 12$ ft. and $h = 9$ ft. (See Exercise 23.) *Ans.* 48π cu. ft.

25. Find the weight of a green fir log 215 ft. long, 4 ft. 6 in. in diameter at one end, and 20 in. in diameter at the other end, the specific gravity of fir being 0.78. *Ans.* 42 tons approx.

26. Hard coal dumped in a pile lies at an angle of 30° with the horizontal, Fig. 200. Estimate the number of tons in a pile of conical shape and 10 ft. high. Large egg size weighs 38 lb. per cubic foot. *Ans.* 60 tons approx.

Fig. 200.

27. Find the number of tons of large egg coal in a pile averaging 20 ft. broad and 100 ft. long with circular ends. *Ans.* 99 tons approx.

28. Find the weight of a tapered brick stack of 10 ft. inside diameter, with a wall 4 ft. thick at the base, 1 ft. 6 in. at the top, and 175 ft. high. A cubic foot of brick weighs 112 lb. *Ans.* 1095.5 tons.

29. It is known that the most economical proportions for a conical tent of given capacity are $h = r\sqrt{2}$. Find the least amount of canvas to make a conical tent with $V = \dfrac{1000\pi\sqrt{2}}{3}$ cu. ft.

Ans. $100\pi\sqrt{3}$ sq. ft.

30. A cast-iron driver in the form of a frustum of a square pyramid is used in a pile-driving machine. Find the weight of the driver if it is 16 in. square at the bottom, and 7 in. square at the top. *Ans.* 303.7 lb.

31. A cast-iron cone pulley is 34 in. long. The diameter of one end is 12 in., and that of the other end is 5 in. A circular hole 2 in. in diameter extends the length of the pulley. Find the weight of the pulley. *Ans.* 502.2 lb.

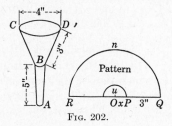

32. Determine how to cut a pattern to make a tin cone of the dimensions shown in Fig. 201.

Suggestion.—Radius of sector is 4 in.

Angle θ of sector is the same part of 360° that the circumference of the cone is of a circumference of radius 4 in.

$$\therefore 8\pi : 3\pi = 360° : \theta, \text{ or } \theta = 135°$$

Fig. 201.

The pattern is a sector of 135° in a circle of 4 in. radius.

33. Determine how to draw a pattern for the upper part of the funnel with dimensions as shown in Fig. 202, the diameter at B being 1 in. and at A $\frac{1}{2}$ in.

Suggestion.—The length $OP = x$ may be determined as follows:

$$x:x + 3 = 1:4, \text{ or } x = 1$$

The radius to use is therefore 4 in.

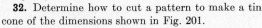

Fig. 202.

To determine the central angle θ, by the same reasoning as in the solution of the previous exercise, we have

$$\text{arc } QnR : 8\pi = \theta : 360°$$

But arc $QnR = 4\pi$, which, substituted in the proportion, gives $\theta = 180°$.

34. Determine how to draw a pattern for the lower part of the funnel shown in Fig. 202.

CHAPTER XVII

THE SPHERE

196. Definitions.—A **sphere** is a solid bounded by a curved surface, every point of which is equally distant from a point within, called the **center.** A straight line passing through the center and ending in the surface is called a **diameter.** A line extending from the center to the surface is a **radius.**

If the sphere is cut by a plane, the section is a circle. If the section is through the center of the sphere, it is called a **great circle;** if not through the center, it is called a **small circle.** The **circumference of a sphere** is the same as the circumference of a great circle.

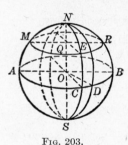

Fig. 203.

In Fig. 203, circles *ACB* and *NCS* are great circles and *MER* is a small circle.

The parallels of latitude on the surface of the earth are small circles. The meridians of the earth all run through both the north and the south poles and, therefore, are great circles.

197. Area.—The following is proved in geometry:

Rule.—*The area of the surface of a sphere equals four times the area of a circle of the same radius.*

Or stated as a formula:

[55]
$$S = 4\pi r^2 = \pi d^2$$

where

S = the area of the surface of the sphere.

r = the radius.

d = the diameter.

278

The student may satisfy himself that this is true by winding evenly the surface of a ball with heavy cord and then coiling the same cord into four circles of the same radius as the radius of the sphere.

The rule can be derived from the fact that a sphere has the same area as the lateral area of a cylinder having the same radius as the sphere and an altitude equal to the diameter of the sphere. Area of lateral surface of cylinder $= 2\pi r \times 2r = 4\pi r^2$.

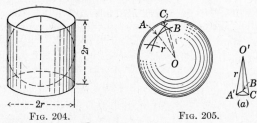

FIG. 204.   FIG. 205.

198. Volume.—Geometry gives the following:

RULE.—*The volume of a sphere equals the area of the surface times one-third of the radius.*

Or stated as a formula:

$$[56] \qquad V = \tfrac{1}{3}Sr = \tfrac{4}{3}\pi r^3 = \tfrac{1}{6}\pi d^3 = 0.5236d^3$$

The reasonableness of this may be seen by thinking of the surface of the sphere as divided into a large number of small polygons. Let these be so small that they may be considered as planes. Now if we think of the sphere cut into pyramids having these polygons as bases and having their vertices at the center of the sphere, as shown in Fig. 205, the volume of one of these small pyramids, represented in (*a*) of the figure, is found by formula [51] to be $\tfrac{1}{3}r$ times the area of the small polygon. And the volume of all the small pyramids is equal to the whole surface of the sphere times $\tfrac{1}{3}r$. Hence, $V = \tfrac{1}{3}Sr$.

199. Zone and segment of sphere.—A portion of the volume of a sphere included between two parallel planes is a **segment of the sphere.** If both the planes cut the surface of the sphere, the segment is a **segment of two bases.** In Fig. 206, the segment between the planes *ABC* and *DEF* is a segment of two bases. The part of the sphere above *DEF* is a **segment of one base.**

That portion of the surface of the sphere between two

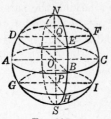

FIG. 206.

parallel planes is a **zone.** The **altitude** of the segment or zone is the perpendicular between the parallel planes.

Thus, *OQ* is the altitude of the segment between the planes *ABC* and *DEF* in Fig. 206.

Here we can neither derive the rules for the area of a zone and the volume of a segment nor make them seem reasonable by any discussion. They are of some importance practically, especially the volume of the segment.

RULE.—*The area of a zone is equal to the circumference of a great circle of the sphere times the altitude of the zone.*

This rule is stated in the formula

[**57**] $$Z = 2\pi rh$$

where

Z = the area of the zone.

h = the altitude.

r = the radius of the sphere.

It is readily seen from formula [**57**] that the area of any two zones on the same or equal spheres are to each other as their altitudes. It also follows that any zone is to the surface of the sphere as the altitude of the zone is to the diameter of the sphere.

If a sphere is cut by parallel planes that are equal distances apart, as the planes cutting the sphere in Fig. 206, then the zones are all equal. Since the parallels of 30° north and south latitude are in planes that bisect the radii drawn to the north and south poles, then one half of the surface of the earth is within 30° of the equator.

The volume of a spherical segment (Fig. 207) is given by the formula

[58] $$V = \tfrac{1}{2}h\pi(r_1{}^2 + r_2{}^2) + \tfrac{1}{6}\pi h^3$$

where

V = the volume.

h = the altitude.

r_1 and r_2 = the radii of the bases of the segment.

If the segment has only one base, one of the radii is zero.

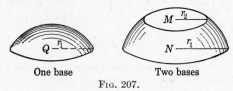

One base   Two bases

FIG. 207.

Example 1.—Find the surface, volume, and weight of a cast-iron ball of radius $12\tfrac{1}{2}$ in.

Solution.—By formula [55],

$$S = 4\pi r^2 = 4 \times 3.1416 \times 12.5^2$$
$$= 1963.5 \text{ sq. in. } Ans.$$

By formula [56]

$$V = \tfrac{1}{3}Sr = \tfrac{1}{3} \times 1963.5 \times 12.5 = 8181.25 \text{ cu. in. } Ans.$$

Since 1 cu. in. of cast iron weighs 0.26 lb., the weight

$$= 0.26 \times 8181.25 = 2127.125 \text{ lb.}$$
$$Ans.$$

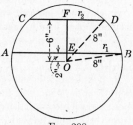

FIG. 208.

Example 2.—A sphere 8 in. in radius is cut by two parallel planes, Fig. 208, one passing 2 in. from the center and the other 6 in. from the center. Find the area of the zone and the volume of the segment between the two planes if both planes are on the same side of the center.

Solution.—By formula [**57**],

$$Z = 2\pi rh = 2 \times 3.1416 \times 8 \times 4 = 201.06 \text{ sq. in.} \quad Ans.$$
$$r_1 = \sqrt{(OB)^2 - (OE)^2} = \sqrt{8^2 - 2^2} = \sqrt{60}$$
$$r_2 = \sqrt{(OD)^2 - (OF)^2} = \sqrt{8^2 - 6^2} = \sqrt{28}$$

By formula [**58**]

$$V = \tfrac{1}{2}h\pi(r_1^2 + r_2^2) + \tfrac{1}{6}\pi h^3$$
$$= \tfrac{1}{2} \times 4 \times 3.1416(60 + 28) + \tfrac{1}{6} \times 3.1416 \times 4^3$$
$$= 586.43 \text{ cu. in.} \quad Ans.$$

EXERCISES

1. The bottom part of an art piece is a square pyramid whose base is a square with edges 6 in. and whose altitude is 1 ft.; the top part of the art piece is a sphere 6 in. in diameter. Find the ratio of the weights of the top part and the bottom part. *Ans.* $\pi : 4$.

2. How many square feet of varnish surface are in 100 of the art pieces of Exercise 1? *Ans.* 206.6.

3. The decorations of the top part of a gatepost are spheres 8 in. in diameter. If these spheres are cut from 8 in. cubes, what part of the volume is wasted? *Ans.* 48% approx.

4. The bottom part of a container is a hemisphere with a 4 ft. diameter. The top part is a right circular cone; $r = h = 2$ ft. How many gallons will this container hold? Use 7.5 gal. = 1 cu. ft. *Ans.* 60π.

5. How many square feet of paint surface in 20 of the containers of Exercise 4? Only the outside is to be painted. *Ans.* 858+.

6. Do you think that you could carry 10 lead balls 3 in. in diameter? A cubic foot of lead weighs 712 lb.

7. The nose of an army plane is a hemisphere with a 4 ft. diameter. A hole with a 6-in. radius passes through the nose. Find the area of the zone left. *Ans.* 24.33 sq. ft.

8. A hubcap is a hemisphere of three different zones. The radius of the hubcap is R in., and this radius is divided into three equal parts by planes parallel to the flat part of the hubcap. Find the ratio of the areas of the three zones formed. *Ans.* 1:1:1.

9. A cast-iron ball 3 in. in diameter is covered with a coating of ice 1 in. thick. Find the weight of the ice. *Ans.* 1.7 lb. approx.

10. A hollow copper sphere used as a float weighs 10 oz. and is 5 in. in diameter. How heavy a weight will it support in water? *Ans.* 27.9 − oz.

11. Find how many acres of land on the surface of the earth if one-fourth of the surface is land and the radius is 4000 miles.

Ans. 32,170,000,000 approx.

12. The radius of the earth is 3960 miles, and the radius of the moon is 1080 miles. Find the ratio of their areas. *Ans.* 121:9.

13. Discuss the relative positions of two spheres:

(1) When the line of centers is greater than the sum of the radii.

(2) When the line of centers is equal to the sum of the radii.

(3) When the line of centers is less than the sum and greater than the difference of the radii.

(4) When the line of centers is equal to the difference of the radii.

(5) When the line of centers is less than the difference of the radii.

14. If two spheres intersect, the circle of intersection is perpendicular to the line connecting their centers. Two spheres of radii 8 and 5 in., respectively, intersect. If the distance between their centers is 10 in., find the distance from the center of each to the circle of intersection of the two spheres and find the radius of the circle of intersection.

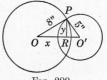

FIG. 209.

Solution.—Let x = distance from the center of the larger sphere to the circle of intersection in inches, and let y = radius of circle of intersection in inches.

In Fig. 209, ORP and $O'RP$ are right triangles.

(1) $$x^2 + y^2 = 8^2$$
(2) $$(10 - x)^2 + y^2 = 5^2$$

(1) $-$ (2) gives (see Part III)

(3) $$-100 + 20x = 39$$

Solving

$$x = 6\tfrac{19}{20}, \text{ and } 10 - x = 3\tfrac{1}{20}$$

From (1)

$$y = \sqrt{8^2 - x^2} = 3.96$$

The distances from the centers of the spheres to the circle of intersection are $6\tfrac{9}{20}$ and $3\tfrac{1}{20}$ in., respectively, and the radius of the circle of intersection is 3.96 in.

15. A model for a light bulb is two intersecting spheres of radii 10 and 12 cm., respectively. The distance between the centers of the spheres is 16 cm. Find the radius of the circle of intersection of the two spheres.

Ans. 7.49+ cm.

16. Two spheres whose radii are 6 and 8 in., respectively, have their centers 10 in. apart. Find the volume of the portion common to the two spheres. This is the form of a spherical lens. *Ans.* 105.9− cu. in.

17. There are as many square feet in the surface of a certain sphere as there are cubic feet in its volume. Find its radius.   *Ans.* 3 ft.

18. Find the volume of a cylinder 2 ft. in diameter and 2 ft. in altitude of a sphere 2 ft. in diameter; and of a cone 2 ft. in diameter and 2 ft. in altitude.   Compare the three volumes, showing that their volumes are in the ratio 3:2:1; that is, the volume of the sphere is two-thirds that of the cylinder, and the volume of the cone is one-third the volume of the cylinder or one-half the volume of the sphere.

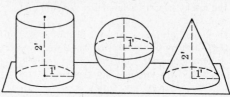

Fig. 210.

Note.—Archimedes who lived from 287 to 212 B.C. was, perhaps, the greatest mathematician of antiquity.   He proved the relation of the cylinder, sphere, and cone as stated in the previous exercise.   This is regarded as one of the most beautiful theorems of elementary geometry

19. A ball of lead 2 in. in diameter is pounded into a circular sheet 0.01 in. thick.   How large in diameter is the sheet?

Ans. 23 in. approx.

20. A water tank, 6 ft. in total length and 18 in. in diameter, is in the form of a circular cylinder with two hemispherical ends.   Find its capacity in gallons.   *Ans.* 72.7+.

21. Find the ratio of the cubes of the areas of a cube and a sphere that each have 1 cu. ft. for their volume.   *Ans.* 6:π.

Note.—It is known that among all the solids with the same given volume the sphere has the least surface area.

22. A silo is made in the form of a cylinder with a hemispherical roof. If the diameter of the silo equals its total height, find its total area.   (Let diameter = *d* ft.)

$$Ans. \; \frac{5\pi d^2}{4} \; \text{sq. ft.}$$

Note.—It is known that this is the most economical proportion for building this silo.   (Takes less material to build for a given volume.)

23. In Exercise 22, if the floor is twice as thick as the walls and roof, then the most economical shape is height of the cylinder equal to its diameter.   Find the number of board feet of lumber to build this silo if the floor is 2 in. thick and the radius equals *r* in.

$$Ans. \; \frac{\pi r^2}{18}.$$

24. A circular flower bed in a park is 25 ft. in diameter and is raised 1 ft. 6 in. in the center, making a spherical segment. How many loads of soil did it take to build it up if one load is $1\frac{1}{2}$ cu. yd.?

Ans. $15\frac{1}{3}$ approx.

25. In a practical handbook the following rule is given as *nearly correct*. In fact, it *is correct*. The area of a flanged spherical segment, a vertical section of which is shown in Fig. 211, is equal to the area of a circle of radius equal in length to the line drawn from the top of the segment to the edge of the flange, that is, equal to a circle of radius AB.

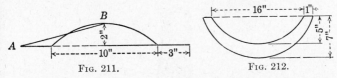

FIG. 211.   FIG. 212.

Find the area of a flanged segment having dimensions as given in Fig. 211. Work both by the rule and by using the formulas for area of a ring and of a zone.

Ans. $213.63-$ sq. in.

26. Find the per cent of error in using the following rule: To find the weight of a cast-iron ball multiply the cube of the diameter in inches by 0.1377, and the product is the weight in pounds.

27. Find the volume of the segment between two parallel planes 6 in. apart that cut a sphere 12 in. in radius if one plane passes 2 in. from the center. There are two cases; (*a*) when the center of the sphere lies outside of the segment and (*b*) when the center lies in the segment.

Ans. (*a*) 2186.6 cu. in.; (*b*) 2638.9 cu. in.

28. Figure 212 is the vertical cross section of a casting, the inner and outer "skins" being spherical zones. Find the weight of metal at 0.35 lb. per cubic inch necessary to make the casting. *Ans.* 176 lb. approx.

29. A hemispherical cap of aluminum is $3\frac{1}{2}$ in. in diameter. Find the diameter of the blank from which it is pressed. *Ans.* $4.95-$ in.

30. Find the diameter of the blank if the cap in the preceding exercise has a flat ring $\frac{1}{2}$ in. wide around it. *Ans.* $5.70+$ in.

31. Show that the volume of a round or button head of a machine screw is given by the formula

$$V = \pi h \left(\frac{D^2}{8} + \frac{h^2}{6} \right)$$

where

D = the diameter of the head.

h = height of the head.

Suggestion.—In formula [**58**]

$$V = \tfrac{1}{2} h \pi (r_1{}^2 + r_2{}^2) + \tfrac{1}{6} \pi h^3$$

But

$$r_1 = \frac{D}{2} \text{ and } r_2 = 0$$

$$\therefore V = \frac{1}{2} h\pi \frac{D^2}{4} + \frac{1}{6} \pi h^3 = \pi h \left(\frac{D^2}{8} + \frac{h^2}{6} \right)$$

32. Find the volume of the head of a round-head machine screw if the diameter of the head is 0.731 in. and the height is 0.279 in.

Ans. 0.070 cu. in.

Fig. 213.

33. The water tank shown in Fig. 213 consists of a cylinder with a hemisphere below. The diameter is 20 ft., and the height of the cylindrical part is 22 ft. Find the capacity of the tank in gallons.

Ans. 67,369 gal.

CHAPTER XVIII

VARIOUS OTHER SOLIDS

200. Anchor ring.—A ring formed of a cylinder bent into a circular form, as in Fig. 214, is called an **anchor ring or torus.**
The mean length of the rod in such a ring is the circumference of a circle of radius ON.

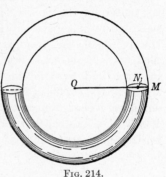

Any cross section of such a ring will be a circle. Since the ring may be considered as a cylinder bent into circular form, the area of the surface is the lateral area of the surface of the cylinder that forms the ring and equals $2\pi \times ON \times$ circumference of a cross section. If $ON = R$,

FIG. 214.

and the radius of the cross section NM is r, we have for the area the formula

59] $$A = 2\pi R \times 2\pi r = 4\pi^2 Rr$$

The volume is the same as the volume of a cylinder with an altitude that is equal to the mean circumference of the ring; hence the following:

60] $$V = 2\pi R \times \pi r^2 = 2\pi^2 Rr^2$$

These rules may be generalized so as to apply to *any circular ring*. In general, the area of the surface equals the perimeter of the cross section times the circumference drawn through the center of gravity of the cross section. The volume equals the area of the cross section times the circumference drawn through the center of gravity of the cross section. This means that the cross section may be a square, a triangle, or any other shape; but it is necessary to be able to find the center of gravity of the cross section.

If the meaning of the term center of gravity is not understood, one may gain a fair idea of it, at least for an area, by thinking of the center of gravity as the balancing point of the area. For instance, a circular piece of tin would balance on a pencil point if it rested with its center on the pencil point. A square piece of tin would likewise be balanced by placing its center on the point of support. Any triangle could be balanced by placing it so that the point of support was under the point of the triangle that is the intersection of the medians. If one could take any irregular-shaped piece of thin material and by trial find its balancing point, that point would be the center of gravity of the piece. Any solid of any shape has a center of gravity, but it is not so easily determined. If a wire, a baseball bat, or a billiard cue were balanced in a horizontal position on one's finger, the center of gravity would be over the finger.

EXERCISES

1. The cross section of a wedding ring is a circle of $\frac{1}{16}$ in. in radius. The inner radius of this torus is $\frac{3}{8}$ in. If the ring is solid gold, find its weight. *Ans.* 0.34 + troy oz.

2. If a solid cork float is a torus with ON equal to 1 ft. and NM equal to 4 in., Fig. 214, find its weight. *Ans.* 33 lb. approx.

3. In Exercise 2, 1000 of the floats are to be painted; find the number of square feet of painted surface. *Ans.* 13,159.

4. The top part of a smokestack is an anchor ring. The circular cross section has a radius of 4 in. The inner radius of the ring is 3 ft. Find the amount of concrete in the ring. *Ans.* 12,633 cu. in.

5. The cross section of the rim of a flywheel is a rectangle 6 by 8 in. the shorter dimension being in the diameter of the wheel. The wheel is 22 ft. in outer diameter. Find the volume of the rim and its weight if of cast iron. *Ans.* 22.515 cu. ft.; 10,132 lb.

6. Find the weight of a cast-iron water main 12 ft. in length, 2 ft. in outer diameter, and 1 in. thick. Solve by considering it both as a ring and as a hollow cylinder. *Ans.* 2710 lb. approx.

7. Find the area of the surface and the volume of a ring of outer diameter 10 in., made of round iron 1 in. in diameter. What is its weight at 0.28 lb. per cubic inch? *Ans.* 88.83 sq. in.; 22.207 cu. in.; 6.218 lb.

8. An anchor ring, 13 in. in outer diameter, of $1\frac{1}{4}$-in. round iron, has the same volume as what length of a bar $1\frac{1}{4}$ by $1\frac{1}{2}$ in. in cross section?
Ans. 24.16 in.

9. Find the weight of an anchor ring of cast iron, outer diameter 3 ft., the iron being circular in cross section and 6 in. in diameter. (Use 450 lb. per cubic foot.) *Ans.* 693.9 lb.

201. Prismatoids.—A **prismatoid** is a solid whose bases are parallel polygons and whose faces are quadrilaterals or triangles. As special cases: (*a*) one base may be a point, in which case the prismatoid is a pyramid; or (*b*) one base may be a line,

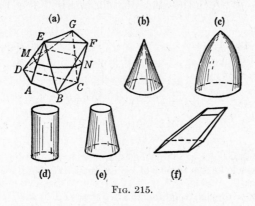

Fig. 215.

n which case it is wedge shaped. The rule for finding the volumes of prismatoids holds in many cases when the faces become curved surfaces and the prismatoid has become a cone, frustum of a cone, a cylinder, a sphere, a spindle of some kind, or one of various other forms that cannot well be described here. The rule is as follows:

RULE.—*To find the volume of a prismatoid, add together the areas of the two bases and four times the area of a section midway between them and parallel to them, then multiply the sum by one-sixth the perpendicular distance between the bases.*

The rule may be stated in the formula

[61] $V = \frac{1}{6}h(B_1 + 4M + B_2)$

where

    B_1 and B_2 = the area of the two bases.

        M = the area of the mid-section.

In Fig. 215 are given forms to which the rule for the volume

of a prismatoid will apply.   The dimensions of the mid-section may be found by actually measuring the lines or by computing them.

Example.—By formula [61], find the volume of a frustum of a pyramid in which the bases are regular hexagons 10 and 6 in. on a side, respectively, and in which the whole altitude is 18 in.   (See Fig. 216.)

Fig. 216.

Solution: $AB = \frac{1}{2}(10 \text{ in.} + 6 \text{ in.}) = 8 \text{ in.}$

    Area of lower base $= 5^2 \times 1.732 \times 6 = B_1$

    Area of upper base $= 3^2 \times 1.732 \times 6 = B_2$

  $4 \times$ area of mid-section $= 4 \times 4^2 \times 1.732 \times 6 = 4M$

      $\therefore B_1 + 4M + B_2 = 1018.416$

and

    $V = \frac{1}{6} \times 18 \times 1018.416 = 3055.2 \text{ cu. in.}$ *Ans.*

EXERCISES

1. Use the rule for the volume of a prismatoid, and find the volume of the following:

    (1) A cube with edge equal to x.

    (2) A right circular cylinder with radius and height equal to r and h, respectively.

Fig. 217.

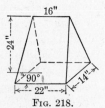

Fig. 218.

    (3) A right circular cone with radius r and altitude h.

    (4) A hemisphere of radius r.

2. Use formula [**61**] to find the volume of the solid shown in Fig. 217.

Ans. 3420 cu. in.

3. Use formula [**61**] to find the volume of the solid shown in Fig. 218.

Ans. 3630 cu. in.

4. A concrete pier for a railway bridge has the dimensions shown in Fig. 219, the bases being rectangles with semicircles. Find the number of cubic yards of concrete in 21 such piers. *Ans.* 793.3.

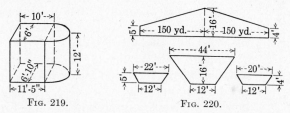

Fig. 219.   Fig. 220.

5. A railroad cut has the dimensions given in Fig. 220, which shows the vertical section and three cross sections. Find the volume of the earth removed in cubic yards. *Ans.* 7972⅔ cu. yd.

PART THREE

Algebra

CHAPTER XIX

INTRODUCTION TO ALGEBRA

202. This and the following chapters of Part III are devoted to the subject of algebra. If one wishes, they may be studied before the chapters on geometry. However, familiarity with the formulas used in geometry will help in grasping the meaning and uses of the forms used in algebra.

The understanding of any subject in mathematics presupposes a clear and definite knowledge of the preceding subjects upon which it is based. One cannot "burn his bridges" behind him as he advances in mathematics and hope to master more advanced subjects. It is because of this dependence of each subject upon what precedes that "there is no royal road" to mathematics and that the study is discouraging to weak and indolent minds, those who are not able and willing to master each subject as presented.

In mathematics, the attempt is made to do certain things more easily and in less time than they can otherwise be done. In arithmetic, many processes were learned that saved time and labor. In performing these processes, certain signs and symbols were used to express the ideas. New signs and symbols were introduced as they were needed to express the new ideas that were involved.

Thus, there were used the numerals 0, 1, 2, 3, 4, 5, 6, 7, 8, and 9; the letters of the alphabet; and various signs among which are $+$, $-$, $\times$, $\div$, (), and $\sqrt{}$.

203. Algebra.—The subject of **algebra** is a continuation of arithmetic. Arithmetic deals with number; so does algebra. Number is not essential in geometry, for geometric figures can be constructed, compared, and studied without numbers. It is when they are measured and computations made that numbers are used.

This algebra of number, as we may call it, is an old subject and was slowly formed through many centuries. The object of algebra is to investigate the properties of number and deal with its relations and combinations. It deals with the subjects to which it is applied by means of numbers. It is then of the greatest importance that one should examine the idea of number and clarify its meaning to himself.

In the study of algebra we shall expect that many new, simpler, and more powerful methods of procedure will be developed; in fact, this is the chief aim in continuing the study of mathematics.

From time to time as we proceed, we shall find it convenient to add to the symbols and signs, in order that we may express new ideas or perform new processes.

204. Numbers.—Many of the numbers used, especially those used in practical work, are obtained by counting a group of objects or from the measurement of something. However, the concept of number is fundamental and precedes counting and measurement instead of following them. The measure of an object, for instance, the length of a room, is the *number* of times that it contains a unit of measure. If 1 ft. is the unit of measure used, the measure of the length of a room 20 ft. long is the number 20. Number is connected with a group of things by counting them. It is customary, in answering a question regarding the measure of some object, to give the *measure* and also the *unit of measure*. For instance, the length of a room is 20 ft., the weight of a fish is 11 lb. or 5 kg. (See Art. 78.)

205. Definite numbers.—The numerals 0, 1, 2, 3, etc., have definite meanings. For instance, the symbol 4 represents the idea that we call four. It may be 4 yd., $4, 4 lb., or 4 of any other units but, in any case, is a **definite number.** We have learned that the letter π represents a definite number, the ratio of the circumference to the diameter of a circle. This cannot be expressed exactly by the numerals 1, 2, 3, etc., but has, none the less, a fixed value.

206. General numbers.—We have used the letter b to represent the number of units in the base of a triangle. Its value changed for different triangles; that is, it represented in a general way the length of the base of a triangle. Its value might be given as 10 ft., 6 in., or any number of any sized units of length. Likewise, r represents the radius of a circle; but when it occurs in the formula $A = \pi r^2$, we do not think of a particular value for it. Such an idea as we represent by b or by r cannot be represented by the numerals. The idea is a **general number-idea.** It is usually represented by a letter of the alphabet.

In a particular discussion, the letter or letters used stand for the same value throughout the discussion. For example, when we are considering a particular circle, the letter r represents a definite length, as 10 ft.

207. Signs.—The signs $+$, $-$, $\times$, and $\div$ are **signs of operation.** They continue to have the same meaning as in arithmetic. As we have already seen, the sign $\times$ is not often expressed where a multiplication is indicated between numbers expressed by letters. The symbol $(\cdot)$ may be used instead; but usually no sign is expressed. Thus, $a \times b$ is written $a \cdot b$ or simply ab. Similarly, $2axy$ means 2 times a times x times y.

The **signs of grouping** are the **parentheses** ( ), the **brackets** [ ], the **braces** { }, and the **vinculum** ————. The first three are placed around the parts grouped, and the vinculum is usually placed over what is grouped. They all indicate the same thing; namely, the parts enclosed are to be taken as a single quantity.

Thus, $12 - (10 - 4)$ indicates that 4 is to be subtracted from 10 and then the remainder is to be taken from 12. Hence $12 - (10 - 4) = 6$.

Exactly the same thing is indicated by $12 - [10 - 4]$, $12 - \{10 - 4\}$, and $12 - \overline{10 - 4}$.

The vinculum is most frequently used with the radical sign. Thus, $\sqrt{6425}$.

It is to be noted that in the form $\dfrac{7 - 4}{3 + 4}$ the horizontal line serves as a vinculum and as a sign of division. It thus performs three duties: (1) indicates a division, (2) binds together the numbers in the numerator, and (3) binds together the numbers in the denominator.

In performing the operations in a problem containing the signs of grouping, the operations within the grouping signs must be considered first.

208. Algebraic expression.—An **algebraic expression** is any expression that represents a number by means of the signs and symbols of algebra.

A **numerical algebraic expression** is one made up wholly of numerals and signs. A **literal algebraic expression** is one that contains letters.

Thus, $14 + 13 - (4 + 3)$ and $3ab - 4cd$ are algebraic expressions; the first is numerical, and the second is literal.

The value of an algebraic expression is the number that it represents.

209. Coefficient.—If we have such an expression as $8abx$, 8, a, b, and x are factors of the expression. Any one of these factors or the product of any two or more of them is called the **coefficient** of the remaining part.

Thus, $8ab$ may be considered the coefficient of x, or $8a$ the coefficient of bx, but usually, by the coefficient, we mean the numerical part only. It may then be called the **numerical coefficient.** If no numerical part is expressed, 1 is understood. Thus, $1axy$ is the same as axy.

210. Power, exponent.—If all the factors in a product are equal as $a \cdot a \cdot a \cdot a$, the product of the factors is called a **power** of one of them. The form $a \cdot a \cdot a \cdot a$ is usually written

a^4. The small number to the right and above indicates how many times a is taken as a factor. (See Arts. 88 and 89.)

In the foregoing power, a is called the **base** and 4 the **exponent.**

The **exponent** of a **power** is a *number* written at the right and a little above the base. When it is a positive whole number, it shows how many times the base is to be taken as a factor.

Thus, c^2 is read c square or c second power and indicates that c is taken twice as a factor; c^3 is read c cube or c third power and indicates that c is taken three times as a factor; c^4 is read c fourth power and indicates that c is taken four times as a factor; c^n is read c nth power or c exponent n and indicates that c is taken n times as a factor.

When no exponent is written, the exponent is understood to be 1. Thus, a is the same as a^1.

211. A **term** in an algebraic expression is a part of the expression not separated by a plus or a minus sign. Furthermore, the $+$ or the $-$ sign that precedes the term is a part of the term.

Thus, in $4ax + 3c - d$, $+4ax$, $+3c$, and $-d$ are terms.

It is convenient to have names for algebraic expressions having different numbers of terms. A **monomial** is an algebraic expression consisting of one term; a **binomial** consists of two terms; and a **trinomial** consists of three terms. Any algebraic expression of two or more terms is called a **polynomial** or a **multinomial.**

Terms that are exactly the same or that differ only in their coefficients are called **like terms** or **similar terms.** Terms that differ otherwise than in their coefficients, are **unlike,** or **dissimilar,** terms.

Thus, $6a^3x^2$, $-7a^3x^2$, and $16a^3x^2$ are like terms; whereas $6ax^2$, $-7a^3x^2$, and $16ayz$ are unlike terms.

212. Remarks.—The exercises of this chapter are to recall the meanings and uses of signs and symbols and to fix in mind the new ideas that have been given here. The doing of these exercises must not be slighted by the student. He should become familiar with the mathematical way of stating ideas in order that he may be prepared for the work that comes later.

EXERCISES

Find the value of each of the following:
1. $2 + 7 - 3 + 5 - 1 + 9$.   *Ans.* 19.
2. $8 + (3 \times 5) - 2(5 - 9)$.   *Ans.* 31.
3. $10(9 + 8) - 7(6 - 5) + 11$.   *Ans.* 174.
4. $12 + 21 - 3(7 - 5) + 2(6 \times 8)$.   *Ans.* 123.
5. $175 - 152 + 11(8 \times 11) - 5$.   *Ans.* 986.
6. $[144 \div (3 \times 12)] + 4(2 \div 4)$.   *Ans.* 6.

In the following list, name the monomials, the binomials, and the trinomials. Which of them are multinomial?

7. $at^2 + vt$.
8. $x^2 + bx + c$.
9. $ma - nu^2$.
10. $200a^2bc^3$.
11. $x^2 - 20 + y^2$.
12. $11x^2 - 12y^2$.
13. $87d^2t^3$.
14. $PLAN + 144r^2$.
15. $ax^3 - ay^3$.
16. $2\pi r^2 + 2\pi rh$.
17. $xyz - abc + 4$.
18. $45 + 73x$.
19. $rt + \frac{2}{3}at^3 - 0.9s$.
20. $at - bt + ct^2$.
21. $12c^2 + CD^2 - 32h^2$.

22. What is the coefficient of x in Exercise 18? In Exercise 8? Of t^3 in Exercise 13? Of b in Exercise 10? Of s in Exercise 19? Of y^2 in Exercise 12?

23. Name the numerical coefficients in Exercises 12, 19, and 21.

24. Name the exponents in Exercises 10, 15, and 19.

25. How many factors are there in Exercise 10? In Exercise 13?

Write the following algebraic symbols:

26. The result of adding 9 times x to a times y.

27. The result of subtraction 6 times h from 34 times k.

28. The product of 5 times x^4 times w cube.

29. The product of 3 times a fifth power times s cube times t.

30. The product of the sum of h and k times the difference found by subtracting h from k.   *Ans.* $(h + k)(h - k)$.

31. The square of the sum of 4, x, and y.   *Ans.* $(4 + x + y)^2$.

32. The quotient of the sum of a and b divided by the difference when a is subtracted from b.   *Ans.* $\dfrac{a + b}{a - b}$.

33. Express the product of v^3 and the sum of the two fractions, 5 divided by x and 6 divided by y.   *Ans.* $v^3 \left(\dfrac{5}{x} + \dfrac{6}{y} \right).$

34. Express the product of the sum of p, $3q$, and $5r$ and the sum of $4p$, $6q$, and $8r$.   *Ans.* $(p + 3q + 5r)(4p + 6q + 8r).$

35. Express the square of the sum of u and v plus the cube of the sum of a, b, and c.   *Ans.* $(u + v)^2 + (a + b + c)^3.$

Translate the following algebraic expressions into words:

36. $10 + ax.$

37. $x^2 - 2pm.$

38. $(a + bt) \div abt.$

39. $7x - 5(4a - b)c.$

40. $al + b(c \div d).$

41. $\dfrac{x^2 - y^2}{(x - y)^2}.$

42. $(x^2 - t^2)(x - t)^2.$

43. $[a(b - c) - d] + h^2.$

44. $a(b + c^2).$

45. $3.4 + (4.3 - 9).$

46. $\dfrac{1}{x - y} \div \dfrac{1}{z}.$

47. $[1 \div x(3 - y)]t^3.$

48. Write the following in a more compact form by using exponents.

(1) $9aaabbbc.$

(2) $(3)(3)xyyzzzz.$

(3) $4(2)2aac - 16hhkkk.$

(4) $5abcabc + 10abbc - 15abbc.$

49. Write the following in more compact form by using exponents:

(1) $2(2)(2)(a + b)(a + b).$

(2) $11(11)[ax](ax)11.$

(3) $a(ab)[a(ab)]ab.$

(4) $(ab - c)(ab - c)(ab - c).$

50. Express each of the following as a single number without an exponent [NOTE: $(10)^4 = 10(10)(10)(10) = 10,000$]:

(1) $2(10)^4.$ *Ans.* 20,000.

(2) $2 \div 10^3.$ *Ans.* 0.002.

(3) $a(10)^{10}.$ *Ans.* 10,000,000,000a.

(4) $9.37 \times 10^7.$ *Ans.* 93,700,000.

(5) $6.27 \times 10^2.$ *Ans.* 627.

(6) $2.8 \div (10)^{11}.$ *Ans.* 0.000000000028.

51. Express each of the following large numbers as a small number times a power of 10: [NOTE: $800,000 = 8 \times 10 \times 10 \times 10 \times 10 \times 10 = 8(10)^5.$]

(1) 500,000.   *Ans.* $5(10)^5.$

(2) 480,000,000.   *Ans.* $4.8(10)^8.$

(3) 123,000.   *Ans.* $1.23(10)^5.$

(4) 10,100,000.   *Ans.* $1.01(10)^7.$

(5) 3,468,100,000. *Ans.* $3.4681(10)^9$.

(6) 9,463,780,000,000,000. *Ans.* $9.46378(10)^{15}$.

52. Separate into prime factors and express compactly by using exponents [NOTE: $36 = 4 \times 9 = 2^2 \times 3^2$; 2 and 3 are prime numbers]:

(1) 60. *Ans.* $2^2 \times 3 \times 5$.

(2) 1080. *Ans.* $2^3 \times 3^3 \times 5$.

(3) 6084. *Ans.* $2^2 \times 3^2 \times 13^2$.

(4) 14,400. *Ans.* $2^6 \times 3^2 \times 5^2$.

53. Find the value of:

(1) $2^2 3^3$.

(2) $3^2 (10)^3$.

(3) $5^2 6^3 7^2$.

54. If $a = 4$, what is the value of $2a$? Of $4a^2$? Of $10a^4$?

55. What is the value of $12a$ if a is 3.5? 1.2? $6\frac{2}{3}$? 0? $8\frac{1}{3}$?

56. If I have d dollars and you have four times as much, how many dollars have you?

57. If a team wins 11 games in one month and 15 games in the second month, how many games have they won? If they win n games one week and m the next week, how many games have they won these two weeks? They have now won $26 + (n + m)$ games, but the next week they lose p games. How many games have they now to their credit as won?

58. If s is the number of feet in the length of a line, how many feet are there in twice this length? In half the length? In three-fourths the length?

59. A boy can run a yards in 1 sec. How far can he run in 10 sec.? In c sec.? In 1 min.? In d min.?

60. If a train runs a miles in c hr., how far does it run in 1 hr.? In q hr.? *Ans.* $\frac{a}{c}$ miles; $\frac{aq}{c}$ miles.

61. A grocer receives c cents for 1 lb. of tea. How much does he receive for 20 lb.? For p lb.?

62. A boy can walk m miles an hour. How many miles can he walk in c hr.? In d min.? How many feet can he walk in e min.?

Ans. mc; $\frac{md}{60}$; $88me$.

63. What number does $10t + u$ represent if $t = 8$ and $u = 3$?

Ans. 83.

64. What number does $100h + 10t + u$ represent if $h = 4$, $t = 5$, and $u = 6$? If $h = 7$, $t = 8$, and $u = 0$? *Ans.* 456; 780.

65. What number does $1000a + 100b + 10c + d$ represent if $a = 5$, $b = 7$, $c = 9$, and $d = 1$? *Ans.* 5791.

66. If a, b, c, and d have the same values as in Exercise 65, what number does $abcd$ represent? What does 5791 mean? *Ans.* 5791.

67. If u, t, and h stand, respectively, for the units, tens, and hundreds figures of a number, give a general expression for a number consisting of two figures; for one consisting of three figures.

Ans. $10t + u$; $100h + 10t + u$.

68. Is twice any whole number always an even number? If n is any whole number, represent any even number.

69. If n is any whole number, does $2n - 1$ represent an even number or an odd number? Does $2n + 1$ represent an even number or an odd number?

70. What interesting conclusions can be drawn from the following:
1; $(1 + 3)$; $(1 + 3 + 5)$; $(1 + 3 + 5 + 7)$; $(1 + 3 + 5 + 7 + 9)$;
$[1 + 3 + 5 + 7 + 9 + \cdots (2n - 1)]$.

Ans. All are perfect squares.

213. Formulas.—In previous chapters, especially in those parts dealing with geometry, many formulas have been used. In Art. 118, a formula was defined as a rule stated in letters and other symbols. We may now define a formula as a rule written in algebraic language. The rule is the statement of the same thing in words. The formula is the rule translated into algebraic language.

To some extent the derivation of the formulas previously used was made clear; but one cannot thoroughly understand the derivation of formulas and the changes that can be made in them without a considerable knowledge of algebra. It is only through a thorough understanding of the *equation* that one gains the ability to change a formula to other forms that are more convenient for certain computations. The equation, in its turn, requires an understanding of the fundamental operations, factoring, and fractions in algebra for its manipulation. For these reasons we shall expect a more complete treatment of formulas later.

214. Evaluation of algebraic expressions and formulas.— To evaluate an algebraic expression is to find its value. In Art. 208, it was stated that the value of an algebraic expression is the number that it represents. This value can be a *definite* number only when definite values are assigned to the letters in the expression. Much drill has already been given in substituting values for the letters in formulas and computing results in problems in geometry.

A *numerical algebraic expression* has a definite value that may be found by performing the indicated operations.

Thus, $21 - (10 + 3) + 14 - 10 = 21 - 13 + 14 - 10 = 12$.

A *literal algebraic expression* has a definite value depending upon the values given the letters.

Thus, the expression abc, which means $a \times b \times c$, has a definite value if $a = 3$, $b = 4$, and $c = 10$. Putting these values in place of the letters, we have $3 \times 4 \times 10 = 120$.

If any other set of values are assigned to a, b, and c, a definite value will be obtained for the product.

Example 1.—Find the value of $\pi r^2 h$ if $\pi = 3.1416$, $r = 6$, and $h = 10$.

Substituting these values for the letters, the expression becomes $3.1416 \times 6^2 \times 10 = 1130.976$, the definite value.

Example 2.—Find the value of $a^3 + 3a^2b + 3ab^2 + b^3$, when $a = 2$ and $b = 3$.

Substituting the values in place of the letters,

$$a^3 + 3a^2b + 3ab^2 + b^3 = 2^3 + 3 \times 2^2 \times 3 + 3 \times 2$$
$$\times 3^2 + 3^3 = 125, \text{ the definite value}$$

Example 3.—Find the value of $\sqrt{s(s - a)(s - b)(s - c)}$ if $s = \dfrac{a + b + c}{2}$ and $a = 36$, $b = 22$, and $c = 20$.

Substituting in $s = \dfrac{a + b + c}{2}$,

$$s = \frac{36 + 22 + 20}{2} = 39$$

Substituting in $\sqrt{s(s - a)(s - b)(s - c)}$, we have

$$\sqrt{39(39 - 36)(39 - 22)(39 - 20)} = \sqrt{37791} = 194.4-$$
$$Ans.$$

EXERCISES

1. Express without exponents and find the value of the following:

(1) $2^2 3^3$.   *Ans.* 108.

(2) $4^2 5^3 10^2$.   *Ans.* 200,000.

(3) $3^2 7^2 11^2$.

(4) $4^2 3^3 2^4$.

(5) $11(9^2)3^2$.

(6) $12^2 13^2 3^4$.

If $a = 3$, $b = 4$, and $c = 10$, find the value of the following:

2. $2abc^2$.   *Ans.* 2400.

3. $(2abc)^2$.   *Ans.* 57,600.

4. $3a^2 - b^2$.   *Ans.* 11.

5. $3(a^2 b^2 - c^2)$.   *Ans.* 132.

6. $(3ab^2 - c)^2$.   *Ans.* 17,956.

7. $(3a + b - c)^2$.   *Ans.* 9.

8. $3a + (b + c)^2$.   *Ans.* 205.

9. $(ab)^2(c - b)^2$.   *Ans.* 5184.

10. $[ab(c - b)^2]$.   *Ans.* 5184.

11. $(a + b)^2(c - b)^2$.   *Ans.* 1764.

12. $a + b^2(c - b)^2$.   *Ans.* 579.

13. $[c + (a + b)][c - (a + b)]$.

                    Ans. 51.

14. $(a + b)^3$.   *Ans.* 343.

15. $a^3 + 3a^2 b + 3ab^2 + b^3$.

                    Ans. 343.

16. Find the value of the following when $d = 9$:

(1) $S = \pi d^2$.   *Ans.* 254.4696$-$.

(2) $V = \frac{1}{6}\pi d^3$.   *Ans.* 381.7044$-$.

17. Find the value of the following when $r = 5$ and $h = 10$:

(1) $S = 2\pi r h$.   *Ans.* 314.16$-$.

(2) $V = \pi r^2 h$.   *Ans.* 785.4$-$.

If $a = 1$, $b = 3$, $c = 5$, and $d = 0$, find the numerical values of the following:

18. $a^2 + 2b^2 + 3c^2 + 4d^2$.   *Ans.* 94.

19. $a^4 + 4a^3 b + 6a^2 b^2 - 4ab^3 + b^4$.   *Ans.* 40.

20. $\dfrac{12a^3 - b^2}{3a^2} + \dfrac{2c^2}{a + b^2} - \dfrac{a + b^2 + c^3}{5b^6}$.   *Ans.* 5.

Suggestion.—Remember that the lines in the fractions are vinculums and bind the terms in the numerators or denominators together, as well as indicate division. The multiplications, additions, and subtractions indicated in the numerators and denominators must be performed first. Thus, after substituting the values,

$$\frac{12 \times 1^3 - 3^2}{3 \times 1^2} + \frac{2 \times 5^2}{1 + 3^2} - \frac{1 + 3^2 + 5^3}{5 \times 3^3} = \frac{3}{3} + \frac{50}{10} - \frac{135}{135}$$

21. $(c^2 - b^2 - a^2) \div (abc - b^2)$.   *Ans.* $\frac{5}{2}$.

22. $(c - b - a)^2 \div (abc - b)^2$.   *Ans.* $\frac{1}{144}$.

23. $\dfrac{10ab + cd}{(d + 2ab - c)^2} + \dfrac{(2c)^2}{a^2 + b} - \dfrac{8a^2}{2b^2}.$ *Ans.* $54\dfrac{5}{9}.$

If $a = 1$, $b = 2$, $c = 3$, $d = 4$, and $e = 5$, evaluate the following:

24. $\sqrt{(a + c)}\ \sqrt{(d + e)}.$ *Ans.* 6.

25. $\sqrt{(c^2 + d^2)} - e.$ *Ans.* 0.

26. $\dfrac{\sqrt{(a + c + e)} + \sqrt[3]{(c + e)}}{b^2 + 2be + e^2 + (a + c + d)^2}.$ *Ans.* $\dfrac{5}{113}.$

27. $(a + b)(b + c) - (b + c)(c + d) + (c + d)(d + e).$ *Ans.* 43.

28. $(a - 2b + 3c)^2 - (b - 2c + 3d)^2 + (c - 2d + 3e)^2.$ *Ans.* 72.

29. $\sqrt{4c^2 + 5d^2 + e}.$ *Ans.* 11.   **30.** $\sqrt{e^2 + d^2 + c^2 - a^2}.$ *Ans.* 7.

31. Evaluate $(ac - bd)\sqrt{a^2bc + b^2cd + c^2ad - 2}$ if $a = 1$, $b = 2$, $c = 3$, and $d = 0$. *Ans.* 6.

32. Find the value of the expression $\dfrac{a(b - c)}{d(e - b)}$, when $a = 500$, $b = 98$, $c = 8$, $d = 150$, and $e = 100$. *Ans.* 150.

33. Given $J = \dfrac{ab}{T} \div (c - d)$, find J, when $T = 273$, $a = 1{,}013{,}250$, $b = (1 \div 0.001293)$, $c = 0.2375$, and $d = 0.1684$.   (See Art. 303.)

Ans. 4.188(10)[7] approx.

34. If A stands for the number of square units in the area of a circle, and r stands for the number of lineal units in the radius, state in words the following formula: $A = \pi r^2$.

35. In the preceding formula, can r be any number that we please to make it? Can A? If we make $r = 5$ in., can we then make A anything that we please? Can π be any number that we wish to make it? Is π a general number? Is A? Is r?

36. Using A, a, and b, state the following as a formula: The area of any triangle equals one-half the base times the altitude.

37. Write the following as a formula: The horsepower H of an electric machine is found by multiplying the number of volts V by the number of amperes I and dividing by 746.

38. To find the horsepower H of an engine, take the continued product of the mean effective pressure in pounds per square inch P, the length of the stroke in feet L, the area of the piston in square inches A, and the number of strokes per minute N, and divide the product by 33,000. Write this as a formula, and compare the length of the formula with that of the rule.

39. If S is the distance in miles between two cities, R the average rate in miles per hour that a car is driven, and T the time in hours that it takes to go from one city to the other, write a formula connecting S, R, and T. *Ans.* $S = RT$.

40. If P stands for the principal, I for the interest, t for the time in years, r for the rate in per cent, and A for the amount, translate the following formulas into words:

(1) $I = Prt.$

(2) $A = P + Prt.$

(3) $A = P + I.$

(4) $P = \dfrac{I}{rt}.$

(5) $t = \dfrac{I}{Pr}.$

(6) $r = \dfrac{I}{Pt}.$

(7) $r = \dfrac{A - P}{Pt}.$

41. State in words the process of adding two fractions having a common denominator. State the same as a formula, using a and b for the numerators and d for the common denominator.

42. Do the same as in Exercise 41, for subtracting fractions having a common denominator.

43. Translate the following into words:

(1) $\dfrac{a}{b} \div \dfrac{c}{d} = \dfrac{a}{b} \times \dfrac{d}{c}.$

(2) $\dfrac{n \times m}{d \times m} = \dfrac{n}{d}.$

(3) $\dfrac{n \div m}{d \div m} = \dfrac{n}{d}.$

(4) $\dfrac{n}{d} \times m = \dfrac{n \times m}{d}.$

44. Find the perimeter of each form in Fig. 221.

Ans. (1) $4x$; (2) $2(a + b)$; (3) $2(x + y) + 4b$;

(4) $2(b + c + d + y) + 4x$; $2(a + b + d)$.

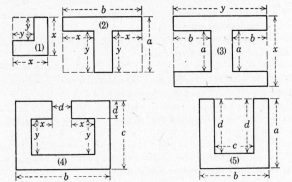

Fig. 221.

45. Find the area of each form in Fig. 221.

Ans. (1) $x^2 - y^2$; (2) $ab - 2xy$; (3) $xy - 2ab$;
(4) $bc - y(2x + d) - d^2$; (5) $ab - cb$.

46. Write the formula that states that a times the sum of b, c, and d equals s.

47. In Exercise 46, find s (1) if $a = 7$, $b = 6$, $c = 8$, and $d = 10$; (2) if $a = \frac{2}{3}$, $b = \frac{7}{8}$, $c = \frac{3}{4}$, and $d = \frac{7}{24}$. *Ans.* 168; $1\frac{5}{18}$.

48. Let L be the cost of a city lot and H the cost of the house on the lot. Write in algebraic symbols the fact that if \$500 is added to the cost of the lot and this sum is multiplied by 4, the total cost of the house and lot will be obtained. *Ans.* $4(L + 500) = H + L$.

49. Using b_1 and b_2 for the bases and h for the altitude, state the following as a formula: The area of a trapezoid equals one-half the sum of the two bases times the altitude. *Ans.* $A = \frac{1}{2}(b_1 + b_2)h$.

50. Using the formula of the preceding exercise, find the areas of the following trapezoids:

(1) $b_1 = 22.33$ in.; $b_2 = 46.39$ in.; $h = 26.43$ in. *Ans.* 908.13 sq. in.
(2) $b_1 = 7.203$ in.; $b_2 = 5.826$ in.; $h = 3.243$ in. *Ans.* 21.127 sq. in.

51. Write the formula stating that the area S of the surface of a sphere equals four times π times the square of the radius r. Use the formula, and find the area of the surface of a sphere 15 in. in radius.

Ans. 2827.4 sq. in.

52. Write a formula stating that the volume V of a sphere equals $\frac{4}{3}$ of π times the cube of the radius r. Use this formula, and find the volume of a sphere 12 in. in radius. *Ans.* 7238.2 cu. in.

53. Write a formula stating that the volume V of a rectangular solid equals the length l times the breadth b times the height h. Use this formula, and find the number of cubic feet in a room 40 by 30 by 12 ft.

Ans. 14,400.

54. If a man is thirty-five years old, what was his age a years ago? What will it be b years from now?

55. If x years was the age of a man a years ago, what is his age now? What will it be in c years from now?

Ans. $x + a$ years; $x + a + c$ years.

56. Write in algebraic language: x diminished by a; y increased by b; x divided by n; the nth part of x; one mth of a.

57. The sum of two numbers is a, and one of the numbers is x. What is the other number? Express one mth of the first plus one nth of the second number. *Ans.* $a - x$; $\dfrac{x}{m} + \dfrac{a - x}{n}$.

58. What is the next whole number larger than 10? If n is a whole number, what is the next larger whole number?

59. What is the next larger even number than 6? If $2n$ is an even number, what is the next larger even number? The next smaller?

60. If x is the first of two consecutive numbers, what is the second? What will represent each of three consecutive numbers if x stands for the middle one? *Ans.* $x + 1$; $x - 1$, x, $x + 1$.

61. Represent three consecutive even numbers if x is the middle one.
Ans. $x - 2$, x, $x + 2$.

62. If the length of a stick is a ft., how many inches is it in length? How many rods? How many miles? *Ans.* $12a$; $\dfrac{a}{16\frac{1}{2}}$; $\dfrac{a}{5280}$.

63. If d is the number of dollars that an article costs, what is the number of cents?

64. If a room is a yd., b ft., and c in. long, how many inches in length is it?

65. Given the product p and the multiplier m, find the multiplicand n.

66. Given the dividend d and the quotient q, find the divisor b.

67. Given the divisor d, the quotient q, and the remainder r, find the dividend D.

68. The difference between two numbers is n, and the smaller one is a; what is the larger?

69. A number exceeds a by c; what is the number? *Ans.* $a + c$.

70. Write in symbols that a exceeds b as much as c is less than d.
Ans. $a - b = d - c$.

71. Express in symbols that one-half of m equals the nth part of the sum of a, b, and c. *Ans.* $\dfrac{1}{2} m = \dfrac{a + b + c}{n}$.

72. If a cents is the price per quart for beans, what is the price per bushel?

73. The provisions that will keep a family of 9 persons 30 days will keep a family of 5 persons how many days? The provisions that will keep a family of a persons l days will keep b persons how many days?
Ans. 54; $\dfrac{al}{b}$.

74. If it takes m men d days to dig a ditch, how many days will it take c men to dig it? *Ans.* $\dfrac{md}{c}$.

75. How many pounds of sugar at c cents per pound will d dozen eggs at e cents per dozen buy? *Ans.* $\dfrac{de}{c}$.

76. A cubical tank e ft. on an edge will hold how many barrels if 1 bbl. equals 4.211 cu. ft.? *Ans.* $\dfrac{e^3}{4.211}$.

77. A box a ft. long, b ft. wide, and c ft. deep will hold how many bushels if 1 bu. equals 2150.42 cu. in.? *Ans.* $\dfrac{1728abc}{2150.42}$.

78. A man earned a dollars per day and his son b dollars. How many dollars did they both earn in a month if the man worked 26 days and the son 21 days? *Ans.* $26a + 21b$.

79. A man walks a miles in an hour; how many miles does he walk in h hr.? In m min.? How long will it take him to walk s miles?

80. If the European cash made up $\dfrac{P}{100}$ of the trading on the New York Stock Exchange from 1935 to 1937, and if the European traders invested D billion dollars for these two years, what was the total amount traded on the New York Stock Exchange for the whole world during 1935 and 1937? In fact, P equaled 9 and D equaled 11.4 (that is, 11.4 billion dollars) for the two years mentioned. Find the total amount traded for the two years. *Ans.* $126\frac{2}{3}$ billion dollars.

POSITIVE AND NEGATIVE NUMBERS

215. The degrees of temperature, indicated by the thermometer scale, are counted in two opposite directions from the zero point. We may speak of a temperature as so many degrees above or below zero. In mathematics, it is convenient to indicate that a temperature reading is above zero by placing a plus sign before the number, as $+30$ deg. Likewise a reading below zero is indicated by placing a minus sign before the number, as -10 deg. This method is even used in newspapers when giving temperatures with the thermometer showing readings both below and above zero. This use of these signs is different from the ordinary use in which they indicate addition and subtraction. Here they indicate the *sense* or *direction* in which the temperature is measured or counted from the zero reading.

One also frequently finds the signs $+$ and $-$ used in connection with stock quotations to show that there has been an increase or a decrease in the prices for the day. In mathematics, it is common practice to make use of the $+$ and $-$ signs to show these qualities of numbers.

A number preceded by a $+$ sign is called a **positive number**, and one preceded by a $-$ sign, a **negative number**. Two numbers so related, one positive and one negative, may be called **relative numbers**. The following are further examples of relative numbers. They will help to fix the negative number-idea in mind.

Time is commonly measured forward and backward from a certain date. This might be shown by using the + and − signs.

Thus, A.D. 1930 might be written +1930, whereas 325 B.C. might be written −325.

A force acting in one direction and another in an opposite direction are designated as a + and a − force, respectively. Money gained and resources are +, and money lost and liabilities are −.

The negative number is a good illustration of the long centuries that must sometimes elapse before an idea can become commonly accepted by people in general. In early times many students of algebra encountered the negative number. Usually this was in solving an equation. Sometimes an attempt was made to explain the significance of the new number, but usually it was pushed aside and labeled inadequate, absurd, impossible, or fictitious. No decided progress in bringing about its general acceptance was made until a picture of it was presented to the eye.

216. Need of negative number.—The desirability of extending the number system so as to include negative numbers may be seen from the following subtractions, where the minuend remains the same but the subtrahend increases by steps of 1 as we pass from left to right. This causes the difference to diminish by steps of 1 from left to right. When the difference becomes less than zero, we indicate it by the sign − placed before the number.

$$
\begin{array}{cccccccc}
6 & 6 & 6 & 6 & 6 & 6 & 6 & 6 \\
3 & 4 & 5 & 6 & 7 & 8 & 9 & 10 \\
\hline
3 & 2 & 1 & 0 & -1 & -2 & -3 & -4 \text{ etc.}
\end{array}
$$

217. Representation of negative and positive numbers.—For convenience, the positive and negative numbers may be represented on a horizontal line as in Fig. 222; the +, or positive, numbers to the right of a certain point, called zero and the −, or negative, numbers to the left of the zero point. This method of representing them is very convenient in explaining addition and subtraction.

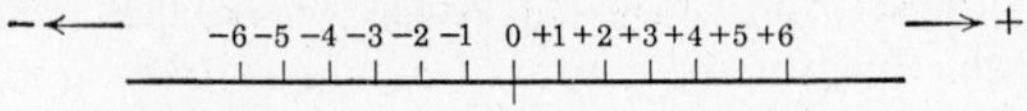

Fig. 222.

It should be carefully noted that toward the right is the **positive direction** and toward the left is the **negative direction** no matter from what point we start.

The idea of negative number is opposite to that of positive number. For example, if a man walks 5 miles east, or in the positive direction, and then 5 miles west, or in the negative direction, he is at the starting point. The negative distance has destroyed the opposite or positive.

218. Definitions.—Positive and negative numbers, together with zero, form the system called **algebraic numbers**. In this book the term "algebraic numbers" is used in a general sense but is more expressive for the beginner.

The **absolute** or **numerical value** of a number is the value that it has without reference to its sign.

Thus, +5 and −5 have the same absolute value 5.

The signs + and − when used to show direction or sense are called **signs of quality** to distinguish them from the **signs of operation** used indicate an addition or a subtraction.

The sign +, used as a sign of quality, is usually omitted but the sign −, when a sign of quality, is expressed.

To show that the sign is one of quality, it is sometimes written with the number and enclosed in parentheses, as (−3) (+4). (−5) + (+2) indicates that a −5 is to be added to a +2.

219. Remarks on numbers.—What is the negative number and why do we need to trouble ourselves about it? The examples given above should help us to get the idea of negative number and to see how it is forced upon us when we try to subtract a larger number from a smaller one.

In mathematics when a new number-idea appears, the first thing to do is to represent it by a symbol and, second, to find a way of operating with it. That is, we must determine how to add, subtract, multiply, and divide such numbers.

One of the first things that we did in arithmetic was to determine methods of operating with positive whole numbers; then a little later, we did the same thing for the fractional numbers. In fact, much of the time spent in studying mathematics is spent in finding how to add, subtract, multiply, and divide numbers of different kinds, whole, positive, negative, fractional, and combinations of these.

It now remains to devise methods and rules for operating with algebraic numbers. This must be done if possible in such a way that no old rules or principles shall be violated. The student is asked to consider carefully each step taken and *to make every part seem reasonable.* The operating with negative numbers is one of the ways in which algebra is an extension of arithmetic.

EXERCISES

1. Suppose that longitude east of Greenwich 180° to the international date line is designated by positive direction, whereas longitude west of Greenwich 180° to the international date line is designated by negative direction. Designate by means of the proper sign the fact that New York is 74° west longitude. Two places are (1) 10° east longitude and (2) 88° west longitude. What sign may be used instead of the words east and west to designate the longitude of each of these two places?

2. From the equator to the north pole the latitude may be designated as positive, and from the equator to the south pole the latitude would be thought of as negative. Chicago is 41°45′ north latitude, and Melbourne 37° south latitude. Designate each of these two cities with its proper algebraic sign.

3. If the weight of a stone that weighs 100 lb. is written +100 lb., how may the upward lift of 500 lb. of a balloon be written?

4. A man weighs +180 lb. He enters a balloon with a lifting force of 400 lb. How may this lifting force be written?

5. A man overdraws his bank account.   How may the banker indicate this on his books?

6. What is meant by saying that a man is worth +$3000?   By −$2000?

7. If a man has a −$200, a +$300, and a −$100, what is he worth?

8. A boy earned $2.50 on Monday, $1.75 on Tuesday, 95 cents on Wednesday.   On Thursday he spent $1.40, and on Friday he spent 75 cents.   Write as a numerical algebraic expression the amount of money that the boy had left.

9. If a man has assets of $3000 and we represent it by a line 3 in. long drawn to the right of 0, how could we represent a liability of $1500?

10. A man walks 10 miles east and then 6 miles west.   Write this in symbols.

11. If a body is heated 37 deg. and then cooled 42 deg., indicate the facts in symbols.

12. Yesterday it was 12 deg. below zero; today it is 20 deg. above zero. Write these two numbers with their proper algebraic signs.

13. Remembering the positive and negative directions, draw a line; locate a zero point; and with a unit of 1 in. locate positive and negative numbers to the right and left of zero.   Start at +10, and go +2, −8, −3, +6, −10, +2, +1, and +3.   Where do you stop?   *Ans.* +3.

CHAPTER XX

ADDITION AND SUBTRACTION

220. Definitions.—The aggregate value of two or more algebraic numbers is called their **algebraic sum.** The process of finding this sum is called **addition.**

221. Addition of algebraic numbers.—If we wish to add 3 to 4, we start with 4 and count 3 more, arriving at 7 which is the sum. If we consider the system of algebraic numbers arranged on a horizontal line, Fig. 223, we add a positive num-

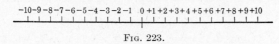

$$-10\,-9\,-8\,-7\,-6\,-5\,-4\,-3\,-2\,-1\quad 0\ +1\,+2\,+3\,+4\,+5\,+6\,+7\,+8\,+9\,+10$$

Fig. 223.

ber by starting with the number that we wish to add to and counting toward the right as many units as there are in the number added.

Thus, to add 3 to 4, we start at 4 and count 3 toward the right to 7.

To add $+5$ to -3, we start at -3 and proceed 5 units toward the right, arriving at $+2$.

To add $+3$ to -7, we start at -7 and proceed 3 units toward the right, arriving at -4.

Since adding -3 to $+7$ is the same as adding $+7$ to -3 the result of adding -3 to $+7$ is $+4$. In order to start with $+7$ and arrive at $+4$, we must move in the negative direction, or toward the left. Therefore, we conclude that to add a negative number, we go toward the left, that is, in the negative direction.

Thus, to add -4 to $+9$, we start at $+9$ and go 4 units toward the left, arriving at $+5$. To add -7 to $+2$, we start at $+2$ and go 7 units toward the left, arriving at -5. To add -4 to -5, we start with -5 and proceed 4 units toward the left arriving at -9.

313

The foregoing results are given here:

$$
\begin{array}{ccccccc}
+4 & -3 & -7 & +7 & +9 & +2 & -5 \\
+3 & +5 & +3 & -3 & -4 & -7 & -4 \\
\hline
+7 & +2 & -4 & +4 & +5 & -5 & -9
\end{array}
$$

222. Principles.—A careful consideration of the preceding operations will disclose the following principles:

(1) *The algebraic sum of two numbers with like signs is the sum of their absolute values, with the common sign prefixed.*

(2) *The algebraic sum of two numbers with unlike signs is the difference between their absolute values, with the sign of the one greater in absolute value prefixed.*

In adding three or more algebraic numbers, differing in signs, find the sum of the positive numbers and then the sum of the negative numbers by principle (1), and then add these sums by principle (2).

Thus, in finding the sum of $+2$, $+10$, -6, -3, -7, $+9$, we take $+2 + 10 + 9 = 21$ and $(-6) + (-3) + (-7) = -16$, then $+21 + (-16) = +5$, the sum.

223. Subtraction of algebraic numbers.—Subtraction is the *inverse* of addition. If we are given *one* of two numbers and their *sum*, subtraction is the process of finding the other number.

In arithmetic it is assumed that the minuend is always greater than the subtrahend. In the subtraction of algebraic numbers not only may we have the subtrahend larger than the minuend when the numbers are positive, but either or both subtrahend and minuend may be negative numbers.

Since subtraction is the inverse of addition, if we consider the system of algebraic numbers arranged along the horizontal line as in Art. 221, we have the following principles:

(1) *Subtracting a positive number is equivalent to adding a numerically equal negative number.*

(2) *Subtracting a negative number is equivalent to adding a numerically equal positive number.*

These may be combined in the following:

RULE.—*Subtraction of algebraic numbers is performed by considering the sign of the subtrahend changed and proceeding as in addition of algebraic numbers.*

Applying the rule, we find the following algebraic differences:

$$
\begin{array}{rrrrrr}
+7 & +4 & -6 & -3 & -8 & +7 \\
+3 & +6 & -2 & -7 & +3 & -2 \\
\hline
+4 & -2 & -4 & +4 & -11 & +9
\end{array}
$$

It should be carefully noted that $4 - 3$ may be considered as a $+4$ minus a $+3$, or as a $+4$ plus a -3. It is this choice which causes more or less trouble to the beginner.

If the number with its sign of quality is enclosed in parentheses, we have, for example, $(+4) + (-6) - (+7) - (-11) + (+7)$. This may also be written $(+4) - (+6) - (+7) + (+11) + (+7)$, which is the same as $4 - 6 - 7 + 11 + 7$ where the signs indicate operations and all the numbers are positive.

EXERCISES

1. Add each of the following:

$$
\begin{array}{rrrrrrrrr}
+6 & -7 & -5 & 14 & -14 & +10 & 13 & 19 & 45 & -97 \\
+8 & -3 & +5 & 19 & 17 & -15 & -18 & -\ 8 & -\ 9 & 791
\end{array}
$$

$$
\begin{array}{rrrrrrrrr}
5 & -\ 7 & 11 & -\ 9 & -191 & -90 & 107 & 74 & -10 & 111 \\
-4 & -\ 3 & 12 & 10 & 190 & 40 & 100 & -\ 74 & 11 & 100 \\
3 & 100 & -11 & 9 & 1 & 50 & -200 & 444 & -\ 1 & -300 \\
-1 & -\ 90 & -12 & 20 & 77 & 30 & -\ 8 & -440 & -\ 5 & -\ 11
\end{array}
$$

Ans. 14; -10; 0; 33; 3; -5; -5; 11; 36; 694; 3, 0; 0; 30; 77; 30; -1; 4; -5; -100.

2. Subtract each of the following, and check the result by adding the remainder and the subtrahend:

$$
\begin{array}{rrrrrrrr}
6 & -8 & 11 & 17 & +80 & -95 & -87 & -240 & -0.1 \\
-3 & -5 & +10 & -13 & 70 & 90 & -88 & +260 & -1.1
\end{array}
$$

3. What number added to 10 gives 5? -1? -10?   9?

4. What number added to -10 gives 5?   15? -15?   0?   22?

5. What number subtracted from 15 gives −15? 15? 0? 30? 1?
60? −115? −17?

6. What number subtracted from −15 gives 15? −15? 0? −30?
−1? 60? −115? −17?

7. Find the sum of each of the following:

575	−8008	7070	−1940	$1.07	95%
−500	1008	− 70	− 60	−$0.77	−15%

Ans. 75; −7000; 7000; −2000; $0.30; 80%.

8. Find the remainder in each of the following:

201	−707	−333	5280 ft.	$4.04	33⅓%
102	93	−333	5200 ft.	−$4.96	30 %

Ans. 99; −800; 0; 80 ft.; $9.00; 3⅓%.

Find the sum in Exercises 9 to 15:

9. 3, −4, −15, 10, 15. *Ans.* 9.

10. 37, −67, 96, 105, −3. *Ans.* 167.

11. 1.9, 9.1, −20, 15, −6. *Ans.* 0.

12. $\frac{1}{2}$, $\frac{3}{4}$, $\frac{9}{12}$, $-\frac{18}{24}$, $-\frac{4}{8}$. *Ans.* $\frac{3}{4}$.

13. $-5\frac{2}{3}$, $-6\frac{3}{4}$, $11\frac{7}{12}$, 10. *Ans.* $\frac{55}{6}$.

14. −4.26, −6.74, −10.1, +3. *Ans.* −18.1.

15. $2.90, −$1.90, $9.75. *Ans.* $10.75.

16. From 12.5% take 8%. *Ans.* 4.5%.

17. From −200 take −150. *Ans.* −50.

18. From −65 take 100. *Ans.* −165.

19. Is the absolute value of an algebraic number ever increased by subtraction? Illustrate.

20. Is the absolute value of an algebraic number ever decreased by addition? Illustrate.

21. How many degrees of latitude between places at +37° 45′ 17″ and at −16° 14′ 53″? *Ans.* 54° 0′ 10″.

22. If a steamer is moving through still water at the rate of 20 miles per hour, and a man walks forward on the deck at the rate of 4 miles per hour, express the rate at which the man is moving with reference to the water. Suppose that the man walks toward the stern of the boat at the same rate, how may the rate of the boat and the rate of the man with reference to the boat be expressed?

224. Addition and subtraction of literal algebraic expressions.—We add 5, 8, 10 bu., and get 23 bu. So we have 5 bu. + 8 bu. + 10 bu. = 23 bu.

Similarly,

$$6d + 4d + 7d = 17d$$
$$4xy + 7xy + 8xy = 19xy$$
$$16x^2y + 23x^2y + 3x^2y = 42x^2y$$

In subtraction, we have

$$17a - 5a = 12a$$
$$46x^3y^2 - 6x^3y^2 = 40x^3y^2$$

We know that in arithmetic we cannot add or subtract unlike things; neither can we do so here. If we wish to add $3a$ to $2b$, we indicate the addition, thus, $3a + 2b$.

From these considerations, we have the following principle:

Monomials that are alike, or similar, can be added or subtracted by adding or subtracting the coefficients. If the monomials are unlike, the operations can only be indicated.

Examples of addition:

(1)	(2)	(3)
$+ \ 3abc$	$-16xy^3$	$17ab$
$- \ 6abc$	$+ \ 3xy^3$	$-3xy$
$+10abc$	$- \ 4xy^3$	$-4c^2$
$-16abc$	$- \ 7xy^3$	$+3a^2$
$- \ 3abc$	$+28xy^3$	
$-12abc$	$+ \ 4xy^3$	$17ab - 3xy - 4c^2 + 3a^2$

Examples of subtraction:

(1)	(2)	(3)
$4ax^2$	$-21x^2y$	$14ab$
$-6ax^2$	$3x^2y$	$-6c$
$10ax^2$	$-24x^2y$	$14ab + 6c$

225. Polynomials.—The addition or subtraction of polynomials is similar to that of monomials. *Write them so that like terms are in the same column, and combine the terms in each column as with monomials.*

Example of addition

$+\ 3ax^2 + 14y^2 -\ \ 3z$
$-\ 7ax^2 - 16y^2 +\ \ 7z$
$+10ax^2 -\ \ 4y^2 +\ \ 9z$
$-\ 7ax^2 + 10y^2 - 11z$

$-\ \ \ ax^2 +\ \ 4y^2 +\ \ 2z$

Example of subtraction

$17xy^2 - 14c^2 +\ \ 4a$
$10xy^2 -\ \ 5c^2 -\ \ 8a$

$7xy^2 -\ \ 9c^2 + 12a$

226. Test or proof of results.—It is very important that one should be able to *test* the results. The problems in addition or subtraction of literal algebraic expressions may be tested by substituting some definite values for the general numbers. Thus, if $a = 1$, $b = 1$, and $x = 1$ in the following example, the test is as given.

Example

$-\ 7ab +\ \ 4x^2 - 3bx$
$-\ 8ab - 10x^2 - 4bx$
$-\ 9ab + 11x^2 + 6bx$

$-24ab +\ \ 5x^2 -\ \ bx$

Test

$-\ 7 +\ \ 4 - 3 = -\ 6$
$-\ 8 - 10 - 4 = -22$
$-\ 9 + 11 + 6 =\ \ \ \ 8$

$-24 +\ \ 5 - 1 = -20$

The test depends upon the fact that the letters used may have any values whatever. We could just as well take $a = 1$, $b = 2$, $x = 3$. Of course, we usually choose values that make the computations as simple as possible.

EXERCISES

Write sums in Exercises 1 to 11.

1. a, $3a$, $5a$, $7a$.   *Ans.* $16a$.
2. $5ax$, $-2ax$, $8ax$, $-ax$.   *Ans.* $10ax$.
3. $10ax^2$, $-3ax^2$, $-5ax^2$, $11ax^2$.   *Ans.* $13ax^2$.
4. $17m^2n^2$, $13m^2n^2$, $-11m^2n^2$.   *Ans.* $19m^2n^2$.
5. $3x + y$, $7x - 2y$, $5x + 4y$.   *Ans.* $15x + 3y$.
6. $2a + 3b - 4c$, $5a - 3b$.   *Ans.* $7a - 4c$.
7. $6x - 7a$, $4a$, $4x + 10a + 17$.   *Ans.* $10x + 7a + 17$.
8. $-3d + 3m - 7z$, $8d - 2m + 3z$.   *Ans.* $5d + m - 4z$.
9. $10s - 8t + 7u$, $-19s - 12t - 7u$.   *Ans.* $-9s - 20t$.
10. $a + b - 3c$, $3a + 4b - 10c$, $-3a - 4b + 17c$.   *Ans.* $a + b + 4c$.
11. $7x^2y - 9xy^2$, $-x^2y - 11xy^2$, $-6x^2y + 10xy^2$.   *Ans.* $-10xy^2$.
12. Subtract in Exercises 8 and 9.

Ans. $-11d + 5m - 10z$; $29s + 4t + 14n$.

13. From $7mn - 11pq$ take $9mn + pq$. *Ans.* $-2mn - 12pq$.

14. From $6xy - 13h$ take $10xy + 4k$. *Ans.* $-4xy - 13h - 4k$.

15. From $a^2 + 2ab + b^2$ take $a^2 - 2ab + b^2$. *Ans.* $4ab$.

16. From $20 - 15axh^2 + t$ take $20m^2 + 4t - xh^2$.
$$\text{\textit{Ans.} } 20 - 15axh^2 - 3t - 20m^2 + xh^2.$$

17. Collect the terms, that is, unite the like terms in the following:
$$12a + 12 - a - 4 + 10a - 5 + a - 20a + 14. \quad \textit{Ans. } 2a + 17.$$

18. Collect similar terms in the following:
$$6x^4 - 7x^3 + 8x^2 - 9x + 5 - 5x^4 + 8x^3 - 7x^2 + 9x - 4.$$
$$\textit{Ans. } x^4 + x^3 + x^2 + 1.$$

19. Simplify the following by collecting the like terms:
$$5x - 7t + 30 + 10t - x + 4t - 20 - x + t + 11 - 12t.$$
$$\textit{Ans. } 2x - 4t + 21.$$

20. Add and test by putting $a = 1$, $b = 3$, $c = 2$: $3a - 2b + c$, $+ 20b - 8c$, $-9a + 8b - 7c$. *Ans.* $-5a + 26b - 14c$.

21. Add and test by putting $s = 2$, $t = 1$: $4s - 5t + 6st$, $7s + 8t - 9st$.
$$\textit{Ans. } 11s + 3t - 3st.$$

22. Subtract and test by putting $s = 2$, $t = 1$, and $u = 3$: $s^3 - s^2t + s^2u$ $- t^3 + t^2u - tu^2 + u^3 - stu$ from $3s^3 - 4t^3 + 5u^3 - 6stu$.
$$\textit{Ans. } 2s^3 + s^2t - s^2u - 3t^2 - t^2u + tu^2 + 4u^3 - 5stu.$$

23. From $8x^3 - 10y^3 + 11z^3 - 12xyz$ take $-13x^3 + 14y^3 - 15z^3$.
$$\textit{Ans. } 21x^3 - 24y^3 + 26z^3 - 12xyz.$$

24. Add $x^3 - 3x^2y + 3xy^2 - y^3$, $x^3 + y^3 - 5x^2y$, $-2x^3 - 4xy^2 + 6x^2y$.
$$\textit{Ans. } -2x^2y - xy^2.$$

25. Add $4abc - 5abd + 6bcd - 7abcd$, $6abc - 7bcd + 8abcd + 9abd$.
$$\textit{Ans. } 10abc + 4abd - bcd + abcd.$$

26. Add $8xy^4 - 4y^5$, $-6x^4y + 8xy^4$, $-3x^3y^2 + 7y^5$, $9xy^4 + 4x^4y$ $- 2x^3y^2$.
$$\textit{Ans. } 25xy^4 + 3y^5 - 2x^4y - 5x^3y^2.$$

27. Add $a^2 - b^2$, $a^2 - 2ab + b^2$, $2a^2 + 3b^2$, $-4a^2 - 6ab - 7b^2$, $10a^2$.
$$\textit{Ans. } 10a^2 - 8ab - 4b^2.$$

28. Add $10stu - 11stv + 12tuv$, $8stv + 9tuv$, $2stu + 10stv$, $4stu - tuv$.
$$\textit{Ans. } 16stu + 7stv + 20tuv.$$

29. Add $450xyz - 36x^2y + 200xy^2$, $10x^3 - 650y^3 + 140xyz$, $100x^2y$ $+ 75xy^2 + 10y^3$, $560x^3 - 100xyz$.
$$\textit{Ans. } 570x^3 + 490xyz + 64x^2y + 275xy^2 - 640y^3.$$

30. Add and test by letting $x = 1$, $y = 2$, and $z = 3$: $4x^2 - xyz + yz$ $- xz$, $30xyz - 10yz + 5xz$, $2x^2 - 3xz$, $16xyz - 10$, $-6x^2 - 2yz + 11$.
$$\textit{Ans. } 45xyz - 11yz + xz + 1.$$

31. Add and test by letting $x = 2$, and $y = 3$: $3x^2 + xy - 2y^2$, $4x^2 + 5xy - 3y^2$, $x^2 - 2xy + y^2$, $2xy - 5y^2$. *Ans.* $8x^2 + 6xy - 9y^2$.

32. Add and test by letting $m = 2$, $n = 1$, $p = 3$, $q = -1$: $9m + 2n$ $- 3p$, $7p - 2q$, $-5m + 2n - q$, $m + 2q$, $4n - 3p$, $-m - 1 - n + q$,
$$\textit{Ans. } 4m + 7n + p - 1.$$

33. Add $7aby - 4xy + 3ax - naby + 4ax - bz - 3ax + aby + 2b$ $+ 2naby.$ *Ans.* $8aby + naby - 4xy + 4ax + bz.$

34. Add $4uv^2 - 5u^2v + tuv - 6uv^2 - 2tuv + 3u^2v + 10 - 10uv^2 -$ $+ 4tuv - 3.$ *Ans.* $-12uv^2 - 2u^2v + 3tuv + 2.$

35. Subtract $2abc - 3ab + 4bc^2 - 10$ from $5ab - 4abc - 3bc^2 + 8.$
                              Ans. $8ab - 6abc - 7bc^2 + 18.$

36. Subtract $2mn^2 - 3m^2n^2 + 7m^2n - 8mn - 6$ from $4m^2n^2 + 8mn$ $- 10.$ *Ans.* $7m^2n^2 + 6mn^2 - 7m^2n + 8mn - 4.$

37. From $3abx^2 - 2abxy - 5aby^2$ subtract $4abxy + 5aby^2 - 2abx^2$
                              Ans. $5abx^2 - 6abxy - 10aby^2.$

38. From $10uvw^2 - 9uv^2w + 8u^2vw - 4$ subtract $5 - 3uv^2w + 7uvw^2$
                              Ans. $3uvw^2 - 6uv^2w + 8u^2vw - 9.$

39. Take $3a^2b + 3ab^2 + b^3$ from the sum of $a^3 - 2b^3 + 3a^2b$ and $4ab^2 - 5a^3 + 2a^2b.$ *Ans.* $-4a^3 - 3b^3 + 2a^2b + ab^2.$

Given $A = m^3 - 3m^2n + 3mn^2 - n^3$, $B = 2mn^2 - 3n^2m - 3n^3$, and $C = 4m^3 - n^3$, find the results in Exercises 40 to 47.   Test the result by substituting numbers for m and n.

40. $A + B.$	**43.** $B + C.$	**46.** $A - C.$
41. $A - B + C.$	**44.** $B - C.$	**47.** $A + C.$
42. $A - B.$	**45.** $A - B - C.$	**48.** $C - B - A.$

49. From the sum of $0.1x^2 - 2.3y^2 + 4.4xy$ and $0.2xy - 2.2x^2$ take $3.3y^2 - 2.4x^2 - xy.$ *Ans.* $0.3x^2 + 5.6xy - 5.6y^2.$

50. From $\dfrac{xy^2}{2} - \dfrac{2x^2y}{3} + \frac{3}{4}xy$ take   the   sum   of $\frac{1}{3}xy^2 - \frac{1}{2}x^2y$ and $xy^2 + \frac{2}{3}xy.$

$$\textit{Ans. } - \frac{5xy^2}{6} - \frac{x^2y}{6} + \frac{xy}{12}.$$

227. Terms with unlike coefficients.

—It often happens that we wish to add or subtract terms where the coefficients that are to be united are not all numerical.   For example, add d^2x, e^2x and cx by uniting the coefficients of x.   Here the coefficients of x are d^2, e^2, and c.   Since these are unlike terms, the addition can only be indicated, thus, $d^2 + e^2 + c$.   We may write the sum then of d^2x, e^2x, and cx as $(d^2 + e^2 + c)x$.   Similarly the sum of $6x$, $5x$, and $2x$ may be written $(6 + 5 + 2)x$; but here the coefficients can actually be united and expressed as one symbol, thus $13x$.

EXERCISES

1. Find the sum of the following:

$3x$	$7x + 3ay$	$222s + 3t - 4u$
ax	$3ax + 4by$	$31as - bt + cu$
bx	$-10ax - 4ay$	$- 4s + kt - mu$

Ans. $x(3 + a + b)$; etc.

2. Find the remainder in the following:

$2bx$	$-15ay$	$4x - 7y$	$ax - by + cz$
$2ax$	$-10by$	$mx + ny$	$-cx + by - az$

Ans. $2x(b - a)$; etc.

Add the following by uniting the coefficients of the letter that is common in the terms:

3. $2hay$, $-2hy$, $4ky$, and $15ay$.   *Ans.* $y(2ha - 2h + 4k + 15a)$.

4. $4a^2x$, $-4ax$, and x.   *Ans.* $x(4a^2 - 4a + 1)$.

5. $4kx$, $-ak$, $-10k$, and $10x$.   *Ans.* $x(4k + 10) - k(a + 10)$.

6. $(a + 2)x$, bx, $-2ax$, and $-2x$.   *Ans.* $x(-a + b)$.

7. $(ax - by)t$, $-4at$, $(a - 5)t$, and $16t$.   *Ans.* $t(ax - by - 3a + 11)$.

8. $(2 - a + b)x$, $-hx$, $(2 + a - b)x$, and $(h - 4)x$.   *Ans.* 0.

9. $(2a - 3b + 4c)x$, $(4a - 3b + 2c)x$, and $(-a + 7b - 7c)x$.
 Ans. $x(5a + b - c)$.

Subtract the second expression from the first in the following by uniting the coefficients of the common letters:

10. $4y$ and xy.   *Ans.* $y(4 - x)$.

11. $4ay$ and $7by$.   *Ans.* $y(4a - 7b)$.

12. $7mnx$ and am^2x.   *Ans.* $mx(7n - am)$.

13. $(m + n)t$ and $(m - 3n)t$.   *Ans.* $4nt$.

14. $(3a - 4b + 5c)uv$ and $(-a + 2b - 3c)uv$.
 Ans. $2uv(2a - 3b + 4c)$.

15. $(ax - by + cz)u$ and $(-2ax + 3by - 4cz)u$.
 Ans. $u(3ax - 4by + 5cz)$.

16. $(-2 + 3a - 2c)(a + b)$ and $(4 - 4a + 4c)(a + b)$.
 Ans. $(a + b)(-6 + 7a - 6c)$.

17. A man saved $3a - 4b$ dollars the first year, $6a + 7b$ dollars the second year, $-5a + 10b$ dollars the third year, and $10a - 100b$ dollars the fourth year.   For the four years what was the total amount saved?
 Ans. $14a - 87b$.

18. Find the perimeter of an irregular hexagon having sides of the following lengths: $2a + b$, $3a - 2b$, $4a + b$, $2a - 3b$, $2a + 2b$, and $7a - 5b$
 Ans. $20a - 6b$.

228. Signs of grouping.—When a sign of grouping is preceded by a $+$ or $-$ sign, it indicates that the expression enclosed by the sign of grouping is to be added to or subtracted from what precedes. It is often desirable to remove signs of grouping that appear in an expression and not change the value of the expression.

When a plus sign precedes a sign of grouping, we may remove the sign of grouping without making any change in signs.

Thus, $a + (b - c) = a + b - c$.

When preceded by a minus sign, the sign of grouping may be removed if the signs within it are changed.

Thus, $a - (b - c + d) = a - b + c - d$.

The reason for this change is the same as for the changing of the signs in the subtrahend when subtracting.

When there are several signs of grouping, one within another, they may be removed by first removing the innermost one and then the next outer one, continuing till all are removed.

Example 1.—Simplify $4x^2 - 5y^2 + x - [6x^2 - 3x - (y^2 - x)]$.
Beginning with the inner sign of grouping,

$$4x^2 - 5y^2 + x - [6x^2 - 3x - (y^2 - x)]$$
$$= 4x^2 - 5y^2 + x - [6x^2 - 3x - y^2 + x]$$
$$= 4x^2 - 5y^2 + x - 6x^2 + 3x + y^2 - x$$
$$= -2x^2 - 4y^2 + 3x \quad Ans.$$

Example 2.—Simplify $8 - \{7 - [4 + (2 - x)]\}$.
Solution:

$$8 - \{7 - [4 + (2 - x)]\} = 8 - \{7 - [4 + 2 - x]\}$$
$$= 8 - \{7 - 4 - 2 + x\}$$
$$= 8 - 7 + 4 + 2 - x$$
$$= 7 - x \quad Ans.$$

The terms may be united as soon as like terms appear within a sign of grouping.

Thus, in the first step in Example 2, the $4 + 2$ within the signs [ ] may be united; it then would be

$$8 - \{7 - [6 - x]\}$$
$$= 8 - \{7 - 6 + x\}$$
$$= 8 - \{1 + x\}$$
$$= 8 - 1 - x$$
$$= 7 - x \quad Ans.$$

EXERCISES

Simplify by removing the signs of grouping and uniting the like terms in the following:

1. $2a + 5b - (a + 4b)$. *Ans.* $a + b$.

2. $7 - 3x + (-4 - 6x)$. *Ans.* $3 - 9x$.

3. $10y - 10 - (-3y + 4)$. *Ans.* $13y - 14$.

4. $z + 4z^2 - 14 - (3z^2 + 4 - 2z)$. *Ans.* $z^2 + 3z - 18$.

5. $m - (3m - 2n + p) - m - n + p$. *Ans.* $-3m + n$.

6. $x - 2y + 3z - (2x - 3y + 4z) - (-3x + z)$. *Ans.* $2x + y - 2z$.

7. $-9 - 4u + 3v - 2w - (-9 + 4w) + (5v - 7u - 10w)$.
   $$Ans. \; -11u + 8v - 16w.$$

8. $a - [b - (a + 4)]$. *Ans.* $2a - b + 4$.

9. $19 - 3 - [4 - (-6 + 10)]$. *Ans.* 16.

10. $17 - [2 + (3 - 7)]$. *Ans.* 19.

11. $2x - [3x - (x - y) - y]$. *Ans.* 0.

12. $-5x - [-3x - (-2x + 3y) - 6y]$. *Ans.* $-4x + 9y$.

13. $(a + 2b) - 3a - 4b - [-a - (-b - 10)]$. *Ans.* $-a - 3b - 10$.

14. Let $a = 5$, $b = -10$, $x = 8$, and $y = -3$, and verify results in Exercises 1, 2, 8, 11, 12, and 13.

15. $x - y - \{-x + y - [x - y - (-x + y)]\}$. *Ans.* $4x - 4y$.

16. $[-(3a + 2b) - (a + 9b)] - [a + (-b - 2) + 2]$.
    $$Ans. \; -5a - 10b.$$

17. $\{-[(2u + 3v) - u - 3v]\} - 5u - 6v$. *Ans.* $-6u - 6v$.

18. $10a - 5b + 2c - [-(-a - 2b + 3c) - 7a + 9b - 10c.]$
    $$Ans. \; 16a - 16b + 15c.$$

19. $8a^2 - 9ab + 10c^2 - [ab + 4a^2 - 3ab - (a^2 + ab + c^2)]$.
    $$Ans. \; 5a^2 - 6ab + 11c^2.$$

229. Insertion of signs of grouping.—For the same reasons as given in the preceding article, any terms of a polynomial may be enclosed in a sign of grouping preceded by a plus sign *without change of signs.* They may be enclosed in a sign of grouping preceded by a minus sign, *provided the sign of each term within is changed from — to +, or from + to —.*

Example.—Enclose the last three terms in the following expression within parentheses: (1) preceded by a $+$ sign, and (2) preceded by a $-$ sign.

$$ax + by + cd - e$$
$$(1) \quad ax + by + cd - e = ax + (by + cd - e)$$
$$(2) \quad ax + by + cd - e = ax - (-by - cd + e)$$

EXERCISES

Insert parentheses around all the terms that follow the first $-$ sign in each of the following:

1. $a - 2b + 3c$.   *Ans.* $a - (2b - 3c)$.

2. $3x - x^2 - 2xy - y^2$.   *Ans.* $3x - (x^2 + 2xy + y^2)$.

3. $8a + b - 64a^2 - 16a - 1$.   *Ans.* $8a + b - (64a^2 + 16a + 1)$.

4. $3s^2 - 4r - 5s + 2t$.   *Ans.* $3s^2 - (4r + 5s - 2t)$.

5. $16z^2 + 10zw - 14z^3w + 15w^2 - 5z^2$.

6. $-2a - 3b - 4c - 5d + 40abc - 30ab - 20cd$.

Write the following with the last three terms of each enclosed in parentheses (1) preceded by a $-$ sign and (2) preceded by a $+$ sign:

7. $4 - 4x^2 + 4x - 1$.   **8.** $10 - 3x + y - 3z$.

9. $9u^2 + 9u - 18v + 24$.

10. $16a^2 + 4b^2 - 16ab - 9abc - c^2$.

11. $81x - 9xy + 4y - 1$.

12. $41ab - 4ac + bc - 4abc$.

Collect all the coefficients of x in the following within parentheses preceded by a $-$ sign.

13. $4x - ax + bx$.   *Ans.* $-(-4 + a - b)x$.

14. $abx - 2bcx + 3dex - x$.   *Ans.* $-(1 + 2bc - ab - 3de)x$.

15. $mx - 4nx + 18mnx - 5x$.   *Ans.* $-(5 + 4n - m - 18mn)x$.

16. $-3ax + 45dx + 19mx - 7nx$.   *Ans.* $-(7n + 3a - 45d - 19m)x$.

In the following, group within parentheses the terms that have the same letter to the same power (1) preceded by a $+$ sign and (2) preceded by a $-$ sign:

17. $-4a + 6mn - dm - ab + 46 - 46ac + m$.

18. $xy - mn + 3x - 4am - 18xz - 45m$.

19. $4ax^3 - 8ay^3 - mx + my - ax^2 + a - m$.

20. $3amn^2 - 4cmu^2 + 5m + 4h^3 - ah^3$.

21. $9m^2 - adm^2 + bct^3 - 34t^3 + 34m^2$.

CHAPTER XXI

EQUATIONS

230. Remarks on equations.—Many problems that are solved by means of algebra involve the equation in one form or another. This makes the equation the most important tool of algebra; in fact, it may be looked upon as a more or less complicated piece of machinery with which the student should become very familiar. Some equations are very easy to solve; but in many cases, the solution of an equation is by no means a simple matter.

To become familiar with the mechanism of the equation and its applications requires a great deal of time and much drill. A considerable part of the work in solving equations may, by sufficient drill, become mechanical, in that it will not require much thought in its performance. However, there is a reason for doing each step that is taken, and one should be able to give this reason.

In studying algebra, the efforts of the practical man should be especially devoted to a thorough understanding of the equation, its solution, and its uses. In gaining this understanding, he will be impressed with the fact that the solutions of equations involve most of the other parts of algebra.

231. Definitions.—An **equation** is a statement that two expressions are equal in value.

Thus, $A = \frac{1}{2}ab$ is an equation. So are $A = \pi r^2$, $V = \frac{4}{3}\pi r^3$, and $3x + 4 = 10$.

The part to the left of the equality sign is called the **first member** of the equation, and the part to the right, the **second member**.

If the area of a rectangle is 36 sq. ft. and the altitude is 4 ft., we have $36 = 4b$, where b stands for the base. Now it is easy to see that the statement, or equation, is true if, and only if, $b = 9$. Such an equation as this, where the letter whose value we wish to find has a certain value, is called a **conditional equation.** That is, this equation is true on the condition that $b = 9$ and for no other value of b.

Not all statements of equality are conditional. For instance, $4x + 3x = 7x$ is evidently always true no matter what the value of x. Also $\dfrac{x^2 - 4}{x + 2} = x - 2$ is an equation; but x may have any value whatever and still make the equation true, except that $x \neq -2$; that is, x is not -2.

Thus, if $x = 3$, the equation becomes $\dfrac{9 - 4}{3 + 2} = 3 - 2$ or $+1 = +1$. If $x = 4$, we get $2 = 2$. Similarly, for any value we give, $x \neq -2$.

An equation like these where, by uniting terms, one member is exactly the same as the other or an equation that is true for any value of the letter is called an **identical equation,** or an **identity.**

The number asked for in an equation or the letter standing for it is called the **unknown number,** the **unknown quantity,** or, briefly, the **unknown.**

The following definitions are stated for equations involving one unknown but may easily be extended.

An equation that is true only on condition that the unknown has particular values is called a **conditional equation** or, briefly, an **equation.**

An equation that either involves no unknown or is true for any value whatever that may be given to the unknown is called an **identical equation** or, briefly, an **identity.**

To **solve** an equation is to find the value or values of the unknown that will make the equation true.

It may be noted that an equation in mathematics corresponds to a sentence. It is a declarative sentence stated in mathematical language.

232. Solution of equations.—As already stated, to solve an equation is to determine the value or values of the unknown number or numbers in the equation. This may be an easy matter, but it is often difficult. Here we shall start with very simple equations and endeavor to discover certain general methods of procedure in the solution.

One who is taking up the study of equations for the first time is urged to give careful thought to the treatment of the following very simple cases.

Example 1.—Find the value of x, if $x - 5 = 3$.

Here one readily sees by inspection that $x = 8$, but this does not help in solving a more complicated equation. If, however, we notice that in order to determine $x = 8$, 5 is added to each member of the given equation, we have a method of procedure that we can apply to another like problem. We have then the *solution:*

Given equation

$$x - 5 = 3$$

Adding 5 to each member,

$$x = 3 + 5$$

Collecting the terms,

$$x = 8 \quad Ans.$$

Example 2.—Solve for x, if $x + 3 = 10$.
Solution.—Given equation

$$x + 3 = 10$$

Subtracting 3 from each member,

$$x = 10 - 3$$

Collecting the terms,

$$x = 7 \quad Ans.$$

Example 3.—Solve for b, if $4b = 36$.
Solution.—Given equation

$$4b = 36$$

Dividing each member by 4,

$$b = 9 \quad Ans.$$

Example 4.—Solve for x, if $4x + 5 - 7 = 2x + 6$.

Solution.—Given equation

$$4x + 5 - 7 = 2x + 6$$

Adding 7 to both members,

$$4x + 5 = 2x + 6 + 7$$

Subtracting 5 from both members,

$$4x = 2x + 6 + 7 - 5$$

Subtracting $2x$ from both members,

$$4x - 2x = 6 + 7 - 5$$

Collecting the terms,

$$2x = 8$$

Dividing both members by 2,

$$x = 4 \quad Ans.$$

Notice that when a term is added to or subtracted from both members of an equation, it is *transposed* from one member to the other and its sign is changed. For instance, in the first line of the solution of Example 4, -7 in the *first* member appears as $+7$ in the *second* member of the second line. Now by this transposing we can bring all the terms that contain the unknown into the *first member* and all the others into the *second member*. This gives a convenient form, for we wish finally to have an equation in which the form is

Unknown = some number

Steps in solution.—The solution of an equation that is in a simple form may then be carried out in the following three steps:

(1) *Transpose all terms containing the unknown to the first member and all other terms to the second member. In each case change the sign of the term transposed.*

(2) *Collect the terms in each member.*

(3) *Divide each member by the coefficient of the unknown.*

It will be found later that there are other changes to be made in an equation that is not in a simple form before these three steps are to be performed.

233. Axioms.—An **axiom** is a truth that we accept without proof.

The solutions of the equations and the changes mentioned in the preceding articles suggest the following axioms:

(1) *If equal numbers are added to equal numbers, the sums are equal.*

(2) *If equal numbers are subtracted from equal numbers, the remainders are equal.*

(3) *If equal numbers are multiplied by equal numbers, the products are equal.*

(4) *If equal numbers are divided by equal numbers. not zero. the quotients are equal.*

(5) *Numbers that are equal to the same number or equal numbers are equal to each other.*

(6) *Like powers of equal numbers are equal.*

(7) *Like roots of equal numbers are equal.*

(8) *The whole of anything equals the sum of all its parts.*

234. Testing the equation.—The equation puts the question: What number, if any, must the unknown represent in order that the two members of the equation shall be equal? The solution of the equation answers this question, but it is always well to test or check the work. This may be done by substituting the number obtained for the unknown in place of the unknown letter. If the two members of the equation then become identical, the number substituted is the answer to the equation.

Example.—Solve and test: $47r - 17 = 235 - 37r$.

Solution.—Given equation

$$47r - 17 = 235 - 37r$$

Transposing,

$$47r + 37r = 235 + 17$$

Collecting terms,

$$84r = 252$$

Dividing by the coefficient of r,

$$r = 3$$

Testing by substituting 3 for r in the equation

$$141 - 17 = 235 - 111$$

Collecting gives the identical equation,

$$124 = 124 \quad Ans.$$

EXERCISES

Which of the following are identities and which are equations, that is, conditional equations? They can be tested either by transposing and collecting the terms so as to show that one member is or is not identically equal to the other or by substituting numerical values for the letters and showing that the two members are or are not identical.

1. $4x + 5x - 3x = 6x.$ **3.** $9t + t - 4 = -4 + 10t.$

2. $4x + 5x - 3x = 6.$ **4.** $\dfrac{6y - 2y + 4y}{8} = \dfrac{8y}{8}.$

5. $3u + 2u - u - 24 = 0.$

6. $9w^2 - 8w - 8w^2 = w^2 - 8w.$

7. $4y^4 - 3y^3 + 10 = y^4 - 3y^3 + 3y^4 + 10.$

8. $\dfrac{x^3 - 27}{x - 3} = x^2 + 3x + 9. \quad (x \neq 3)$

Solve and test the following equations:

9. $2x + 3 = x + 4. \quad Ans.\ 1.$ **10.** $4x - 10 = 2x + 2. \quad Ans.\ 6.$

11. $9x - 9 + 3x = 15. \quad Ans.\ 2.$

12. $300x - 250 = 50x + 750. \quad Ans.\ 4.$

13. $17x - 7x = x + 18. \quad Ans.\ 2.$

14. $2.5x + 0.5 = 1.5x + 1.5. \quad Ans.\ 1.$

15. $9y - 19 + y = 11. \quad Ans.\ 3.$

16. $x + 2x + 3 - 4x = 5x - 9. \quad Ans.\ 2.$

17. $2y + 3y - 4 = 5y + 6y - 16$. *Ans.* 2.

18. $75z - 150 = 80z - 300$. *Ans.* 30.

19. $3.3x + 2.7x - 4.6 = 7.4$. *Ans.* 2.

20. $2y - 3y + 4y - 5 = 6y - 7y + 15$. *Ans.* 5.

21. $(4x + 6) - 2x = (x - 6) + 24$. *Ans.* 12.

Suggestion.—First clear of parentheses, and then proceed as before.

22. $15y - [3 - (4y + 4) - 57] = (2 - y)$. *Ans.* $-\frac{14}{5}$.

23. $x - (4x - 8) + 9 + (6x - 8) = 9 - x + 24$. *Ans.* 6.

24. $[2y - (3y - 4) + 5y - 6] + 10y = (12y - 12) + 36$. *Ans.* 13.

25. $4t - (12t - 24) + 38t - 38 = 0$. *Ans.* $\frac{7}{15}$.

235. The equation in solving problems.—As has been stated before, one of the things to be gained in the study of mathematics is to be able to express ideas in mathematical symbols. The student has already had some practice in this. We have stated various principles and rules as formulas and have done much translating from words to mathematical language and from the language of mathematics to words in Chap. XIX.

For this translating we cannot give rules as we can for the operations to be performed in the solutions of exercises. The student must first thoroughly understand the thing to be expressed; and, secondly, he must know the signs and symbols, that is, the language of mathematics. The following suggestions will help the student to state a problem in the form of an equation.

(1) *Read carefully the statement of the problem as it is given in words.*

(2) *Select the unknown number, and represent it by a letter. If there are more unknown numbers than one, try to express the others in terms of the one first selected.*

(3) *Find two expressions that, according to the problem, represent the same number, and set them equal to each other. This forms the equation to be solved.*

EXERCISES

1. A man is S years old. Give in algebraic symbols his age 5 years ago. Give his age T years ago. Give his age $(5 + T)$ years ago. Give his age $(5 + T)$ years from now.

$$Ans. \ S - 5; \ S - T; \ S - (5 + T); \ S + (5 + T).$$

2. A man was S years old 10 years ago. How old will he be 20 years from now? T years from now? When will he be 30 years old?

Ans. $S + 30$ yr.; $S + 10 + T$ yr.; $20 - S$ yr.

3. A car runs d miles in 8 hr. How far does it run in 1 hr.? In t hr.? In t hr. and m min.? *Ans.* $\dfrac{d}{8}$ miles; $\dfrac{dt}{8}$ miles; $\dfrac{d}{8}\left(t + \dfrac{m}{60}\right)$ miles.

4. If a car is driven d miles in h hr., how long will it take to drive 100 miles? *Ans.* $100 \div \dfrac{d}{h}$ hr.

5. How many cents in $20? In a dollars? In 10 dimes? In d dimes? In d dimes and n nickels?

Ans. 2,000; 100a; 100; 10d; 10d + 5h.

6. A man has $2x$ dollars. How many dimes has he? How many nickels? How many cents? *Ans.* 20x; 40x; 200x.

7. You have $100 more than I. If you have x dollars, how much money have I? *Ans.* $x - 100$ dollars.

8. Express five consecutive odd numbers if a is the middle number?

Ans. $a - 4$; $a - 2$; a; $a + 2$; $a + 4$.

Write the following as equations, and solve for the unknown:

9. $4x$ increased by 4 equals 44. *Ans.* 10.

10. $10x$ increased by 4 equals $8x$ decreased by $(2 - 3x)$. *Ans.* 6.

11. $12x$ decreased by 4 equals $4x$ increased by 12. *Ans.* 2.

12. An automobile runs 18 miles on 1 gal. of gasoline. If it runs 360 miles on x gal., find x. *Ans.* 20.

13. A man bought an automobile for $960 and sold it at a loss of d dollars. If he sold it for $450, find d. *Ans.* $510.

14. If 10 is added to twice your money, the result is the same as it would be if your money were subtracted from 43. Let x be your money, and find x. *Ans.* 11.

15. If 10 is added to $10x$ and 15 subtracted from the sum, the result equals $2x$ plus 3. Find x. *Ans.* 1.

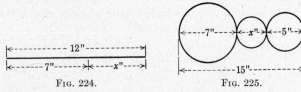

<table>
<tr><td>Fig. 224.</td><td>Fig. 225.</td></tr>
</table>

16–19. Form equations for the relations indicated in Figs. 224, 225, 226, and 227, and solve each equation for the unknown.

Ans. 5; 3; 9; 6.

Suggestion: $7'' + x'' = 12''$, or as it is usually written

$$7 + x = 12$$

20–22. Scales will balance when equal weights are in the pans. Find the values of the unknown weights in pounds for each of the settings shown in Figs. 228, 229, and 230.   *Ans.* 7; 70; 10.

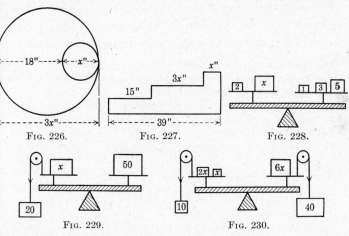

FIG. 226.   FIG. 227.   FIG. 228.

FIG. 229.   FIG. 230.

Suggestion.—The weight of 20 acts in the opposite direction to x, and we have $x - 20 = 50$.   (Fig. 229.)

23. If x represents the number of gallons of oil bought, what was the price per gallon if $140 was the cost of all.   *Ans.* $\dfrac{140}{x}$ dollars.

24. Find the cost per book if eight books at x dollars per book cost $20. State as an equation, and solve.   *Ans.* $2.50.

25. A room is three times as long as it is wide, and its perimeter is 96 ft. Find the length and width.

Solution.—Let

(1) x = number of feet in width

then

(2) $3x$ = number of feet in length

and

(3) $x + x + 3x + 3x$ = perimeter

also

(4) 96 = perimeter
(5) $\therefore x + x + 3x + 3x = 96$, by axiom (5)

Collecting terms,

(6) $8x = 96$

Dividing by 8,

(7) $x = 12$ = number of feet in width
(8) $3x = 36$ = number of feet in the length

Note that in statements (3) and (4) are two expressions for the same thing, the perimeter. These two expressions put equal to each other in statement (5) give the equation to be solved.

26. In a company there are 64 persons, and the number of children is three times the number of adults. How many are there of each?

Solution.—Let

(1) x = the number of adults

then

(2) $3x$ = the number of children

and

(3) $x + 3x$ = number in the company

also

(4) 64 = number in the company
(5) $\therefore x + 3x = 64$
(6) $4x = 64$
(7) $x = 16$ = the number of the adults
(8) $3x = 48$ = the number of the children.

27. A hat and a dress cost together $21. If the hat cost $11 less than the dress, find the cost of each.   *Ans.* $5; $16.

28. Tom, Dick, and Bill are working. Dick earns two times as much as Tom, and Bill earns three times as much as Tom. If the total amount earned by all was $900, how much did each earn?

Ans. $150; $300; $450.

29. Twin steel subway tubes are incased in concrete and sunk under State Street in the Chicago River. The distance from outside to outside of the incasement is 40 ft. One of the tubes is 18 ft. Find the distance between the tubes.   *Ans.* 4 ft.

30. In a tire sale it was found that the regular price of a tire plus the sales price was $21 and that the sales price of four tires was the same as the regular price of three tires. Find the regular and sales prices of the tires.   *Ans.* $12; $9.

31. The sum of two numbers is 300, and their difference is 200. What are the numbers?

Solution.—Let

(1) $$x = \text{the greater number}$$

then

(2) $$300 - x = \text{the lesser number}$$

and

(3) $$x - (300 - x) = \text{the difference}$$

also

(4) $$200 = \text{the difference}$$
(5) $$\therefore x - (300 - x) = 200, \text{ by axiom (5)}$$

Simplifying,

(6) $$x - 300 + x = 200$$

Transposing,

(7) $$x + x = 300 + 200.$$

Collecting terms,

(8) $$2x = 500$$

Dividing by coefficient of x,

(9) $$x = 250, \text{ the greater number}$$
(10) $$300 - x = 50, \text{ the lesser number}$$

Test.—The sum of 250 and 50 is 300, and the difference is 200. Hence, the conditions of the problem are satisfied.

32. Tom has $88 in one-dollar bills and ten-dollar bills. How many bills has Tom if he has the same number of each? *Ans.* 16.

33. I have four times as many five-dollar bills as two-dollar bills. The sum of my money is $110. How many of each kind of bill have I? *Ans.* 5 two-dollar bills; 20 five-dollar bills.

34. In August, 1939, there were 166,000 WPA workers in Illinois. This amount is the same as three times the number that had been on the roll for 18 months or longer plus the 4000 who were dismissed on Aug. 6. How many workers were on the rolls for 18 months or longer?
Ans. 54,000.

35. In 1936 there were 276,500 public and private schools and colleges in the United States. This number multiplied by 100 lacks 29,370 of being the number of students going to these schools. How many students attended school in the United States in 1936? *Ans.* 27,679,370.

36. In 1936 four times the number of men teachers exceeds the number of women teachers by 57,000. If the total number of teachers was 1,073,000, find the number of men and also of women teachers.

Ans. 226,000 men; 847,000 women.

37. A number plus its double equals 18. What is the number?

Ans. 6.

38. Find the three consecutive even numbers whose sum is 216.

Ans. 70; 72; 74.

Suggestion.—Let x = first number.

Then $x + 2$ = second number, and $x + 4$ = third number.

39. Find the four consecutive odd numbers whose sum is 88.

Ans. 19; 21; 23; 25.

40. Find the three consecutive numbers whose sum is 66.

Ans. 21; 22; 23.

41. Divide $210 between A, B, and C so that B shall have $35 less than A and $20 more than C. *Ans.* $100; $65; $45.

42. One angle is the complement of another. If 14° is subtracted from the second and 14° added to the first, the first will be 44° larger than the second. Find the two angles. *Ans.* 53° and 37°.

Two angles are said to be complements of each other if their sum is 90°

43. The difference between two angles is 12°. Find the angles if they are complements of each other. *Ans.* 51° and 39°.

44. Ten times the per capita consumption of beer for the calendar year 1938 (in gallons) for the state of Mississippi increased by twice the amount per capita consumed in Alabama is the same as that consumed for the state of Wisconsin. If Alabama consumes 2.3 gal. per capita and Wisconsin 22.6 gal. per capita, what is the per capita consumption for Mississippi? *Ans.* 1.8 gal.

45. Tom, Dick, and Harry have $4080. Tom has three times as much as Dick and $330 more than Harry. How many dollars has each?

Ans. $630; $1890; $1560.

46. The sum of four angles about a point is 360°. The second is twice the first; the third, three times the second; and the fourth is 10° greater than the first. Find the angles. *Ans.* 35°, 70°, 210°, 45°.

47. One of two supplementary angles is three times the other. How many degrees are there in each angle? *Ans.* 135° and 45°.

48. One of two complementary angles added to 20° equals the other; find the angles. *Ans.* 35° and 55°.

49. Find the angle the sum of whose complement and supplement is 150°. *Ans.* 60°.

50. The greater of two complementary angles exceeds the less by 20°; find the number of degrees in each angle. *Ans.* 55° and 35°.

51. If $2x - 5$ and $3x + 20$ are, respectively, the number of degrees in two complementary angles, find the angles. *Ans.* 25° and 65°.

52. If $2x + 5$ and $3x + 20$ are, respectively, the number of degrees in two supplementary angles, find the angles. *Ans.* 67° and 113°.

53. The number of degrees in the four angles about a point in a plane are, respectively, $2x + 10$, $3x - 10$, $4x + 40$, and $6x + 20$; find the four angles. *Ans.* 50°, 50°, 120°, and 140°.

54. If the three sides of a triangle are $2x + 3$, $3x - 1$, and $4x + 3$ in., respectively, and the perimeter is 23 in., find the length of each side.

Ans. 7, 5, and 11 in.

55. The three angles of a triangle are in the ratio $1:2:3$; find the number of degrees in each angle. *Ans.* 30, 60, and 90.

Suggestion.—Let x, $2x$, and $3x$ represent the number of degrees in each of the three angles respectively.

56. If two angles of a triangle are complements of each other and in the ratio of $2:3$, find the three angles. *Ans.* 36°, 54°, and 90°.

57. If one angle of a triangle is 45° and the others are in the ratio $2:3$, find the two angles. *Ans.* 54° and 81°.

58. The number of degrees in the three angles of a triangle are $x + 10$, $2x - 5$, and $3x + 25$, respectively; find the angles of the triangle.

Ans. 35°, 45°, and 100°.

59. If two adjacent sides of a parallelogram are $2x + 4$ and $5x - 2$ inches, respectively, and the perimeter is 74 in., find each side.

Ans. 14 and 23 in.

60. Five lamps connected in series have a resistance of 1250 ohms. The first has a resistance of 240 ohms; the second, 260 ohms; and the other three are alike. Find the resistance of each of the like lamps.

Ans. 250 ohms.

61. A piece of wire 66 in. long is bent into the form of a rectangle 1 in. longer than it is wide; find the dimensions of the rectangle.

Ans. Width 16 in.; length 17 in.

62. A student earned $1200 his first three years in college. The second year he earned twice as much as the first and the third year $450 more than the second year. How much did he earn each year?

Ans. $150; $300; $750.

63. In one year three college boys earned together $1200. The first earned twice as much as the second, and the third $200 less than twice as much as the first. How much did each earn?

Ans. $400; $200; $600.

64. A spiral spring of initial length 8 in. stretches 0.2 in. for each pound of weight that is suspended from it. Write the equation that connects the length L in inches of the stretched spring with the load W in pounds suspended from it. Calculate from the equation the length of the spring when 35 lb. is suspended from it. Calculate the weight when the length of the stretched spring is $16\frac{1}{2}$ in. *Ans.* 15 in.; $42\frac{1}{2}$ lb.

CHAPTER XXII

MULTIPLICATION

236. Multiplication of whole numbers in arithmetic may be thought of as a *shortened process of addition*.
For instance,

$$(1) \qquad 5 \times 3 = 5 + 5 + 5 = 15$$

We say that the multiplicand is used as an addend* as many times as there are units in the multiplier.

This idea of multiplication must be enlarged in order to include the multiplying by a fraction.

Thus, $8 \times \dfrac{3}{4} = \dfrac{8 \times 3}{4}$; that is, we multiply by the numerator and divide by the denominator of the multiplier.

237. Multiplication with algebraic numbers.—For multiplication in algebra we shall retain its arithmetical meaning when the multiplier is a positive whole number or fraction, but we shall have to extend the meaning to include negative numbers.

From the arithmetical meaning, since the multiplier is positive, we have

$$(2) \qquad (-5) \times (+3) = (-5) + (-5) + (-5) = -15$$

Now we know that when we multiply two positive abstract numbers together, it does not matter which is used as the multiplier. If we assume that this principle holds when one of the numbers is negative, we have

$$(-5) \times (+3) = (+3) \times (-5) = -15$$

---

* An addend is one of the numbers to be added in an addition problem.

338

This gives us the following meaning for multiplication by a negative number:

To multiply by a negative number is to multiply by its absolute value and then change the sign of the product.

Thus, to multiply $+5$ by -3, we multiply $+5$ by $+3$ getting $+15$ and then change the sign of the result. That is,

$$(3) \qquad (+5) \times (-3) = -15$$

Likewise, to multiply -5 by -3, we multiply -5 by $+3$, getting -15, and then change the sign of the result. That is,

$$(4) \qquad (-5) \times (-3) = +15$$

In (1), (2), (3), and (4) we have examples of all the combinations possible in multiplying two algebraic numbers.

From the aforementioned considerations we see that in finding the product of two algebraic numbers:

(1) *The numerical part of the product is the product of the absolute values of the multiplicand and multiplier.*

(2) *The sign of the product is plus when the signs of the multiplicand and multiplier are alike and minus when their signs are unlike.*

This is called the **law of signs in multiplication.** It may be stated as follows:

$$+ \times + = +$$
$$- \times - = +$$
$$+ \times - = -$$
$$- \times + = -$$

238. Concrete illustration.—For those who find the foregoing discussion difficult to understand, the following illustration may clear up matters.

There is a machine shop employing laborers and apprentices. The laborers are paid $15 per week, and the apprentices are charged $3 per week.

Suppose that an increase in the number of men or dollars is positive and a decrease in either is negative. Thus, a number of laborers or apprentices taken in will be called positive, and a number let go will be called negative; also the number of dollars received from an apprentice is positive, and the number of dollars paid a laborer is negative.

On these suppositions we have:

(1) If apprentices are increased by 5, the amount of money is increased $15 per week. That is,

$$(+3) \times (+5) = +15$$

(2) If apprentices are decreased by 5, the amount of money is decreased $15 per week. That is,

$$(+3) \times (-5) = -15 .$$

(3) If laborers are increased by 5, the amount of money is decreased by $75 per week. That is,

$$(-15) \times (+5) = -75$$

(4) If laborers are decreased by 5, the amount of money is increased by $75 per week. That is,

$$(-15) \times (-5) = +75$$

From these considerations, we may deduce the same rules as already given.

239. Continued products.—To find the product of three or more numbers, we find the product of the first two and then multiply this product by the third, and so on, till all the numbers have been used.

By applying principles (1) and (2) of Art. 237, we obtain the following:

(1) *The product of an odd number of negative factors is negative.*

(2) *The product of an even number of negative factors is positive.*

(3) *The product of any number of positive factors is positive.*

Thus, $(-2)(-2)(-2)(-2)(-2) = -32$,
whereas $(-2)(-2)(-2)(-2)(-2)(-2) = +64$.

The first one of these equals $(-2)^5$ and is then read *the fifth power of* -2. The second is $(-2)^6$.

It should be noted that such a form as $(-2)^5$ does not mean the same as -2^5, though they may be equal. The form -2^5 is read *minus 2 to the fifth power*.

Thus, $(-2)^2 = (-2)(-2) = 4 = 2^2$,
$(-2)^3 = (-2)(-2)(-2) = -8 = -2^3$,
$(-2)^4 = (-2)(-2)(-2)(-2) = 16 = 2^4$,
$(-2)^5 = (-2)(-2)(-2)(-2)(-2) = -32 = -2^5$,
$-2^5 = -(2)(2)(2)(2)(2) = -32$,
$(-3)^2(-2)^3 = (-3)(-3)(-2)(-2)(-2) = -72$,
$(4^2)(3^2) = 4 \cdot 4 \cdot 3 \cdot 3 = 144$.

EXERCISES

1. Find the product of -3, $+4$, and -5.   *Ans.* 60.
2. Find the product of $+6$, -20, -10, and $+40$.   *Ans.* 48,000.
3. Find the cube of -4; of $+5$; of -11.   *Ans.* -64; 125; -1331.
Find the values of the following:

4. $(-3)^3$.   *Ans.* -27.
5. $(-1)^{100}$.   *Ans.* 1.
6. $(-6)^4$.   *Ans.* 1296.

7. $(-2)^2(-3)^3$.   *Ans.* -108.
8. $3(-4)^5(-2)^2$.   *Ans.* $-12,288$.
9. $-2(-2)^2(-10)^3$.   *Ans.* 8000.

If $x = -2$, $y = 3$, $z = -4$, find the value of:

10. x^3y^2.   *Ans.* -72.
11. y^3z.   *Ans.* -108.

12. xyz.   *Ans.* 24.
13. $x^2y^2z^2$.   *Ans.* 576.

14. $(6)(-5)(-2)y^3$.   *Ans.* 1620.
Find the values of the following:
15. $4(-10)(-3) + 5(+6)(-30)$.   *Ans.* -780.
16. $+1(-2)(+3) - (-4)(-3)(+10)$.   *Ans.* -126.
17. $3(-4)(5) + 5(-3)(-4)$.   *Ans.* 0.
18. $-(3)^2(-1)^2(-4)^3 + 3(-4)^3(-3)(-1)^3$.   *Ans.* 0.
19. $(-2)^2 - (-3)^2 + (-4)^3 - (-4)^3 + 5$.   *Ans.* 0.
20. $(-12)(-10) - (-10)^2 + (-2)^2(3)(10)$.   *Ans.* 140.
21. $5(4)(3)(2) - (-2)(-3)(-4)(-5)$.   *Ans.* 0.
22. $4(5)(6)(10) - 1(-4)(-5)(-6)(-10)$.   *Ans.* 0.

240. Law of exponents.—The law which applies to exponents that are positive integers is derived from the definition given in Art. 210.

Since

$$a^5 = a \cdot a \cdot a \cdot a \cdot a$$

and

$$a^3 = a \cdot a \cdot a$$

then

$$a^5 \cdot a^3 = a \cdot a \cdot a \cdot a \cdot a \cdot a \cdot a \cdot a = a^8$$

and

$$a^5 \cdot a^3 = a^{5+3} = a^8$$

In general

$$a^n = a \cdot a \cdot a \ldots \text{to } n \text{ factors}^*$$

and

$$a^m = a \cdot a \cdot a \ldots \text{to } m \text{ factors}$$

then

$$a^n \cdot a^m = a \cdot a \cdot a \ldots \text{to } (n + m) \text{ factors}$$

and

$$a^n \cdot a^m = a^{n+m}$$

Similarly, when there are any number of factors we have

$$a^n \cdot a^m \cdot a^p \cdot a^r \ldots = a^{n+m+p+r\ldots}$$

LAW.—*The product of two or more powers of the same base is equal to that base affected with an exponent equal to the sum of the exponents of the powers.*

241. To multiply a monomial by a monomial.

Example.—Multiply $14a^3b^2$ by $-3a^4b^3$.

Process:
$$\begin{array}{r} 14a^3b^2 \\ -\ 3a^4b^3 \\ \hline -42a^7b^5 \quad Ans. \end{array}$$

Discussion.—Since the multiplier is composed of the factors -3, a^4, and b^3, the multiplicand may be multiplied by each successively. In each case the product for any one of these factors is obtained by multiplying a single factor in the multiplicand by it. We multiply by -3, by multiplying 14 by

---

* A repetition of dots, as $a, b, c, \ldots$, is the sign of continuation. It is read "and so on."

-3, which gives $-42a^3b^2$. This is multiplied by a^4, by multiplying the a^3 by a^4, which gives $-42a^7b^2$. This is multiplied by b^3, by multiplying the b^2 by b^3, which gives $-42a^7b^5$, the answer.

The multiplication is carried out by determining in the following order.

(1) *The sign of the product.*
(2) *The coefficient of the product.*
(3) *The letters of the product.*
(4) *The exponents of these letters.*

Thus, in the preceding example the sign is $+ \times - = -$; the coefficient is $14 \times 3 = 42$; the letters are a and b; and the exponents are, for a, $3 + 4 = 7$ and, for b, $2 + 3 = 5$.

This plan should be carefully followed by the beginner.

242. To multiply a polynomial by a monomial.

RULE.—*The product is found by multiplying each term of the multiplicand by the multiplier and taking the algebraic sum of these partial products.*

Example.—Multiply $7ax^3 - 21ab^4 - 3x^2$ by $2a^2b^3x^4$.

Process:
$$7ax^3 - 21ab^4 - 3x^2$$
$$2a^2b^3x^4$$
$$\overline{14a^3b^3x^7 - 42a^3b^7x^4 - 6a^2b^3x^6} \quad Ans.$$

Explanation.—The first term at the left of the product is obtained by multiplying the first term at the left of the multiplicand by the multiplier. The second and third terms in the product are obtained in a similar manner. In each of the multiplications, we have a monomial by a monomial, which has been discussed in the previous article.

EXERCISES

Find the product of the following:

1. $5a^2b^3$ and $4ab^2$. *Ans.* $20a^3b^5$.

2. $21m^4n^5$ and $5m(-n)^3$.
   Ans. $-105m^5n^8$.

3. $8ab^2c^3$ and $-5b^5c^{10}$.
   Ans. $-40ab^7c^{13}$.

4. $-10xyz^4$ and $-6x^4y^6$.
   Ans. $60x^5y^7z^4$.

5. $-8a^4b^5xy^6$ and $-2ab^5x^4y$. *Ans.* $16a^5b^{10}x^5y^7$.

6. $-(-1)x^2y^4$ and $-(-x^2)(-y)^4$. *Ans.* x^4y^8.

7. $2x^2y$, $-3y^2z$, and $4xy^2z^3$. *Ans.* $-24x^3y^5z^4$.

8. $-(\frac{4}{5})x^2y^4$, $(\frac{5}{8})x^3$, and $-2y$. *Ans.* x^5y^5.

9. $3S^3T$, $-5(-t)(T)^4$, and $-(\frac{1}{15}tT^8)$. *Ans.* $-S^3T^{13}t^2$.

10. a^2, a^n, and a^{4n+5}. *Ans.* a^{5n+7}.

11. $(x^3)^3$ or $(x^3)(x^3)(x^3)$. *Ans.* x^9.

12. $(S^2t^3)^4 = ?$ *Ans.* S^8t^{12}.

13. $2(2a^2b^2)^2 = ?$ *Ans.* $8a^4b^4$.

14. $[-2(P^3)Q^4]^3 = ?$ *Ans.* $-8P^9Q^{12}$.

15. $x^2y^3z(xyz^2)x^5 = ?$ *Ans.* $x^8y^4z^3$.

16. $abc(a^2b^2c^2)(abc)^2 = ?$ *Ans.* $a^5b^5c^5$.

17. $3a^3(-2ab^3)(2ab)^3 = ?$ *Ans.* $-48a^7b^6$.

18. $XYZ^2(-Z^2)(-Z)^2 = ?$ *Ans.* $-XYZ^6$.

19. $(ABC)(-ABC^3)(AB)^4C(A)^2(BC)^2$. *Ans.* $-A^8B^8C^7$.

20. $4b^2(-4b^2)(-4b)^2(-4)(b)^2$. *Ans.* $1024b^8$.

21. $-3X^2(3XY^2)(3X^2)(3Y)^2$. *Ans.* $-243X^5Y^4$.

22. $-3x(-3x - 4xy^2)$. *Ans.* $9x^2 + 12x^2y^2$.

23. $-2(-2xy)(-2x + 3y)$. *Ans.* $-8x^2y + 12xy^2$.

24. $+10abcd^3(3a^2b - 3b^2c + 5c^2d^3)$.

Ans. $30a^3b^2cd^3 - 30ab^3c^2d^3 + 50abc^3d^6$.

25. $-10xy^2z(-2x^2yz^2 + 5xy^2z - 4xyz)$.

Ans. $20x^3y^3z^3 - 50x^2y^4z^2 + 40x^2y^3z^2$.

26. $abc^2(a^nb^mc^p - 3ab^2c^n + 2a^mb^nc)$.

Ans. $a^{n+1}b^{m+1}c^{p+2} - 3a^2b^3c^{n+2} + 2a^{m+1}b^{n+1}c^3$.

27. $x^ay^bz^c(-xyz + 4x^2y^3z^4 - ax^ny^nz^n)$.

Ans. $-x^{a+1}y^{b+1}z^{c+1} + 4x^{a+2}y^{b+3}z^{c+4} - ax^{a+n}y^{b+n}z^{c+n}$.

243. To multiply a polynomial by a polynomial.

RULE.—*Multiply every term of the multiplicand by each term of the multiplier, write the like terms of the partial products under each other, and find the algebraic sum of the partial products.*

Example 1.—Multiply $x - 3$ by $x + 7$.

Process:

$$
\begin{array}{r}
x - 3 \\
x + 7 \\
\hline
x^2 - 3x \\
7x - 21 \\
\hline
x^2 + 4x - 21 \quad \textit{Ans.}
\end{array}
$$

x times $(x - 3) =$

7 times $(x - 3) =$

Adding these we get,

Example 2.—Multiply $x^2 + 3xy - 2y^2$ by $2xy - 2y^2$.

Process:

$$x^2 + 3xy - 2y^2$$
$$2xy - 2y^2$$

$2xy$ times $(x^2 + 3xy - 2y^2) =$ $2x^3y + 6x^2y^2 - \quad 4xy^3$

$-2y^2$ times $(x^2 + 3xy - 2y^2) = \qquad\qquad - 2x^2y^2 - \quad 6xy^3 + 4y^4$

Adding these we get, $2x^3y + 4x^2y^2 - 10xy^3 + 4y^4$

Ans.

Example 3.—Multiply $3a^2 + 3b^2 + ab$ by $b^3 - 2a^2b + ab^2$.

Process: $3a^2 + 3b^2 \quad + ab$

$\qquad\qquad\quad b^3 - 2a^2b + ab^2$

$\qquad\qquad 3a^2b^3 + 3b^5 + ab^4$

$\qquad -6a^2b^3 \qquad\qquad\qquad - 6a^4b - 2a^3b^2$

$\qquad\quad a^2b^3 \qquad + 3ab^4 \qquad\qquad + 3a^3b^2$

$\overline{-2a^2b^3 + 3b^5 + 4ab^4 - 6a^4b + \quad a^3b^2}$ *Ans.*

244. Test.—Problems in multiplication can be tested by substituting convenient numerical values for the letters. It is best to use values larger than 1, since with 1 the exponents are not tested, as any power of 1 is 1.

Test of Example 2, by letting $x = 2$ and $y = 2$.

$x^2 + 3xy - 2y^2 \qquad\qquad = 4 + 12 - 8 = 8$

$2xy - 2y^2 \qquad\qquad\qquad = 8 - 8 \qquad = 0$

$2x^3y + 6x^2y^2 - 4xy^3$

$\quad - 2x^2y^2 - 6xy^3 + 4y^4$

$2x^3y + 4x^2y^2 - 10xy^3 + 4y^4 = 32 + 64 - 160 + 64 = 0.$

The work is probably correct if the product of the values of the two factors equals the value of the product. Here it is 0 in each case.

EXERCISES

Multiply each of the following:

1. $x + 1$ by $x - 1$.   *Ans.* $x^2 - 1$.

2. $x - 1$ by $x - 1$.   *Ans.* $x^2 - 2x + 1$.

3. $x - 2$ by $x + 2$.   *Ans.* $x^2 - 4$.

4. $x + 3$ by $x + 4$.   *Ans.* $x^2 + 7x + 12$.

5. $x - 5$ by $x - 6$.   *Ans.* $x^2 - 11x + 30$.

6. $x + 8$ by $x - 3$.   *Ans.* $x^2 + 5x - 24$.

7. $x - 10$ by $x + 1$.   *Ans.* $x^2 - 9x - 10$.

8. $x - 11$ by $x + 11$.   *Ans.* $x^2 - 121$.

9. $x + 20$ by $x - 30$.   *Ans.* $x^2 - 10x - 600$.

10. $x - 14$ by $x + 5$.   *Ans.* $x^2 - 9x - 70$.

11. $3x - 3$ by $x - 4$.   *Ans.* $3x^2 - 15x + 12$.

12. $4x + 5$ by $5x - 6$.   *Ans.* $20x^2 + x - 30$.

13. $10x - 1$ by $x - 10$.   *Ans.* $10x^2 - 101x + 10$.

14. $10x + 1$ by $10x - 1$.   *Ans.* $100x^2 - 1$.

15. $5x - 4$ by $5x + 4$.   *Ans.* $25x^2 - 16$.

16. $x^2 - x + 1$ by $x + 1$.   *Ans.* $x^3 + 1$.

17. $x^2 + 2x + 1$ by $x + 1$.   *Ans.* $x^3 + 3x^2 + 3x + 1$.

18. $x^2 + xy + y^2$ by $x - y$.   *Ans.* $x^3 - y^3$.

19. $a^2 - 4a + 4$ by $a^2 - 2a$.   *Ans.* $a^4 - 6a^3 + 12a^2 - 8a$.

20. $b^2 + 5b$ by $b^2 - 5b$.   *Ans.* $b^4 - 25b^2$.

21. $3a - 4x$ by $4a - 3x$.   *Ans.* $12a^2 - 25ax + 12x^2$.

22. $3x^2 - 4b^2$ by $3x^2 + 4b^2$.   *Ans.* $9x^4 - 16b^4$.

23. $-2ax + b$ by $2ax + b$.   *Ans.* $-4a^2x^2 + b^2$.

24. $-7x^2 + 7x$ by $7x^2 - 7x$.   *Ans.* $-49x^4 + 98x^3 - 49x^2$.

25. $-by + ax$ by $ax - by$.   *Ans.* $a^2x^2 - 2axby + b^2y^2$.

26. $ax^2 - by^2$ by $ax^2 + by^2$.   *Ans.* $a^2x^4 - b^2y^4$.

27. $(ax)^2 - by^2$ by $(ax)^2 + by^2$.   *Ans.* $a^4x^4 - b^2y^4$.

28. $2a + 3x + y$ by $2a + 3x - y$.   *Ans.* $4a^2 + 12ax + 9x^2 - y^2$.

29. $2a^2 + 3x^2 - 4y^2$ by $2a^2 + 3x^2 + 4y^2$.

Ans. $4a^4 + 9x^4 - 16y^4 + 12a^2x^2$.

30. $-(-x^2)^2 + (y^2)^2$ by $x^4 + y^4$.   *Ans.* $y^8 - x^8$.

31. $x^2 - xy + y^2 - 1$ by $x + y$.   *Ans.* $x^3 + y^3 - x - y$.

32. $x^2 + xy + y^2 - 1$ by $x - y$.   *Ans.* $x^3 - y^3 - x + y$.

33. $2x^2 + y^2 - 2z^2$ by $2x^2 + y^2 + 2z^2$.   *Ans.* $4x^4 + 4x^2y^2 + y^4 - 4z^4$.

34. $81x^2 - 16y^2 - 25z^2$ by $81x^2 + 16y^2 + 25z^2$.

Ans. $6561x^4 - 256y^4 - 625z^4 - 800y^2z^2$.

35. $x^2 + 3x + 2$ by $x^2 + 7x + 12$.

Ans. $x^4 + 10x^3 + 35x^2 + 50x + 24$.

36. $x^2 - 1$ by $x^2 - 4$.   *Ans.* $x^4 - 5x^2 + 4$.

37. $m^3 - 3m^2$ by $m^3 - 6m^2 + 9m$.   *Ans.* $m^6 - 9m^5 + 27m^4 - 27m^3$.

38. $(2x)^3 - 3(2x)^2 + 3(2x) - 1$ by $(2x + 1)^2$.

Ans. $32x^5 - 16x^4 - 16x^3 + 8x^2 + 2x - 1$.

39. $(3a - 4b)^2$ by $(3a + 4b)^2$.   *Ans.* $81a^4 - 288a^2b^2 + 256b^4$.

40. $x^2 - y^2$ by $x^4 + x^2y^2 + y^4$.   *Ans.* $x^6 - y^6$.

41. $(a - x)^3$ by $(a + x)^3$.   *Ans.* $a^6 - 3a^4x^2 + 3a^2x^4 - x^6$.

42. $x^{2n} - 2x^n + 1$ by $x^n - 1$.   *Ans.* $x^{3n} - 3x^{2n} + 3x^n - 1$.

43. $x^{2n+2} + y^m$ by $x^{2n+2} - y^m$.   *Ans.* $x^{4n+4} - y^{2m}$.

Signs of grouping are often used to enclose factors of a product. Thus, $(a + b)(a - b)$ means the same as $(a + b)$ times $(a - b)$. To free the expression of these signs of grouping, the indicated multiplications are performed.

Free the following of signs of grouping and simplify:

44. $(2x + 1)(2x - 1)$.   *Ans.* $4x^2 - 1$.

45. $(3t - 4u)(3t + 4u)$.   *Ans.* $9t^2 - 16u^2$.

46. $(ax^2 - by^2)(ax^2 + by^2)$.   *Ans.* $a^2x^4 - b^2y^4$.

47. $4(x - y)^2 + 4(2xy) - 4(x^2 + y^2)$.   *Ans.* 0.

48. $a^3 + x^3 + 3ax(a + x) - (a + x)(a^2 - ax + x^2)$.
$$\text{Ans. } 3a^2x + 3ax^2.$$

49. $-3ax(a - x) + a^3 - x^3 + (x - a)(x^2 + ax + a^2)$.
$$\text{Ans. } -3a^2x + 3ax^2.$$

50. $(x - 2y)(2 + 2y) - 2(-2y + x)$.   *Ans.* $2xy - 4y^2$.

51. $(2x^n - y^3)(2x^n + y^3) - 4(x^n)^2 - (-y)^3$.   *Ans.* $-y^6 + y^3$.

52. $ax^2[x^2 - 2xy + y^2 - (x - y)^2] + x(a - x) + x(x - a)$.   *Ans.* 0.

53. Find the area of a rectangle that is s ft. longer than it is wide.
Hint: $x(x + s)$.

54. Find the volume of a rectangular solid $2x - 3$ ft. wide, $7x - 2$ ft. long, and $x + 4$ ft. deep.   *Ans.* $14x^3 + 31x^2 - 94x + 24$ cu. ft.

55. Find the volume of a right circular cylinder if the altitude is h ft. and the radius $2h - 4$ ft.   Volume of cylinder $= \pi r^2 h$, where r is radius and h is altitude.   *Ans.* $\pi(4h^3 - 16h^2 + 16h)$ cu. ft.

56. A hollow square has dimensions as shown in Fig. 231.   Find its area.   *Ans.* $3s^2 + 28s + 32$.

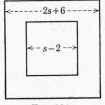

FIG. 231.

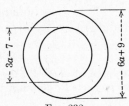

FIG. 232.

57. A ring has dimensions as shown in Fig. 232.   Find its area.   Area of circle $= \frac{1}{4}\pi d^2$.   *Ans.* $\frac{1}{4}\pi(27a^2 + 150a + 32)$.

58. A strip of sheet iron w in. in width is bent up at the edges so as to form an open gutter d in. deep for carrying water.   Find the area A of the cross section of the gutter.   *Ans.* $dw - 2d^2$.

59. A rectangular sheet of tin a in. long and b in. wide is made into an open box by cutting a square c in. on a side from each corner and turning up the sides.   Find the volume of the box.
$$\text{Ans. } abc - 2ac^2 - 2bc^2 + 4c^3.$$

245. Representation of products.—If a is the number o
units in the altitude in Fig. 233 and b is the number of unit
in the base, then the product ab is the number of square unit
in the area of the rectangle in the figure.

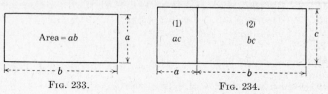

Fig. 233.   Fig. 234.

Similarly, the two rectangles in Fig. 234 represent the prod
uct of $(a + b)$ by c. The part marked (1) represents th
partial product ac, and the part marked (2) represents th
partial product bc.

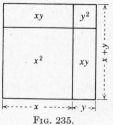

Fig. 235.

Figure 235 shows that $(x + y)(x + y)$
$= x^2 + 2xy + y^2$. The whole figure is
square $x + y$ on a side. This is made u
of a square x units on a side, having x
square units; a square y units on a side
having y^2 square units; and two rec
tangles each x units by y units, havin
xy square units each. Hence, the whol
figure contains $x^2 + 2xy + y^2$ square units.

EXERCISES

Find the product in each of the following, and show the product an
the partial products by drawings:

1. $(a + b + 2)3.$
2. $(a + b + c)d.$
3. $[(2x - b) + c]^2.$

4. $(x - 4)(x + 4).$
5. $(x - a)^2.$
6. $(2 + x + 2y)(a + b + c).$

246. Approximate products.—By multiplication we get th
formula $(1 + a)(1 + b) = 1 + a + b + ab.$

If in this formula a and b are small fractions, the product ab
will be very small compared with a and b. The value o
$(1 + a)(1 + b)$ will then be approximately $1 + a + b.$

Thus, if $a = 0.05$ and $b = 0.02$, the approximate value of $(1 + a)$ $(1 + b) = 1 + 0.05 + 0.02 = 1.07$ but the exact value is $1.05 \times 1.02 = 1.071$. $1.071 - 1.07 = 0.001 = $ difference.

Example.—If $a = 0.01$ and $b = 0.02$, find the per cent of error in the product $(1 + a)(1 + b)$ if the term ab is disregarded.

Solution.—The approximate value of $(1 + 0.01)(1 + 0.02) = 1 + 0.01 + 0.02 = 1.03$.

The exact value $= 1 + 0.01 + 0.02 + 0.0002 = 1.0302$.

The error $= 1.0302 - 1.03 = 0.0002$.

The per cent of error is obtained by finding what per cent 0.0002 is of 1.0302.

$$\therefore \ 0.0002 \div 1.0302 = 0.0002 - \ = 0.02 - \% \quad Ans.$$

EXERCISES

1. Find the per cent of error if term ab in $(1 + a)(1 + b)$ is disregarded when $a = 0.001$ and $b = 0.002$. *Ans.* $0.0002 - \%$.

2. Calculate the value of 1.002×1.05 to three decimal places by using the approximate method. $(a = 0.002, b = 0.05.)$ *Ans.* 1.052.

3. To how many places can the product of 1.02×1.0024 be found by the approximate method? $(b$ has 4 places.$)$ *Ans.* 4.

4. What per cent of error is there in assuming $(1 + a)(1 + b) = 1 + a + b$ where $a = 0.003$ and $b = 0.005$? *Ans.* $0.0015 - \%$.

5. In assuming $(1 + a)^3 = 1 + 3a$, what is the per cent of error when $a = 0.0002$? When $a = 0.002$? When $a = 0.02$? When $a = 0.2$? *Ans.* $0.000012 - \%; 0.0012 - \%; 0.114 - \%; 7.41 - \%$.

6. In measuring the radius of a circle, the correct length of which is 1 ft., there is an error of 1 %. Find the per cent of error in the area of the circle determined from the measured radius. Area of circle is πr^2, where r is the radius. *Ans.* 2%, approx.

7. If in determining the area of a triangle by drawing to scale and measuring the base and altitude the base is measured $1\frac{1}{2}\%$ and the altitude 2 % too large, respectively, find the per cent of error in the area, disregarding the product term. The area of a triangle is one-half the base times the altitude. *Ans.* $3\frac{1}{2}\%$.

8. Find the approximate products of the following:

(1) 1.003×1.012.
(2) 1.02×0.97.
(3) 1.004×0.998.
(4) 0.97×0.98.
(5) 0.996×0.997.
(6) 0.985×0.996.

9. In measuring a rectangle the length is measured 2 % too large an the width 3 % too small. If the area is computed from these measure ments, find the per cent of error in the area.

Ans. 1 % too small, approx.

10. If in measuring a triangle the base is measured 1 % too large an the altitude $1\frac{1}{2}$ % too small, find the per cent of error in the area com puted from these measurements. *Ans.* $\frac{1}{2}$ % too small, approx.

11. If the error in a number is 1 %, what is the per cent of error in th square of the number? In the cube of the number?

Ans. 2 %; 3 %, approx.

247. Equations.—Multiplication is often necessary in solv ing equations. In these equations terms may appear that con tain squares or higher powers of the unknown. For th present we are able to solve such equations only when th terms containing squares or higher powers disappear i the process of transposing and uniting terms.

Example.—Solve $(x + 8)(x - 5) = (x - 7)(x + 3) + 9$.

Solution.—Multiplying,

$$x^2 + 3x - 40 = x^2 - 4x - 21 + 9$$

Transposing,

$$x^2 - x^2 + 3x + 4x = 40 - 21 + 9$$

Collecting terms,

$$7x = 28$$

Dividing by 7;

$$x = 4 \quad Ans.$$

Check.—Substituting 4 for x in the original equation,

$$(4 + 8)(4 - 5) = (4 - 7)(4 + 3) + 9$$
$$12 \cdot (-1) = (-3) \cdot 7 + 9$$
$$-12 = -21 + 9$$
$$-12 = -12$$

EXERCISES

Solve the following equations:

1. $(x - 4)^2 = x^2 - 40$. *Ans.* 7.

2. $(x - 3)^2 = (x + 3)^2 - 24$. *Ans.* 2.

3. $9(x - 10) = -(x - 10)$.   *Ans.* 10.

4. $20(x + 2) = 2(x + 20)$.   *Ans.* 0.

5. $(x - 3)^2 + 40 = (x + 7)^2 + 200$.   *Ans.* -10.

6. $(2x + 1)^2 = 4x^2 + 6x + 9$.   *Ans.* -4.

7. $(3x - 2)^2 = 3x(3x + 1)$.   *Ans.* $\frac{4}{15}$.

8. $(2x - 3)^2 = 4(x + 2)^2$.   *Ans.* $-\frac{1}{4}$.

9. $(6x + 2)(5x - 4) - 30(x - 1)^2 = 34x + 106$.   *Ans.* 12.

10. $6x^2 - 27x + 72 = 3x(2x + 3)$.   *Ans.* 2.

11. $(s + 1)(3s + 1) = 3s^2 + 7s - 13$.   *Ans.* $\frac{14}{3}$.

12. $(h + 1)(h^2 - h + 1) = h^3 - 8h - 31$.   *Ans.* -4.

13. If $x - 14$ is multiplied by $x - 10$, the product is 20 more than x^2. Find x.   *Ans.* 5.

14. If a number plus 6 is multiplied by the same number minus 13, the product is 27 more than the square of the number. Find the number.   *Ans.* -15.

15. A rectangle that is 5 ft. narrower and 10 ft. longer than a square is equal in area to the square. Find the dimensions of the square and the rectangle.   *Ans.* 10 ft.; 5 by 20 ft.

Suggestion.—Let x = number of feet in one side of the square.

Then $x - 5$ and $x + 10$ represent the number of feet in the sides of the rectangle.

16. A rectangle that is 2 ft. wider and 6 ft. longer than a square has an area 84 sq. ft. greater than the area of the square. Find the dimensions of the square and of the rectangle.   *Ans.* 9 ft.; 11 by 15 ft.

17. Show that the product of the first and the third of three consecutive numbers is always 1 less than the square of the second.

18. A man's salary is \$1500 the first year and increases p dollars each year. Write a formula for his salary, s, for the nth year.

$$Ans. \ s = 1500 + (n - 1)p.$$

19. It is known that n men received the same salary of x dollars per year for t years and that for $(m + t)$ years they received together a total sum of P dollars. Write a formula for x; for m; for n.

$$Ans. \ x = \frac{P}{n(m + t)}; \ m = \frac{P}{xn} - t; \ n = \frac{P}{x(m + t)}.$$

CHAPTER XXIII

DIVISION

248. Division is the *inverse* of multiplication. That is, the quotient must be a number that multiplied by the divisor will give the dividend. Stated in other words, if the product of two numbers is divided by one of the numbers, the quotient is the other number.

Since division is the inverse of multiplication, we have

$$(+5) \cdot (+3) = +15, \text{ therefore } (+15) \div (+3) = +5$$
$$(-5) \cdot (+3) = -15, \text{ therefore } (-15) \div (+3) = -5$$
$$(+5) \cdot (-3) = -15, \text{ therefore } (-15) \div (-3) = +5$$
$$(-5) \cdot (-3) = +15, \text{ therefore } (+15) \div (-3) = -5$$

It follows that for division of algebraic numbers we have statements analogous to those for multiplication.

(1) *The numerical part of the quotient is the quotient of the absolute values.* (NOTE.—Divisor $\neq 0$.)

(2) *The sign of the quotient is plus when the signs of the dividend and divisor are alike, and minus when their signs are unlike.* (NOTE.—Divisor $\neq 0$.)

249. Law of exponents.—The law applying to exponents that are positive integers is readily established as follows:

$$\frac{a^5}{a^3} = \frac{\not a \cdot \not a \cdot \not a \cdot a \cdot a}{\not a \cdot \not a \cdot \not a} = a^2, \text{ or } a^5 \div a^3 = a^{5-3} = a^2,$$

by canceling common factors in numerator and denominator.

In general, $a^m \div a^n = a^{m-n}$, where m is greater than n.

When $m = n$, we have a case like $a^3 \div a^3 = 1$, for the dividend and divisor are equal.

The law of exponents in division as stated in the following article is considered established:

LAW.—*In dividing powers of the same base, if the exponent of the dividend is the larger, the exponent of the quotient equals the exponent of the dividend minus the exponent of the divisor. If the exponents of the dividend and divisor are equal, the quotient is* 1. (Base $\neq$ 0.)

Illustrations: $x^7 \div x^2 = x^{7-2} = x^5$
$3^8 \div 3^5 = 3^{8-5} = 3^3 = 27$
$a^5 \div a^5 = 1$
$4^3 \div 4^3 = 1$

It should be noted that nothing has been said about the quotient when the exponent of the divisor is larger than the exponent of the dividend. This will be considered later.

250. Division of one monomial by another.—It is well for the beginner to carry out the work of a division in a regular order as in multiplication. (See Art. 241.) The steps in division are

(1) *Determine the sign of the quotient.*

(2) *Determine the coefficient.*

(3) *Determine letters and exponents.*

Remember that in the process of division we divide where we multiply in multiplication, and we subtract exponents where we add exponents in multiplication.

Example.—Divide $25a^4x^5$ by $-5a^2x^3$.

Process.—Carried out in steps:

$$25 \div -5 = -5$$
$$a^4 \div a^2 = a^2$$
$$x^5 \div x^3 = x^2$$
$$\therefore 25a^4x^5 \div -5a^2x^3 = -5a^2x^2 \quad Ans.$$

Only the last should be written down in performing the work. The first three steps are mental operations and are placed here for guidance.

The division of one monomial by another may also be performed as a cancellation. If we recall that an expression like $4a^2b^3$ means $4 \cdot a \cdot a \cdot b \cdot b \cdot b$, we may write $16a^3b^5c^3 \div 4a^2b^3$ in the form

$$\frac{\not{4} \cdot 4 \cdot \not{a} \cdot \not{a} \cdot a \cdot \not{b} \cdot \not{b} \cdot \not{b} \cdot b \cdot b \cdot c \cdot c \cdot c}{\not{4} \cdot \not{a} \cdot \not{a} \cdot \not{b} \cdot \not{b} \cdot \not{b}}$$

Now cancel the factors common to the dividend and divisor. The product of the factors remaining in the dividend is the quotient.

This process is too long for rapid work, but it may clear up points in division that trouble the student.

251. Test.—The work in division can be tested in the same way as in multiplication by substituting convenient values for the letters. It may also be tested by multiplying the divisor by the quotient, in which the product will be the dividend.

EXERCISES

Divide the following:

1. $12x^3y$ by $6xy$ *Ans.* $2x^2$.
2. $-18ab^3$ by $6ab^2$.   *Ans.* $-3b$.
3. $15m^2n^2$ by $-5mn^2$.   *Ans.* $-3m$.
4. $-30abc^2$ by $-15bc$.   *Ans.* $2ac$.
5. $-100h^5k^4$ by $-10hk^3$.   *Ans.* $10h^4k$.
6. $-144t^4u^3v^2$ by $12tu^2v$.   *Ans.* $-12t^3uv$.
7. $225s^3w^6$ by $25sw^4$.   *Ans.* $9s^2w^2$.
8. $17a^3b^4c^5d^6$ by $-17abcd$.   *Ans.* $-a^2b^3c^4d^5$.
9. $-51ax^9y$ by $17ax^7$.   *Ans.* $-3x^2y$.
10. $44b^5g^6$ by $-44b^5g^6$.   *Ans.* -1.
11. $55h^9k^8$ by $-5h^8k$.   *Ans.* $-11hk^7$.
12. $-55mn^3p$ by $10n^2p$.   *Ans.* $-5.5mn$.
13. $22x^5y^3z$ by $-xyz$.   *Ans.* $-22x^4y^2$.
14. $13t^4u^5v^3$ by $-u^4v^2$.   *Ans.* $-13t^4uv$.
15. $65ab^5c^8$ by $13ac^6$.   *Ans.* $5b^5c^2$.
16. $-21^4ab^4cd^4$ by 21^3abcd^3.   *Ans.* $-21b^3d$.
17. $16x^my^4$ by $-4xy^m$.   *Ans.* $-4x^{m-1}y^{4-m}$.
18. $40a^{n+1}b^mc^2$ by $-10a^nb^{m-1}c$.   *Ans.* $-4abc$.
19. $-100x^{5a}b^{5a-1}c^{-5}$ by $25xb^{-1}c^{-6}$.   *Ans.* $-4x^{5a-1}b^{5a}c$.
20. $-4a^{x-y}b^{x+y}c^4$ by $-2a^{-y}b^zc^2$.   *Ans.* $2a^xb^{x+y-z}c^2$.

252. Division of a polynomial by a monomial.

Example.—Divide $24a^5y^3 - 96a^5y^6$ by $8a^4y^3$.

Process:
$$8a^4y^3)\overline{24a^5y^3 - 96a^5y^6}$$
$$3a \quad - 12ay^3 \quad Ans.$$

The division is carried out by first dividing $24a^5y^3$ by $8a^4y^3$ as one monomial by another and then dividing $-96a^5y^6$ by $8a^4y^3$. This process is stated in the following:

RULE.—*The division is performed by dividing each term of the dividend by the divisor, beginning at the left.*

EXERCISES

Divide the following and test by multiplication:

1. $14ax + 28ay + 84az$, by a; by $14a$.

2. $12x^4 - 16x^3y + 20x^5$ by $2x^2$, by $-4x^3$.

3. $-3ab^4 + 6ab^5 - 9ab^6$ by ab^4, by $-3ab^2$.

4. $5(41)^2 - 4(41) + 7(41)^3$ by $-(41)$.

5. $3(5^2) - 7(5)^3 + 9(5)(5)$ by 5^2.

6. $2.5xyz^2 - 0.5x^2yz + 1.5xyz$ by $0.5xz$.

7. $16a^3b^2c - 20a^2b + 24a^2b^2$ by $-4a^2b$.

8. $4x^3 - 3x^2 + 2x$ by $2x$.

9. $24(xy)^2 - 8(x^2y^2)y - 24(xy)y$ by $-8xy$.

10. $8a^7 - 7a^6 + 6a^5 - 5a^4$ by $2a^3$.

11. $y^4 - 1.5y^3 + 0.5y^2$ by $0.5y^2$.

12. $3x^6 + 2x^4 - x^2$ by $0.5x$.

13. $0.25a^5b^4 - 2a^4b^3 + a^3b^2$ by $\dfrac{3ab}{2}$.

14. $4 - 4x - 5x^2 + 7x^3 - 10x^4$ by 0.5.

15. $a(1 + a)^4 - ab(1 + a)^3 + 7a(1 + a)^2$ by $a(1 + a)$, by a, by $a + 1$.

16. $24(x + y)^3 - 12(x + y)^2 - 6(x + y)$ by $-6(x + y)$.

17. $3(m - n)(a + b)^5 - 6(m - n)(a + b)^{10}$ by $-3(m - n)(a + b)^5$, by $(a + b)^2$.

18. $ax^n - bx^{n-1} + cx^{n-2} - dx^{n-3} + ex^{n-4}$ by x^{n-4}.

19. $(a + b)x^m - (a + b)^2x^{m-1} + (a + b)^3x^{m-2}$ by $(a + b)x^m$.

20. $x^{2n} - x^{2n-2} + x^{2n-4} - x^{2n-6}$ by x^{n-6}.

253. Division of a polynomial by a polynomial.—One can do many things by algebra and solve many practical problems and never find it necessary to divide one polynomial by another. To provide for the cases that seldom arise, attention will now be given to such divisions.

The division of a polynomial by a monomial may be likened to short division in arithmetic and, as has been seen, is carried out like the division of, say, $87,066 \div 9$.

$$\text{Thus, } 9\overline{)87066} \\ \phantom{\text{Thus, } 9)}9674$$

The division of a polynomial by a polynomial may be likened to long division in arithmetic and is quite as easy. The actual work will be readily performed by the guidance of the following:

RULE.—(1) *Arrange the dividend and divisor in descending powers beginning with the highest or in ascending powers beginning with the lowest power of a common letter.*

(2) *Divide the first term, left-hand term, of the dividend by the first term of the divisor to find the first term of the quotient.*

(3) *Multiply the divisor by the first term of the quotient; write the product under the like terms of the dividend; and subtract from the dividend.   Then bring down other terms of the dividend.*

(4) *Divide the first term of this remainder by the first term of the divisor to find the second term of the quotient.*

(5) *Multiply the divisor by the second term of the quotient; write the product under the remainder; subtract; and continue in the same manner for other terms in the quotient.   Finally, there will be no remainder or there will be a remainder that cannot be divided by the divisor as previously.*

Example 1.—Divide $x^2 + 7x + 12$ by $x + 3$.

Process:

$$\begin{array}{r|l} x^2 + 7x + 12 & x + 3 \ \ Divisor \\ \underline{x^2 + 3x} & x + 4 \ \ Quotient \\ 4x + 12 & \\ \underline{4x + 12} & \end{array}$$

Check.—*By multiplying divisor by quotient:*

$$\begin{array}{r} x + 3 \\ \underline{x + 4} \\ x^2 + 3x \\ \underline{ 4x + 12} \\ x^2 + 7x + 12 \ \ Dividend \end{array}$$

Example 2.—Divide $x^2 - x^3 + x^4 - 3x + 2$ by $x^2 + x + 2$.

Process.—First, arrange the dividend by (1) of the rule.

$$
\begin{array}{l}
x^4 - x^3 + x^2 - 3x + 2 \,\big|\, x^2 + x + 2 \quad Divisor \\
\underline{x^4 + x^3 + 2x^2} \big|\, x^2 - 2x + 1 \quad Quotient \\
 - 2x^3 - x^2 - 3x \\
 \underline{- 2x^3 - 2x^2 - 4x} \\
 x^2 + x + 2 \\
 \underline{x^2 + x + 2}
\end{array}
$$

Example 3.—Divide $x^3 - 27$ by $x + 3$.

Note that here there are no terms in x^2 and x in the dividend, and make allowance for these by supplying zero terms.

$$
\begin{array}{l}
Process: x^3 + 0x^2 + 0x - 27 \,\big|\, x + 3 Divisor \\
 \underline{x^3 + 3x^2} \big|\, x^2 - 3x + 9 \quad Quotient \\
 - 3x^2 + 0x \\
 \underline{- 3x^2 - 9x} \\
 9x - 27 \\
 \underline{9x + 27} \\
 - 54 \quad Remainder
\end{array}
$$

The result may be written $x^2 - 3x + 9 - \dfrac{54}{x + 3}$, which is exactly as would be done in arithmetic with a slight exception that the student can readily point out.

In checking, where there is a remainder,

$$Dividend = divisor \times quotient + remainder$$

EXERCISES

Divide the following and check by multiplication:

1. $x^2 + 5x + 4$ by $x + 1$.   *Ans.* $x + 4$.
2. $x^2 - 5x + 4$ by $x - 1$.   *Ans.* $x - 4$.
3. $14 + 9x + x^2$ by $7 + x$.   *Ans.* $2 + x$.
4. $14 - 9x + x^2$ by $7 - x$.   *Ans.* $2 - x$.
5. $x^2 + 16x + 63$ by $x + 9$.   *Ans.* $x + 7$.
6. $x^2 - 16x + 63$ by $x - 7$.   *Ans* $x - 9$.
7. $x^2 - 2x - 63$ by $x - 9$.   *Ans.* $x + 7$.
8. $x^2 + 2x - 63$ by $x + 9$.   *Ans.* $x - 7$.

9. $x^3 - 3x^2 + 3x - 1$ by $x - 1$.   *Ans.* $x^2 - 2x + 1$.

10. $x^3 + 3x^2 + 3x + 1$ by $x^2 + 2x + 1$.   *Ans.* $x + 1$.

11. $x^3 + 2x^2 - 5x - 6$ by $x^2 - x - 2$.   *Ans.* $x + 3$.

12. $x^3 + x - 4x^2 - 4$ by $x - 4$.   *Ans.* $x^2 + 1$.

13. $x^4 + x^2 + 1$ by $x^2 + 1 - x$.   *Ans.* $x^2 + x + 1$.

14. $x^6 - 64$ by $x^2 - 4$.   *Ans.* $x^4 + 4x^2 + 16$.

15. $x^4 - 4x^2 + 16$ by $x^2 + 4$.   *Ans.* $x^2 - 8 + \dfrac{48}{x^2 + 4}$.

16. $x^4 - 16$ by $x + 2$.   *Ans.* $x^3 - 2x^2 + 4x - 8$.

17. $27x^6 + 8$ by $9x^4 - 6x^2 + 4$.   *Ans.* $3x^2 + 2$.

18. $27x^6 - 8y^6$ by $3x^2 - 2y^2$.   *Ans.* $9x^4 + 6x^2y^2 + 4y^4$.

19. $32x^4 - 76x^3 + 93x^2 - 110x + 63$ by $4x^3 - 5x^2 + 6x - 7$.

Ans. $8x - 9$.

20. $2a^3 - 3a^2b + 4ab^2 - 5b^3$ by $a - 2b$.

Ans. $2a^2 + ab + 6b^2 + \dfrac{7b^3}{a - 2b}$.

21. $12x^4 - 10x^3y + 8x^2y^2 - 6xy^3 + 4y^4$ by $x^2 + y^2$.

Ans. $12x^2 - 10xy - 4y^2 + \dfrac{4xy^3 + 8y^4}{x^2 + y^2}$.

22. $x^{5n} - y^{5n}$ by $x^n - y^n$.   *Ans.* $x^{4n} + x^{3n}y^n + x^{2n}y^{2n} + x^ny^{3n} + y^{4n}$.

23. If the area of a rectangle is $x^2 + 3x + 2$ and one side is $x + 1$, find the other side.   Check by substituting $x = 5; x = 0$.   *Ans.* $x + 2$.

24. The area of a rectangle is given by $x^2 + x$.   Find lengths for the two sides in terms of x.   *Ans.* x and $x + 1$.

CHAPTER XXIV

SPECIAL PRODUCTS AND QUOTIENTS, AND FACTORING

254. When one is to do a certain piece of work, it is well that he should have already in mind (1) exactly what is to be done, (2) how it is to be done, and (3), so far as possible, why it is to be done. He can then go about the task in an interested manner and with assurance of success.

There are certain forms in multiplication and division that one meets again and again in using algebra, and much time and labor are saved if these are learned so that when they are met, the results may be written at once from memory. Then, too, the more familiar one is with these forms the easier it is for him to determine the factors of expressions occurring in his work.

Factoring does not involve new processes in computation, but ability to factor depends upon one's insight into the combinations that may have entered into the expression to be factored.

In this chapter will be considered only algebraic expressions and their factors that are of a simple nature and can be readily handled. It must not be thought that factoring is always easy, nor is it always possible to factor an algebraic expression into simple factors.

255. Definitions.—The definitions used are strictly in accordance with those already used in arithmetic.

A **factor** of an algebraic expression is an expression that will exactly divide the given expression.

An expression is said to be **prime** when it has no other factors than itself and one.

Any given expression is said to be **factored** when it is resolved into its prime factors.

Ordinarily all the prime factors are not discovered at once, but the given expression is factored into two factors which may or may not be prime, and then these are further factored, continuing till all factors are prime.

Factoring as a process is very closely connected with multiplication and division. When two or more expressions are multiplied together to form a product, each of the expressions used is a factor of the product. Factoring is the inverse of this process; for in factoring, one starts with the product and endeavors to find the expressions that may have been multiplied together to form the product.

We will suppose now that we have a fairly clear idea of *what* we wish to do and *why*. The *how* it is to be done will follow.

256. Factors of a monomial.—The factors of a monomial, excepting the numerical coefficient, are at once evident from the meaning of the symbols used. For this reason it is not necessary to pay any attention to the factoring of monomials. Of course, the factoring of the numerical coefficient is simple arithmetic.

Thus, the factors of a^4x^2y are a repeated four times, x repeated twice, and y.

The factors of $14x^2y^3$ are $2 \cdot 7 \cdot x \cdot x \cdot y \cdot y \cdot y$.

Because the factors are perfectly evident, a monomial is not usually separated into its prime factors.

257. Factors of a polynomial when one factor is a monomial. In Exercise 1, page 355, each term of $14ax + 28ay + 84az$ can be divided by $14a$. The quotient is $x + 2y + 6z$. Now the product of $x + 2y + 6z$ and $14a$ is $14ax + 28ay + 84az$. We say that $14a$ and $x + 2y + 6z$ are the factors of $14ax + 28ay + 84az$.

The factors of a polynomial similar to the foregoing are a monomial, containing all that is common to each term of the polynomial, and the quotient found by dividing the polynomial by the monomial.

As a help in factoring a polynomial when one factor is a monomial we give the following:

RULE.—(1) *Inspect the terms of the polynomial, and determine a monomial that will divide all the terms. This is one factor.*

(2) *Divide the polynomial by this monomial, and find the quotient, which is the other factor.*

Example.—Factor $4a^2x - 2ax^2 + 6a^2x^2$.

The monomial factor is $2ax$. This is seen by inspection. Dividing the polynomial by $2ax$ we find $2a - x + 3ax$, which is the other factor. The factors are written in the form $2ax(2a - x + 3ax)$.

The work may be tested by finding the product of the factors, which gives the expression that was to be factored.

EXERCISES

Find factors orally of the following and test the work by multiplication:

1. $4b + 8$.
2. $8x - 16$.
3. $12y + 4z$.
4. $6ab - 21ac$.
5. $9x^2 + 6x$.
6. $9x^2y - 19xy^2$.

7. $5 - 10mn - 15my$.
8. $5mn - 10mny + 15my^2$.
9. $2a^2b - 3ab^2 + ab$.
10. $3st^2 - 6tu^2 + 9stu$.
11. $x^2y^2 - 4x^4y^4 + 4x^6y^6$.
12. $15h^2 - 21h^3 + 30h^4$.

13. $100m^2 - 200mn + 300mn^2$.
14. $250x^3 - 1000x^6y$.
15. $5^2x - 5^3x^2$.
16. $17A^2 - 51B^2$.
17. $13(AB)^2 - 65(AB)^3$.
18. $15A^2B^2 + 30A^3B^3$.
19. $(x - 2)a + (x - 2)b$. *Ans.* $(x - 2)(a + b)$.

Suggestion.—Consider $(x - 2)a$ and $(x - 2)b$ as the terms of the polynomial. Then $(x - 2)$ is common to the two terms and is the factor to use as a divisor in finding the other factor.

20. $(a + b)x^2 - (a + b)y^2$. *Ans.* $(a + b)(x^2 - y^2)$.
21. $(2x - 3y)xy + (2x - 3y)$. *Ans.* $(2x - 3y)(xy + 1)$.
22. $5(7ax + 5) - 15(7ax + 5)x$. *Ans.* $5(7ax + 5)(1 - 3x)$.
23. $10x^2(s + t) - 20xy(a + b)$. *Ans.* $10x[x(s + t) - 2y(a + b)]$.

24. $10x^2(s + t) - 20xy(s + t)^3$.   *Ans.* $10x(s + t)[x - 2y(s + t)^2]$.

25. $5^2a^2(x + y)^2 - 10a(x + y)$.   *Ans.* $5a(x + y)[5a(x + y) - 2]$.

258. Squares and square roots of monomials.—By the principles of multiplication already given, the *square* of a monomial may be found as follows:

(1) *The sign is always plus.*

(2) *The numerical coefficient is the square of the numerical coefficient of the monomial.*

(3) *The exponent of any letter is twice the exponent of the same letter in the monomial.*

Thus, $(5a^2b^3)^2 = 25a^4b^6$, $(-4a^3b^2d)^2 = 16a^6b^4d^2$, and $(\frac{1}{3}x^3y)^2 = \frac{1}{9}x^6y^2$.

The *square root* of a monomial can be found by doing the inverse processes to those for finding the *square* of a monomial.

(1) *The square root can be found of a positive number only.*

(2) *The numerical coefficient is the square root of the numerical coefficient of the monomial.*

(3) *The exponent of any letter is one-half the exponent of the same letter in the monomial.*

It follows that the monomial of which the square root is to be taken must have a numerical coefficient that is a perfect square and all the exponents must be even numbers. Otherwise the square root cannot be found exactly.

Thus, $\sqrt{16a^4b^2} = 4a^2b$ and $\sqrt{225x^4y^6z^2} = 15x^2y^3z$; but $\sqrt{10a^4b^6}$ can only be expressed as $\sqrt{10}\,a^2b^3$; and $\sqrt{35a^3b}$ cannot be found.

EXERCISES

Find the indicated square or square root of the following expressions when possible. When not possible, tell what change in the expression would make it possible. Do these orally.

1. $(2ax^2)^2$.

2. $(-2ax^2)^2$.

3. $(-4ab^2c)^2$.

4. $(\frac{2}{3}xy^2z^3)^2$.

5. $[-\frac{3}{4}AB^3C^4]^2$.

6. $[0.5h^3k^6]^2$.

7. $(-0.2ax^2y^8)^2$.

8. $(-25u^4v^9)^2$.

9. $\sqrt{4x^2y^8}$.

10. $\sqrt{25h^4k^{10}}$.

11. $\sqrt{81t^4u^9}$.

12. $\sqrt{8t^4u^8}$.

13. $\sqrt{169X^2Y^6}$.

14. $\sqrt{36AB^2}$.

15. $\sqrt{144a^4b^4}$.

16. $\sqrt{-16x^2}$.

17. $\sqrt{-4y^4}$.

18. $\sqrt{-9x^2y^2}$.

19. $\sqrt{(-9x^2y^2)^2}$.

20. $\sqrt{\left(\dfrac{a}{3}\right)^2 W^2u^2}$.

21. $\sqrt{\left(\dfrac{g}{2}\right)^2 t^4}$.

259. The square of a binomial.—The square of a binomial is a special product that occurs very frequently, and it will well pay one to learn how to write the square without actually multiplying.

By actual multiplication

$$(a + b)^2 = a^2 + 2ab + b^2$$
$$(a - b)^2 = a^2 - 2ab + b^2$$

Here a and b are general numbers, so we may use the statements as formulas to find the square of the sum or the difference of any two numbers. These formulas may be translated into words as follows:

(1) *The square of the sum of two numbers equals the square of the first plus twice the product of the first by the second plus the square of the second.*

(2) *The square of the difference of two numbers equals the square of the first minus twice the product of the first by the second plus the square of the second.*

The use of these principles will save much work in multiplication.

Example 1.—Find the value of $(cd + e)^2$.

The square of the first term $= (cd)^2 = c^2d^2$.

Twice the product of the first by the second $= 2(cd)e = 2cde$.

The square of the second term $= e^2$.

$$\therefore (cd + e)^2 = c^2d^2 + 2cde + e^2 \quad Ans.$$

Example 2: $(2a + b^2)^2 = 4a^2 + 4ab^2 + b^4$.   *Ans.*
Example 3: $(2x^2 - 3y^3)^2 = 4x^4 - 12x^2y^3 + 9y^6$.   *Ans.*

EXERCISES

Write the products of the following without actual multiplication, and then test by actual multiplication.

1. $(x + 6)^2$.
2. $(2x - 6)^2$.
3. $(2x + 6y)^2$.
4. $(2x - 6y)^2$.
5. $(A^2 - 2)^2$.
6. $(2b^2 + 1)^2$.
7. $(4 - 5W^3)^2$.
8. $(2U^2 - aV)^2$.
9. $(2ax - 3by)^2$.
10. $(2x^3 + 3xy^2)^2$.
11. $(3^2 - 2^2)^2$.
12. $(30 - 1)^2$.
13. $(20 + 1)^2$.
14. $(50 - 1)^2$.
15. $(20 - 1)^2$.
16. $(100 - 1)^2$.

260. Factors of a trinomial square.—A *trinomial square* is a trinomial that is the square of a binomial. Thus, $a^2 + 2ab + b^2$ is a trinomial square because it is the square of the binomial $a + b$. Its factors then are evidently $(a + b)(a + b)$. Likewise, the factors of $a^2 - 2ab + b^2$ are $(a - b)(a - b)$. The factors of $4x^2 - 12x + 9$ are $(2x - 3)(2x - 3)$.

How to distinguish whether or not a trinomial is a perfect square should be carefully learned.

(1) *The trinomial must have two positive terms, each of which is the square of a monomial.*

(2) *It must have one term, either positive or negative, that is twice the product of the square roots of the two other terms. If this term is positive, the factors are sums; and if negative, the factors are differences.*

Thus, $9a^4 - 24a^2y^2 + 16y^4$ is a trinomial square; for $9a^4$ and $16y^4$ are each positive and squares of the monomials $3a^2$ and $4y^2$ respectively, and $24a^2y^2$ is twice the product of these square roots. The factors are $(3a^2 - 4y^2)(3a^2 - 4y^2)$.

Since by definition the **square root** of a number is one of its two equal factors, the square root of a trinomial square is one of its two equal factors.

EXERCISES

Determine which of the following are trinomial squares. Factor, and find the square root when possible. Do these orally.

1. $x^2 + 2x + 1$.

2. $x^2 - 4x + 4$.

3. $x^2 - 6xy + 9$.

4. $x^2 - 6xy + 9y^2$.

5. $x^2 + 8xy - 16y^2$.

6. $x^2 + 8xy + 16y^2$.

7. $X^4 + 10XY + 25Y^4$.

8. $X^4 + 10X^2Y^2 + 25Y^4$.

9. $-10xy + 25y^2 + x^2$.

10. $9x^2 + 16y^2 - 24xy$.

11. $9x^6 + 16y^6 - 24x^3y^3$.

12. $625a^2 + 225b^4 + 750ab^2$.

13. $0.25x^2 - 0.25x + \frac{1}{16}$.

14. $4x^6 + 12x^3y^2 + 9y^4$.

15. $-108U^2V^2 + 36U^4 + 81V^4$.

16. $-40ST + 16S^2 + 25T^2$.

17. $-(x^2 + 2x + 1)$.

18. $-(-112R + 49R^2 + 64)$.

261. The product of the sum of two numbers by the difference of the same two numbers.—A very common case of multiplication, and perhaps the most frequently occurring of any, is the product of the sum of any two numbers by their difference. By actual multiplication,

$$(a + b)(a - b) = a^2 - b^2$$

Since a and b are general numbers, we may use this statement as a formula and so write at once, without actual multiplication, the product of the sum and the difference of any two numbers. The formula may be translated into words as follows:

The product of the sum and the difference of two numbers equals the difference of their squares.

Example 1: $(2c + 3b)(2c - 3b) = 4c^2 - 9b^2$. *Ans.*

Example 2: $(16 + 2)(16 - 2) = 16^2 - 2^2 = 256 - 4 = 252$. *Ans.*

Example 3: $102 \times 98 = (100 + 2)(100 - 2) = 10,000 - 4 = 9996$. *Ans.*

EXERCISES

Find the product of each of the following without actual multiplication, and test by actual multiplication:

1. $(x - 3)(x + 3)$.
2. $(3y + 4)(3y - 4)$.
3. $(7h + 8k)(7h - 8k)$.

4. $(11a^2 + 7b)(11a^2 - 7b)$.
5. $(ab^3 + 2c^3)(ab^3 - 2c^3)$.
6. $(4d + 5c^2)(4d - 5c^2)$.

7. $(8m^4 - an^3)(8m^4 + an^3)$.
8. $[(3)(5)^2 - 7][(3)(5)^2 + 7]$.
9. $[(a + 2) - b][(a + 2) + b]$.
10. $[(x - y) + z][(x - y) - z]$.
11. $(2c + d + e)(2c + d - e)$.

Suggestion.—This may be written

$$[(2c + d) + e][(2c + d) - e] = (2c + d)^2 - e^2$$
$$= 4c^2 + 4cd + d^2 - e^2$$

12. $(a + b + 5)(a + b - 5)$.
13. $(a - b + 5)(a + b + 5) = (a + 5 - b)(a + 5 + b) = ?$
14. $(a^2 - b^2 - ab)(a^2 + b^2 + ab)$
$$= [a^2 - (b^2 + ab)][a^2 + (b^2 + ab)] = ?$$
15. $(10 + 2a + 3b)(10 - 2a - 3b)$.
16. $(3 - x + y)(3 + x + y)$.

Suggestion.—This may be written

$$[(3 + y) - x][(3 + y) + x] = (3 + y)^2 - x^2 = ?$$

17. $(a + b + 7)(a - b + 7)$.
18. $(-a - b + 7)(a + b + 7)$.
19. $(10ax^2 + 9bc)(9bc - 10ax^2)$.
20. $98 \times 102 = (100 - 2)(100 + 2) = ?$

21. 97×103.	23. 44×36.	25. 702×698.
22. 87×93.	24. 1105×1095.	26. 1001×999.

262. Factors of the difference of two squares.—From a consideration of the preceding it is easily seen that *the difference of two squares can be factored into two binomial factors that are, respectively, the sum and the difference of the square roots of these squares.*

Example 1: $4 - a^2 = (2 + a)(2 - a)$. *Ans.*

Example 2: $16a^4 - 9y^2 = (4a^2 + 3y)(4a^2 - 3y)$. *Ans.*

Example 3: $(a + b)^2 - 2^2 = (a + b + 2)(a + b - 2)$.
Ans.

Example 4: $a^2 - b^2 + 2bc - c^2 = a^2 - (b^2 - 2bc + c^2) = a^2 - (b - c)^2 = (a + b - c)(a - b + c)$. *Ans.*

EXERCISES

Factor the following and test by multiplication:

1. $9 - x^2$.
2. $1 - 9x^2$.
3. $9y^2 - 16$.
4. $9y^2 - 25b^2$.
5. $25 - 16x^4$.
6. $81u^4 - 9v^2$.

7. $81 - 9$.
8. $81 - 9a^2$.
9. $a^2b^2 - 4c^2$.
10. $4a^2b^4 - 16c^6$.
11. $2^2a^2b^4 - 4^2c^4$.
12. $2^23^4a^2x^4 - 7^2$.

13. $(a + 2)^2 - x^2$. *Ans.* $(a + 2 + x)(a + 2 - x)$.
14. $(a + 2b)^2 - 9c^2$. *Ans.* $(a + 2b + 3c)(a + 2b - 3c)$.
15. $a^2 + 2ab + b^2 - c^2$. *Ans.* $(a + b + c)(a + b - c)$.
16. $a^2 - 4b^2 - 4bc - c^2$. *Ans.* $(a + 2b + c)(a - 2b - c)$.
17. $4 - (x + 2y)^2$. *Ans.* $(2 + x + 2y)(2 - x - 2y)$.
18. $100 - (a - b)^2$. *Ans.* $(10 + a - b)(10 - a + b)$.
19. $4b^2 + 9c^2 - 16x^2 - 12bc$. *Ans.* $(2b - 3c + 4x)(2b - 3c - 4x)$.
20. $(4 - x)^2 - (x - y)^2$. *Ans.* $(4 - y)(4 - 2x + y)$.

263. The product of two binomials having one common term.
The necessity for finding the product of two binomials that
have a common term is of less frequent occurrence, but still
it is of importance. By actual multiplication the following
products are found:

$$(1) \quad (a + 2)(a + 3) = a^2 + 5a + 6$$
$$(2) \quad (a - 2)(a - 3) = a^2 - 5a + 6$$
$$(3) \quad (a + 2)(a - 3) = a^2 - a - 6$$
$$(4) \quad (a - 2)(a + 3) = a^2 + a - 6$$
$$(5) \quad (a + b)(a + c) = a^2 + (b + c)a + bc$$

The two factors in each of these products have a common
term a, and the other terms are different.

From an inspection of these, the truth of the following statement can be seen:

*The product of two binomials, having one common term and
the other terms unlike, is a trinomial consisting of the square
of the common term, the algebraic sum of the unlike terms times
the common term, and the product of the unlike terms.*

Thus, in (1) above, the common term is a and the unlike terms are 2 and 3. The square of the common term is a^2. The algebraic sum of the unlike terms is $2 + 3 = 5$, and this times the common term is 5 times $a = 5a$. The product of the unlike terms is $2 \times 3 = 6$. Hence, the result $(a + 2)(a + 3) = a^2 + 5a + 6$.

Likewise in (3), the square of the common term is a^2. The algebraic sum of the unlike terms is the sum of $+2$ and -3, or -1. This times the common term, a, is $-a$. The product of the unlike terms is $2 \times -3 = -6$. Hence, the result $(a + 2)(a - 3) = a^2 - a - 6$.

EXERCISES

Find the products of the following without actual multiplication, and test by multiplication.

1. $(a + 1)(a + 5)$.
2. $(x - 5)(x - 2)$.
3. $(x + 5)(x - 2)$.
4. $(y - 7)(y + 9)$.
5. $(y + 7)(y - 9)$.
6. $(h + 8)(h + 4)$.
7. $(u - 2)(u - 5)$.
8. $(b - 9)(b + 1)$.
9. $(3k - 4)(3k + 5)$.
10. $(2a + 4)(2a - 2)$.
11. $(7s - 6)(7s - 8)$.
12. $(2h + 3)(2h - 4)$.
13. $(3 + 4)(3 - 2)$.
14. $(3p + 4)(3p - 2)$.
15. $(10 - 2x)(9 + 2x)$.
16. $(5 - xy)(6 + xy)$.
17. $(xy - 5)(xy + 6)$.
18. $(4mn - 8)(4mn + 1)$.
19. $(10 - y)(9 + y)$.
20. $(7ax + 4)(ax + 4)$.
21. $(4x^3 - 9)(4x^3 + 3)$.

264. To factor a trinomial into two binomials with one common term.—By a careful study of the preceding exercises, we may determine how to proceed in factoring such trinomials as the products in those exercises. The method of factoring those forms will best be seen by considering examples.

Example 1.—Factor $a^2 + 9a + 20$.

This has one term, a^2, that is a perfect square; a, the square root of this, is to be the common term of the factors if there are any. The unlike terms of the factors must have a product of $+20$ and a sum of $+9$. By inspection we see that $+5$ and $+4$ have such a product and sum. Hence, the factors of $a^2 + 9a + 20$ are $(a + 5)(a + 4)$. *Ans.*

Example 2.—Factor $a^2 - a - 20$.

As before, the common term is a. The unlike terms have a product of -20 and a sum of -1. The product being $-$, one of the terms is $-$ and one $+$. The sum, being $-$, shows that the larger in absolute value is $-$. This gives -5 and $+4$ as the numbers.

Hence, $a^2 - a - 20 = (a - 5)(a + 4)$. *Ans.*

Many trinomials that, at first glance, appear to be of the kind here considered cannot be factored in this way. For instance, $x^2 + 7x + 5$ cannot be factored as here, for we can find no integral numbers that have a sum of 7 and a product of 5. [See Chap. XXX for a method of factoring the general trinomial.]

EXERCISES

Factor the following by the method of this article if possible; if not, change a term so that they may be factored. Test your work by multiplication.

1. $x^2 + 5x + 4$.
2. $x^2 - 5x + 4$.
3. $x^2 + 4x + 4$.
4. $x^2 - 4x + 4$.
5. $y^2 - 9y + 18$.
6. $y^2 + 9y + 18$.
7. $y^2 - 11y + 18$.
8. $y^2 + 11y + 18$.
9. $y^2 - 19y + 18$.
10. $h^2 + h - 56$.
11. $h^2 - h - 56$.
12. $h^2 - 18h + 56$.
13. $h^2 + 10h - 56$.
14. $h^2 - 10h - 56$.
15. $k^2 + 2k + 2$.

16. $k^2 + 2k + 1$.
17. $k^2 + 2k$.
18. $k^2 + 2k - 8$.
19. $x^2 + 4x + 5$.
20. $x^2 - 4x - 60$.
21. $x^2 + x + 1$.
22. $x^2 + x - 2$.
23. $x^2 - x + 1$.
24. $x^2 - x - 2$.
25. $p^2 - 2p + 3$.
26. $p^2 - 10p$.
27. $p^2 - 10p + 16$.
28. $x^2y^2 + xy - 72$.
29. $m^4 - 7m^2 + 6$.
30. $m^4 - m - 6$.

31. $-10 - 3x + x^2$.

32. $-10 + 3x + x^2$.

33. $40 + 22mn + m^2n^2$.

34. $u^2 - 7uv + 12v^2$.

35. $u^2 + 7uv + 10v^2$.

36. $77 - 4hk + h^2k^2$.

37. $(2 + x)^2 - 5(2 + x) + 6$.

Suggestion.—This may be written

$A^2 - 5A + 6 = (A - 3)(A - 2)$

$= [(2 + x) - 3][(2 + x) - 2]$

$= (2 + x - 3)(2 + x - 2)$

$= (x - 1)(x).$

38. $(x + y)^2 - (x + y)$.

39. $(x + y)^2 - (x + y) + 90$.

265. Trinomials factored into binomials with no common term.—A class of trinomials, those where the binomial factors have no common term, will now be considered. The factoring of these forms will be done by inspection and will require very careful study of the formation of such trinomials as are the products of two binomials having no common term but that have a common letter occurring in a term of each. As illustrations of such products we have by actual multiplication:

(1) $\qquad (x + 3)(2x + 1) = 2x^2 + 7x + 3$

(2) $\qquad (2a + 3)(3a - 5) = 6a^2 - a - 15$

(3) $\qquad (5y - 4)(2y - 7) = 10y^2 - 43y + 28$

(4) $\qquad (3x - 2y)(x + 4y) = 3x^2 + 10xy - 8y^2$

In each of these it is noted that the product has a term containing the square of the common letter, a term containing the first power, and a term that does not contain the letter. This trinomial always contains the square of the letters involved and therefore is called a **quadratic trinomial.** Its general form is $ax^2 + bx + c$, where a, b, and c are any numbers. The trinomials already considered in previous articles are forms of this, in which a, b, and c have special values. The student should point these out.

266. Method for multiplying and factoring.—We will now study carefully the multiplication for (2) of the preceding article.

Perform the multiplication in the usual way and note:

(1) The first term of the product, $6a^2$, is the product of the first two terms of the factors.

$$
\begin{array}{r}
2a + 3 \\
3a - 5 \\
\hline
6a^2 + \ 9a \\
- 10a - 15 \\
\hline
6a^2 - \quad a - 15
\end{array}
$$

(2) The last term of the product, -15, is the product of the second terms of the factors.

(3) The middle term of the product, $-a$, is the sum of what are known as the "cross products," $3a$ by 3 and -5 by $2a$.

Following the inverse of this process enables one to find the factors of such a quadratic trinomial.

Example 1.—Factor $2x^2 + 7x + 3$.

The first term of each factor contains x.

The product of the numerical parts of the first terms is 2. Hence, they must be 1 and 2, as these are the only two factors of 2.

The product of the second terms of the factors is 3. Hence, they must be 1 and 3.

The sum of the cross products is $+7x$.

Keeping these facts in mind, one can determine the factors, at least after a few trials.

$$2x^2 + 7x + 3 = (x + 3)(2x + 1) \quad Ans.$$

Example 2.—Factor $18x^2 + 3x - 10$.

The first term of each factor contains x.

The product of the numerical parts of the first terms is 18. Hence, they may be 1 and 18, 2 and 9, or 3 and 6.

The product of the second terms of the factors is -10. Hence, they may be 1 and -10, -1 and 10, 2 and -5, or -2 and 5.

The sum of the cross products is $3x$.

Fitting these numbers together, after a greater or less number of trials, we have

$$18x^2 + 3x - 10 = (3x - 2)(6x + 5) \quad Ans.$$

EXERCISES

Factor the following by trial, and test by actual multiplication:

1. $2x^2 + 11x + 12$.   *Ans.* $(2x + 3)(x + 4)$.
2. $2x^2 + 6x - 20$.   *Ans.* $2(x + 5)(x - 2)$.
3. $2x^2 - 7x - 30$.   *Ans.* $(2x + 5)(x - 6)$.
4. $6x^2 + 22x + 20$.   *Ans.* $2(x + 2)(3x + 5)$.
5. $6x^2 - 16x - 6$.   *Ans.* $2(x - 3)(3x + 1)$.

6. $6x^2 + 17x + 10$.   *Ans.* $(6x + 5)(x + 2)$.
7. $20x^2 + 41x + 20$.   *Ans.* $(5x + 4)(4x + 5)$.
8. $12x^2 - x - 20$.   *Ans.* $(4x + 5)(3x - 4)$.
9. $15x^2 + 34xy - 77y^2$.   *Ans.* $(5x - 7y)(3x + 11y)$.
10. $45x^2 - 78xy - 63y^2$.   *Ans.* $3(3x - 7y)(5x + 3y)$.

267. Sums and differences of cubes.—By actual division
we have (see Art. 253)

$$\frac{a^3 + b^3}{a + b} = a^2 - ab + b^2$$

$$\frac{a^3 - b^3}{a - b} = a^2 + ab + b^2$$

Stated in words these are:

*The sum of the cubes of two numbers, divided by the sum
of the numbers, gives for a quotient the square of the first number
minus the product of the two numbers plus the square of the
second number.*

*The difference of the cubes of two numbers, divided by the
difference of the numbers, gives for a quotient the square of the
first number plus the product of the two numbers plus the square
of the second number.*

One can, therefore, readily write the factors of the sum of
two cubes or of the difference of two cubes.

Examples: $x^3 + 8 = x^3 + 2^3 = (x + 2)(x^2 - 2x + 4)$.

$a^3 - 27 = a^3 - 3^3 = (a - 3)(a^2 + 3a + 9)$.
$8x^3 + 64y^3 = (2x)^3 + (4y)^3 = (2x + 4y)(4x^2 - 8xy + 16y^2)$
$a^6 + b^6 = (a^2)^3 + (b^2)^3 = (a^2 + b^2)(a^4 - a^2b^2 + b^4)$.

EXERCISES

Factor the following as sums or differences of cubes:
1. $a^3 + x^3$.   *Ans.* $(a + x)(a^2 - ax + x^2)$.
2. $h^3 - k^3$.   *Ans.* $(h - k)(h^2 + hk + k^2)$.
3. $1 + 8x^3$.   *Ans.* $(1 + 2x)(1 - 2x + 4x^2)$.
4. $8x^3 - 27y^3$.   *Ans.* $(2x - 3y)(4x^2 + 6xy + 9y^2)$.
5. $27 + 64a^3$.   *Ans.* $(3 + 4a)(9 - 12a + 16a^2)$.
6. $64x^3 + 8y^6$.   *Ans.* $(4x + 2y^2)(16x^2 - 8xy^2 + 4y^4)$.
7. $125 - h^3$.   *Ans.* $(5 - h)(25 + 5h + h^2)$.

8. $27b^9 - c^6$.   *Ans.* $(3b^3 - c^2)(9b^6 + 3b^3c^2 + c^4)$.

9. $8a^3 + 27b^3$.   *Ans.* $(2a + 3b)(4a^2 - 6ab + 9b^2)$.

10. $x^3y^6 + 1$.   *Ans.* $(xy^2 + 1)(x^2y^4 - xy^2 + 1)$.

11. $x^3 - y^6$.   *Ans.* $(x + y^2)(x^2 - xy^2 + y^4)$.

12. $1000R^3 - 216S^{12}$.   *Ans.* $(10R - 6S^4)(100R^2 + 60RS^4 + 36S^8)$.

13. $(a + b)^3 - 8c^3$.   *Ans.* $[(a + b) - 2c][(a + b)^2 + 2c(a + b) + 4c^2]$.

14. $(x^2 + y^2)^3 + 8x^3y^3$.
   Ans. $[(x^2 + y^2) + 2xy][(x^2 + y^2)^2 - 2xy(x^2 + y^2) + 4x^2y^2]$.

268. Summary of factoring.

In factoring one must first classify the problem as to type and then proceed according to the method for factoring that type.

The types of factoring may be summarized as follows:

(1) $\mathbf{ax + ay + az = a(x + y + z)}$	See Art. 257.
(2) $\mathbf{a^2 \pm 2ab + b^2 = (a \pm b)^2}$	See Art. 260.
(3) $\mathbf{a^2 - b^2 = (a + b)(a - b)}$	See Art. 262.
(4) $\mathbf{a^2 + (b + c)a + bc = (a + b)(a + c)}$	See Art. 264.
(5) $\mathbf{ax^2 + bx + c}$	See Art. 265.
(6) $\mathbf{a^3 + b^3}$ **and** $\mathbf{a^3 - b^3}$	See Art. 267.

Frequently various types will develop as one proceeds in factoring an expression. Remember that the expression is not completely factored till all factors are prime.

Example.—Factor $a^6 - b^6$.

This may be taken as the difference of two squares or as the difference of two cubes. Taking it as the difference of two squares is the easier.

$$a^6 - b^6 = (a^3)^2 - (b^3)^2 = (a^3 + b^3)(a^3 - b^3)$$
$$= (a + b)(a^2 - ab + b^2)(a - b)(a^2 + ab + b^2)$$
$$Ans.$$

EXERCISES

Classify and factor the following expressions:

1. $4x + 8y - 12z$.   *Ans.* $4(x + 2y - 3z)$.

2. $4x^2 + 8xy + 4y^2$.   *Ans.* $4(x + y)^2$.

3. $8x + x^4$.   *Ans.* $x(2 + x)(4 - 2x + x^2)$.

4. $10x^2 + 23x + 12$.   *Ans.* $(5x + 4)(2x + 3)$.

5. $x^2 - 6x + 8$.   *Ans.* $(x - 4)(x - 2)$.

6. $100 - x^4$.   *Ans.* $(10 - x^2)(10 + x^2)$.

7. $16 - x^4$.   *Ans.* $(4 + x^2)(2 + x)(2 - x)$.

8. $(x^2 + 4)^2 - (4x)^2$.   *Ans.* $(x - 2)^2(x + 2)^2$.

9. $6a^2 - a - 2$.   *Ans.* $(2a + 1)(3a - 2)$.

10. $5b^2 - 24b - 5$.   *Ans.* $(5b + 1)(b - 5)$.

11. $14x^2 + 29x - 15$.   *Ans.* $(7x - 3)(2x + 5)$.

12. $25x^4 - 25x$.   *Ans.* $25x(x - 1)(x^2 + x + 1)$.

13. $25x^2 - 10xy + y^2$.   *Ans.* $(5x - y)^2$.

14. $mn^2 - 6mn + 9m$.   *Ans.* $m(n - 3)^2$.

15. $6y^3 - 48$.   *Ans.* $6(y - 2)(y^2 + 2y + 4)$.

16. $a^2 - b^2 - 4bc - 4c^2$.   *Ans.* $(a - b - 2c)(a + b + 2c)$.

17. $4x^2 - 100$.   *Ans.* $4(x - 5)(x + 5)$.

18. $(x - y)^2 - 25$.   *Ans.* $(x - y - 5)(x - y + 5)$.

19. $(x - y)^3 - 125$.   *Ans.* $(x - y - 5)[(x - y)^2 + 5(x - y) + 25]$.

20. $27 + (a - 2b)^3$.

   Ans. $[3 + (a - 2b)][9 - 3(a - 2b) + (a - 2b)^2]$.

21. $8x - 2xy^2$.   *Ans.* $2x(2 - y)(2 + y)$.

22. $10x^2 + 23xy$.   *Ans.* $x(10x + 23y)$.

23. $2x^2y^4 - 16x^2y$.   *Ans.* $2x^2y(y - 2)(y^2 + 2y + 4)$.

24. $(x^2 + 4)^2 - 16x^2$.   *Ans.* $(x - 2)^2(x + 2)^2$.

25. $a^2x^2 + 2axb + b^2$.   *Ans.* $(ax + b)^2$.

26. $a^2 + 8a^5$.   *Ans.* $a^2(1 + 2a)(1 - 2a + 4a^2)$.

27. $22x^2 + 69x + 35$.   *Ans.* $(11x + 7)(2x + 5)$.

28. $Ax^5 - Ax^2$.   *Ans.* $Ax^2(x - 1)(x^2 + x + 1)$.

29. $(2x + y)^2 + 2(2x + y) + 1$.   *Ans.* $(2x + y + 1)^2$.

30. $-x^2 - y^2 + 2xy + a^2$.   *Ans.* $(x - y + a)(-x + y + a)$.

31. $4(x - y)^2 - 4(x - y) + 1$.   *Ans.* $[2(x - y) - 1]^2$.

32. $(a - 2b)^3 + (a + 2b)^3$.   *Ans.* $2a(a^2 + 12b^2)$.

CHAPTER XXV

EQUATIONS

269. Equations that were comparatively easy of solution were considered in Chap. XXI. In the present chapter further equations will be given, which will be of a slightly more difficult nature. In solving some of these, factoring will be used.

If an equation has indicated multiplications and signs of grouping, it is usually best to perform the multiplications and remove the signs of grouping before proceeding with the solution of the equation.

Example 1.—Find the value of c from

$$4c + 3[2c - 4(c - 2)] = 72 - 6c$$

Solution.—Given equation

(1) $$4c + 3[2c - 4(c - 2)] = 72 - 6c$$

Simplifying,

(2) $$4c + 3[2c - 4c + 8] = 72 - 6c$$

Simplifying,

(3) $$4c + 6c - 12c + 24 = 72 - 6c$$

Transposing,

(4) $$4c + 6c - 12c + 6c = 72 - 24$$

Collecting terms,

(5) $$4c = 48$$

Dividing by the coefficient of c,

(6) $$c = 12 \quad Ans.$$

Test: $48 + 3[24 - 4(12 - 2)] = 72 - 72$, or $0 = 0$

Example 2.—Solve for x:

$$(1 + 3x)^2 = (5 - x)^2 + 4(1 - x)(3 - 2x)$$

Solution.—Given equation

(1) $(1 + 3x)^2 = (5 - x)^2 + 4(1 - x)(3 - 2x)$

Removing parentheses,

(2) $1 + 6x + 9x^2 = 25 - 10x + x^2 + 12 - 20x + 8x^2$

Transposing,

(3) $9x^2 - x^2 - 8x^2 + 6x + 10x + 20x = 25 + 12 - 1$

Collecting terms,

(4) $36x = 36$

Dividing by 36,

(5) $x = 1$ *Ans.*

Test: $(1 + 3)^2 = (5 - 1)^2 + 4(1 - 1)(3 - 2)$

or

$$4^2 = 4^2 + 0, \text{ or } 16 = 16$$

EXERCISES

Solve for x, and test:

1. $5x - 8 = 2x + 7$. *Ans.* 5.   3. $4x - 5 = 6x - 15$.   *Ans.* 5.

2. $8x + 3 = 3x + 13$. *Ans.* 2.   4. $2x - 2 = 4(x - 1)$.   *Ans.* 1.

5. $7(2x - 6) - 8 = 10x + 10$. *Ans.* 15.

6. $4(3x + 4) = 15(x - 2) + 1$. *Ans.* 15.

7. $6(5x - 4) + 30 = 29x - 12$. *Ans.* -18.

8. $3(2x - 10) - 20 = x + 50$. *Ans.* 20.

9. $4(4x - 6) + 2(2x - 3) = 5(2x - 6) - 10$. *Ans.* -1.

10. $7(5x - 8) + 9(2x - 5) = 3x + 4$. *Ans.* 2.1.

11. $(x - 1)(x + 1) + x(1 - x) = 4x(2x + 1) - 8x(x - 2)$.

Ans. $-\frac{1}{19}$.

12. $2x(3 - 4x) + (x - 2)(x + 3) = 7x(10 - x) + 12$. *Ans.* $-\frac{2}{7}$.

13. $(x - 4)(x + 5) = 2x(x - 6) - x(x - 10) + 80$. *Ans.* $33\frac{1}{3}$.

14. $14(x - 9) - 4x + 26(1 - x) = 0$. *Ans.* $-6\frac{1}{4}$.

15. $(x + 8)(x - 7) - (x - 4)(x + 3) + 5(2x - 10) = 0$. *Ans.* $7\frac{5}{6}$.

16. $(2x - 3)(3x - 2) = (6x - 7)(x - 8) + 9x - 15$. *Ans.* $1\frac{2}{33}$.

17. $10(x - 2) - 10(2 - x) = 4x - 40$. *Ans.* 0.

Find the value of a in Exercises 18 to 24:

18. $6a - 3(a + 2)(a - 3) + 3a^2 = (a - 2)(a - 3)$
$$- (a + 2)(a + 3). \quad Ans. -\tfrac{18}{19}.$$

19. $4.4a + 5.6 = 2.4a - 0.4.$ *Ans.* $-3.$

20. $12a - 8 = 10(a - 2).$ *Ans.* $-6.$

21. $5 - 5a - 5.2 = 10a + 9.8.$ *Ans.* $-\tfrac{2}{3}.$

22. $9.8a - 9.4 = 6.8a + 0.6.$ *Ans.* $\tfrac{10}{3}.$

23. $(a + 4)(5 - 2a) - a(10 - 2a) = 1.5.$ *Ans.* $1\tfrac{11}{26}.$

24. $4a - 4 + 6a - 7 = 8a - 9 + (9 - a)(9 + a) + a + a(a - 10).$
$$Ans. \ 7\tfrac{6}{11}.$$

Find the value of y in Exercises 25 to 30:

25. $(y - 2)(y + 4) + (y - 10)(y + 10) + y(1 - y)$
$$= (y - 6)(y - 2). \quad Ans. \ 10\tfrac{10}{11}.$$

26. $y(y + 4) - (y - 4)(y - 5) + 10 = 8(y + 2).$ *Ans.* $5\tfrac{1}{5}.$

27. $y^2 - (y - 1)(y + 1) = 4(y + 8).$ *Ans.* $-7\tfrac{3}{4}.$

28. $(y - 1)^2 - (y - 1)(y + 1) + 8 = 7y - 9.$ *Ans.* $2\tfrac{1}{9}.$

29. $4y + 4y(y - 4) + 4(1 - y)(1 + y) = 0.$ *Ans.* $\tfrac{1}{3}.$

30. $5[y + 24(y - 1) - 20(y + 1)] + 18 = 0.$ *Ans.* $8\tfrac{2}{25}.$

Find the value of p in Exercises 31 and 32:

31. $p(p + 4) - p[p - 5)(p + 5) + p] = 4 - p^3.$ *Ans.* $\tfrac{4}{29}.$

32. $p^2 - 2p + 1 - (p + 2)(p + 3) = 10(p - 4) + 8.$ *Ans.* $1\tfrac{10}{17}.$

33. Find two numbers whose difference is 10 and whose sum is $4\tfrac{1}{5}$ times their difference. *Ans.* 26 and 16.

Suggestion.—Let $x =$ the smaller number and $10 + x =$ the larger number.

34. Find two numbers whose difference is 25 and whose sum is $4\tfrac{1}{5}$ times their difference. *Ans.* 40, 65.

35. A rectangular field is 5 rods longer than it is wide. If it was 2 rods wider and 3 rods shorter, it would contain 4 square rods less. Find dimensions of the field.

Solution.—Let $x =$ number of rods in width.

Then $x + 5 =$ number of rods in length

and $x(x + 5) =$ number of square rods in field

Also $x + 2 =$ number of rods in width of second field

and $x + 2 =$ number of rods in length of second field

Then $(x + 2)(x + 2) =$ number of square rods in second field

$$\therefore x(x + 5) - (x + 2)(x + 2) = 4$$
$$x^2 + 5x - x^2 - 4x - 4 = 4$$
$$x^2 - x^2 + 5x - 4x = 4 + 4$$
$$x = 8$$
$$x + 5 = 13$$

$\therefore$ Field is 13 rods long and 8 rods wide   *Ans.*

36. The difference between the squares of two consecutive eve: numbers is 44. What are the numbers?   *Ans.* 10; 12.

37. The height of a flagstaff is unknown; but it is noticed that the fla rope, which is 4 ft. longer than the staff, when stretched out just reache the ground at a point 25 ft. from the foot of the staff. If the ground i level, find the height of the staff.   *Ans.* $76\frac{1}{8}$ ft.

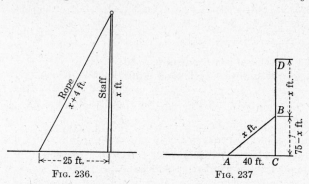

Fig. 236.   Fig. 237

Suggestion.—Figure 236 shows the rope stretched to a point 25 ft. from the foot of the staff. This makes a right triangle that has the rope a hypotenuse. We then have the equation

$$(x + 4)^2 = 25^2 + x^2$$

38. A flagstaff CD, Fig. 237, 75 ft. high, breaks at point B, and end *I* strikes at A, a distance of 40 ft. from C. Find the length BD that i broken off.   *Ans.* $48\frac{1}{6}$ ft.

Suggestion.—Let $BD = x$; then $CB = 75 - x$.

39. At what rate simple interest will \$85 amount to \$110.50 in 15 years $(A = P + Prt.$ See page 385.)   *Ans.* 2%.

270. Equations solved by aid of factoring.—The equation: considered so far have reduced to a form in which a certair number of times the unknown equaled some number. Thus $6x = 12$ is such a form. They may be called **simple equations**

All equations do not reduce to such a form as this. Fo instance, when the equation has been reduced, we may have an equation in which the *square* of the unknown equals number. Thus, $x^2 = 5$ is such a form. Such an equation i called a **pure quadratic equation.**

Again, when the equation is simplified and reduced, we may have a form containing the *square* and the *first power* of the unknown equaling some number. Thus, $x^2 - 5x = 24$ is such a form. Such an equation is called an **affected quadratic equation.**

Some of these forms of equations, together with certain other forms, can be solved by the *aid of factoring.*

Example 1.—Solve the equation $x^2 - 5x + 6 = 0$.

Discussion.—This equation puts the question: For what values of x does $x^2 - 5x + 6$ equal zero? If we factor the expression in the first member, we get $(x - 2)(x - 3) = 0$. The question now is: For what values of x does the product $(x - 2)(x - 3)$ have the value zero? We know that the product of two factors is zero if either or both factors are zero and not otherwise. Hence, the product is zero if $x - 2 = 0$ or if $x - 3 = 0$. Thus, the solution of $x^2 - 5x + 6 = 0$ depends upon the solution of the two simple equations $x - 2 = 0$ and $x - 3 = 0$. These give the values 2 and 3 for x.

That these are the values of x may be tested by substituting each one separately in the equation

$$x^2 - 5x + 6 = 0$$

Substituting $x = 2$, gives $4 - 10 + 6 = 0$, or $0 = 0$.
Substituting $x = 3$, gives $9 - 15 + 6 = 0$, or $0 = 0$.

The values of the unknown number that satisfy the equation, that is, answer the question, are called **roots** of the equation.

A quadratic equation having one unknown letter always has two roots.

Example 2.—Solve the equation $x^2 - 25 = 0$.

First solution.—Given equation

(1) $$x^2 - 25 = 0$$

Factoring,

(2) $$(x + 5)(x - 5) = 0$$

Putting each factor equal to zero,

(3) $\qquad x + 5 = 0$, and $x - 5 = 0$

Transposing,

(4) $\qquad x = -5$ and $x = 5$ *Ans.*

Test for $x = -5$, $25 - 25 = 0$.
Test for $x = 5$, $25 - 25 = 0$.
Second solution.—Given equation

(1) $\qquad\qquad x^2 - 25 = 0$

Transposing,

(2) $\qquad\qquad\qquad x^2 = 25$

Taking the square root of each member of the equation,

(3) $\qquad\qquad\qquad x = \pm 5$

Here the sign $\pm$ is read "plus or minus." It means that is a plus as well as a minus quantity. It should be noted her that we are saying that 25 has the two square roots, $+5$ an -5. Either of these is the square root of 25, for $(+5)^2 = 2$ and also $(-5)^2 = 25$. Hence, both fulfill the definition of square root, that is, one of the two equal factors into which number may be divided.

Any positive number has two square roots, one positive an one negative, both equal in absolute value.

Example 3.—Solve $(x + 1)(x - 3)(2x - 16) = 0$.
Equating each factor to zero,

$$x + 1 = 0,\ x - 3 = 0,\ \text{and}\ 2x - 16 = 0$$

Solving these,
$$x = -1,\ x = 3,\ \text{and}\ x = 8\quad Ans.$$

We have the following rule of procedure when solving a equation by the aid of factoring:

RULE.—(1) *Simplify the equation as much as possible.*

(2) *Transpose all terms to the first member of the equation.*

(3) *Factor the expression in the first member.*

(4) *Equate each factor to zero.*

(5) *Solve each of these equations.*

EXERCISES

Solve the following by the aid of factoring:

1. $(x - 1)(x - 5) = 0$. *Ans.* 1, 5.

2. $(x + 3)(x - 7) = 0$. *Ans.* -3, 7.

3. $(x - 7)(x + 8)(x - 9) = 0$. *Ans.* 7, -8, 9.

4. $(x + 5)(x + 6)(x - 8) = 0$. *Ans.* -5, -6, 8.

5. $(3x - 9)(2x - 3) = 0$. *Ans.* 3, $\frac{3}{2}$.

6. $x(x + 4)(4x - 2) = 0$. *Ans.* 0, -4, $\frac{1}{2}$.

7. $x^2(x^2 - 36) = 0$. *Ans.* 0, ± 6.

8. $(x + 5)(x^2 - 25) = 0$. *Ans.* ± 5.

9. $(x^2 - 4)(x^2 - 9) = 0$. *Ans.* ± 2, ± 3.

10. $x^2 - x = 72$. *Ans.* -8, 9.

11. $(2x + 1)(x + 3) = x^2 - 9$. *Ans.* -3, -4.

Suggestion.—It is necessary first to clear of parentheses, transpose, and nite before factoring.

Clearing of parentheses,

$$2x^2 + 7x + 3 = x^2 - 9$$

Transposing,

$$2x^2 - x^2 + 7x + 3 + 9 = 0$$

Collecting terms,

$$x^2 + 7x + 12 = 0$$

Factoring,

$$(x + 3)(x + 4) = 0$$

12. $(3x + 2)(x - 4) = 2x^2 - 17$. *Ans.* 1, 9.

13. Find the number that when added to its square equals 42.

Ans. 6, -7.

14. Twice a number added to its square equals 63. Find the number.

Ans. 7, -9.

15. Twice a number subtracted from its square equals 63. Find the number. *Ans.* -7, 9.

16. If 16 is added to the square of a number, the sum equals 10 times he number. Find the number. *Ans.* 8, 2.

17. If 44 be subtracted from the square of a number, the difference quals 7 times the number. Find the number. *Ans.* -4, 11.

18. If 2 is added to a number, the square of the sum is 4 more than 13 times the number. What is the number? *Ans.* 9, 0.

19. A rectangle is 8 in. longer than it is wide. Find the dimensions i the area is 560 sq. in. *Ans.* 20 in.; 28 in.

20. Find the dimensions of a rectangle that is 4 rods longer than it i wide and, when the length is increased by 4 rods and the width by 4 rods the area is doubled. *Ans.* 8 rods, 12 rods.

21. The base of a triangle is 3 in. longer than the altitude, and the area is 54 sq. in. Find the length of the base and the altitude.

Ans. 12 in.; 9 in.

22. The altitude of a triangle is three times the base, and the area is $73\frac{1}{2}$ sq. in. Find the length of the base and the altitude.

Abs. 7 in.; 21 in.

271. Formulas.—A formula as given usually stands solved for one letter in terms of several others. For instance, formula [**34**] is $T = ph + 2A$. Here T is stated in terms of p, h, and A. As this formula stands, it is suitable for finding T when p, h, and A are given but is not suitable for finding, say, p when h, A, and T are given. To find a formula for finding p it is necessary to solve the equation $T = ph + 2A$ for p in terms of h, A, and T. In this way a knowledge of the methods for solving equations enables one to derive several formulas from a single formula.

Example.—Solve the formula $T = ph + 2A$ for each of the other letters.

Solution.—Here there are three other letters than T, and we will solve for p, h, and A in turn.

Given equation

(1) $$T = ph + 2A$$

Transposing,

(2) $$-ph = -T + 2A$$

Dividing by the coefficient of p which is $-h$, and indicating the division, since it cannot be performed,

(3) $$p = \frac{T - 2A}{h} \quad Ans.$$

Solving (2) for h, since it is properly transposed,

4) $$h = \frac{T - 2A}{p} \quad Ans.$$

To solve for A transpose (1),

5) $$-2A = -T + ph$$

Dividing by the coefficient of A,

6) $$A = \frac{T - ph}{2} \quad Ans.$$

EXERCISES

In the following, the numbers in the brackets are the numbers of the formulas as given in previous chapters, where their meaning can be found. The ability to do such problems as these is very important.

1. [**31**] $A = \pi ab$. Solve for a and b.   *Ans.* $\dfrac{A}{\pi b}$; $\dfrac{A}{\pi a}$.

2. [**33**] $S = ph$. Solve for p and h.   *Ans.* $\dfrac{S}{h}$; $\dfrac{S}{p}$.

3. [**42**] $S = 2\pi rh$. Solve for r.   *Ans.* $\dfrac{S}{2\pi h}$.

4. [**43**] $V = \pi r^2 h$. Solve for h.   *Ans.* $\dfrac{V}{\pi r^2}$.

5. [**46**] $V = \pi R^2 h - \pi r^2 h$. Solve for h.   *Ans.* $\dfrac{V}{\pi(R^2 - r^2)}$.

6. [**59**] $A = 4\pi^2 Rr$. Solve for R.   *Ans.* $\dfrac{A}{4\pi^2 r}$.

7. [**57**] $Z = 2\pi rh$. Solve for r.   *Ans.* $\dfrac{Z}{2\pi h}$.

8. Using the answer of Exercise 7, find the radius of a sphere on which a zone of altitude 3 ft. has an area of 32 sq. ft.   *Ans.* 1.698− ft.

9. [**35**] $T = 6a^2$. Solve for a^2 and then for a.   *Ans.* $\dfrac{T}{6}$; $\sqrt{\dfrac{T}{6}}$.

10. Using the second answer of Exercise 9, find the edge of a cube whose total surface area is 3258 sq. ft.   *Ans.* 23.302+ ft.

11. [**60**] $V = 2\pi^2 Rr^2$. Solve for r.   *Ans.* $\sqrt{\dfrac{V}{2\pi^2 R}}$.

12. [**55**] $S = 4\pi r^2$. Solve for r.   *Ans.* $\sqrt{\dfrac{S}{4\pi}}$.

13. Using the answer of Exercise 12, find the radius of a sphere that has a surface area of 2756 sq. ft.   *Ans.* 14.82 − ft.

14. [43] $V = \pi r^2 h$. Solve for r.   *Ans.* $\sqrt{\dfrac{V}{\pi h}}$

15. Using the answer of Exercise 14, find the radius of a right circular cylinder whose altitude is 16 in. and volume 2674 cu. in.

Ans. 7.294 − in.

16. Disregarding the resistance of the air, $v = \sqrt{2gh}$ is a formula that gives the velocity in feet per second that a body will have after falling from a height of h ft. Solve this for h, and get a formula for the height to which a body will rise if thrown upward with a velocity of v ft. per second.

Ans. $h = \dfrac{v^2}{2g}$.

Suggestion.—First square both members of the equation, which gives $v^2 = 2gh$.

17. Use the formulas of Exercise 16, and find (1) the velocity that a stone will have after falling 125 ft., (2) the height to which a stone will go if thrown upward with a velocity of 200 ft. per second. ($g = 32.2$.)

Ans. $v = 89.72+$ ft. per second; $h = 621.1$ ft.

18. The formula $v_t = v_o + 32.2t$ gives the velocity that a falling body will have.

$t =$ the time in seconds that the body has been falling.

$v_o =$ velocity in feet per second that the body has at the start, that is, v_o is the initial velocity.

$v_t =$ the velocity in feet per second after t sec.

Solve for v_o and for t.   *Ans.* $t = \dfrac{v_t - v_o}{32.2}$.

19. Using the formulas of Exercise 18, find (1) the time for a falling body to have a velocity of 600 ft. per second if it started with a velocity of 40 ft. per second; (2) the initial velocity in order that a falling body may have a velocity of 340 ft. per second after falling 5 sec.

Ans. 17.39+ sec.; 179 ft. per second.

20. Use the formula given in Exercise 5, and find the height of a hollow cylinder having outer and inner radii of 14 and 10 in., respectively, that it may have a volume of 4.211 cu. ft.   *Ans.* 24.13 − in.

21. Given the formula $V = \frac{1}{3}\pi r^2 h = 1.0472 r^2 h$, for finding the volume of a circular cone, solve for h and for r.   *Ans.* $\dfrac{V}{1.0472 r^2}$; $\sqrt{\dfrac{V}{1.0472 h}}$.

22. Using the formulas of Exercise 21, find (1) the altitude of a circular cone having a volume of 800 cu. in. and a radius of 8 in.; (2) the radius of the base of a circular cone having a volume of 456 cu. in. and an altitude of 10 in.

Ans. 11.94 − in.; 6.6 − in.

23. In the formula, $A = td + b(s + n)$. Solve this for t, d, b, s, and n successively.

$$Ans.\ t = \frac{A - b(s + n)}{d};\ s = \frac{A - td - bn}{b}.$$

Suggestion.—Here, from the single formula, five other formulas can be found. To find s, first clear of parentheses, and we have

$$A = td + bs + bn$$

Transposing, $\qquad -bs = -A + td + bn.$

Dividing by $-b$, $\qquad s = \dfrac{A - td - bn}{b}.$

24. Using the formulas of Exercise 23, find (1) t when $A = 3.35$ sq. in., $= 2.04$ in., $s = 0.22$ in., $n = 0.56$ in., and $d = 8$ in.; (2) b when $d = 10$ in., $t = 0.24$ in., $n = 0.63$ in., $s = 0.24$ in., and $A = 4.45$ sq. in.; (3) when $d = 5$ in., $t = 0.19$ in., $b = 1.56$ in., $n = 0.45$ in., and $A = 1.95$ q. in. *Ans.* 0.22 in.; 2.36 in.; 0.19 in.

25. In finding the area of a trapezoid, $2A = (b_1 + b_2)h$. Find b_1 if $= 400$ sq. in., $b_2 = 15$ in., and $h = 20$ in. *Ans.* 25 in.

26. Find the volume of a sphere that has a surface of 201.0624 sq. in.
Ans. 268.08 cu. in.

Suggestion.—First use the answer of Exercise 12 to find r. Then use the formula $V = \frac{1}{3}Sr$ from formula [**56**] to find the volume.

27. In reckoning simple interest,

$$A = Prt + P$$

where
$A =$ the amount.
$P =$ the principal.
$t =$ the time in years.
$r =$ the rate per cent.
Solve for each letter.

$$Ans.\ P = \frac{A}{rt + 1};\ t = \frac{A - P}{Pr};\ r = \frac{A - P}{Pt}.$$

28. Using the formulas of Exercise 27, find (1) t when $P = \$250$, $= 6\%$, and $A = \$300$; (2) r when $t = 3$ years, $P = \$328$, and A $\$377.20$; (3) P when $A = \$500$, $t = 5$ years, and $r = 4\%$.
Ans. $3\frac{1}{3}$ years; 5 %; \$416.67.

CHAPTER XXVI

FRACTIONS

272. In our previous work in algebra, fractions have been avoided except when occasionally an indicated division has been used. In many problems that arise it is necessary to use algebraic fractions.

The same names and terms are used when referring to fractions in algebra as are used in fractions in arithmetic, and these terms have the same meanings. The same principles are applied and the same operations performed as in arithmetic.

In working with fractions in algebra, one is apt to lose sight of the number concept involved and be content to operate mechanically with meaningless symbols. This should be guarded against, for a person who does this, though he may perform very well so long as the machinery runs in an orderly fashion, will be in trouble when something unusual arises.

The operations in fractions as given in arithmetic are readily carried over into algebra. In fact, if one understands these operations and has factoring in arithmetic at ready command, he can have no trouble with operations in fractions in algebra.

Here only those processes will be considered which are necessary for the understanding of what follows.

When in doubt about an operation in algebra, carry out a similar operation using numerical numbers, and from this determine what the operation with the algebraic expression should be.

273. Definitions.—An indicated division is called a **fraction.**

Thus, $\frac{3}{4}$, $\frac{25}{2}$, $\frac{2ab}{c}$, and $\frac{x^2 + y}{xy}$ are fractions.

The part above the line is the **numerator,** and the part below the line the **denominator.** Together they are called the **terms of the fraction.**

A fraction whose numerator is of less degree than the denominator is called a **proper fraction.** If the degree of the numerator is equal to or greater than that of the denominator, the fraction is an **improper fraction.**

The **degree** of an algebraic expression is determined by the greatest number of literal factors in any term.

Thus, $a^2 + a$ is of the second degree, $x^3y + 1$ is of the fourth degree. $\dfrac{a}{a^2 + 1}$, $\dfrac{x^2 + 2}{x^3 + 1}$, and $\dfrac{2}{3x^2 - 1}$ are proper fractions. $\dfrac{x^3 - 1}{x - 1}$ and $\dfrac{x + 1}{x - 3}$ are improper fractions.

The sum of an integral expression and a fraction is a **mixed expression.**

Thus, $3x + 2 + \dfrac{x}{x^2 + 1}$ is a mixed expression.

The **value of a fraction** is the number that it represents.

274. Principles used in operating with fractions.—The well-known principles used in fractions in arithmetic are given here for reference. [Remember the denominator $\neq 0$.]

(1) *Multiplying or dividing both numerator and denominator of a fraction by the same number does not change the value of the fraction.*

(2) *Multiplying the numerator or dividing the denominator of a fraction multiplies the value of the fraction.*

(3) *Dividing the numerator or multiplying the denominator of a fraction divides the value of the fraction.*

REDUCTION OF A FRACTION TO ITS LOWEST TERMS

275. A fraction is in its **lowest terms** when there is no factor common to both numerator and denominator.

Example 1.—Reduce $\frac{105}{120}$ to its lowest terms.

Process: $\qquad \dfrac{105}{120} = \dfrac{3 \cdot 5 \cdot 7}{3 \cdot 5 \cdot 8} = \dfrac{7}{8}$

Here each term of the fraction is factored, and then the common factors are canceled. We handle an algebraic fraction in the same way.

Example 2.—Reduce $\dfrac{6x^2y^3}{12x^4y^4}$ to its lowest terms.

Process: $\dfrac{6x^2y^3}{12x^4y^4} = \dfrac{2 \cdot 3 \cdot \not{x} \cdot \not{x} \cdot \not{y} \cdot \not{y} \cdot \not{y}}{2 \cdot 2 \cdot 3 \cdot \not{x} \cdot \not{x} \cdot x \cdot x \cdot \not{y} \cdot \not{y} \cdot \not{y} \cdot y} = \dfrac{1}{2x^2y}$

Example 3.—Reduce $\dfrac{x^2 - y^2}{x^2 + 2xy + y^2}$ to its lowest terms.

Process: $\dfrac{x^2 - y^2}{x^2 + 2xy + y^2} = \dfrac{\cancel{(x + y)}(x - y)}{\cancel{(x + y)}(x + y)} = \dfrac{x - y}{x + y}$

Example 4: $\dfrac{x^2 + 16x + 63}{x^2 + 4x - 21} = \dfrac{\cancel{(x + 7)}(x + 9)}{\cancel{(x + 7)}(x - 3)} = \dfrac{x + 9}{x - 3}$

EXERCISES

Reduce the following fractions to their lowest terms:

1. $\dfrac{36}{64}$. *Ans.* $\dfrac{9}{16}$.

2. $\dfrac{122}{244}$. *Ans.* $\dfrac{61}{122}$.

3. $\dfrac{175}{275}$. *Ans.* $\dfrac{7}{11}$.

4. $\dfrac{28x^2y^3}{35xy^2}$. *Ans.* $\dfrac{4xy}{5}$.

5. $\dfrac{22x^3yz^4}{33x^2yz^2}$. *Ans.* $\dfrac{2xz^2}{3}$.

6. $\dfrac{20ab^4c^2}{36abc^4}$. *Ans.* $\dfrac{5b^3}{9c^2}$.

7. $\dfrac{360r^5st^7}{720r^2st^6}$. *Ans.* $\dfrac{r^3t}{2}$.

8. $\dfrac{16w^8xyz^4}{64wxyz^2}$. *Ans.* $\dfrac{w^7z^2}{4}$.

9. $\dfrac{72a^4b^5c^6}{9a^2b^8c^2}$. *Ans.* $\dfrac{8a^2c^4}{b^3}$.

10. $\dfrac{625uvw^3}{25u^3w^6}$. *Ans.* $\dfrac{25v}{u^2w^3}$.

11. $\dfrac{1028a^8b}{64a^9b^4}$. *Ans.* $\dfrac{257}{16ab^3}$.

12. $\dfrac{(a - b)(a + b)^2}{a(a + b)}$. *Ans.* $\dfrac{(a - b)(a + b)}{a}$.

13. $\dfrac{x^2 - 6x + 9}{x^2 - 5x + 6}$. *Ans.* $\dfrac{x - 3}{x - 2}$.

14. $\dfrac{m^2 + 2m - 24}{m^2 - 2m - 48}$. *Ans.* $\dfrac{m - 4}{m - 8}$.

15. $\dfrac{n^3(n - m)^2}{n^2 - 2mn + m^2}$. *Ans.* n^3.

16. $\dfrac{2a^2 - 4ab + 2b^2}{10a^2b - 10ab^2}$. *Ans.* $\dfrac{a - b}{5ab}$.

17. $\dfrac{100 - 25x^2}{50(2 + x)(x - 2)}$. *Ans.* $-\dfrac{1}{2}$.

18. $\dfrac{x(x^2 + 5x - 14)}{x^3 + 2x^2 - 35x}$. *Ans.* $\dfrac{x - 2}{x - 5}$.

19. $\dfrac{36a^2 - 81b^2}{9(2a - 3b)^2}$. *Ans.* $\dfrac{2a + 3b}{2a - 3b}$.

20. $\dfrac{4(a + b)(-a + b)}{16a - 16b}$. *Ans.* $\dfrac{-b - a}{4}$.

21. $\dfrac{4 - (a + b)^2}{4(2 + a + b)(2 - a - b)}$. *Ans.* $\dfrac{1}{4}$.

22. $\dfrac{(a + b) - (a + b)^2}{(a + b)(1 - a - b)}$. *Ans.* 1.

23. $\dfrac{(x + y)^2}{x^3 + y^3}$. *Ans.* $\dfrac{x + y}{x^2 - xy + y^2}$.

24. $\dfrac{2 - h}{8 - h^3}$. *Ans.* $\dfrac{1}{4 + 2h + h^2}$.

25. $\dfrac{24h - 48k}{h^2 - 4hk + 4k^2}$. *Ans.* $\dfrac{24}{h - 2k}$.

26. $\dfrac{6x^2 - 2xy - 20y^2}{2(x^2 - 4y^2)}$. *Ans.* $\dfrac{3x + 5y}{x + 2y}$.

Reduce the following to lowest terms and then to mixed expressions:

27. $\dfrac{x^2 - 16}{x(x - 4)}$. *Ans.* $1 + \dfrac{4}{x}$.

28. $\dfrac{x^4 - 9x^2}{x + 3}$. *Ans.* $x^3 - 3x^2$.

29. $\dfrac{6x^4 - x^2 - 35}{(x + 1)(3x^2 + 7)}$. *Ans.* $2x - 2 - \dfrac{3}{x + 1}$.

30. $\dfrac{10x^2 + 29x + 21}{(2x + 3)^2}$. *Ans.* $\dfrac{5}{2} - \dfrac{1}{4x + 6}$.

Express the following mixed expressions as improper fractions:

31. $2x + 3 + \dfrac{4}{2x - 3}$. *Ans.* $\dfrac{4x^2 - 5}{2x - 3}$.

32. $x + 2 - \dfrac{5}{x + 3}$. *Ans.* $\dfrac{x^2 + 5x + 1}{x + 3}$.

33. $x^2 - x + 1 - \dfrac{1}{x + 1}$. *Ans.* $\dfrac{x^3}{x + 1}$.

34. $4 - y^2 - \dfrac{4}{16 + 4y^2}$. *Ans.* $\dfrac{60 - 4y^4}{16 + 4y^2}$.

REDUCTION OF FRACTIONS TO COMMON DENOMINATORS

276. In arithmetic, fractions are reduced to a least common denominator before adding, so in literal fractions we change the fractions to fractions having the lowest common denominator before adding them.

The **lowest common denominator,** L. C. D., is the lowest common multiple, L. C. M., of the denominators of the fractions. We must then first consider the finding of the L. C. M. of algebraic expressions.

It should be noticed that in arithmetic we can tell the relative size, or magnitude, of the numbers and therefore can speak of the *least* common multiple. In algebra the magnitude cannot always be told, and we speak of the *lowest* common multiple, referring to the degree of the expression. For instance, x^3 is of higher degree than x^2, but one cannot say which of these is the larger unless the value of x is known. If $x = 2$, x^3 is the larger; if $x = 1$, they are equal; and, if $x = \frac{1}{2}$, x^3 is the smaller.

277. Lowest common multiple. *Example* 1.—Find the L. C. M. of 24, 32, and 40.

First separate into prime factors, and then find a number that contains all the factors of each.

$$\begin{aligned}
\textit{Process:} \qquad 24 &= 2^3 \cdot 3 \\
32 &= 2^5 \\
40 &= 2^3 \cdot 5 \\
\therefore \text{ L. C. M. } &= 2^5 \cdot 3 \cdot 5 = 480
\end{aligned}$$

Remark.—The L. C. M. may also be found by the method of Art. 21, but that method is not so easily applied to algebraic expressions.

Example 2.—Find the L. C. M. of $12x^2y$, $16xy^3$, and $24x^3y$.

$$\begin{aligned}
\textit{Process:} \qquad 12x^2y &= 2^2 \cdot 3 \cdot x^2 \cdot y \\
16xy^3 &= 2^4 \cdot x \cdot y^3 \\
24x^3y &= 2^3 \cdot 3 \cdot x^3 \cdot y \\
\therefore \text{ L. C. M. } &= 2^4 \cdot 3 \cdot x^3 \cdot y^3 = 48x^3y^3
\end{aligned}$$

The L. C. M. is found by taking each factor the greatest number of times that it is found in any expression.

Example 3.—Find the L. C. M. of $x^2 + 2xy + y^2$ and $x^2 - y^2$.

Process:
$$x^2 + 2xy + y^2 = (x + y)^2$$
$$x^2 - y^2 \quad = (x + y)(x - y)$$
$$\therefore \text{ L. C. M. } = (x + y)^2(x - y)$$

To find the L. C. M. of two or more algebraic expressions we may state the following:

RULE.—*Separate each algebraic expression into its prime factors. The lowest common multiple is the continued product of all the distinct factors, each used the greatest number of times that it occurs in any expression.*

EXERCISES

Find the L. C. M. of the following:

1. 90, 45, 135. *Ans.* 270.
2. 1020, 625, 75. *Ans.* 127,500.
3. $3x^2y^3$, $6xy^2$, $12x^3y$. *Ans.* $12x^3y^3$.
4. $5a^4b$, $6ab^5$, $7a^3b^3$. *Ans.* $210a^4b^5$.
5. $4 - a^2$, $4 - 4a + a^2$. *Ans.* $(2 - a)^2(2 + a)$.
6. $x^2 - 5x + 6$, $x^2 - 7x + 12$. *Ans.* $(x - 2)(x - 3)(x - 4)$.
7. $8 - 2x^2$, $2(2 + x)^2$, $4(2 - x)^2$. *Ans.* $4(2 - x)^2(2 + x)^2$.
8. $x^3 - 2x^2y + xy^2$, $x^2y - xy^2$. *Ans.* $xy(x - y)^2$.
9. $5x^2 - 75x + 280$, $25(x - 7)^2$. *Ans.* $25(x - 7)^2(x - 8)$.
10. $2(x^2 - 6x - 7)$, $x^2 - 1$, $(x + 1)^2$.
   Ans. $2(x + 1)^2(x - 1)(x - 7)$.

278. Fractions having a L. C. D. *Example* 1.—Change $\frac{9}{16}$, $\frac{7}{24}$, and $\frac{17}{32}$ to equivalent fractions having a L. C. D.

The L. C. D. is found by the method of the preceding article to be 96. Now multiply both numerator and denominator of each fraction by such a number as will make the denominator in each case 96. How is the multiplier in each case found?

Process:
$$\frac{9}{16} = \frac{9 \times 6}{16 \times 6} = \frac{54}{96}$$
$$\frac{7}{24} = \frac{7 \times 4}{24 \times 4} = \frac{28}{96}$$
$$\frac{17}{32} = \frac{17 \times 3}{32 \times 3} = \frac{51}{96}$$

Example 2.—Change $\dfrac{x}{y-2}$, $\dfrac{z}{y^2+4y-12}$, and $\dfrac{v}{y^2+6y}$ to fractions having a L. C. D.

Process.—By the preceding article

$$\text{L. C. D.} = y(y-2)(y+6)$$

$$\frac{x}{y-2} = \frac{x \cdot y(y+6)}{(y-2) \cdot y(y+6)} = \frac{xy^2+6xy}{y^3+4y^2-12y}$$

$$\frac{z}{y^2+4y-12} = \frac{z \cdot y}{(y^2+4y-12) \cdot y} = \frac{yz}{y^3+4y^2-12y}$$

$$\frac{v}{y^2+6y} = \frac{v \cdot (y-2)}{(y^2+6y) \cdot (y-2)} = \frac{vy-2v}{y^3+4y^2-12y}$$

The multiplier in each case is found by dividing the L. C. D. by the denominator of the fraction. The division is most easily performed by striking out those factors in the L. C. D. which are found in the denominator of the fraction considered. For this reason it is best not to multiply together the factors of the L. C. D.

Thus, in the foregoing the L. C. D. is left in the form $y(y-2)(y+6)$ during the process, instead of in the form y^3+4y^2-12y.

EXERCISES

Reduce the following to equivalent fractions having a L. C. D.:

1. $\dfrac{11}{35}$, $\dfrac{13}{42}$, $\dfrac{17}{30}$. *Ans.* $\dfrac{66}{210}$, $\dfrac{65}{210}$, $\dfrac{119}{210}$.

2. $\dfrac{11}{5a}$, $\dfrac{12}{10a}$, $\dfrac{21}{25a}$. *Ans.* $\dfrac{110}{50a}$, $\dfrac{60}{50a}$, $\dfrac{42}{50a}$.

3. $\dfrac{3}{a+2b}$, $\dfrac{2}{a-2b}$. *Ans.* $\dfrac{3a-6b}{a^2-4b^2}$, $\dfrac{2a+4b}{a^2-4b^2}$.

4. $\dfrac{2}{x}$, $\dfrac{a}{x(2-y)}$, $\dfrac{b}{2x^2-x^2y}$. *Ans.* $\dfrac{4x-2xy}{2x^2-x^2y}$, $\dfrac{ax}{2x^2-x^2y}$, $\dfrac{b}{2x^2-x^2y}$.

5. $\dfrac{10}{(x+2)^2}$, $\dfrac{5}{x^2+6x+8}$. *Ans.* $\dfrac{10(x+4)}{(x+2)^2(x+4)}$, $\dfrac{5(x+2)}{(x+2)^2(x+4)}$.

6. $2+x$, $\dfrac{x^2}{2-x}$. *Ans.* $\dfrac{4-x^2}{2-x}$, $\dfrac{x^2}{2-x}$.

7. $x+2y$, $x-2y$, $\dfrac{x^2+4y^2}{x-2y}$.

$$\text{Ans. } \frac{x^2-4y^2}{x-2y}, \frac{x^2-4xy+4y^2}{x-2y}, \frac{x^2+4y^2}{x-2y}.$$

8. $\dfrac{x-1}{x+1}, \dfrac{x^2}{x-1}, \dfrac{1}{x^2-1}, \dfrac{x}{(x-1)^2}.$

Ans. $\dfrac{(x-1)^3}{(x+1)(x-1)^2}, \dfrac{x^2(x^2-1)}{(x+1)(x-1)^2}, \dfrac{x-1}{(x+1)(x-1)^2},$

$$\dfrac{x(x+1)}{(x+1)(x-1)^2}.$$

ADDITION AND SUBTRACTION OF FRACTIONS

279. Fractions can be added or subtracted as in arithmetic, by first reducing them to fractions having a common denominator and then adding or subtracting the numerators. The result should then be reduced to its lowest terms.

Example 1.—Find the sum of $\dfrac{x}{a-x}, \dfrac{a}{a+x},$ and $\dfrac{a^2+x^2}{a^2-x^2}.$

Process: L. C. D. $= (a+x)(a-x) = a^2 - x^2$

$$\frac{x}{a-x} = \frac{x(a+x)}{(a-x)(a+x)} = \frac{ax+x^2}{a^2-x^2}$$

$$\frac{a}{a+x} = \frac{a(a-x)}{(a+x)(a-x)} = \frac{a^2-ax}{a^2-x^2}$$

$$\frac{a^2+x^2}{a^2-x^2} = \qquad\qquad \frac{a^2+x^2}{a^2-x^2}$$

Adding the numerators, the sum of the fractions is $\dfrac{2a^2+2x^2}{a^2-x^2}.$

Example 2.—From $\dfrac{a+x}{a^2-ax}$ take $\dfrac{a+2x}{a^2-x^2}.$

Process: L. C. D. $= a(a+x)(a-x) = a^3 - ax^2$

$$\frac{a+x}{a^2-ax} = \frac{(a+x)(a+x)}{(a^2-ax)(a+x)} = \frac{a^2+2ax+x^2}{a^3-ax^2}$$

$$\frac{a+2x}{a^2-x^2} = \frac{(a+2x)a}{(a^2-x^2)a} = \frac{a^2+2ax}{a^3-ax^2}$$

Subtracting the numerator of the second fraction from the numerator of the first, the result is $\dfrac{x^2}{a^3-ax^2}.$

EXERCISES

1 to **8**.   Add the fractions in the preceding set of exercises.

Ans. **1.** $1\dfrac{4}{21}$.

Ans. **2.** $\dfrac{106}{25a}$.

Ans. **3.** $\dfrac{5a - 2b}{a^2 - 4b^2}$.

Ans. **4.** $\dfrac{4x - 2xy + ax + b}{2x^2 - x^2y}$.

Ans. **5.** $\dfrac{15x + 50}{(x + 2)^2(x + 4)}$.

Ans. **6.** $\dfrac{4}{2 - x}$.

Ans. **7.** $\dfrac{3x^2 - 4xy + 4y^2}{x - 2y}$.

Ans. **8.** $\dfrac{x^4 + x^3 - 3x^2 + 5x - 2}{(x + 1)(x - 1)^2}$.

9. Add $\frac{2}{3}, \frac{3}{5}, \frac{5}{6}, \frac{7}{10}$.   *Ans.* $2\dfrac{4}{5}$.

10. Add $\dfrac{2x}{3y}, \dfrac{3x}{4y}, \dfrac{4x}{y}, \dfrac{x}{2y}$.   *Ans.* $\dfrac{71x}{12y}$.

11. Add $\dfrac{2x}{3y}, \dfrac{x - y}{6y}, \dfrac{x + y}{9y}$.   *Ans.* $\dfrac{17x - y}{18y}$.

12. Add $\dfrac{5x - 6}{9}, \dfrac{6x + 5}{18}$.   *Ans.* $\dfrac{16x - 7}{18}$.

13. Add $\dfrac{4 - h}{4h}, \dfrac{h - 8}{8h}, \dfrac{2h + 3}{6h}$.   *Ans.* $\dfrac{12 + 5h}{24h}$.

14. Add $x, \dfrac{x + 3}{10} + x$ and $\dfrac{x - 3}{20}$.   *Ans.* $\dfrac{43x + 3}{20}$.

15. From $\dfrac{12m - 5n}{8}$ take $\dfrac{3m + 2n}{2}$.   *Ans.* $\dfrac{-13n}{8}$.

16. From $\dfrac{ax}{2}$ take $\dfrac{ax + 12}{3}$.   *Ans.* $\dfrac{ax - 24}{6}$.

17. From $\dfrac{ab - c}{2ab}$ take $\dfrac{ab + c}{4ab}$.   *Ans.* $\dfrac{ab - 3c}{4ab}$.

18. Combine $\dfrac{2x - 3y}{7} - \dfrac{4x - 5y}{14} + \dfrac{5x + 6y - 7}{21} - \dfrac{x + y}{2}$.

Ans. $\dfrac{-11x - 12y - 14}{42}$.

19. From $6ab + \dfrac{12 - 5ab}{6}$ take $8ab - \dfrac{2ab + 3}{8}$.   *Ans.* $\dfrac{57 - 62ab}{24}$.

20. Add $\dfrac{3}{x - 2}, \dfrac{4}{x + 2}$, and $\dfrac{5}{x^2 - 4}$.   *Ans.* $\dfrac{7x + 3}{x^2 - 4}$.

21. Combine $\dfrac{2}{m} - \dfrac{3}{n} - \dfrac{1}{m - n} - \dfrac{6}{m^2n - mn^2}$.

Ans. $\dfrac{4mn - 2n^2 - 3m^2 - 6}{m^2n - mn^2}$.

22. Combine $\dfrac{1}{x^2 - 9x + 18} + \dfrac{1}{x^2 - 8x + 12}$.

$$Ans.\ \dfrac{2x - 5}{(x - 6)(x - 3)(x - 2)}.$$

23. Combine $\dfrac{1}{x(x - 1)} - \dfrac{2}{x(x + 1)} + \dfrac{3}{x^2 - 1}$. $\quad Ans.\ \dfrac{2x + 3}{x(x^2 - 1)}.$

24. Combine $\dfrac{1}{x^2 - x - 2} + \dfrac{1}{x^2 + x - 6} - \dfrac{1}{6 + 5x + x^2}$.

$$Ans.\ \dfrac{x^2 + 9x + 10}{(x - 2)(x + 1)(x + 2)(x + 3)}.$$

25. Combine $\dfrac{x + y}{x^2 - y^2} - \dfrac{x - y}{x^2 + 2xy + y^2} + \dfrac{y - x}{(x - y)^2}$.

$$Ans.\ \dfrac{(y - x)^3}{(x + y)^2(x - y)^2}.$$

26. Add $\dfrac{1}{f} + \dfrac{1}{f'} - \dfrac{1}{f''} + \dfrac{1}{F}$. $\quad Ans.\ \dfrac{f'f''F + ff''F - ff'F + ff'f''}{ff'f''F}.$

27. Simplify $\dfrac{6}{x + 7} - \dfrac{8}{x + 9}$, and verify the work by using $x = 1$.

Verify by using $x = -1$. $\quad Ans.\ \dfrac{-2x - 2}{(x + 7)(x + 9)}.$

28. Combine $\dfrac{1}{x^2 + x - 2} + \dfrac{1}{x^2 - x - 6} - \dfrac{1}{x^2 - 4x + 3}$.

$$Ans.\ \dfrac{x - 6}{(x + 2)(x - 1)(x - 3)}.$$

29. Combine $\dfrac{a - b}{a^2 - b^2} + \dfrac{b - a}{a^2 + 2ab + b^2} - \dfrac{2}{a - b}$.

$$Ans.\ \dfrac{-2a^2 - 2ab - 4b^2}{(a + b)^2(a - b)}.$$

30. Add $\dfrac{1}{r_1} + \dfrac{1}{r_2} + \dfrac{1}{r_3} + \dfrac{1}{r_4}$. $\quad Ans.\ \dfrac{r_2 r_3 r_4 + r_1 r_3 r_4 + r_1 r_2 r_4 + r_1 r_2 r_3}{r_1 r_2 r_3 r_4}.$

31. If $pv = c$, find the decrease in the value of p when v changes from v_1 to $v_1 + h$.

$$Ans.\ \dfrac{ch}{v_1^2 + hv_1}.$$

Suggestion.—Solving for p, $p = \dfrac{c}{v}$.

When

$$v = v_1,\ p = \dfrac{c}{v_1}$$

When

$$v = v_1 + h,\ p = \dfrac{c}{v_1 + h}$$

Decrease in $p = \dfrac{c}{v_1} - \dfrac{c}{v_1 + h}$.

32. The area of a rectangle is A, and one side is b.   Find in the form of a simple fraction the perimeter of the rectangle.   *Ans.* $\dfrac{2A + 2b^2}{b}$.

33. A man can row m miles an hour in still water.   How long will it take him to row s miles up a river flowing a miles an hour?   How long will it take him to row s miles down the river?   How much longer does it take him to row up the river than down?

$$Ans. \ \frac{s}{m - a}; \ \frac{s}{m + a}; \ \frac{2as}{m^2 - a^2}$$

34. Two places A and B are m miles apart on a river that flows c miles an hour.   A man who can row a miles an hour in still water goes from A to B and back; find the time for the journey.   *Ans.* $\dfrac{2am}{a^2 - c^2}$.

MULTIPLICATION AND DIVISION OF FRACTIONS

280. Multiplication of fractions.—As in arithmetic, the product of two or more fractions is the product of their numerators divided by the product of their denominators.

If we first cancel all factors common to both numerator and denominator, the result will be in its lowest terms when the multiplying is done.

Example 1.—Multiply $\dfrac{35}{99}$ by $\dfrac{45}{91}$.

Process: $\dfrac{35}{99} \times \dfrac{45}{91} = \dfrac{5 \cdot 7}{9 \cdot 11} \times \dfrac{5 \cdot 9}{7 \cdot 13} = \dfrac{25}{143}$

Here we cancel 7 and 9 in both numerator and denominator.

Example 2.—Multiply 42 by $\frac{27}{28}$

Process: $42 \times \dfrac{27}{28} = \dfrac{2 \cdot 3 \cdot 7}{1} \times \dfrac{3 \cdot 3 \cdot 3}{2 \cdot 2 \cdot 7} = \dfrac{81}{2} = 40\frac{1}{2}$

Example 3.—Multiply $\dfrac{x - y}{x^2 + 2xy + y^2}$ by $\dfrac{x + y}{x^2 - 2xy + y^2}$ by $\dfrac{x^2 - y^2}{x^3}$.

Process: $\dfrac{x - y}{x^2 + 2xy + y^2} \times \dfrac{x + y}{x^2 - 2xy + y^2} \times \dfrac{x^2 - y^2}{x^3}$

$= \dfrac{\cancel{x - y}}{(x + y)(x + y)} \times \dfrac{\cancel{x + y}}{(x - y)(x - y)} \times \dfrac{(x + y)(x - y)}{x^3} = \dfrac{1}{x^3}$

281. Division of fractions.—One fraction is divided by another by multiplying the reciprocal of the divisor by the dividend.

The **reciprocal** of a number is 1 divided by that number. The reciprocal of a fraction is then the fraction inverted.

Thus, the reciprocal of 4 is $\frac{1}{4}$, of $\frac{2}{3}$ is $\frac{3}{2}$ and of $\frac{c}{b}$ is $\frac{b}{c}$.

Example.—Divide $\dfrac{x^2 - 11x - 26}{x^2 - 3x - 18}$ by $\dfrac{x^2 - 18x + 65}{x^2 - 9x + 18}$.

Process: $\dfrac{x^2 - 11x - 26}{x^2 - 3x - 18} \div \dfrac{x^2 - 18x + 65}{x^2 - 9x + 18}$

$$= \frac{x^2 - 11x - 26}{x^2 - 3x - 18} \times \frac{x^2 - 9x + 18}{x^2 - 18x + 65}$$

$$= \frac{(x - 13)(x + 2)}{(x - 6)(x + 3)} \times \frac{(x - 6)(x - 3)}{(x - 13)(x - 5)}$$

$$= \frac{(x + 2)(x - 3)}{(x + 3)(x - 5)} = \frac{x^2 - x - 6}{x^2 - 2x - 15}$$

EXERCISES

1. Multiply $\frac{16}{75}$ by $\frac{125}{64}$.   *Ans.* $\frac{5}{12}$.

2. Find the product of $13(2 \div 65)(5 \div 6)$.   *Ans.* $\frac{1}{3}$.

3. Divide $\frac{36}{55}$ by $\frac{12}{77}$.   *Ans.* $\frac{21}{5}$.

4. Multiply $\frac{4x}{5y}$ by $\frac{10y}{16}$.   *Ans.* $\frac{x}{2}$.

5. Find the product of $\dfrac{6xy}{13a} \times \dfrac{16a^2b^2}{14xy^2} \times \dfrac{26mn^3}{15mb^2}$.   *Ans.* $\dfrac{32an^3}{35y}$.

6. Divide $\dfrac{21u^3v^2}{24ab^5}$ by $\dfrac{22u^2v^3}{12a^5b}$.   *Ans.* $\dfrac{21a^4u}{44b^4v}$.

Perform the operations indicated in the following:

7. $\dfrac{3h^3}{49a^2b} \times \dfrac{7ab^3}{9hk}$.   *Ans.* $\dfrac{b^2h^2}{21ak}$.

8. $\dfrac{25ax}{7cmn} \times \dfrac{3bx}{2mn}$.   *Ans.* $\dfrac{75abx^2}{14cm^2n^2}$.

9. $\dfrac{3xyz^2}{4a^2b} \times \dfrac{7z^3}{2ab^4}$.   *Ans.* $\dfrac{21xyz^2}{8a^3b^5}$.

10. $\dfrac{a^2 - ab}{1 + b^2} \times \dfrac{a + ab^2}{a^2 - b^2}$.   *Ans.* $\dfrac{a^2}{a + b}$.

11. $\dfrac{x^2 - 4}{xy + 2y} \times \dfrac{y^2 + y}{x - 2}$.   *Ans.* $y + 1$.

12. $\dfrac{x^3}{y^4} \times \dfrac{x^6}{y^n}$.   *Ans.* $\dfrac{x^9}{y^{4+n}}$.

13. $\dfrac{5pq^3}{6xy} \div 5p$.   *Ans.* $\dfrac{q^3}{6xy}$.

14. $\dfrac{5a - 3b}{8} \div \dfrac{16ab}{3}$.   *Ans.* $\dfrac{15a - 9b}{128ab}$.

15. $\dfrac{1 - b^2}{3a} \div \dfrac{1 + b}{6a}$.   *Ans.* $2(1 - b)$.

16. $\dfrac{3x + 4y}{3x - 4y} \div \dfrac{9x^2 - 16y^2}{3x - 4y}$.   *Ans.* $\dfrac{1}{3x - 4y}$.

17. Simplify $\left(\dfrac{3a^2}{5y} \times \dfrac{15ay^3}{7c}\right) \div \dfrac{45a^3}{14c}$.   *Ans.* $\dfrac{2y^2}{5}$.

18. Simplify $\left(\dfrac{2 - x}{3 + y} \times \dfrac{9 - y^2}{x - 2}\right) \div \dfrac{3 - y}{3 + x}$.   *Ans.* $-3 - x$.

19. Multiply $\dfrac{x^2 + 2x + 1}{y(x + 1)}$ by $\dfrac{y(x^2 - 1)}{x - 1}$.   *Ans.* $(x + 1)^2$.

20. Divide $\dfrac{x^2 - 5x + 6}{x^2 - 9x + 20}$ by $\dfrac{x^2 - 3x + 2}{x^2 - 5x + 4}$.   *Ans.* $\dfrac{x - 3}{x - 5}$.

21. Simplify $\left(\dfrac{x^2 + x - 12}{x^2 + x - 20} \div \dfrac{x^2 - 7x + 12}{x^2 + 9x + 20}\right) \times \dfrac{(x + 4)^2}{(x - 4)^2}$.

Ans. $\dfrac{(x + 4)^4}{(x - 4)^4}$.

22. Multiply $x^2 + 4x + 4$ by $\dfrac{4}{x^2 - 4}$.   *Ans.* $\dfrac{4(x + 2)}{x - 2}$.

23. Multiply $\dfrac{1}{a} - \dfrac{1}{b}$ by $a - \dfrac{a^2}{b}$.   *Ans.* $\dfrac{(a - b)^2}{b^2}$.

Suggestion: $\dfrac{1}{a} - \dfrac{1}{b} = \dfrac{b}{ab} - \dfrac{a}{ab} = \dfrac{b - a}{ab}$

$$a - \dfrac{a^2}{b} = \dfrac{ab}{b} - \dfrac{a^2}{b} = \dfrac{ab - a^2}{b}$$

Now multiply $\dfrac{b - a}{ab}$ by $\dfrac{ab - a^2}{b}$.

24. Multiply $\dfrac{a}{b} + \dfrac{b}{a}$ by $a - \dfrac{b^2}{a}$.   *Ans.* $\dfrac{a^4 - b^4}{a^2b}$.

25. Multiply $1 + \dfrac{3a}{1 - a}$ by $1 + \dfrac{a}{1 + a}$.   *Ans.* $\dfrac{(1 + 2a)^2}{1 - a^2}$.

26. Multiply $4 + \dfrac{2a}{4 - a}$ by $4 - \dfrac{2a}{8 - a}$.   *Ans.* $\dfrac{4(16 - 3a)}{4 - a}$.

27. Multiply $\dfrac{axy}{ax^2 + by^2}$ by $\dfrac{x}{by} + \dfrac{y}{ax}$.   *Ans.* $\dfrac{1}{b}$.

28. Multiply $\dfrac{x^3y^4z^5}{xy + xz + yz}$ by $\dfrac{1}{x} + \dfrac{y + z}{yz}$.   *Ans.* $x^2y^3z^4$.

Simplify the following:

29. $\left(\dfrac{2-a}{3-a} \times \dfrac{5abc}{6xyz} \times \dfrac{9-a^2}{4-a^2}\right) \div \dfrac{5ab^2-5a^2b}{6x^2y+6xy^2}.$

$$Ans. \ \dfrac{c(3+a)(x+y)}{z(2+a)(b-a)}.$$

30. $\dfrac{x^2-2xy+y^2}{4xy+4y} \times \dfrac{(x+1)^2}{2x^2-2xy} \times \dfrac{16xy}{x^2-1}.$ $Ans. \ \dfrac{2(x-y)}{x-1}.$

31. $\dfrac{x^2+xy}{x^2-xy} \times \dfrac{(x-y)^2}{(x+y)^2} \times \dfrac{4x+4y}{4x-4y}.$ $Ans. \ 1.$

32. $\dfrac{x^2-5x+6}{x^2-9x+20} \times \dfrac{x^2-16}{x^2-9} \times \dfrac{x^2-2x-15}{x^2+x-12}.$ $Ans. \ \dfrac{x-2}{x-3}.$

33. $\left[\dfrac{a^2x^2-x^4}{4a^2-5ax+x^2} \div \dfrac{(ax-x^2)^2}{(4a-x)^2}\right] \div \dfrac{a+x}{4a+x}.$ $Ans. \ \dfrac{16a^2-x^2}{(a-x)^2}.$

34. $\dfrac{x^2+8x+16}{4x+x^2} \div \left(\dfrac{x^2+9x+20}{x^2-25} \div \dfrac{x^2+5x}{x^2-5x}\right).$ $Ans. \ \dfrac{x+5}{x}.$

35. $\left[\dfrac{x^2-3x+2}{x^2+3x+2} \times \dfrac{x^2+10x+16}{(x-1)^2}\right] \div \dfrac{x^2+6x-16}{x^2-x-2}.$ $Ans. \ \dfrac{x-2}{x-1}.$

36. $\dfrac{6x^2-7x+2}{6x^2+5x+1} \times \dfrac{12x^2-5x-3}{12x^2-17x+6} \times \dfrac{2x^2+x}{4x^2-1}.$ $Ans. \ \dfrac{x}{2x+1}.$

37. $\left(\dfrac{8a}{a^2-9}+a\right) \div \left(\dfrac{2a}{a-3}+a\right).$ $Ans. \ \dfrac{a+1}{a+3}.$

38. $\left(\dfrac{x}{y}-\dfrac{y}{x}\right) \div \left(\dfrac{y}{x}-1\right).$ $Ans. \ \dfrac{-x-y}{y}.$

39. $\left(\dfrac{4}{x^2}-1\right) \div \left(1-\dfrac{16}{x^4}\right).$ $Ans. \ \dfrac{-x^2}{x^2+4}.$

40. $\left(\dfrac{6}{h+1}-1\right) \div \left(\dfrac{8-2h}{h^2-1}+h\right).$ $Ans. \ \dfrac{(5-h)(h-1)}{h^3-3h+8}.$

41. $\left(\dfrac{-x-y}{3x}\right)\left(\dfrac{-x^2+y^2}{-m}\right)\left[\dfrac{-2mx}{(x+y)^2}\right].$ $Ans. \ \dfrac{2(x-y)}{3}.$

42. $\left(\dfrac{a}{a+1}-\dfrac{1}{1-a}\right) \div \left(\dfrac{a}{1-a}+\dfrac{1}{a+1}\right).$ $Ans. \ -1.$

43. $\left(\dfrac{a-b}{a+b}+\dfrac{a+b}{a-b}\right) \div \left(\dfrac{a-b}{a+b}-\dfrac{a+b}{a-b}\right).$ $Ans. \ \dfrac{-(a^2+b^2)}{2ab}.$

44. $\left(\dfrac{4y}{a-y}+4\right)\left(\dfrac{a-y}{a+y}-1\right).$ $Ans. \ \dfrac{-8ay}{a^2-y^2}.$

45. $\left(\dfrac{a^2-4}{b+2}\right)\left(\dfrac{4-b^2}{a^2+2a}\right)\left(\dfrac{a}{1-a}+1\right).$ $Ans. \ \dfrac{(a-2)(b-2)}{a(a-1)}.$

46. $(a^2+a+1) \div \left(1+\dfrac{1}{a}+\dfrac{1}{a^2}\right).$ $Ans. \ a^2.$

47. $\left(\dfrac{4x^2-9x+2}{3x^2+5x-2}\right)\left(\dfrac{5x^2+9x-2}{6x^2-13x+2}\right)\left(\dfrac{6x^2-7x+1}{20x^2-9x+1}\right).$

$$Ans. \ \dfrac{x-1}{3x-1}.$$

48. $\dfrac{a^3 - b^3}{a^2 + 5ab + 6b^2} \times \dfrac{a^2 + 3ab}{a^2 - 6ab + 5b^2} \times \dfrac{a^2 - 3ab - 10b^2}{a^2 + ab + b^2}.$ *Ans. a.*

49. $\dfrac{64a^2b^2 - z^2}{x^2 - 4} \times \dfrac{(x - 2)^2}{8ab + z} \div \dfrac{x^2 - 4}{(x + 2)^2}.$ *Ans. 8ab − z.*

50. Simplify $\dfrac{ah^2x}{4} - \left(\dfrac{ax^2}{2}\right)\dfrac{2x}{3} - ax(h - x)\dfrac{x}{2}$ and   put   in   form $\dfrac{a}{12}(3h^2x - 6hx^2 + 2x^3)$.

51. A can do a piece of work in 10 hr., and B can do it in 6 hr.   How many hours would be required for them to complete the work if working together?   (Together they can do $\frac{1}{10} + \frac{1}{6}$ per hour.)   *Ans. $3\frac{3}{4}$.*

52. A can do a piece of work in 10 hr., and B can do it in m hr.   How many hours would be required for them to complete the work if working together?   *Ans. $\dfrac{10m}{10 + m}$.*

53. A can do a piece of work in m hr., and B can do it in n hr.   How many hours would be required for them to complete the work if working together?   *Ans. $\dfrac{mn}{m + n}$.*

CHAPTER XXVII

EQUATIONS AND APPLICATIONS

282. In previous chapters a number of equations were presented for solution. These involved simplifications of various kinds but were not what are called **fractional equations,** that is, equations in which fractions occur. In the present chapter, besides equations like those previously considered will appear fractional equations.

283. Order of procedure.—The main steps in the solution of a simple equation have already been given, but for the sake of clearness they are repeated here.

(1) *Simplify the equation; that is, free signs of grouping, perform indicated operations of multiplication and division if possible, clear of fractions, etc.*

(2) *Transpose all the terms containing the unknown to the first member and all other terms to the second member.*

(3) *Collect terms.*

(4) *Divide both members of the equation by the coefficient of the unknown.*

(5) *Test the results by substituting each in the original equation.*

284. Clearing of fractions.—A fraction is an indicated division and usually a division that cannot be performed. Hence, when an equation contains fractions, these must be removed by a method other than division.

An equation can be cleared of fractions by multiplying both members of the equation by the lowest common denominator of all the fractions in the equation.

Example 1.—Solve $\dfrac{x}{5} + \dfrac{x}{8} = 17 - \dfrac{x}{10}.$

Solution.—Given equation

(1) $$\frac{x}{5} + \frac{x}{8} = 17 - \frac{x}{10}$$

Clearing of fractions by multiplying each term by the L. C. D., 40, we have

(2) $$8x + 5x = 680 - 4x$$

Transposing,

(3) $$8x + 5x + 4x = 680$$

Collecting terms,

(4) $$17x = 680$$

Dividing by coefficient of x,

(5) $$x = 40 \quad Ans.$$

Test: $\quad \frac{40}{5} + \frac{40}{8} = 17 - \frac{40}{10}$, or $13 = 13$

Example 2.—In the equation $S = \dfrac{E - IR}{0.220}$ solve for I.

Solution.—Given equation

(1) $$S = \frac{E - IR}{0.220}$$

Clearing of fractions,

(2) $$0.220S = E - IR$$

Transposing,

(3) $$IR = E - 0.220S$$

Dividing by coefficient of I,

(4) $$I = \frac{E - 0.220S}{R} \quad Ans.$$

EXERCISES

Solve the following equations for the unknown letters, and test the results:

1. $2x + 3 + \dfrac{11x - 11}{3} = 22.$ *Ans.* 4.

2. $\dfrac{6 - 2x}{3} + x - 1 = \dfrac{2x + 2}{5}.$ *Ans.* 9.

3. $\dfrac{x + 3}{8} + \dfrac{x + 1}{4} = 1.$ *Ans.* 1.

4. $\dfrac{3x}{2} + \dfrac{x}{2} - 10 = 0.$ *Ans.* 5.

5. $\dfrac{4x}{5} + \dfrac{x}{4} = \dfrac{x}{2} + \dfrac{11}{20}.$ *Ans.* 1.

6. $\dfrac{x + 1}{6} - \dfrac{x + 1}{12} = \dfrac{3(x + 2)}{8}.$ *Ans.* $-\dfrac{16}{7}.$

7. $\dfrac{2(x + 1)}{3} - \dfrac{3(x + 2)}{4} = \dfrac{x + 1}{6}.$ *Ans.* $-4.$

Solution: $\dfrac{2(x + 1)}{3} - \dfrac{3(x + 2)}{4} = \dfrac{x + 1}{6}.$

Clearing of parentheses,

$$\frac{2x + 2}{3} - \frac{3x + 6}{4} = \frac{x + 1}{6}$$

Clearing of fractions,

$$8x + 8 - 9x - 18 = 2x + 2$$

Transposing,

$$8x - 9x - 2x = -8 + 18 + 2.$$

Collecting terms,

$$-3x = 12$$

Dividing by coefficient of x,

$$x = -4$$

8. $\dfrac{9x - 7}{12} + \dfrac{8x}{9} = \dfrac{11x}{36} + \dfrac{3}{2}.$ *Ans.* $1\dfrac{9}{16}.$

9. $\dfrac{5x - 15}{2} + \dfrac{21 + x}{4} = \dfrac{3x + 5}{16}.$ *Ans.* 1.

10. $-(5x + 15) = 5x + 21 - \dfrac{5(2 - x)}{2}.$ *Ans.* $-2\dfrac{12}{25}.$

Note that as in Exercise 7, when a fraction is preceded by a minus sign, all the terms obtained from it when clearing of fractions must have their signs changed. This is because the vinculum is a sign of grouping; and in clearing of a sign of grouping preceded by a minus sign, the signs of the terms within are changed according to Art. 228.

11. $\dfrac{x + 1}{4} - \dfrac{2(x - 1)}{3} = 3.$ *Ans.* $-5.$

12. $\dfrac{2 - x}{2} - \dfrac{5x + 21}{5} = x + 3.$ *Ans.* $-2\dfrac{12}{25}.$

13. $(x + 1)^2 + 2(x + 3)^2 = 3x(x + 2) + 35.$ *Ans.* 2.

14. $\dfrac{x + 1}{2} + \dfrac{x + 2}{3} + \dfrac{x + 4}{4} + 8 = 0.$ *Ans.* $-9\dfrac{5}{13}.$

15. $\dfrac{3x + 5}{8} - \dfrac{21 + x}{2} = 5x - 15.$ *Ans.* 1.

16. $x - \left(3x - \dfrac{2x - 5}{10}\right) = \dfrac{1}{6}(2x - 57) - \dfrac{5}{8}.$ *Ans.* 5.

17. $\frac{5}{6}x + 0.25x - \frac{1}{3}x = x - 3.$ *Ans.* 12.

18. $1.5 = \dfrac{0.36}{0.2} - \dfrac{0.09x - 0.18}{0.9}.$ *Ans.* 5.

19. Given $3ac - 5c = 17$, solve for c.   *Ans.* $\dfrac{17}{3a - 5}.$

20. Given $4abc - 5bc + 16 = 3bc$, solve (1) for a, (2) for b, (3) for c.

$$Ans.\ a = \frac{2bc - 4}{bc};\ b = \frac{4}{2c - ac};\ c = \frac{4}{2b - ab}.$$

Solution for a.—Given equation

(1) $4abc - 5bc + 16 = 3bc$

Transposing,

(2) $4abc = 5bc + 3bc - 16$

Collecting terms,

(3) $4abc = 8bc - 16$

Dividing by $4bc$,

(4) $a = \dfrac{8bc - 16}{4bc} = \dfrac{2bc - 4}{bc}$

Solution for b.—
Transposing,

(5) $4abc - 5bc - 3bc = -16$

Collecting terms,

(6) $(4ac - 8c)b = -16$

Dividing by $4ac - 8c$,

(7) $b = \dfrac{-16}{4ac - 8c} = \dfrac{4}{2c - ac}$

21. Given $(b - x)(b + 2x) = b^2 - 2x^2 - 3b + 4$; solve (1) for b, (2) for x.

$$Ans.\ b = \frac{4}{x + 3};\ x = \frac{4 - 3b}{b}.$$

22. Given $(a + b)x + (a - b)x = a^2$, solve for x.   *Ans.* $\dfrac{a}{2}.$

23. Given $\frac{1}{2}(a + x) + \frac{1}{3}(2a + x) + \frac{1}{4}(3a + x) = 3a$, solve for x.

Ans. a.

24. Given $4(t + b + y) + 3(t + b - y) = y$, solve for t.

Ans. $-b$.

The following are formulas that occur in physics, electricity, etc.

25. Given $PD = WD_1$, solve for P. *Ans.* $\dfrac{WD_1}{D}$.

26. Given $F = \dfrac{WV^2}{gr}$, solve for W, g, r, and V, successively.

Ans. $\dfrac{Fgr}{V^2}$, $\dfrac{WV^2}{Fr}$; $\dfrac{WV^2}{Fg}$; $\sqrt{\dfrac{Fgr}{W}}$.

27. Given $I = \dfrac{En}{R + nr}$, solve for E, R, r, and n, successively.

Solution for E.—Given equation

(1) $$I = \frac{En}{R + nr}$$

Clearing of fractions,

(2) $$IR + Inr = En$$

Dividing by coefficient of E,

(3) $$E = \frac{IR + Inr}{n} = \frac{I(R + nr)}{n}$$

Ans. $\dfrac{I(R + nr)}{n}$; $\dfrac{n(E - Ir)}{I}$; $\dfrac{nE - IR}{In}$; $\dfrac{IR}{E - Ir}$.

28. Given (1) $I = \dfrac{E}{R + r}$, (2) $I = \dfrac{nE}{R + nr}$, and (3) $I = \dfrac{E}{R + \dfrac{r}{n}}$; what

value of n will make (1), (2), and (3) identical? Solve for n in (2) and (3).

Ans. 1; $\dfrac{IR}{E - Ir}$, $\dfrac{Ir}{E - IR}$.

29. Given $\dfrac{1}{f} = \dfrac{1}{p} + \dfrac{1}{q}$, solve for each letter in terms of the others.

Ans. $f = \dfrac{pq}{p + q}$; $p = \dfrac{fq}{q - f}$; $q = \dfrac{fp}{p - f}$.

Solution for p.—Given equation

(1) $$\frac{1}{f} = \frac{1}{p} + \frac{1}{q}$$

Multiplying by L. C. D., fpq,

(2) $$pq = fq + fp$$

Transposing,

(3) $$pq - fp = fq$$

Collecting terms,

(4) $$(q - f)p = fq$$

Dividing by $(q - f)$,

(5) $$p = \frac{fq}{q - f}$$

30. If $\frac{1}{k} = \frac{1}{a} + \frac{1}{b} + \frac{1}{l}$, solve for k; and find the value of k if $a = 19,000$, $b = 90,000$, and $l = 3180$. *Ans.* $\frac{abl}{ab + al + bl}$; 2644.

31. Given $\frac{E}{r} = \frac{E}{r_1} + \frac{E}{r_2}$, solve for r. *Ans.* $r = \frac{r_1 r_2}{r_1 + r_2}$.

32. Given $E = RI + \frac{rI}{n}$, find $I = \frac{E}{R + \dfrac{r}{n}}$.

Solution.—This can be done without clearing of fractions.   By factoring out I from the second member of the equation, we have

$$E = I \left(R + \frac{r}{n} \right)$$

Dividing by the coefficient of I, $I = \dfrac{E}{R + \dfrac{r}{n}}$.   *Ans.*

33. Given $nE = RI + \frac{nrI}{m}$, find $I = \dfrac{E}{\dfrac{R}{m} + \dfrac{r}{n}}$.

34. Given $R_t = R_0(1 + \alpha t)$, solve for R_0, α, and t, successively, in terms of the other quantities. *Ans.* $\dfrac{R_t}{1 + \alpha t}$; $\dfrac{R_t - R_0}{R_0 t}$; $\dfrac{R_t - R_0}{R_0 \alpha}$.

In the following exercises, the numbers in the brackets are the numbers of the formulas as given in previous chapters, where their meaning can be found.

35. [30] Given $A = \frac{2}{3} hw$, solve for w. *Ans.* $w = \dfrac{3A}{2h}$.

36. [60] Given $V = 2\pi^2 R r^2$, solve for R. *Ans.* $\dfrac{V}{2\pi^2 r^2}$.

37. [46] Given $V = \pi R^2 h - \pi r^2 h$, solve for r^2 and then for r.

Ans. $\dfrac{\pi R^2 h - V}{\pi h}$; $\sqrt{\dfrac{\pi R^2 h - V}{\pi h}}$.

38. A hollow cylindrical cast-iron pillar 12 ft. high and 10 in. in outside diameter is to weigh 1200 lb.   Find the diameter of the hollow.

Ans. 7.7 in.

Suggestion.—Use the answer of Exercise 37, and take cast iron at 450 lb. per cubic foot.

39. [**47**] Given $S = \frac{1}{2} ps$, solve for s. *Ans.* $\frac{2S}{p}$.

40. [**48**] Given $T = \frac{1}{2} ps + A$, solve for p. *Ans.* $\frac{2(T - A)}{s}$.

41. [**49**] Given $S = \frac{1}{2} (P + p)s$, solve for p. *Ans.* $\frac{2S - Ps}{s}$.

42. [**50**] Given $T = \frac{1}{2} (P + p)s + B + b$, solve for s.

Ans. $\frac{2(T - B - b)}{P + p}$.

43. Given $F = -\frac{4\pi^2 mx}{T^2}$, solve for x. *Ans.* $-\frac{FT^2}{4\pi^2 m}$.

44. Given $E = \frac{Ff}{(P - x)p}$, solve for x. *Ans.* $\frac{EPp - Ff}{Ep}$.

45. Given $C = K \frac{rr'}{r + r'}$, solve for r'. *Ans.* $\frac{Cr}{Kr - C}$.

46. Given $Q = K \frac{(t_2 - t_1)aT}{d}$, solve for t_1 and a.

Ans. $\frac{aKt_2T - dQ}{aKT}$; $\frac{dQ}{KT(t_2 - t_1)}$.

47. Given $p_t v_t = p_0 v_0 \left(1 + \frac{t}{273}\right)$, solve for t.

Ans. $\frac{273(p_t v_t - p_0 v_0)}{p_0 v_0}$.

48. Given $H = 1{,}600{,}000 \frac{b_1 - b_2}{b_1 + b_2} (1 + 0.0004t)$, solve for t.

Ans. $\frac{H(b_1 + b_2) - 1{,}600{,}000(b_1 - b_2)}{6400(b_1 - b_2)}$.

49. Given R = radius of a circle, h = height of a segment, and W = length of the chord. If W and h are known, find R. (See Art. 148.)

Solution.—In Fig. 238, AB is the chord, DC is the height, and AO is the radius. ADO is a right triangle. Hence,

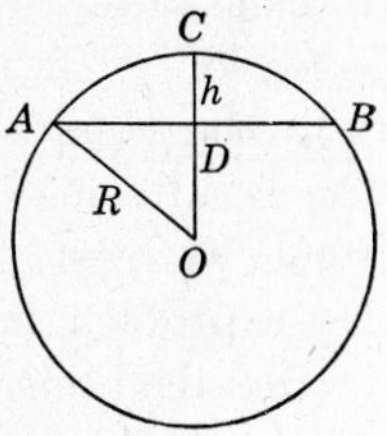

Fig. 238.

$$\overline{AO}^2 - \overline{DO}^2 = \overline{AD}^2$$
$$R^2 - (R - h)^2 = (\tfrac{1}{2}W)^2$$

Simplifying $\quad R^2 - (R^2 - 2hR + h^2) = (\tfrac{1}{2}W)^2$

Simplifying, $\quad R^2 - R^2 + 2hR - h^2 = (\tfrac{1}{2}W)^2$

Transposing and collecting, $\quad 2hR = (\tfrac{1}{2}W)^2 + h^2$

$$R = \frac{(\tfrac{1}{2}W)^2 + h^2}{2h} \quad Ans.$$

APPLICATIONS TO PROBLEMS

285. Solving problems by equations.—When one attempts to apply mathematics to problems, real or otherwise, he is often unable to select the proper mathematical machine; or if that is selected, he does not know how to feed the raw material to the machine; or, finally, he may not be able to run the machine. The second of these is the cause of the greatest trouble, as it involves an intimate knowledge of the field in which the problem lies as well as a knowledge of mathematics.

One should select the problems from the following pages that appeal to him. For instance, one not familiar with electricity may omit those problems dealing with that subject.

For the solving of a problem by means of algebraic equations, we cannot give rules as we can for the operations to be performed in the solution of an equation. For convenience the suggestions of Art. 235 are repeated here.

(1) Read the statement of the problem carefully to understand exactly what it means.

(2) Select the unknown number, and represent it by some letter. If there are more unknown numbers than one, express the others in terms of the one first selected.

(3) Find two expressions that, according to the statement of the problem, represent the same number and set them equal to each other. This gives the equation to be solved.

(4) Solve the equation, and test the results by checking them into the conditions of the problem. It often happens that the results may satisfy the equation and still be such that some, at least, will not fulfill the conditions of the problem. If the problem has any solution, it must be among the solutions of the algebraic equation that correctly states the conditions of the problem, no matter how many inapplicable solutions may also be yielded. If none of the solutions of the equation is applicable to the problem, it is impossible; that is, the conditions given are contradictory in some manner. Thus, if the solution of the problem was the number of children in a

family, and the solution of the equation was $4\frac{1}{2}$, we would know that impossible conditions had been given.

Example 1.—Find a side of a square room such that if its length and width are increased by 3 ft. the area is increased by 81 sq. ft.

Solution.—Let x = number of feet in side of square room. Then

$$x + 3 = \text{number of feet in side after increase}$$
$$x^2 = \text{number of square feet in area at first}$$
$$(x + 3)^2 = \text{number of square feet in area after increase}$$
$$\therefore (x + 3)^2 = x^2 + 81$$
$$x^2 + 6x + 9 = x^2 + 81$$
$$x^2 - x^2 + 6x = 81 - 9$$
$$6x = 72$$
$$x = 12$$

Hence, a side of the square room is 12 ft.   *Ans.*

This result checks in the conditions of the problem, for the area of room is 144 sq. ft.; and after the side is increased by 3 ft., it is 225 sq. ft., which is 81 sq. ft. larger.

Example 2.—A man invested $15,000 as follows: He paid a certain amount for a city lot and twice as much for a second lot and invested in bonds $2500 less than he paid for the second lot. How much did he invest in each?

Solution.—Let x = number of dollars invested in first lot.

Then $2x$ = number of dollars invested in second lot, and $2x - 2500$ = number of dollars invested in bonds.

Then

$$x + 2x + 2x - 2500 = \text{number of dollars invested}$$

Also

$$15,000 = \text{number of dollars invested}$$
$$\therefore x + 2x + 2x - 2500 = 15,000$$
$$x + 2x + 2x = 15,000 + 2500$$
$$5x = 17,500$$
$$x = 3500$$
$$2x = 7000$$
$$2x - 2500 = 4500$$

Hence he invested $3500 in first lot, $7000 in second lot, and $4500 in bonds.

Note that the letter representing the unknown always stands for an abstract number. One should never use a careless statement like x = first lot or x = horses but always say x = *number* of dollars or *number* of horses.

EXERCISES

1. A man is paid twice as much per day as his son is paid. Together they are paid $15 per day. How much is each paid per day? Solve first by inspection; then write an equation, and solve.   *Ans.* $5; $10.

2. A company finds that the labor cost of making an article is three times as much as the material to make it and that advertising cost is one-half as much as the material. The total cost was $27. Find each separate cost.   *Ans.* $6; $18; $3.

3. When the marked price of an article was reduced one-third, it still sold for six-fifths of $320. What was the marked price?

Ans. $576.

4. The marked price of an article was increased one-fifth, which made the selling price 0.75 of $160. Find the marked price.   *Ans.* $100.

5. A number, plus its half, plus its third, is eleven-tenths of 100. What is the number?   *Ans.* 60.

6. The list price of an electric fan was reduced 20 % and still sold for $4.80, which was 20 % more than it cost. Find the cost. Also find the list price.   *Ans.* $4; $6.

7. A reduced the list price of a car 10 % and sold it to B. Then B increased his cost price 10 % and sold it to C for $99. Find the list price.   *Ans.* $100.

8. A man's weekly salary was increased 50 %. Then his new salary was increased $33\frac{1}{3}$ % so that he now made $128 per week. Find his first weekly salary.   *Ans.* $64.

9. The sum of $1100 is invested, part at 5 % and part at 6 % per annum. If the total annual income is $59, how much is invested at each rate?   *Ans.* $700; $400.

Suggestion.—Let x = the number of dollars invested at 5 %. Then

$$1100 - x = \text{number of dollars invested at 6 \%}$$
$$\therefore \ 0.05x + 0.06(1100 - x) = 59$$

10. A total sum of $1300 is invested, part at 2 % and part at 2.5 % per annum. The total annual income is $30. How much is invested at each rate?   *Ans.* $800 at $2\frac{1}{2}$ %; $500 at 2 %.

11. The interest on $1200 for t years at 3 % is $84. Find t.

Ans. $2\frac{1}{3}$ years.

12. The interest on $1200 for 3.25 years at i % is $117. Find i.

Ans. 3 %.

13. If air is a mixture of 4 parts nitrogen to 1 part oxygen, how many cubic feet of each are there in a room 40 by 30 and 12 ft. high?

Ans. 11,520; 2880.

Suggestion.—Let x = the number of cubic feet of oxygen in the room. Then $4x$ = the number of cubic feet of nitrogen in the room.

14. If a mixture is 3 parts water and 1 part oil, find how many gallons of oil in 88 gal. of the mixture. *Ans.* 22.

15. A company employs three men. The first man receives 6 parts, the second receives 4 parts, and the third receives 3 parts of a weekly pay roll of $169. Find the weekly pay of each man.

Ans. $78; $52; $39.

16. A jug when filled with water weighed 6 lb. When the jug was filled with gasoline of specific gravity 0.9, it weighed 5.5 lb. Find the weight of the jug. *Ans.* 1 lb.

17. Seven times the amount that the average person spends at the cleaning and dyeing shops in Mississippi in 1 year is 6 cents less than the average person in New York spends in similar shops. The total sum that they both spend in 1 year is $2.46. What amount does each spend per year? *Ans.* 30 cents; $2.16.

18. If $19\frac{1}{4}$ lb. of gold and $10\frac{1}{4}$ lb. of silver each lose 1 lb. when weighed in water, find the weight of gold in an alloy of gold and silver when 20 lb. of its loses 1.25 lb. when weighed in water. *Ans.* 15.37 lb.

19. If 50 % of x plus 10 % of x is $12\frac{1}{2}$ % of 480, find x. *Ans.* 100.

20. There were 110,000 patrons on one occasion in Soldier's Field in Chicago. A week later the admission was increased 15 cents, with 5000 patrons less; but $10,250 more was realized. Find the two admission prices. *Ans.* $1.10 and $1.25.

21. A man made a journey of 560 miles, part at the rate of 40 miles per hour and part at 50 miles per hour. If it took him 13 hr., how far did he go at each rate? *Ans.* 360 mi.; 200 mi.

Suggestion.—Let x = number of miles at 40 miles per hour; then $560 - x$ = number of miles at 50 miles per hour.

$$\frac{x}{40} + \frac{560 - x}{50} = 13$$

The important idea here is that distance divided by rate equals time.

22. A bus traveling at the rate of 40 miles per hour from Omaha to Detroit made the trip in $15\frac{1}{4}$ hr. less than a truck making the same trip at 25 miles per hour. Find the distance between the two cities.

Ans. $1016\frac{2}{3}$ miles.

23. A tree 189 ft. tall was broken into two pieces by falling. If two thirds the length of the longer piece equals three-fourths the length of the shorter piece, how long is each piece?   *Ans.* $100\frac{1}{7}$ ft.; $88\frac{16}{17}$ ft.

24. Sirloin steak costs $1\frac{1}{2}$ times as much as round steak. Find the cost of each per pound if 3 lb. of sirloin and 5 lb. of round cost $2.28?
Ans. 36 cents; 24 cents.

25. If 2 lb. of butter costs as much as 5 lb. of lard, and $4\frac{1}{2}$ lb. of lard and 6 lb. of butter cost $5.46, find the cost of each per pound.
Ans. 70 cents; 28 cents.

26. There are two cylinders containing water. In one the water is 26 in. deep and is sinking at the rate of $1\frac{1}{2}$ in. a minute. In the other the water is 4 in. deep and is rising at the rate of $1\frac{1}{4}$ in. a minute. When is the depth in the two cylinders the same and what is that depth?

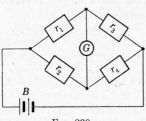

Ans. In 8 min.; 14 in.

27. In measuring an electrical resistance by Wheatstone's bridge, three known resistances are used together with the unknown. The unknown may be any one of the resistances r_1, r_2, r_3 and r_4 shown in Fig. 239. The three known resistances are adjusted to make $\dfrac{r_1}{r_2} = \dfrac{r_3}{r_4}$.

Fig. 239.

From this formula the unknown resistance can readily be found.

(1) Given $r_1 = 3.6$, $r_2 = 4.7$, $r_3 = 5$; find r_4.   *Ans.* 6.53.

(2) Given $r_1 = 500$, $r_2 = 300$, $r_4 = 125$; find r_3.   *Ans.* 208.3.

(3) Given $r_1 = 19.3$, $r_3 = 27.8$, $r_4 = 17.8$; find r_2.   *Ans.* 12.36.

(4) Given $r_2 = 16.4$, $r_3 = 28.2$, $r_4 = 16$; find r_1.   *Ans.* 28.905.

286. Levers.—A lever is often used to gain advantage in using forces. A lever consists of a rigid bar that may move

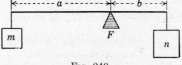

Fig. 240.

about a point called the fulcrum. The position of the fulcrum determines the advantage that may be gained by using the lever.

When a bar is balanced on a fulcrum F, Fig. 240, that is at a distance a from one end and b from the other, with weights m and n suspended from either end as shown, we have found (see Art. 82) that

$$m:n = b:a$$

Taking the product of the means of this proportion and the product of the extremes, we have the equation

$$am = bn$$

The weight at one end of the lever in Fig. 240 has a tendency to pull that end down; that is, it tends to make the lever turn about the fulcrum in that direction. The amount of this turning effect is known as a **moment** and is the product of the weight by the length of its lever arm. Thus am is the moment of the weight m acting on the lever arm of length a.

Two moments that tend to turn in opposite directions balance each other when they are equal. *Two such moments put equal to each other give the equation used in solving a problem in levers.*

We can now state a problem in levers in the form of an equation without using proportion.

Example.—A lever 10 ft. in length has a weight of 1000 lb. on one end. Where must the support be placed so that a weight of 250 lb. at the other end will make it balance? Disregard the weight of the lever.

Solution.—Let d = the number of feet from support to heavier weight.

Then $10 - d$ = the number of feet from support to lighter weight.

The moments are $1000d$ and $250(10 - d)$.

$$\therefore 2500 - 250d = 1000d$$

Transposing,

$$-250d - 1000d = -2500$$

Collecting terms,

$$-1250d = -2500$$

Dividing,

$d = 2$ = the number of feet from the 1000-lb. weight to the support. *Ans.*

EXERCISES

1. If a lever 16 ft. long is supported at a point 18 in. from one end, how heavy a weight can a man weighing 150 lb. on the long part of the lever balance?   Disregard the weight of the lever.   *Ans.* 1450 lb.

2. Two men are carrying a load, weighing 350 lb., on a pole 10 ft long.   Find the weight carried by each if the weight is 4 ft. from one end of the pole.   Disregard the weight of pole.   *Ans.* 210 lb.; 140 lb.

3. Place a fulcrum under a lever 12 ft. long so that a force of 150 lb. at one end will balance a weight of 1750 lb. at the other end if the lever weighs 10 lb. per foot.   *Ans.* Approx. 1 ft. 3 in. from the weight.

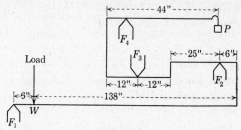

FIG. 241.

Suggestion.—When the weight of the lever is taken into consideration the moment of each arm of the lever is the weight of that arm multiplied by half the length of the arm.   Thus, in Exercise 3:

Let

$$x = \text{the length of the short arm in feet}$$

Then

$$12 - x = \text{the length of the long arm in feet}$$
$$1750x = \text{the moment due to weight}$$
$$150(12 - x) = \text{the moment due to force}$$
$$\tfrac{1}{2}x \cdot 10x = \text{the moment due to short arm}$$
$$\tfrac{1}{2}(12 - x) \cdot 10(12 - x) = \text{the moment due to long arm}$$

The sum of the moments on one arm is equal to the sum on the other arm if the lever is in balance.   Then the equation is

$$1750x + 5x^2 = 150(12 - x) + 5(12 - x)^2$$

4. In the arrangement of levers for a platform scale shown in Fig 241, find the lengths of the arms of the lever resting on F_4 so that a weight of 1 lb. at P will balance a load of 1000 lb. at W.   *Ans.* 4 in.; 40 in.

287. Thermometers.—Two kinds of thermometers are in common use.   The Fahrenheit, which is used for common purposes, has the freezing point marked 32 deg., and the boiling point marked 212 deg. The centigrade, which is used for all scientific purposes, has the freezing point marked 0 deg. and the boiling point marked 100 deg.

It is seen then that on the Fahrenheit scale there are 212° − 32° = 180° between the freezing point and the boiling point whereas on the centigrade scale there are 100 deg. in the same space. Hence 180 deg. of the Fahrenheit scale = 100 deg. of the centigrade scale. These relations are shown in Fig. 242.

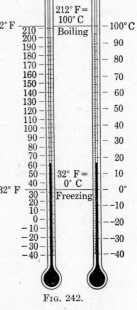

Fig. 242.

EXERCISES

1. If F stands for the number of degrees on the Fahrenheit scale and C for the number of degrees on the centigrade scale, find that

$$(1)\ \ C = \tfrac{5}{9}(F - 32)$$
$$(2)\ \ F = \tfrac{9}{5}C + 32$$

2. A temperature of 176 deg. F. is what temperature centigrade? [Use (1) of Exercise 1.]   *Ans.* 80 deg.

3. A reading of 24 deg. C. is how many degrees Fahrenheit?

Ans. $75\tfrac{1}{5}$ deg.

4. Given that the following metals melt at the given temperatures in Fahrenheit scale, find the melting point of each in the centigrade scale: wrought iron, 2822 deg.; steel, 2462 deg.; cast iron, 2210 deg.; silver, 1832 deg.; lead, 620 deg.; tin, 475 deg.

Ans. Wrought iron, 1550 deg.; steel, 1350 deg.; cast iron, 1210 deg.; silver, 1000 deg.; lead, $326\tfrac{2}{3}$ deg.; tin, $246\tfrac{1}{9}$ deg.

5. 60 deg. below 0 deg. F. is what on the centigrade scale?

Ans. $51\tfrac{1}{9}$ deg. below 0 deg.

6. At what temperature are the readings on the two thermometers the same?   *Ans.* 40 deg. below 0 deg.

Solution.—Let x = the reading on each thermometer scale. Then by the formulas of Exercise 1,

$$\tfrac{5}{9}(x - 32) = \tfrac{9}{5}x + 32$$
$$25x - 800 = 81x + 1440$$
$$25x - 81x = 1440 + 800$$
$$- 56x = 2240$$
$$x = -40. \quad Ans.$$

∴ Reading is the same when temperature is −40 deg.

7. With the oxyacetylene process of welding, the temperature of th flame is sometimes over 6000 deg. F. What is this on the centigrad scale? *Ans.* Over 3315 deg.

288. Horsepower.—The term **horsepower** was first usec by James Watt, the inventor of the steam engine. He ascer tained that a London draught horse was capable of doing work for a short time, equivalent to lifting 33,000 lb. 1 ft. high i 1 min. This value was used by Watt in expressing the powe of his engines and has since been universally adopted i mechanics.

The expression **foot-pounds** is used to denote the unit o work. *It is equivalent to a force of 1 lb. acting through a distanc of 1 ft.* or a force of $\frac{1}{2}$ lb. acting through a distance of 2 ft. o $\frac{1}{10}$ lb. through a distance of 10 ft., etc. *Horsepower is the* measure of the rate at which work is performed. One horse power is equivalent to 33,000 lb. lifted 1 ft. in 1 min. or 1 lb lifted 550 ft. in 1 sec. We say then that *one horsepowe equals* 33,000 *ft.-lb. per minute,* or 550 *ft. lb. per second.*

Therefore, the horsepower of *any machine* can be found by dividing the number of foot-pounds of work done in 1 min. by 33,000, or

$$Horsepower = \frac{number\ of\ foot\text{-}pounds\ of\ work\ per\ minute}{33,000}$$

In *electric-power machines* where the *watt* is used, since 746 watts equal 1 hp., we have

$$Horsepower = \frac{volts \times amperes}{746}$$

EXERCISES

1. What horsepower is necessary to raise a block of stone, weighing 3 tons, to the top of a wall 40 ft. high in 2 min.?

Solution.—The number of foot-pounds per minute is $\dfrac{6000 \times 40}{2}$; and

ence,

$$\text{the horsepower} = \frac{6000 \times 40}{2 \times 33,000} = 3\frac{7}{11} \quad Ans.$$

2. What horsepower is required to lift an elevator, weighing 4 tons, o the top of a building 240 ft. high in $1\frac{1}{2}$ min.?   *Ans.* 39 hp. approx.

3. What horsepower is required to pump 30,000 bbl. of water per our to a height of 45 ft.?   (Use 1 bbl. = 4.211 cu. ft.)

$$Ans. \; 179.4+ \text{hp.}$$

4. The following formula gives the horsepower of a steam engine:

$$H = \frac{PLAN}{33,000}$$

vhere

H = the indicated horse-power.

P = the mean effective pressure of the steam in pounds per square inch.

L = the length of stroke in feet.

A = the area of piston in square inches.

N = the number of strokes of piston (twice the number of revolutions) per minute.

Solve the formula for each of the letters P, L, A, and N in terms of he others,

$$Ans. \; P = \frac{33,000H}{LAN}; L = \frac{33,000H}{PAN}; A = \frac{33,000H}{PLN}; N = \frac{33,000H}{PLA}.$$

Remark.—It is to be noticed that the formula $H = \dfrac{PLAN}{33,000}$ has, in the

umerator, an expression for the number of foot-pounds per minute. To see this, note that PA is the pressure on the piston in pounds.   This imes L, or PLA, is the foot-pounds for one stroke of the piston.   Finally, nultiplying this by the number of strokes per minute N gives $PLAN$, he number of foot-pounds per minute.

5. What horsepower will a steam engine with a cylinder 4 in. in liameter and a stroke of 6 in. develop at 300 R. P. M. of the crank, if he mean effective pressure is 95 lb.   *Ans.* 10.85+ hp.

Suggestion.—Express in form of cancellation,

$$H = \frac{4 \times 4 \times 0.7854 \times 95 \times 1 \times 600}{33,000 \times 2}$$

ancel what you can and compute by slide rule if you wish.

6. Find the horsepower of an engine with a cylinder 10 in. in diameter, a stroke of 30 in., the crank making 96 R. P. M., and the mean effective pressure 120 lb. *Ans.* 137+ hp.

7. Find the diameter of a cylinder to develop 95 hp. with a stroke of 34 in., the crank making 110 R. P. M., the boiler pressure being 8 lb., and the mean effective pressure 65 % of the boiler pressure.

Ans. 11.1− in.

Suggestion.—Find the area of the piston by the formula of Exercise and then the diameter by formula [27].

8. An engine is required to develop 50 hp. with an average effective pressure of 46 lb. on a piston 13 in. in diameter and a crankshaft speed of 100 R. P. M. Find the length of the stroke.

Ans. 1.351+ ft. or 1 ft. $4\frac{3}{16}$ in.

9. Find the mean effective pressure on the piston of a steam engine with a cylinder 12 in. in diameter and a piston stroke of 18 in. if the number of revolutions is 110 per minute and developed horsepower 40.

Ans. 35.37− lb. per square inch.

10. In gas engines it is not easy to determine the mean effective pressure, so the formula $H = \dfrac{PLAN}{33,000}$ cannot well be used. As a result of experiments with engines used in automobiles, the formula $H = \dfrac{D^2N}{2.5}$ is often used. Here D is the diameter of the cylinders in inches, and N is the number of cylinders. Find H if $D = 4\frac{3}{4}$ in. and $N = 6$.

Ans. 54.15.

11. In "Locomotive Data" of the Baldwin Locomotive Works, the following formula is given for the tractive power of a locomotive:

$$T = \frac{C^2SP}{D}$$

where

C = the diameter of cylinders in inches.

S = the stroke of piston in inches.

P = the mean effective pressure in pounds per square inch = 85 % of boiler pressure.

D = the diameter of driving wheels in inches.

T = the tractive power in pounds.

Solve for each of the letters C, S, P, and D in terms of the others.

Ans. $C = \sqrt{\dfrac{DT}{SP}}$; $S = \dfrac{DT}{C^2P}$; $P = \dfrac{DT}{C^2S}$; $D = \dfrac{C^2SP}{T}$.

12. Use the formula of Exercise 11, and find T when $C = 16$ in., $S = 2$ in., and $D = 64$ in., if the boiler pressure is 160 lb. per square inch.

Ans. 11,968 lb.

13. To find the pressure on a lathe tool in turning steel multiply the area in square inches of a section of the chip cut by 230,000. In cutting cast iron use 168,000.

What horsepower does it take to turn a 6-in. steel axle making 30 R. P. M. if the cut is $\frac{1}{32}$ in. deep with a feed of $\frac{1}{8}$ in.?

Ans. 1.3 approx.

14. The power that is transmitted by a belt depends upon the pull of the belt and the rate at which it travels. The power may be given as a number of foot-pounds per minute or may be given as horsepower. Different makers of belts and writers on the subject give different values as the working strength for belts. The allowed pull for single belts is from 30 to 60 lb. per inch of width of belt. For double belts it is from 60 to 100 lb. per inch of width.

Show that the following formula gives the horsepower transmitted by a belt:

$$H = \frac{FWS}{33,000}$$

where

H = the horsepower.

F = the pull in pounds per inch of width.

W = the width in inches.

S = the speed of belt in feet per minute.

Solve for each letter involved in the formula.

15. Find the horsepower that can be transmitted by a belt 14 in. wide if the pull allowed per inch of width is 90 lb. and the speed is 5000 ft. per minute. *Ans.* $190\frac{10}{11}$.

16. Find the horsepower transmitted by a single belt 6 in. wide, running over a pulley 16 in. in diameter and making 350 R. P. M., if the pull of the belt is 45 lb. per inch of width. Allow 2 % for slipping.

Ans. 11.75.

17. If a single belt 6 in. wide transmits 7 hp., find its speed per minute, allowing 35 lb. pull per inch of width.

Ans. 1100 ft. per minute.

18. Find the horsepower transmitted by a 10-in. double belt, running over a 36-in. pulley, making 420 R. P. M. Use a pull of 75 lb. per inch of width. *Ans.* 89.96.

19. Assuming a tension of 50 lb. per inch of width for a single belt, and using D for diameter of pulley in inches, W for width of belt in inches, R for the number of R. P. M., and H for the horsepower transmitted, then

$$H = \frac{DRW}{2520}$$

Use $\pi = \frac{22}{7}$, and derive this formula. Solve for W, D, and R in terms of the other letters.

Remark.—In the preceding formula it is assumed that the pulleys are practically of the same size so that the arc of contact is 180°. If the pulleys differ in diameter, the arc of contact of the belt on the smaller pulley should be found and the following table used in finding the horsepower that can be transmitted.

If angle of contact is.......	90°	100°	110°	120°	130°	140°	150°	160°	170°
Multiply by....	0.65	0.70	0.75	0.79	0.83	0.87	0.91	0.94	0.97

20. Using the notation of the preceding exercise and 80 lb. for the tension per inch of width for double belts,

$$H = \frac{DRW}{1575}$$

Derive this formula if $\pi = \frac{2\,2}{7}$. Solve for D, R, and W in terms of the other letters.

21. Find the width of a single belt to transmit 3 hp. when running over a pulley 15 in. in diameter, making 220 R. P. M. Allow a pull of 50 lb. per inch of width. *Ans.* 2.3 in.

22. Find the number of R. P. M. that a pulley 4 ft. in diameter must make that transmits 120 hp. through a double belt 10 in. wide, having a pull of 80 lb. per inch of width. *Ans.* $393\frac{3}{4}$.

23. How much work is done in lifting 150 lb. from a mine 1100 ft. deep? How many horsepower would it take to lift this weight from the mine in $1\frac{1}{2}$ min.? *Ans.* $3\frac{1}{3}$ hp.

289. Relation of resistance, electromotive force, and current.—Resistance, R, is measured in **ohms**; voltage or electromotive force, E. M. F. or E, in **volts**; and current, I, in **amperes**. The law connecting these is stated as follows:

$$Amperes = \frac{volts}{ohms} \text{ or } I = \frac{E}{R}$$

This law is **Ohm's Law** and is the fundamental law for electrical work. It is an algebraic equation, and any one of the numbers can be found if the two others are given.

Exercises 27, 28, 32, and 33, pages 405 and 406, are forms of this equation.

EXERCISES

1. Solve the equation $I = \dfrac{E}{R}$ for E and R. *Ans.* $E = IR$; $R = \dfrac{E}{I}$.

2. In a certain circuit the voltage is measured and found to be 1.5 volts. If the total resistance is 12 ohms, what is the current in amperes?

Ans. 0.125 ampere.

3. Find the number of amperes of current sent through a circuit of 20 ohms resistance by one Daniell's cell which has an E. M. F. of 1.03 volts. *Ans.* 0.0515.

4. Find the strength of current from 50 Daniell's cells united in series, assuming the E. M. F. of each cell to be 1.03 volts, the resistance within each cell 0.3 ohm, and the external resistance 25 ohms.

Ans. 1.2875 amp.

Remark.—The student not familiar with the meaning of "cells united in series" can note the fact that 50 cells in series have fifty times the E. M. F. of a single cell and the resistance within the cells is fifty times that of one cell. The formula of Exercise 27, page 405, can be used.

5. An electric bell has a resistance of 450 ohms and will not ring with a current of less than 0.06 amp. Neglecting battery and line resistance, what is the smallest E. M. F. that will ring the bell? *Ans.* 27 volts.

6. If an electric car heater is supplied with 500 volts from the trolley, how great must its resistance be so that the current may not exceed 2.5 amp.? *Ans.* 200 ohms.

7. A certain wire has a resistance of 1 ohm for every 30 ft. of its length. What must be the E. M. F. in order that a current of 0.4 ampere may flow through 1 mile of the wire? *Ans.* 70.4 volts.

290. Resistance of conductors.—Consider the formula,

$$R = \frac{l}{a} k$$

where

$R =$ the resistance in ohms.

$l =$ the length of the conductor in *some unit.*

$a =$ the area of the cross section of the conductor in *some unit.*

$k =$ a constant value depending upon the *material in the conductor and upon the units of length and cross section used.*

This formula is the fundamental formula in wiring calculations.

In engineering practice, the length l is taken in *feet;* the area a is taken in *circular mils,* which equals the square of the diameter in thousandths of an inch when the conductor is circular (see Art. 164); and k is the resistance in *ohms* of 1 *ft. length of the conductor having a cross section of one circular mil.* That is, k is the *mil-foot* resistance of the conductor. The formula can then be written.

$$R = \frac{l}{d^2} k$$

If then it is required to find the resistance of any length of any size wire of any material, it is necessary only to know the mil-foot resistance for the material and substitute the values in the formula.

The following table gives the mil-foot resistances for the materials named at 0 deg. C.:

	Ohms
Aluminum	17.5
Copper (commercial)	9.6
German silver	125.7
Iron (pure)	58.3
Iron (telegraph wire)	90.0
Platinum	54.3
Silver	9.1
Zinc	33.8

Example 1.—What is the resistance of 2 miles of No. 12 B. & S. gage commercial copper wire?

Solution.—No. 12 B. & S. gage has an area of 6530 C. M.

$$2 \text{ miles} = 2 \times 5280 \text{ ft.}$$

$$\therefore R = \frac{2 \times 5280 \times 9.6}{6530} = 15.1 \text{ ohms} \quad Ans.$$

If it is required to determine the size of wire of a given length to have a given resistance, the formula is solved for d^2. This gives $d^2 = \dfrac{lk}{R}$.

Example 2.—Find the B. & S. gage of pure iron wire to have a resistance of 3 ohms per mile.

COPPER WIRE TABLE. B. & S., AND A. W. G. GAGE

Gage No.	Diameter in inches	Area Circular mils	Area Square mils	Pounds per foot	Gage No.	Diameter in inches	Area Circular mils	Area Square mils	Pounds per foot
0000	0.460	211,600	166,190	0.6405	21	0.02846	810.1	636.3	0.002452
000	0.4096	167,800	131,790	0.5080	22	0.02535	642.4	504.6	0.001945
00	0.3648	133,100	104,518	0.4028	23	0.02257	509.5	400.2	0.001542
0	0.3249	105,500	82,887	0.3195	24	0.02010	404.0	317.3	0.001223
					25	0.01790	320.4	251.7	0.0009699
1	0.2893	83,690	65,732	0.2533					
2	0.2576	66,370	52,128	0.2009	26	0.01594	254.1	199.6	0.0007692
3	0.2294	52,630	41,339	0.1593	27	0.0142	201.5	158.3	0.0006100
4	0.2043	41,740	32,784	0.1264	28	0.01264	159.8	125.5	0.0004837
5	0.1819	33,100	25,999	0.1002	29	0.01126	126.7	99.53	0.0003836
					30	0.01003	100.5	78.94	0.0003042
6	0.1620	26,250	20,618	0.07946					
7	0.1443	20,820	16,351	0.06302	31	0.008928	79.70	62.60	0.0002413
8	0.1285	16,510	12,967	0.04998	32	0.007950	63.21	49.64	0.0001913
9	0.1144	13,090	10,283	0.03963	33	0.007080	50.13	39.37	0.0001517
10	0.1019	10,380	8,155	0.03143	34	0.006305	39.75	31.22	0.0001203
					35	0.005615	31.52	24.76	0.00009543
11	0.09074	8,234	6,467	0.02493					
12	0.08081	6,530	5,129	0.01977	36	0.0050	25.0	19.64	0.00007568
13	0.07196	5,178	4,067	0.01568	37	0.004453	19.83	15.57	0.00006001
14	0.06408	4,107	3,225	0.01243	38	0.003965	15.72	12.35	0.00004759
15	0.05707	3,257	2,558	0.009858	39	0.003531	12.47	9.79	0.00003774
					40	0.003145	9.888	7.77	0.00002993
16	0.05082	2,583	2,029	0.007818					
17	0.04526	2,048	1,609	0.006200					
18	0.04030	1,624	1,276	0.004917					
19	0.03589	1,288	1,012	0.003899					
20	0.03196	1,022	802	0.003092					

Solution.—Substituting in the formula,

$$d^2 = \frac{5280 \times 58.3}{3} = 102,608 \text{ C. M.}$$

$$d = \sqrt{102,608} = 320.3 \text{ mils} = 0.3203 \text{ in.}$$

The nearest to this size is No. 0 B. & S. which is 0.3249 in. in diameter.

If it is required to find the length of wire of a given size to

have a given resistance, the formula is solved for l.   This gives
$$l = \frac{Ra}{k}.$$

Example 3.—Find the length of a No. 20 B. & S. gage silver wire to have a resistance of 5 ohms.

Solution.—No. 20 B. & S. has an area of 1022 C. M.

$$\therefore l = \frac{5 \times 1022}{9.1} = 561.5 \text{ ft. approx.}   Ans.$$

EXERCISES

1. Find the resistance of 340 ft. of No. 25 B. & S. gage German silver wire.   *Ans.* 133.4− ohms.

2. Find the resistance of 20 miles of trolley wire, made of commercial copper and No. 00 B. & S.   *Ans.* 7.6+ ohms.

3. Find the resistance of 10 miles of the "third-rail" conductor on an elevated railroad.   The "third rail" is iron and has a cross section of 5.88 sq. in.   *Ans.* 0.63 ohm.

4. Find the resistance of 500 turns of No. 30 B. & S. gage silver wire, about a core $\frac{3}{4}$ in. in diameter.   *Ans.* 8.69+ ohms.

5. Find the B. & S. gage of commercial copper wire to give a resistance of 40 ohms per mile.   *Ans.* No. 19.

6. Find the length of No. 16 B. & S. gage commercial copper wire to have a resistance of 20 ohms.   *Ans.* 5381 ft.

7. The resistance of a certain commercial copper wire, 1 ft. long and 1 C. M. in cross section, is 10.79 ohms.   A wire, 525 ft. long, has a cross section of 4117 C. M.; what is its resistance?   *Ans.* 1.376 ohms.

CHAPTER XXVIII

EQUATIONS WITH MORE THAN ONE UNKNOWN

291. Indeterminate equations.—In previous chapters the equations solved have involved only one unknown letter. In the present chapter will be considered equations involving more than one unknown letter. These letters will occur to the first power only or, if squared, will be such as are easily handled.

If we have the equation $x - y = 2$ and try to solve it for the unknown numbers x and y, it is evident that we can get numerous pairs of values for these numbers.

Thus, $x = 3$ and $y = 1$ is a pair of values that satisfy the equation; so are $x = 4$ and $y = 2$; $x = 5$ and $y = 3$; $x = 10$ and $y = 8$.

Such an equation is called an **indeterminate equation.**

EXERCISES

For each of the following equations find several pairs of values that will satisfy:

1. $x + y = 7$.

2. $x - y = 1$.

3. $2x + 3y = 20$.

4. $3x - 4y = 12$.

5. $4x + 5y = 20$.

6. $-2x + 4y = 8$.

7. $-4x - 5y = 40$.

8. $-6x - 8y = -14$.

9. $0.5x + 1.5y = 7.5$.

292. Simultaneous equations.—Take the two indeterminate equations

(1) $\qquad\qquad x - y = 2$

(2) $\qquad\qquad x + y = 12$

Pairs of values that satisfy (1) are as follows:

x	-4	-3	-2	-1	0	1	2	3	4	5	6	7	8	9
y	-6	-5	-4	-3	-2	-1	0	1	2	3	4	5	6	7

Pairs of values that satisfy (2) are as follows:

x	-4	-2	0	1	2	3	4	5	6	7	8	10	12	14
y	16	14	12	11	10	9	8	7	6	5	4	2	0	-2

It is noticed that the pair of values $x = 7$ and $y = 5$ is found in both sets of values; that is, these values satisfy both equations. Such a set of two equations satisfied by a pair of values for the unknown is called a **system of simultaneous equations.**

If, as in the system just considered, there is only one pair of values that satisfy both equations, the equations are called **independent.**

When one is asked to solve a system of simultaneous equations like the equations just discussed, it is necessary to find the pair of values for the unknowns that satisfy both equations. Not every set of equations that may appear like these can be solved; for a set of equations may not have a pair of values that will satisfy each equation, and, again, a set of equations may be such that any pair of values that satisfy one equation will also satisfy the other. Two equations of the first kind are called **inconsistent equations,** and two of the second kind are called **equivalent equations.**

The equations $x + 2y = 7$ and $3x + 6y = 15$ are inconsistent equations, for there is no pair of values for x and y that will satisfy both equations.

The equations $2x + y = 10$ and $6x + 3y = 30$ are equivalent equations, for any pair of values that satisfy one of these will also satisfy the other, as one can readily show by trial. For instance $x = 4$ and $y = 2$ will satisfy both equations. So will $x = 3$ and $y = 4$.

The equations discussed here and their relations will be explained more fully in Chap. XXXII by graphical methods.

293. Solution of independent equations.—It is evidently not convenient to find a pair of values that will satisfy two independent equations, by writing a table of pairs of values for each equation and then selecting the pair that is the same in each table. It remains then to devise a way that is shorter.

The different methods of solution that have been devised are alike in that an equation is obtained that has only one unknown. We say then that one unknown has been **eliminated.** There are three ways of eliminating an unknown. They are:

(1) *Elimination by adding or subtracting.*

(2) *Elimination by substitution.*

(3) *Elimination by comparison.*

294. Elimination by adding or subtracting.

Example 1.—Solve $x - y = 2$ and $x + y = 12$ for x and y.

Solution

$$(1) \qquad x - y = 2$$
$$(2) \qquad x + y = 12$$

Adding equations (1) and (2), first member to first member and second member to second member, and we have

$$(3) \qquad 2x = 14$$
$$(4) \qquad x = 7$$

Substituting this value of x in (1) gives

$$(5) \qquad 7 - y = 2$$
$$(6) \qquad y = 5$$

Hence, the pair of values that will satisfy both equations is $x = 7$ and $y = 5$. Always test in (1) and (2).

Example 2.—Solve $3x + 2y = 21$ and $7x - 5y = 20$ for x and y.

Solution

(1) $$3x + 2y = 21$$
(2) $$7x - 5y = 20$$

Multiplying (1) by 7 gives

(3) $$21x + 14y = 147.$$

Multiplying (2) by 3 gives

(4) $$21x - 15y = 60$$

Subtracting (4) from (3) gives

(5) $$29y = 87$$
(6) $$y = 3$$

Substituting in (1) gives

(7) $$3x + 6 = 21$$
(8) $$3x = 21 - 6$$
(9) $$3x = 15$$
(10) $$x = 5$$

Hence, $x = 5$ and $y = 3$ are the required values. (Test.)

This way of eliminating one of the unknown numbers is called **elimination by adding or subtracting.** The following rule may be given for the process:

RULE.—(1) *Multiply each equation, if necessary, by such a number as will make the absolute values of the coefficients of one of the unknown numbers the same in both of the resulting equations.*

(2) *Add or subtract the corresponding members of the resulting equations so as to eliminate the unknown number having coefficients equal in absolute value.*

It should be noticed that we add when the coefficients are of opposite signs and subtract when they are of like signs.

295. Elimination by substitution.—The elimination can often be performed more easily by using a method called substitution. Consider the following system of equations:

$$y = 42 - 7x \text{ and } 3x - y = 8$$

Solution

(1) $$y = 42 - 7x$$
(2) $$3x - y = 8$$

Substituting the value of y from (1) into (2) gives

(3) $$3x - (42 - 7x) = 8$$
(4) $$3x - 42 + 7x = 8$$
(5) $$3x + 7x = 42 + 8$$
(6) $$10x = 50$$
(7) $$x = 5$$

Substituting in (1) gives

(8) $$y = 42 - 35$$
(9) $$y = 7$$

Hence, $x = 5$ and $y = 7$ are the values. (Test.)

This method of eliminating is called **elimination by substitution** and can generally be used to good advantage when one equation is much simpler in form than the other. The following rule may be given for the process:

RULE.—*Solve one of the equations for the value of one of the unknown numbers, and substitute this value in place of that number in the other equation. This will give an equation with but one unknown number.*

296. Elimination by comparison.

Example.—Solve $x + 4y = 21$ and $3x - y = 11$.

Solution

(1) $$x + 4y = 21$$
(2) $$3x - y = 11$$

Solving (1) for x gives

(3) $$x = 21 - 4y$$

Solving (2) for x gives

(4) $$x = \frac{11 + y}{3}$$

By axiom (5), equations (3) and (4) give

(5) $$21 - 4y = \frac{11 + y}{3}$$

Clearing of fractions,

(6) $$63 - 12y = 11 + y$$
(7) $$-12y - y = 11 - 63$$
(8) $$-13y = -52$$
(9) $$y = 4$$

Substituting in (3) gives

(10) $$x = 21 - 16$$
(11) $$x = 5$$

Hence, $x = 5$ and $y = 4$ are the values.   (Test.)

This method of elimination is called **elimination by comparison.**   The following rule may be given for the process:

RULE.—*Solve each of the equations for the value of one of the unknowns, and equate these values. This forms an equation having but one unknown.*

297. Suggestions.—Any method of elimination may be used. Usually one of the methods is shorter than the others.   Elimination by adding or subtracting can generally be used to the best advantage.

Free the equations of signs of grouping before eliminating. Usually clear of fractions before eliminating.

Much practice and dealing with examples will help one to determine what method to use.

Always test by substituting the determined values in both of the original equations.

EXERCISES

In Exercises 1 to 10 eliminate in each by all three methods.

 1. $x + y = 4$ and $x - y = 2$.   *Ans.* 3, 1.
 2. $x + 2y = 7$ and $x - y = 1$.   *Ans.* 3, 2.
 3. $x + 3y = 1$ and $x - y = 9$.   *Ans.* 7, -2.
 4. $2x + 3y = 2$ and $2x - 3y = 0$.   *Ans.* $\frac{1}{2}$, $\frac{1}{3}$.

5. $x + y = 1$ and $4x + 3y = 0$. *Ans.* $-3, 4$.

6. $2x + 3y = 1$ and $-x + y = 1$. *Ans.* $-\frac{2}{5}, \frac{3}{5}$.

7. $3x + 5y = 11$ and $15x - 15y = 7$. *Ans.* $1\frac{2}{3}, 1\frac{1}{5}$.

8. $2x - y = 3$ and $4x + 2y = 50$. *Ans.* $7, 11$.

9. $5x - 11y = 1$ and $5x + 11y = 3$. *Ans.* $\frac{2}{5}, \frac{1}{11}$.

10. $x + y = 1$ and $4x - 4y = 6$. *Ans.* $\frac{5}{4}, -\frac{1}{4}$.

Solve the following by some method of elimination:

11. $3x + 5y = 8$ and $2x - 3y = 12$. *Ans.* $x = 4\frac{8}{19}, y = -\frac{20}{19}$.

Solution

(1) $$3x + 5y = 8$$
(2) $$2x - 3y = 12$$

Multiplying (1) by 2 gives

(3) $$6x + 10y = 16$$

Multiplying (2) by 3 gives

(4) $$6x - 9y = 36$$

Subtracting (4) from (3) gives

(5) $$19y = -20$$
$$\therefore y = -\frac{20}{19}$$

Substituting in (1),

$$x = 4\frac{8}{19}.$$

12. $5x + 6y = 17$ and $6x + 5y = 16$. *Ans.* $x = 1, y = 2$.

13. $x - 11y = 1$ and $111y - 9x = 99$. *Ans.* $x = 100, y = 9$.

14. $\dfrac{x + 1}{2} = \dfrac{y + 2}{3}$ and $\dfrac{x + y}{4} = \dfrac{y + 2}{3}$. *Ans.* $x = 5, y = 7$.

Suggestion.—Clear of fractions and simplify before eliminating.

15. $(y + 1)(x + 5) = (y + 5)(x + 1)$ and $xy + y + x = (y + 2)(x + 2)$ *Ans.* $x = -2, y = -2$.

16. $\dfrac{a}{3} - \dfrac{b}{6} = \dfrac{1}{2}$ and $\dfrac{a}{5} - \dfrac{3b}{10} = \dfrac{1}{2}$. *Ans.* $a = 1, b = -1$.

17. $\dfrac{a}{5} + \dfrac{b}{2} = 5$ and $a - b = 4$. *Ans.* $a = 10, b = 6$.

18. $\dfrac{n + 1}{10} = \dfrac{3m - 5}{2}$ and $\dfrac{n + 1}{10} = \dfrac{n - m}{8}$. *Ans.* $m = 3, n = 19$.

19. $\dfrac{x - 2}{3} - \dfrac{y + 2}{4} = 0$ and $\dfrac{2x - 5}{5} - \dfrac{11 - 2y}{7} = 0$.

Ans. $x = 5, y = 2$.

20. $\frac{x}{2} - \frac{y}{5} = 4$ and $\frac{x}{7} + \frac{y}{15} = 3$.　　　　　*Ans.* $x = 14$, $y = 15$.

21. $\frac{x}{a} + \frac{y}{b} = \frac{1}{ab}$ and $\frac{x}{c} - \frac{y}{d} = \frac{1}{cd}$.　*Ans.* $x = \dfrac{a + c}{ad + bc}$, $y = \dfrac{d - b}{ad + bc}$.

Solution

(1)　　　　　　　　　　　$\dfrac{x}{a} + \dfrac{y}{b} = \dfrac{1}{ab}$

(2)　　　　　　　　　　　$\dfrac{x}{c} - \dfrac{y}{d} = \dfrac{1}{cd}$

Clearing of fractions,

(3)　　　　　　　　　　　$bx + ay = 1$
(4)　　　　　　　　　　　$dx - cy = 1$

Multiplying (3) by c,

(5)　　　　　　　　　　　$bcx + acy = c$

Multiplying (4) by a,

(6)　　　　　　　　　　　$adx - acy = a$

Adding (5) and (6),

(7)　　　　　　　　　　　$(ad + bc)x = a + c$
(8)　　　　　　　　　　　$\therefore x = \dfrac{a + c}{ad + bc}$

Here it is best to solve for y by eliminating x rather than to substitute the value of y in (1) or (2).

22. The sum of two numbers is 15, and their difference is 1. What are the numbers?　　　　　　　　　　*Ans.* 7 and 8.

Suggestion.—Let $x =$ smaller number and $y =$ larger number. Then the equations are

$$x + y = 15$$
and　　　　　　　　　　　$$y - x = 1$$

This problem could be as readily solved by using one unknown.

23. Three times one number plus four times another number is 10, and four times the first plus the second is 9. What are the two numbers?
　　　　　　　　　　　　　　　　　Ans. 2 and 1.

24. What is the fraction that equals $\frac{1}{3}$ when 1 is added to the numerator but equals $\frac{1}{4}$ when 1 is added to the denominator?　*Ans.* $\frac{4}{15}$.

Suggestion.—Let x = numerator and y = denominator. Then $\dfrac{x}{y}$ is the fraction. The equations are

$$\frac{x+1}{y} = \frac{1}{3}$$

and

$$\frac{x}{y+1} = \frac{1}{4}$$

In Exercises 25 and 26 solve for $\dfrac{1}{x}$ and $\dfrac{1}{y}$ without clearing of fractions.

25. $\dfrac{2}{x} - \dfrac{3}{y} = 4$ and $\dfrac{1}{x} + \dfrac{2}{y} = 3.$ *Ans.* $\dfrac{1}{x} = \dfrac{17}{7}, \dfrac{1}{y} = \dfrac{2}{7}.$

26. $\dfrac{3}{x} - \dfrac{4}{y} = 5$ and $\dfrac{6}{x} + \dfrac{7}{y} = 8.$ *Ans.* $\dfrac{1}{x} = \dfrac{67}{45}, \dfrac{1}{y} = \dfrac{-2}{15}.$

27. Find two numbers whose sum is 1 and whose difference is 6.
Ans. 3.5; -2.5.

28. A rectangle is 3 ft. longer than it is wide. Its perimeter is 4.5 times its shorter side. Find its width.   *Ans.* 12 ft.

29. I bought a suit and a topcoat and had $19 left of a hundred-dollar bill. One-sixth of the cost of the suit is $1 more than one-ninth of the cost of the coat. Find the price of each.

Ans. Suit, $36; topcoat, $45.

30. Today a father is three times as old as his son. Ten years ago he was seven times as old. Find the ages of both today.

Ans. 15 years; 45 years.

31. I am thinking of two numbers such that the double of one is one-half the triple of the other. Find three pairs of these numbers.

32. For an odd lot of rugs a man paid $240. He sold one-third of them at $2 each, one-fourth of them at $3 each, one-sixth of them at $4 each, and one-fourth of them at $5 each. He gained $80 on the lot. How many were in the lot?   *Ans.* 96.

33. A contractor employed three types of laborers. On one-half of the total men employed he cleared $10 per man; on one-third of them he cleared $20 per man; and on one-sixth of them he cleared $30 per man. He cleared a total of $200. How many laborers were there in each type?
Ans. 6; 4; 2.

34. The sum of two consecutive numbers (x and $x + 1$) exceeds half the smaller by 25. Find the numbers.   *Ans.* 16, 17.

35. Given $S = \dfrac{\pi DN}{12}$ and $T = \dfrac{LF}{N}.$ Eliminate N, and find the value of T in terms of the remaining letters.   *Ans.* $T = \dfrac{\pi DFL}{12S}.$

Suggestion.—Solve each equation for N, and eliminate by comparison.

36. The formulas of Exercise 35 are used in lathe work. In these formulas, T is the time in minutes, S is the cutting speed in feet per minute, D is the diameter of the work in inches, N is the number of R. P. M., L is the length of the part to be turned in inches, F is the feed and is expressed as the number of turns to give a sidewise movement of 1 in. Thus, a feed of 16 means that each cut is $\frac{1}{16}$ in. wide. Find the time to turn a piece 3 in. in diameter and 2 ft. long if the feed is 20 and the cutting speed 15 ft. per minute. *Ans.* 25.13+ min.

37. In locating and boring holes in a drill jig, it is necessary to find the diameters of three circular disks tangent two and two, whose centers are at distances of 0.765 in., 0.710 in., and 0.850 in. Find the diameters of the three circles.

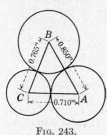

Fig. 243.

Solution.—The disks are placed as shown in Fig. 243.

Let x, y, and z = the radii in inches of the circles centered at A, B, and C, respectively

Then

(1) $\qquad x + y = 0.850$
(2) $\qquad x + z = 0.710$
(3) $\qquad y + z = 0.765$

Subtracting (2) from (1),

(4) $\qquad\qquad y - z = 0.140$

Adding (3) and (4),

(5) $\qquad\qquad 2y = 0.905$
(6) $\qquad\qquad y = 0.4525$

Substituting value of y in (1) gives

$$x + 0.4525 = 0.850$$
$$\therefore x = 0.3975$$

Substituting value of y in (3) gives

$$0.4525 + z = 0.765$$
$$\therefore z = 0.3125$$

The diameters of the circles are at A, 0.795 in.; at B, 0.905 in.; at C, 0.625 in.

38. As in the last exercise, three holes are to be bored, the distances between whose centers shall be 0.650 in., 0.790 in., and 0.865 in., respectively. Find the diameters of the required disks.

Ans. 0.725 in.; 0.575 in.; 1.005 in.

39. Three points A, B, and C are located as shown in Fig. 244. Three disks are centered at these points and tangent two and two. Find the diameters of the disks.

Suggestion.—Let x, y, and z = radii in inches of circles centered at A, B, and C, respectively. Then

$$x + y = \sqrt{0.680^2 + 0.640^2}$$
$$x + z = \sqrt{0.880^2 + 0.310^2}$$
$$y + z = \sqrt{0.950^2 + 0.2^2}$$

Ans. 0.8960 in.; 0.9716 in.; 0.9700 in.

40. A man has $98 in dollar bills, half dollars, and quarters. Half of the dollars and one-fifth of the half dollars are worth $31; and one-seventh of the half dollars and one-third of the quarters are worth $10. How many pieces has he of each?

Ans. 48; 70; 60.

41. In a factory where 700 men and women are employed, the average daily pay for the men is $6.20 and for the women $4.50. If $4000 is paid daily for labor, find the number of men and the number of women employed.

Ans. 500 men; 200 women.

42. A lever is balanced on a fulcrum with a weight of 40 lb. at one end and 50 lb. at the other. If 5 lb. are added to the 40-lb. weight, the 50-lb. weight will have to be placed 1 ft. farther from the fulcrum to balance the lever. Find the lengths of the two arms of the lever at first.

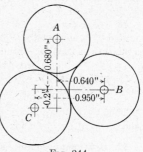

FIG. 244.

Ans. 10 ft.; 8 ft.

Suggestion.—Let x = the length in feet of the long arm and y = the length in feet of the short arm.

Then $40x = 50y$
and $45x = 50(y + 1)$

43. A lever is balanced on a fulcrum with a weight w_1 on one arm and w_2 on the other. If p lb. are added to w_1, w_2 has to be moved over f ft. to balance the lever. Find the lengths of the two arms of the lever.

Ans. $\dfrac{fw_2}{p}$; $\dfrac{fw_1}{p}$.

44. A beam that is supported at its ends has a weight of 50 lb. placed upon it so that it causes an increase in pressure on the support at one end of 20 lb. It is also found that the same pressure is produced at this

end by a weight of 60 lb. placed 3 ft. farther from this end.   How lon
is the beam?   *Ans.* 45 ft.

Suggestion.—Consider the support where the increase is 20 lb. as th
fulcrum.   Then there is a pressure of 30 lb. at the other end.

Let y = the length in feet of the beam and x = the distance the 50-lb
weight is from the fulcrum.

Then $$30y = 50x$$

Similarly, when the 60-lb. weight is applied

$$40y = 60(x + 3)$$

45. A glass full of water weighs 18 oz.   When the same glass is full o
sulphuric acid of specific gravity 1.75, it weighs 27 oz.   Find the weigh
of the glass when empty.   *Ans.* 6 oz.

46. Given two grades of zinc ore, the first containing 45 % zinc and th
second 25 % zinc, find how many pounds of each must be taken to mak
a mixture of 2000 lb. containing 40 % zinc.

Ans. 1500 lb. of 45 % ore and 500 lb. of 25 % ore.

Suggestion.—Let x = the number of pounds of 45 % ore and y = num
ber of pounds of 25 % ore.

Then $$x + y = 2000$$
and $$0.45x + 0.25y = 0.40 \times 2000$$

47. How many gallons of cream containing 35 % fat and milk con
taining 4 % fat should be mixed to give 20 gal. of cream containing 25 %
fat?   *Ans.* $13\frac{17}{31}$ and $6\frac{14}{31}$.

48. Find the number of ounces each of silver 70 % pure and silver 87 %
pure to make 12 ounces 82 % pure.   *Ans.* $3\frac{9}{17}$ and $8\frac{8}{17}$.

49. The specific gravity of one liquid is 1.75 and of another it is 1.4
How many ounces of each of these two liquids should be used to giv
10 oz. of a liquid of specific gravity of 1.7?   *Ans.* $8\frac{4}{7} : 1\frac{3}{7}$.

CHAPTER XXIX

EXPONENTS, POWERS, AND ROOTS

298. General statement.—In previous chapters, we have used **positive integral exponents.** In Art. 210, a positive integral exponent was defined as showing how many times the base is to be used as a factor.

The **negative exponent,** the **fractional exponent,** and the **zero exponent** are other kinds of exponents that occur in mathematics. They will be dealt with to some extent in the present chapter. **Logarithms** are exponents that will be considered in Chap. XXXIII.

The few facts and theorems concerning exponents, given in this chapter, are not intended to be a complete treatment of the subject, but they are sufficient for what follows and will give the proper viewpoint for logarithms.

It should be carefully noted that the definition of a *positive integral exponent* cannot apply to an exponent that is *negative, zero,* or a *fraction.* For instance, in 8^2, the 2 shows that 8 is taken twice as a factor; but in $8^{\frac{1}{3}}$, the $\frac{1}{3}$ can in no sense show how many times 8 is taken as a factor. To say that 8 is taken $\frac{1}{3}$ times as a factor is to make a meaningless statement.

We shall therefore find it necessary to enlarge the definition of an exponent so as to make it include these new kinds of exponents.

299. Laws of exponents.—The **law of exponents in multiplication** (see Art. 240) has been stated and proved for *positive integral exponents.* It may be restated here in symbols as follows:

$$a^m a^n = a^{m+n}$$

437

Likewise the **law of exponents in division** (see Art. 249) has been stated for *positive integral exponents.* A restatement in symbols is as follows:

$$a^m \div a^n = a^{m-n} \text{ when } m \text{ is greater than } n$$
$$a^m \div a^n = 1 \text{ when } m = n, a \neq 0$$

In finding the **power of a power,** *the exponents are multiplied.* That is

$$(a^m)^n = a^{mn}$$

This is found from the definition of a positive integral exponent.

Thus, $(a^m)^n = a^m a^m a^m \ldots$ to n factors $= a^{m+m+m \cdots}$ to n terms $= a^{mn}$.

A numerical illustration is $(a^6)^3 = a^6 \cdot a^6 \cdot a^6 = a^{18}$.

The **power of a product** *is the same as the product of the powers of the factors.* That is,

$$(abc \ldots)^n = a^n b^n c^n \ldots$$

A numerical illustration is $(2 \cdot 3 \cdot 4)^3 = 2^3 \cdot 3^3 \cdot 4^3$.

The **power of a fraction** *equals the power of the numerator divided by the power of the denominator.* That is,

$$\left(\frac{a}{b}\right)^m = \frac{a^m}{b^m} \ (b \neq 0)$$

A numerical illustration is $\left(\frac{2}{3}\right)^3 = \frac{2^3}{3^3} = \frac{8}{27}$.

If we take the **root of a power,** *we have the inverse of the operation by which we get* a^{mn} *and have* $\sqrt[n]{a^m} = a^{m \div n}$.

A numerical illustration is $\sqrt[2]{3^4} = 3^{4 \div 2} = 3^2 = 9$.

The definition of a positive integral exponent gives us the right to state the foregoing only when $m \div n$ is an integer.

A summary of the six laws of exponents mentioned is:

(**1**) $\qquad\qquad \mathbf{a^m a^n = a^{m+n}}$

(**2**) $\qquad\qquad \mathbf{a^m \div a^n = a^{m-n}} \ (a \neq 0)$

(**3**) $\qquad\qquad \mathbf{(a^m)^n = a^{mn}}$

(**4**) $\qquad \mathbf{(a \cdot b \cdot c \ldots)^m = a^m b^m c^m} \ldots$

(5) $$\left(\frac{a}{b}\right)^m = \frac{a^m}{b^m} \ (b \neq 0)$$

(6) $$\sqrt[n]{a^m} = a^{m \div n} = a^{\frac{m}{n}} \ (a \text{ is positive})$$

Example 1.—Find the fourth power of $3a^2x^3y^4$.

$$(3a^2x^3y^4)^4 = 3^4(a^2)^4(x^3)^4(y^4)^4 = 81a^8x^{12}y^{16}$$

Example 2.—Find the cube of $\dfrac{3a^3b^4x}{2y^2}$.

$$\left(\frac{3a^3b^4x}{2y^2}\right)^3 = \frac{3^3(a^3)^3(b^4)^3x^3}{2^3(y^2)^3} = \frac{27a^9b^{12}x^3}{8y^6}$$

Example 3.—Find the cube root of $3^6b^9x^{12}$.

$$\sqrt[3]{3^6b^9x^{12}} = 3^{6\div3}b^{9\div3}x^{12\div3} = 3^2b^3x^4$$

It should be noted that in order that a root may be found, each exponent must be exactly divisible by the index of the root.

EXERCISES

Raise to the indicated powers, or find the root indicated:

1. $(2x^2y^3)^4$.   *Ans.* $16x^8y^{12}$.
2. $(-2ab^2c)^3$.   *Ans.* $-8a^3b^6c^3$.
3. $(5x^4y^5)^6$.   *Ans.* $15{,}625x^{24}y^{30}$.

4. $(-2a^3b^4c)^2$.   *Ans.* $4a^6b^8c^2$.
5. $(4hk^4m)^4$.   *Ans.* $256h^4k^{16}m^4$.
6. $(7abc^x)^2$.   *Ans.* $49a^2b^2c^{2x}$.

7. $(-2x^3y^4z)^x$.   *Ans.* $-2^xx^{3x}y^{4x}z^x$.
8. $(8^a9^bmn^3)^x$.   *Ans.* $8^{ax}9^{bx}m^xn^{3x}$.
9. $-(-2xyz^a)^2$.   *Ans.* $-4x^2y^2z^{2a}$.
10. $(-2abc^m)^2$.   *Ans.* $4a^2b^2c^{2m}$.
11. $\left(\dfrac{4x}{5y}\right)^6$.   *Ans.* $\dfrac{4096x^6}{15625y^6}$.
12. $\left(\dfrac{2^2x^2y}{3abc^3}\right)^4$.   *Ans.* $\dfrac{256x^8y^4}{81a^4b^4c^{12}}$.
13. $\left[\left(\dfrac{2ax^3}{3by^3}\right)^3\right]^n$.   *Ans.* $\dfrac{8^na^{3n}x^{9n}}{27^nb^{3n}y^{9n}}$.

14. $\sqrt{2^2x^4y^6}$.   *Ans.* $2x^2y^3$.

15. $\sqrt[3]{27x^6y^9z^{12}}$.   *Ans.* $3x^2y^3z^4$.

16. $\sqrt[4]{\dfrac{2^2x^4y^8}{3^4h^4k^8}}$.   *Ans.* $\dfrac{\sqrt{2}\,(xy^2)}{3hk^2}$.

17. $[4(abc^2)^3]^3$.   *Ans.* $64a^9b^9c^{18}$.

18. $-[-(2x^2y^4)^2]^2$.   *Ans.* $-16x^8y^{16}$.

300. Zero exponent.—If we assume that $a^m \div a^n = a^{m-n}$ holds when $m = n$, we have $a^m \div a^n = a^{m-n} = a^0$, for $m - n = 0$.

Also $a^m \div a^n = 1$ by Art. 249, if $m = n$.

$$\therefore \mathbf{a^0 = 1}\,(a \neq 0)$$

Making the foregoing assumption is the same as stating by definition: *Any number other than zero affected by a zero exponent equals one.*

Example 1: $0.8^0 = 1$
Example 2: $100^0 = 1$
Example 3: $0.01^0 = 1$

301. Negative exponent.—Assuming that the law $a^m \div a^n = a^{m-n}$ holds when n is greater than m, we have

$$a^2 \div a^6 = a^{-4}$$

But

$$a^2 \div a^6 = \frac{a^2}{a^6} = \frac{1}{a^4}$$

$$\therefore a^{-4} = \frac{1}{a^4}$$

Similarly,

$$\mathbf{a^{-n} = \frac{1}{a^n}}$$

By definition then, *a number other than zero affected by a negative exponent equals 1 divided by the same number affected by a positive exponent, equal in absolute value to the negative exponent.*

Example 1: $\qquad 2^{-3} = \dfrac{1}{2^3} = \dfrac{1}{8}$

Example 2: $\qquad 4^{-3} = \dfrac{1}{4^3} = \dfrac{1}{64}$

302. Fractional exponent.—If we apply the law $\sqrt[n]{a^m} = a^{m \div n}$, when m and n have any values, we have

$$\sqrt[n]{a^m} = a^{\frac{m}{n}}$$

Also $\qquad \sqrt[n]{a} = a^{1 \div n} = a^{\frac{1}{n}}$

By definition then, *a fractional exponent indicates a root.*
The denominator is the index of the root, and the numerator is
he exponent of a power.

A form like $a^{\frac{m}{n}}$ means either $\sqrt[n]{a^m}$ or $(\sqrt[n]{a})^m$; that is, the
umber a may be raised to the mth power and then the nth
oot taken, or the nth root may be taken first and then the
esult raised to the mth power. The base a is to be positive
f n is even.

Thus, $8^{\frac{2}{3}} = \sqrt[3]{8^2} = \sqrt[3]{64} = 4$, or $8^{\frac{2}{3}} = (\sqrt[3]{8})^2 = 2^2 = 4$.

Example 1: $\qquad 4^{\frac{1}{2}} = \sqrt{4} = 2$

Example 2: $\qquad 64^{\frac{1}{3}} = \sqrt[3]{64} = 4$

Example 3: $\qquad 32^{\frac{3}{5}} = (\sqrt[5]{32})^3 = 2^3 = 8$

Example 4: $\qquad 4^{-\frac{3}{2}} = \dfrac{1}{4^{\frac{3}{2}}} = \dfrac{1}{\sqrt{4^3}} = \dfrac{1}{8}$

Example 5.—Divide $a + b$ by $a^{\frac{1}{3}} + b^{\frac{1}{3}}$.
This is readily carried by long division as follows:

$$
\begin{array}{r|l}
a + \phantom{a^{\frac{2}{3}}b^{\frac{1}{3}}} b & a^{\frac{1}{3}} + b^{\frac{1}{3}} \\
\underline{a + a^{\frac{2}{3}}b^{\frac{1}{3}}} & a^{\frac{2}{3}} - a^{\frac{1}{3}}b^{\frac{1}{3}} + b^{\frac{2}{3}} \\
- a^{\frac{2}{3}}b^{\frac{1}{3}} \\
\underline{- a^{\frac{2}{3}}b^{\frac{1}{3}} - a^{\frac{1}{3}}b^{\frac{2}{3}}} \\
a^{\frac{1}{3}}b^{\frac{2}{3}} + b \\
\underline{a^{\frac{1}{3}}b^{\frac{2}{3}} + b}
\end{array}
$$

303. Numbers affected by radicals.—From the work already done in square root, we know that the root cannot always be found exactly. For this reason it is often of advantage to be able to work with numbers affected by radicals. These can be changed in various ways that will make them much easier to handle. Some of these changes have already been made. In Art. 98, Example 2, we write $\sqrt{32} = \sqrt{16 \cdot 2} = \sqrt{16}$ $\sqrt{2} = 4\sqrt{2}$. This change depends upon the fourth law of exponents, Art. 299.

In a similar manner

$$\sqrt{a^4b^3c} = \sqrt{a^4b^2} \cdot \sqrt{bc} = a^2b\sqrt{bc}$$

When this change has been made, we say that the radical expression has been **simplified.** As here the simplifying is done by separating the expression under the radical into two factors, one of which the root can be found.

304. Expressions with fractions under the radical sign.— When a fraction is affected by a radical, the expression can often be changed to advantage by obtaining a form in which the denominator is not affected by a radical. The denominator is then said to be **rationalized.**

For instance, if both numerator and denominator of $\sqrt{\frac{1}{2}}$ are multiplied by 2, the square root of the denominator can be found.

This gives $\sqrt{\frac{1}{2}} = \sqrt{\frac{2}{4}} = \sqrt{\frac{1}{4}} \cdot \sqrt{2} = \frac{1}{2}\sqrt{2}$.

Likewise, $\sqrt{\frac{2}{3}} = \sqrt{\frac{6}{9}} = \sqrt{\frac{1}{9}} \cdot \sqrt{6} = \frac{1}{3}\sqrt{6}$.

By this process a radical expression with a fraction under the radical is said to be simplified. It is done by multiplying both numerator and denominator by a number that will make the denominator so that the indicated root can be extracted. It is evident that this process will, in many cases, make the work less when the result is to be found as a decimal.

Thus, $\sqrt{\frac{1}{2}} = \frac{1}{2}\sqrt{2} = 0.7071$.

EXERCISES

Find the values of the following:

1. $[(20)^2]^0$. *Ans.* 1.

2. 8^{-3}. *Ans.* $\frac{1}{512}$.

3. $(2^4)^{-2}$. *Ans.* $\frac{1}{256}$.

4. 27^{-3}. *Ans.* $\frac{1}{19683}$.

5. 100^{-0}. *Ans.* 1.

6. 100^{-2}. *Ans.* $\frac{1}{10000}$.

7. $1000^{-\frac{2}{3}}$ *Ans* $\frac{1}{100}$

8. $10^0(0)^{10}$ *Ans* 0.

9. $(0.04)^{-\frac{3}{2}}$. *Ans.* 125.

10. $(-27)^{-\frac{2}{3}}$. *Ans.* $\frac{1}{9}$.

11. $(27)^{-\frac{2}{3}}$. *Ans.* $\frac{1}{9}$.

12. $32^{-\frac{2}{5}}$. *Ans.* $\frac{1}{4}$.

13. $3(3)^0$. *Ans.* 3.

14. $[3(3)]^0$. *Ans.* 1.

15. $5(5)^{-1}$. *Ans.* 1.

16. $5^{-1}(25)$. *Ans.* 5.

17. Divide $4x^{-2}y^{-1}$ by $2^{-2}xy^{-2}$. *Ans.* $\frac{16y}{x^3}$.

18. Multiply $3a^{-\frac{4}{5}}$ by $3^{-1}a$. *Ans.* $a^{\frac{1}{5}}$.

19. Multiply $16ab^{-3}c^2$ by $2^{-2}a^{-1}b^4c^{-2}$. *Ans.* $4b$.

20. Divide $a^2 - b^2$ by $(a - b)^{-1}$. *Ans.* $(a - b)^2(a + b)$.

21. Divide $a^{-2} - b^{-2}$ by $a^{-1} - b^{-1}$. *Ans.* $\frac{a + b}{ab}$.

22. Multiply $a^{-1} + b$ by $a^{-1} - b$. *Ans.* $\frac{1 - a^2b^2}{a^2}$.

23. Multiply $a^{\frac{1}{3}} - a^{\frac{1}{3}}$ by $a^{\frac{2}{3}} + (ab)^{\frac{1}{3}} + b^{\frac{2}{3}}$. *Ans.* $a - b$.

24. Divide $4 - x$ by $2 - x^{\frac{1}{2}}$. *Ans.* $2 + x^{\frac{1}{2}}$.

Express with the smallest root.

25. $\sqrt[4]{144} = (144)^{\frac{1}{4}} = (12^2)^{\frac{1}{4}} = 12^{\frac{1}{2}} = \sqrt{12}$.

26. $\sqrt[4]{16}$. *Ans.* 2.

27. $\sqrt[6]{9}$. *Ans.* $\sqrt[3]{3}$.

28. $\sqrt[12]{27x^9y^6z^{15}}$. *Ans.* $z\sqrt[4]{3x^3y^2z}$.

29. $\sqrt[2n]{(x - y)^{2mn}(x + y)^{4n}}$. *Ans.* $(x - y)^m(x + y)^2$.

Express each with the same and the smallest possible root sign.

30. $\sqrt{2}; \sqrt[3]{3}; \sqrt[4]{4}; \sqrt[12]{5}$.

$$2^{\frac{1}{2}}; 3^{\frac{1}{3}}; 4^{\frac{1}{4}}; 5^{\frac{1}{12}}$$
$$= (2^6)^{\frac{1}{12}}; (3^4)^{\frac{1}{12}}; (4^3)^{\frac{1}{12}}, 5^{\frac{1}{12}}$$
$$= \sqrt[12]{2^6}; \sqrt[12]{3^4}; \sqrt[12]{4^3}; \sqrt[12]{5}$$

Notice that the smallest root sign is the L.C.D. of the fractional exponents.

31. $\sqrt[2]{3}; \sqrt[3]{2}; \sqrt[4]{5}$. *Ans.* $\sqrt[12]{3^6}, \sqrt[12]{2^4}, \sqrt[12]{5^3}$.

32. $\sqrt[4]{a^3}; \sqrt[3]{a}; \sqrt[10]{a^3}$. *Ans.* $\sqrt[60]{a^{45}}; \sqrt[60]{a^{20}}; \sqrt[60]{a^{18}}$.

33. $\sqrt[4]{4}; \sqrt{3}; \sqrt[8]{6}$. *Ans.* $\sqrt[8]{4^2}; \sqrt[8]{3^4}; \sqrt[8]{6}$.

34. $\sqrt{2}$; $\sqrt[3]{3}$; $\sqrt[4]{4}$; $\sqrt[5]{5}$; $\sqrt[21]{16}$.   *Ans.* $\sqrt[6]{2^3}$; $\sqrt[6]{3^2}$; $\sqrt[6]{2^3}$; $\sqrt[6]{5}$; $\sqrt[6]{4}$.

35. Which is greater, (1) $\sqrt{2}$ or $\sqrt[3]{3}$? (2) $\sqrt[3]{3}$ or $\sqrt[4]{4}$? (3) $\sqrt[4]{4}$ or $\sqrt[5]{5}$

Ans. (2) $\sqrt[3]{3}$; (3) $\sqrt[4]{4}$.

NOTE: $\sqrt{2} = 2^{\frac{1}{2}} = 2^{\frac{3}{6}} = \sqrt[6]{2^3} = \sqrt[6]{8}$.

$$\sqrt[3]{3} = 3^{\frac{1}{3}} = 3^{\frac{2}{6}} = \sqrt[6]{3^2} = \sqrt[6]{9}.$$

Hence, $\sqrt[3]{3}$ is greater.

Combine the following:

36. $\sqrt[3]{24} + (50)^{\frac{1}{2}} + \sqrt[3]{3} - \sqrt{2} - (81)^{\frac{1}{3}} - \sqrt{32}$.

$\sqrt[3]{2^3(3)} + \sqrt{5^2(2)} + \sqrt[3]{3} - \sqrt{2} - \sqrt[3]{3^3(3)} - \sqrt{4^2(2)}$

$= (2^3)^{\frac{1}{3}}3^{\frac{1}{3}} + (5^2)^{\frac{1}{2}}2^{\frac{1}{2}} + 3^{\frac{1}{3}} - 2^{\frac{1}{2}} - (3^3)^{\frac{1}{3}}3^{\frac{1}{3}} - (4^2)^{\frac{1}{2}}2^{\frac{1}{2}}$.

$= 2\sqrt[3]{3} + 5\sqrt{2} + \sqrt[3]{3} - \sqrt{2} - 3\sqrt[3]{3} - 4\sqrt{2}$

$= (2\sqrt[3]{3} + 1\sqrt[3]{3} - 3\sqrt[3]{3}) + (5\sqrt{2} - 1\sqrt{2} - 4\sqrt{2})$

$= \qquad\qquad 0 \qquad\qquad + \qquad\qquad 0$

$= 0$

37. $\sqrt{3} + \sqrt{27} + \sqrt{12}$.   *Ans.* $6\sqrt{3}$.

38. $\sqrt{3} + 2\sqrt{27} - 4\sqrt{75} + 3\sqrt[4]{9}$.   *Ans.* $-10\sqrt{3}$.

39. $\sqrt{a} + 2\sqrt{a^3} + \sqrt{a^5}$.   *Ans.* $\sqrt{a}(1+a)^2$.

40. $2\sqrt{\frac{3}{4}} - \sqrt{\frac{1}{3}} + \sqrt{\frac{1}{12}} + 2\sqrt{\frac{1}{2}}$.   *Ans.* $\frac{5}{6}\sqrt{3} + \sqrt{2}$.

41. $2\sqrt{24} - 3(54)^{\frac{1}{2}} + 4(96)^{\frac{1}{2}}$.   *Ans.* $11\sqrt{6}$.

42. $3(\frac{1}{2})^{\frac{1}{2}} + (\frac{2}{3})^{\frac{1}{2}} - 2\sqrt{\frac{9}{8}}$.   *Ans.* $\frac{1}{3}\sqrt{6}$.

Simplify and express with integers under the root sign:

43. $(\sqrt{\frac{1}{8}})(\sqrt{12})(5)(18)^{\frac{1}{6}}$.

$5\sqrt{\frac{2}{16}}\sqrt{12}\sqrt[6]{18} = 5\frac{\sqrt{2}}{\sqrt{16}}\sqrt{12}\sqrt[6]{18} = \frac{5}{4}\sqrt{2}\sqrt{12}\sqrt[6]{18}$

$= \frac{5}{4}\sqrt{2}\sqrt{2^2(3)}\sqrt[6]{18} = \frac{5}{4}\sqrt{2}(2)\sqrt{3}\sqrt[6]{18} = \frac{5}{2}\sqrt{6}\sqrt[6]{18}$

$= \frac{5}{2}(6)^{\frac{3}{6}}(18)^{\frac{1}{6}} = \frac{5}{2}\sqrt[6]{6^3(18)} = \frac{5}{2}\sqrt[6]{[(3)(2)]^3 3^2(2)}$

$= \frac{5}{2}\sqrt[6]{(3^5)(2^4)}$

Notice that the number under the root sign is factored into its prime factors. This shows whether any prime factor has a power equal to or greater than the indicated root.

Thus, the problem could be solved:

$\frac{5}{4}\sqrt{2}\sqrt{12}\sqrt[6]{18} = \frac{5}{4}\sqrt{(2)(12)}\sqrt[6]{18} = \frac{5}{4}\sqrt{(2)(2^2)(3)}\sqrt[6]{18}$

$= \frac{5}{4}[(2^3)3]^{\frac{1}{2}}[(3^2)2]^{\frac{1}{6}} = \frac{5}{4}\sqrt[6]{2^9 3^3 3^2 2} = \frac{5}{4}\sqrt[6]{2^{10}3^5}$

$= \frac{5}{4}\sqrt[6]{(2^6)2^4 3^5} = \frac{5}{4}(2^6)^{\frac{1}{6}}[(2^4)(3^5)]^{\frac{1}{6}} = \frac{5}{4}(2)\sqrt[6]{(2^4)3^5}$

$= \frac{5}{2}\sqrt[6]{2^4 3^5}$

44. $(3\sqrt{3})(2\sqrt{27})$.   *Ans.* 54.

45. $(2\sqrt[3]{4})(\sqrt[3]{16})$.   *Ans.* 8.

46. $(\sqrt[3]{\frac{1}{2}})(\sqrt[3]{\frac{1}{3}})(\sqrt[3]{\frac{1}{5}})$.   *Ans.* $\frac{1}{30}\sqrt[3]{900}$.

47. $(3 \sqrt{4})(\sqrt[3]{25})$.   *Ans.* $6 \sqrt[3]{25}$.

48. $(\frac{1}{2} \sqrt[3]{12})(\frac{1}{3} \sqrt[4]{\frac{16}{81}})(12 \sqrt[3]{\frac{9}{4}})$.   *Ans.* 4.

49. $[\sqrt{x(a-b)^5}][\sqrt[3]{x^4(a-b)}][\sqrt[6]{(a-b)}]$.   *Ans.* $x \sqrt[6]{5}(a-b)^3$.

50. $[\sqrt[4]{4(a^2-b^2)^2}][\sqrt[5]{8(a-b)^3}][\sqrt[10]{2(a-b)}$.

Ans. $2(a-b) \sqrt[10]{4(a+b)^5(a-b)^2}$.

51. $3 \sqrt{20} \div 6 \sqrt{5}$.   *Ans.* 1.

52. $3 \sqrt{24} \div 5 \sqrt{27}$.   *Ans.* $\frac{2}{5} \sqrt{2}$.

53. $11 \div \sqrt{3}$.   *Ans.* $\frac{11}{3} \sqrt{3}$.

54. $2 \sqrt[4]{2} \div \sqrt{32}$.   *Ans.* $0.25 \sqrt[4]{8}$.

55. $\sqrt[3]{\frac{1}{4}} \div \sqrt{\frac{1}{8}}$.   *Ans.* $\sqrt[6]{32}$.

56. $\frac{3}{2} \frac{\sqrt{98}}{\sqrt{11}} \div \frac{5 \sqrt{22}}{7}$.   *Ans.* $\frac{147}{110}$.

Find an approximate result in the following:

57. $\dfrac{1}{\sqrt{2}} = \dfrac{1}{1.4145 \ldots}$ approx.

t would be necessary to divide here by long division, but

$$\frac{1}{\sqrt{2}} = \frac{1}{\sqrt{2}} \left(\frac{\sqrt{2}}{\sqrt{2}}\right) = \frac{\sqrt{2}}{2} = \frac{1.4145 \ldots}{2} = 0.707 \ldots$$

58. $\dfrac{1}{\sqrt{3} - \sqrt{2}} = \dfrac{1}{1.732 \ldots - 1.4145 \ldots} = \dfrac{1}{0.318 \ldots} =$

etc.

But

$$\frac{1}{\sqrt{3} - \sqrt{2}} = \left(\frac{1}{\sqrt{3} - \sqrt{2}}\right)\left(\frac{\sqrt{3} + \sqrt{2}}{\sqrt{3} + \sqrt{2}}\right) = \frac{\sqrt{3} + \sqrt{2}}{(\sqrt{3})^2 - (\sqrt{2})^2}$$

$$= \frac{\sqrt{3} + \sqrt{2}}{1} = 1.732 + 1.414 = \text{etc.}$$

59. $\dfrac{\sqrt{2}}{\sqrt{3} - \sqrt{2}}$.   *Ans.* 4.449+.

60. $\dfrac{\sqrt{3}}{\sqrt{3} - 1}$.   *Ans.* 2.366+.

61. $\dfrac{\sqrt{3} + \sqrt{2}}{\sqrt{3} - \sqrt{2}}$.   *Ans.* 9.899−.

305. Exponents used to write numbers in the scientific notation.—Often in engineering subjects we see such expressions as 4.25×10^9 or 726×10^{-8}. These forms are the result of an attempt to write certain expressions in a scientific notation. Keeping in mind the meaning of an exponent,

$$4.25 \times 10^9 = 4.25 \times 1,000,000,000 = 4,250,000,000$$

This last number means the same as the given expression but in some ways is not so convenient a form to handle, nor is it so easily compared with others of its kind as is the first form. Moreover, the eye does not catch its value so quickly as it does that of the scientific notation.

$$\text{The form } 726 \times 10^{-8} = 726 \times \frac{1}{10^8} = 726$$

$$\times \frac{1}{100,000,000} = 0.00000726$$

EXERCISES

The numbers in the following statements are expressed in scientific notation. Write them in ordinary positional notation.

1. The tensile strength of *catalin* in pounds per square inch is approximately $4(10)^3$.   *Ans.* 4000 lb. per square inch.

2. The velocity of light in a vacuum is $2.99766(10)^{10}$ cm. per second   *Ans.* 29,976,600,000 cm. per second.

3. The fractional part of *radium* transformed per second is $1.30(10)^{-11}$.   *Ans.* 0.0000000000130.

4. The attraction in dynes between two gram masses 1 cm. apart is $6.664(10)^{-8}$.   *Ans.* 0.00000006664.

The numbers in the following statements are expressed in the ordinary positional notation. Write them in scientific notation, that is, as a number, between 1 and 10, multiplied by an integral power of 10.

5. The mean wave length of sodium light is 0.00005893 mm.   *Ans.* $5.893(10)^{-5}$ mm.

6. An oil film is half a ten millionth of an inch thick.   *Ans.* $0.5(10)^{-6}$ in.

7. The diameter of the electron is estimated to be about 1 ft. divided by a hundred million million.   *Ans.* $(10)^{-13}$ ft.

8. The total area of the earth is about 196,400,000 sq. miles.   *Ans.* $1.964 \ (10)^8$.

9. The number 6.28 multiplied by a million million million gives the number of electrons flowing past a point per second. This is the electric current known as the **ampere.**   *Ans.* $6.28(10)^{17}$.

CHAPTER XXX

QUADRATIC EQUATIONS

306. The equations already solved have been, for the most part, such as involved only the first powers of the unknowns. A few equations, having the unknowns to higher powers than the first, were solved in Art. 270, but these were such as could be handled by factoring.

In the present chapter, general methods will be given for solving equations with one unknown and of the second degree.

307. Definitions.—An equation that contains the square of the unknown number and no higher power of it is a **quadratic equation.**

A **pure quadratic equation** is one that has the square only of the unknown number, as $2x^2 = 4$.

An **affected quadratic equation** is one that has both the square and the first power of the unknown, as $x^2 + 3x = 10$.

THE PURE QUADRATIC EQUATION

308. Solution.—The solution of the pure quadratic equation is the same as that of the simple equation until the value of the square of the unknown is found. The next step is to take the square root of each member of the equation.

Example 1.—Solve $3x^2 + 8 = 7x^2 - 8$ for x.

Solution.—Given equation,

1)
$$3x^2 + 8 = 7x^2 - 8$$

Transposing,

2)
$$3x^2 - 7x^2 = -8 - 8$$

Collecting terms,

3)
$$-4x^2 = -16$$

447

Dividing by -4,

(4) $$x^2 = 4$$

Extracting the square root of both x^2 and 4,

(5) $$x = \pm 2.$$

Here we use the sign $\pm$, and it indicates that the answer is either a $+2$ or a -2.   (See Art. 270.)

Since the product of two minus numbers gives the same value as the product of the same plus numbers, we may always call a square root either plus or minus.

Example 2.—Find the radius of a circle whose area is 4932 in.^{2}

Solution.—Let

(1) $$r = \text{the radius}$$

then

(2) $$3.1416r^2 = \text{the area of the circle}$$

But

(3) $$4932 \text{ in.}^2 = \text{the area of the circle}$$
(4) $$\therefore 3.1416r^2 = 4932, \text{ by axiom (5)}$$
(5) $$r^2 = 1569.9007$$
(6) $$r = \pm 39.622 \text{ in.}$$

It should be noticed that the radius cannot be negative, hence, the only value of r permissible is $+39.622$ in.

EXERCISES

Solve for x in Exercises 1 to 20 and test.

1. $x^2 = 99 - 10x^2$.   *Ans.* ± 3.
2. $80 - 2x^2 = 3x^2$.   *Ans.* ± 4.
3. $-5 + 0.75x^2 - 22 = 0$.   *Ans.* ± 6.
4. $\dfrac{6}{x+8} - \dfrac{6}{x-8} = 1 - \dfrac{33}{x^2 - 64}$.   *Ans.* ± 1.
5. $8 = \dfrac{3}{1+x} + \dfrac{3}{1-x}$.   *Ans.* $\pm \dfrac{1}{2}$.

6. $(x + 3)(x + 3) + (x - 3)^2 = 4(x^2 - 9)$. *Ans.* $\pm 3\sqrt{3}$.

7. $\dfrac{15}{8} - \dfrac{x - 3}{x - 2} = \dfrac{x + 3}{x + 2}$. *Ans.* ± 6.

8. $(x - 4)^2 + 4 = -8x + 29$. *Ans.* ± 3.

9. $(a - x)^2 - (x - a)(3x + a) = 0$. *Ans.* $\pm a$.

10. $x^2 + a^2 x^2 = (a^2 - 1)^2 - 2ax^2$. *Ans.* $\pm(a - 1)$.

11. Given $\dfrac{u - 2}{u + 2} + \dfrac{u + 2}{u - 2} = \dfrac{40}{u^2 - 4}$, find the values of u.

Ans. ± 4.

12. Given $E = 0.5Mv^2$, find the values of v. *Ans.* $\pm\sqrt{\dfrac{2E}{M}}$.

13. Given $S = 0.5gt^2$, find values of t if $g = 32.16$ and $S = 100.5$.

Ans. ± 2.5 approx.

14. Given $4m^2 = -c^2 + 2(a^2 + b^2)$, solve for m.

Ans. $\pm\dfrac{1}{2}\sqrt{2a^2 + 2b^2 - c^2}$.

15. Given $F = \dfrac{mna}{d^2}$, solve for d.

16. Given $n^2 = \dfrac{KS^2 t}{l^2 d}$, solve for S, l, and n, successively.

Ans. $\pm\sqrt{\dfrac{dl^2 n^2}{Kt}}$; $\pm\sqrt{\dfrac{KS^2 t}{dn^2}}$; $\pm\sqrt{\dfrac{KS^2 t}{dl^2}}$.

17. Find the radius of a cylinder of altitude 12 ft. and volume 1400 cu. ft. Use the formula $V = h\pi r^2$; substitute values; and solve for r.

Ans. $6.09+$ ft.

18. Find the radius of a right circular cone of altitude 20 in. and volume 145 in.^{3} Use the formula $V = \frac{1}{3}\pi r^2 h$. *Ans.* $2.62+$ in.

19. Find two numbers whose product is 90 and the quotient of the greater divided by the less is $3\frac{3}{5}$. *Ans.* 18 and 5, or -5 and -18.

20. The S. A. E. standard for automobile engines is

$$P = \dfrac{D^2 N}{2.5}$$

where

$P =$ the horsepower.

$D =$ the diameter of a cylinder in inches.

$N =$ the number of cylinders.

Given $P = 25.35$ and $N = 6$, find D *Ans.* $3\frac{1}{4}$.

21. Solve $r = \dfrac{(\frac{1}{2}w)^2 + h^2}{2h}$, which is formula 16, for w and obtain formula 18.

THE AFFECTED QUADRATIC EQUATION

309. Solution by factoring.—An affected quadratic equation in x, when simplified, can have a term in x^2, a term in x, a term not containing x, and no other term. Thus, $x^2 - 5x = -6$ is such an equation.

The solution of this equation has been discussed in Art. 270.

The steps in the solution of a quadratic equation that can be solved by factoring are restated here.

(1) *Simplify the equation.*

(2) *Transpose all terms to the first member of the equation.*

(3) *Factor the expression in the first member.*

(4) *Equate each factor to zero.*

(5) *Solve each of these equations.*

Example.—Solve $x^2 + 23x = -102$.

Solution.—Given equation

$$(1) \qquad x^2 + 23x = -102$$

Transposing,

$$(2) \qquad x^2 + 23x + 102 = 0$$

Factoring,

$$(3) \qquad (x + 6)(x + 17) = 0$$
$$(4) \qquad \therefore \ x + 6 = 0, \text{ and } x + 17 = 0$$
$$(5) \qquad \therefore \ x = -6, \text{ and } x = -17$$

Test.—For $x = -6$,

$$(-6)^2 + 23(-6) = -102$$
$$36 - 138 = -102$$
$$-102 = -102$$

For $x = -17$,

$$(-17)^2 + 23(-17) = -102$$
$$289 - 391 = -102$$
$$-102 = -102$$

EXERCISES

Solve the following equations by factoring, and test:

1. $x^2 - 3x + 2 = 0$. *Ans.* 1, 2.

2. $x^2 + 7x + 12 = 0$. *Ans.* -3, -4.

3. $x^2 = 11x - 18$. *Ans.* 2, 9.

4. $x = -x^2 + 6$. *Ans.* -3, 2.

5. $-20 = -x - x^2$. *Ans.* -5, 4.

6. $x^2 = 19x - 90$. *An* 9, 10.

7. $18x = 77 + x^2$. *Ans.* 7, 11.

8. $x^2 + 35x + 250 = 0$. *Ans.* -10, -25.

9. $6x^2 + 7x + 2 = 0$. *Ans.* $-\frac{1}{2}$, $-\frac{2}{3}$.

10. $2x^2 + 7x + 6 = 0$. *Ans.* $-\frac{3}{2}$, -2.

11. $12x^2 + 5 = 19x$. *Ans.* $\frac{1}{3}$, $\frac{5}{4}$.

12. $x^2 + x = 30$. *Ans.* 5, -6.

13. $10x^2 = 13x + 30$. *Ans.* $-\frac{6}{5}$, $\frac{5}{2}$.

14. $x^2 - (a + b)x + ab = 0$. *Ans.* a, b.

310. Completing the square.—Because of the difficulties in factoring a quadratic trinomial, it is well to have a method other than factoring for solving affected quadratic equations. In Arts. 259, and 260, we learned the form of a trinomial square. The first and last terms are perfect squares of monomials, and the middle term is twice the product of the square roots of the first and last terms. Keeping this in mind, we can find the last term if we know the first two.

Thus, if we know that $a^2 + 2ab$ are the first two terms, we can find the third term by taking the square of the quotient obtained by dividing the second term by twice the square root of the first. Twice the square root of the first term is $2a$. The second term divided by this gives b, which squared is b^2, the third term. We say then that we have **completed the square,** which is $a^2 + 2ab + b^2$.

Example.—Complete the square of $x^2 + 4x$.

Twice the square root of x^2 is $2x$, $4x \div 2x = 2$, and the square of 2 is 4. Hence, the completed square is $x^2 + 4x + 4$.

When the coefficient of x^2 is 1, all that is necessary is to *add the square of one-half the coefficient of x.*

EXERCISES

Supply the missing term in the following quadratic trinomials so as to form perfect squares:

1. $x^2 - 2x + \cdots$.

2. $x^2 + \cdots + 1$.

3. $x^2 - 6x + \cdots$.

4. $x^2 + 5x + \cdots$.

5. $x^2 - \cdots + 4$.

6. $1 + \cdots + 4x^2$.

7. $36 - \cdots + x^2$.

8. $36 - \cdots + 9x^2$.

9. $x^2 + \dfrac{x}{2} + \cdots$.

10. $\frac{1}{4} - \cdots + x^2$.

11. $4ax + a^2 + \cdots$.

12. $4bu^2 - \cdots + 9cv^2$.

311. Solution by completing the square.—We can best show how this is applied to the solution of affected quadratic equations by examples.

Example 1.—Given $x^2 + 4x = 12$, find x.

(1) Completing the square of the first member we have $x^2 + 4x + 4$. Since 4 is added to $x^2 + 4x$, we must also add 4 to 12 in order that the equality may be true.

$$\therefore\ x^2 + 4x + 4 = 16.$$

Extracting the square root of both members, we have

(2) $$x + 2 = \pm 4$$

Transposing,

(3) $$x = -2 \pm 4$$
(4) $$\therefore\ x = 2 \text{ and } -6$$

Each of these results checks the original equation and is therefore a root of the equation.

Example 2.—Given $x^2 + 12x = -35$, find x.

Solution.—Given equation

(1) $$x^2 + 12x = -35$$

Completing square,

(2) $$x^2 + 12x + 36 = 1$$

Extracting roots,

(3) $x + 6 = \pm 1$
(4) $\therefore x = -7$ and -5

Example 3.—Given $2r^2 + 4r = 48$, find r.
Solution.—Given equation

(1) $2r^2 + 4r = 48$

Dividing by 2,

(2) $r^2 + 2r = 24$

Completing square,

(3) $r^2 + 2r + 1 = 25$

Extracting roots,

(4) $r + 1 = \pm 5$
(5) $\therefore r = 4$ and -6

Example 4.—Given $3x^2 - 7x = 6$, find x.
Solution.—Given equation

(1) $3x^2 - 7x = 6$

Dividing by 3,

(2) $x^2 - \tfrac{7}{3}x = 2$

Completing square,

(3) $x^2 - \tfrac{7}{3}x + \tfrac{49}{36} = \tfrac{121}{36}$

Extracting roots,

(4) $x - \tfrac{7}{6} = \pm \tfrac{11}{6}$
(5) $\therefore x = 3$ and $-\tfrac{2}{3}$

It should be noticed that we always divide by the coefficient of x^2, unless it is 1, before completing the square.
Example 5.—Given $9x = 4 - 3x^2$, find x.

Solution.—Given equation

(1) $$9x = 4 - 3x^2$$

Transposing,

(2) $$3x^2 + 9x = 4$$

Dividing by 3,

(3) $$x^2 + 3x = \tfrac{4}{3}$$

Completing square,

(4) $$x^2 + 3x + \tfrac{9}{4} = \tfrac{4}{3} + \tfrac{9}{4} = \tfrac{4\,3}{1\,2}$$

Extracting roots,

(5) $$x + \tfrac{3}{2} = \pm \sqrt{\tfrac{4\,3}{1\,2}} = \pm 1.893 -$$
(6) $$x = -\tfrac{3}{2} \pm 1.893 -$$
(7) $$\therefore\ x = 0.393 \text{ and } -3.393$$

The method of solving an affected quadratic equation may be summarized in the following:

RULE.—(1) *Simplify and transpose all terms containing x to the first member and others to the second member.*

(2) *Divide by the coefficient of x^2 if it is not 1, giving the form $x^2 + ax = c$.*

(3) *Complete the square by adding to both members the square of one-half the coefficient of x.*

(4) *Equate the square root of the first member to $\pm$ square root of second member.*

(5) *Solve the two equations thus found.*

EXERCISES

Solve for x by completing the square.

1. $x^2 - 6x = 7$.   *Ans.* $-1, 7$.
2. $x^2 + 8x = 9$.   *Ans.* $1, -9$.
3. $x^2 + 9x = 4.75$.   *Ans.* $-9.5, 0.5$.
4. $x^2 - 7x = 3.75$.   *Ans.* $-0.5, 7.5$.
5. $2x^2 - 5x + 1 = 0$.   *Ans.* $0.2192+, 2.2808-$.
6. $3x^2 + 2x = 1$.   *Ans.* $-1, \tfrac{1}{3}$.

7. $5 = 5x^2 + 10x$. *Ans.* $0.414+$, $-2.414-$.

8. $0.5x^2 = x + 0.5$. *Ans.* $-0.586-$, $2.414+$.

9. $5x^2 + 2x - 20 = 0$. *Ans.* $-2.21+$, $1.81-$.

10. $11x^2 + 121x - 1 = 0$. *Ans.* $0.008+$, $11.008-$.

312. Solution of affected quadratic equation by formula.— The equation $ax^2 + bx + c = 0$, where a, b, and c are any numbers, positive or negative, can represent any quadratic equation in one unknown. If we solve this equation, we will have a formula that may be used to find the values of the unknown in any quadratic equation.

Example 1.—Given $ax^2 + bx + c = 0$, find x.

Solution.—Given equation

(1) $$ax^2 + bx + c = 0$$

Transposing,

(2) $$ax^2 + bx = -c$$

Dividing by a,

(3) $$x^2 + \frac{b}{a}x = -\frac{c}{a} \ (a \neq 0)$$

Completing square,

(4) $$x^2 + \frac{b}{a}x + \frac{b^2}{4a^2} = \frac{b^2}{4a^2} - \frac{c}{a}$$

Extracting roots,

(5) $$x + \frac{b}{2a} = \pm\sqrt{\frac{b^2 - 4ac}{4a^2}}$$

Transposing,

(6) $$x = -\frac{b}{2a} \pm \frac{\sqrt{b^2 - 4ac}}{2a}$$

Uniting we have the important quadratic formula,

$$\mathbf{x = \frac{-b \pm \sqrt{b^2 - 4ac}}{2a}}$$

Substituting these values of x in $ax^2 + bx + c = 0$ shows that they are roots.

The method of solution may be stated in the following:

RULE.—*To solve a quadratic equation by the quadratic formula, reduce the equation to the form $ax^2 + bx + c = 0$, substitute the values of a, b, and c in the formula, and evaluate.*

The formula can be used in solving any quadratic equation. In using the formula, care must be taken as regards the signs. They must be considered a part of the values of a, b and c.

Thus, in $3x^2 - 2x - 4 = 0$, $a = 3$, $b = -2$, and $c = -4$.

Example 2.—Substitute in the formula of example 1, and find the value of x in $6x^2 + 17x + 7 = 0$,

Solution.—Here $a = 6$, $b = 17$, and $c = 7$.

Substituting these values in the formula

$$x = \frac{-17 \pm \sqrt{17^2 - 4 \cdot 6 \cdot 7}}{2 \cdot 6} = \frac{-17 \pm 11}{12} =$$

$$-\tfrac{1}{2} \text{ and } -2\tfrac{1}{3}$$

Example 3.—By formula, find the value of x in $6x^2 + 8x - 30 = 0$.

Solution.—Here $a = 6$, $b = 8$, and $c = -30$.

$$\therefore x = \frac{-8 \pm \sqrt{8^2 - 4 \cdot 6(-30)}}{2 \cdot 6} = \frac{-8 \pm 28}{12} =$$

$$1\tfrac{2}{3} \text{ and } -3$$

EXERCISES

Solve the following equations by the most efficient method that you can discover:

1. $x^2 - 5x + 4 = 0$. *Ans.* 4, 1.
2. $x^2 + 4x = 5$. *Ans.* 1, -5.
3. $2x^2 + 5x + 2 = 0$. *Ans.* $-\tfrac{1}{2}$, -2.
4. $3x^2 - 10x = -3$. *Ans.* $\tfrac{1}{3}$, 3.
5. $2x^2 - 5x + 3 = 0$. *Ans.* 1, $1\tfrac{1}{2}$.
6. $30x^2 = 17x - 2$. *Ans.* $\tfrac{1}{6}$, $\tfrac{2}{5}$.

7. $15x^2 = 75x - 90$.   *Ans.* 2, 3.

8. $6x^2 - 13x + 6 = 0$.   *Ans.* $\frac{2}{3}$, $\frac{3}{2}$.

9. $u^2 + 2u - 2 = 0$.   *Ans.* $0.732+$, $-2.732-$.

10. $h^2 - 3h - 1 = 0$.   *Ans.* $-0.3027-$, $3.3027+$.

11. $2t^2 + 3t - 4 = 0$.   *Ans.* $-2.351+$, $0.851-$.

12. $3s^2 = 4s + 5$.   *Ans.* $-0.786+$, $2.119+$.

13. $7y^2 = 23y - 6$.   *Ans.* $\frac{2}{7}$, 3.

14. $9p^2 - 2p = 0$.   *Ans.* 0, $\frac{2}{9}$.

15. $9p^2 - 2p = 1$.   *Ans.* $-0.24-$, $0.46+$.

16. $q^2 - 2q = 9$.   *Ans.* $4.2-$; $-2.2+$.

17. $0.25k^2 - 0.2k = 1$.   *Ans.* -1.64 and 2.44 approx.

18. $1.2z^2 + 2.1z - 0.3 = 0$. -1.88 and 0.13 approx.

19. $\dfrac{U^2}{2} + \dfrac{U}{3} = \dfrac{1}{6}$.   *Ans.* $-1, \dfrac{1}{3}$.

20. $N\left(\dfrac{1}{a} + \dfrac{1}{b}\right) + N^2 + \dfrac{1}{ab} = 0$.   *Ans.* $\dfrac{-1}{a}, \dfrac{-1}{b}$.

21. Given $h = a + vt - 16t^2$, solve for a, v, and t, successively.

Ans. $a = h + 16t^2 - vt; \; v = \dfrac{h + 16t^2 - a}{t}; \; t = \dfrac{v \pm \sqrt{v^2 - 64(h - a)}}{32}$.

22. Given $T = \dfrac{22R^2}{7} + \dfrac{22RH}{21}$, solve for R.

$$Ans. \; \dfrac{-11 \pm \sqrt{121H + 1386T}}{66}.$$

23. Think of a number; take twice its square; and add 6.   This sum is seven times the number.   What is the number? $\dfrac{3}{2}$, 2.

24. Think of two consecutive numbers; square them; and add.   Note this sum is 25.   What are the numbers?   *Ans.* 3, 4.

25. Is there a number such that if you add it to its reciprocal, the sum is unity?   The sum is 2?   The sum is any number greater than 2?

26. I bought x articles for \$625 and paid x dollars per article for them. How many articles did I buy?   *Ans.* 25.

27. I worked 4 days; you worked 3 days; and we completed a job that you can do in 2 days less than I.   How long does it take me to do the job?   *Ans.* 8 days.

28. I worked 4 days; you worked 10 days; and we completed a job that I can do in 3 days less than you.   How long does it take me to do the job?   *Ans.* 12 days.

29. What is the width of a uniform border around a plot 6 ft. by 8 ft. if its area is 72 sq. ft.?   *Ans.* 2 ft.

30. A walk containing 784 sq. ft. is to be built around a garden 50 by 40 ft.   How wide must the walk be?   *Ans.* 4 ft.

Suggestion.—Let x = width of walk in feet.

Then the number of square feet in both garden and walk is $(50 + 2x)$ $(40 + 2x)$.

$$\therefore (50 + 2x)(40 + 2x) = 50 \times 40 + 784$$

31. There are as many square feet in the surface of a certain sphere as there are cubic feet in its volume.   Find its radius.   *Ans.* 3 ft.

Solution.—Let r = number of feet in radius.

Then $4\pi r^2$ = number of square feet in surface,

and $\frac{4}{3}\pi r^3$ = number of cubic feet in volume.

$$\therefore \frac{4}{3}\pi r^3 = 4\pi r^2$$
$$4\pi r^3 - 12\pi r^2 = 0$$

Factoring,

$$4\pi r^2(r - 3) = 0$$
$$\therefore 4\pi r^2 = 0 \text{ and } r - 3 = 0$$

or $r = 0$ and $r = 3$

32. Same as last exercise, but substitute cube for sphere and find the edge.   *Ans.* 6 ft.

33. There are 728 cu. in. of wood in a covered cubical box.   The boards are 1 in. thick.   Find the outside dimensions of the box.

Ans. 12 in.

34. If a car traveled 4 miles per hour faster, it would take 1 hr. less to go 360 miles.   Find the speed of the car.   *Ans.* 36 miles per hour.

35. A merchant sold a hat for $11 and gained as many per cent as the hat cost.   Find the cost of the hat.   *Ans.* $10.

36. A merchant bought x hats for $60.   If he had bought two less for the same money, they would have cost $1 more apiece.   Find x.

Ans. 12.

37. I bought a number of radios for $480; had they cost $8 apiece less, I should have had two more radios for the same money.   Find the cost of each.   *Ans.* $48.

38. A rectangular piece of ground is 40 by 60 ft.   A strip of uniform width is marked off around it to contain one-half the area of the rectangle. Find the width of the strip.   *Ans.* 6 ft. $11\frac{5}{8}$ in. approx.

39. Two railroads cross at right angles.   A train on one road passes the crossing moving at 40 miles per hour, and 15 min. later a train on the other road passes the crossing moving at 60 miles per hour.   How long after the first train passes the crossing will they be 80 miles apart? Explain the two answers.   *Ans.* 1.276+ hr. or −0.930+ hr.

40. A window screen has a total area of 10 sq. ft. and its length is 4 in. greater than its width.   The area inside the frame is 8 sq. ft.   The frame is of a constant width; find this width.   *Ans.* 2 in.

41. A flower garden that has the shape of a right triangle with one leg 3 yd. longer than the other has a perimeter of 36 yd. How long is each side of the garden?   *Ans.* 9 by 12 by 15 yd.

42. An airplane started $2\frac{1}{2}$ hr. late but finished its flight of 1200 miles on time by going 40 miles per hour faster than usual. What was the usual rate?   *Ans.* 120 miles per hour.

43. A gasoline tank was filled by two pipes in 3 hr. 40 min. The larger pipe alone could fill the tank in $2\frac{1}{2}$ hr. less time than the smaller pipe alone could. Find the time in which each pipe could fill the tank.
                              Ans. 8.79− hr., 6.29 hr.

44. The circumference of the hind wheel of a wagon is 5 ft. more than that of the front wheel. If the hind wheel makes 150 fewer revolutions than the front wheel in going one mile, find the circumference of each wheel.   *Ans.* 16 ft.; 11 ft.

45. An airplane that is at an altitude of 1200 ft. and moving at the rate of 100 miles per hour in a northerly direction drops a bomb. Disregarding the resistance of the air, where will the bomb strike the ground?
                              Ans. 1270 ft. north of starting point.

Suggestion.—Find the number of seconds that it will take the bomb to reach the ground from the formula $s = \frac{1}{2}gt^2$, where s = height of airplane in feet, $g = 32$, and t = time in seconds. This gives $t = 8.66$ sec.

Then the bomb will strike as many feet north of the starting point as the airplane will travel in 8.66 sec.

46. Let a be the difference between any number and its reciprocal, and let b be the difference between the square of the same quantity and the square of its reciprocal. Show that

$$a^2(a^2 + 4) = b^2$$

CHAPTER XXXI

VARIATION

313. The thoughtful student who has gone thus far in the study of mathematics must realize, at least to some extent, that a constant effort is being made to deal with everyday happenings and relations by means of the mathematical machinery that has been developed; and this should be realized more and more as he proceeds in his study. All happenings in this universe of ours are related to other happenings more or less closely; and when we can see these relations, we are sometimes able to predict what may happen from a certain setting. When we can state these relations in the language of mathematics, we are greatly assisted in telling exactly what will happen. In the present chapter we shall study some of the simple ways in which one thing depends on others and shall learn how to state these relations in mathematical language. In the following chapter under the topic of functions, more general relations will be considered.

We depend upon the ideas dealt with in variation for many of our physical laws and formulas. The meaning of many of the formulas already used will be made much clearer by considering their meaning from the viewpoint of variation.

The relations considered in variation are those considered in ratio and proportion. In many ways, however, it will be found that the methods used in variation are more convenient than the methods of ratio and proportion. Familiarity with them gives the student another powerful mathematical instrument.

For the principles of ratio and proportion used in the present chapter the student is referred to Chap. VII.

314. Constants and variables.—A number whose value does not change is called a **constant**.

In mathematical problems, certain constants occur that are always the same. The value of π, the ratio of the circumference to the diameter of a circle, is such a constant.

Other constants also occur that do not change in the same problem but that may have another value in a different problem. The radius of a circle and the side of a square are such constants.

Constants are usually represented by numerals or by the earlier letters of the alphabet. Thus, we may be thinking of a certain rectangle whose base is 10 in. and altitude 6 in. Here 10 and 6 are constants. Again the base may be designated by length b and the altitude as of length a and still be thought of as constants.

A **variable** is a number that may take an unlimited number of values. It may change arbitrarily or according to some law.

The number expressing the speed of an automobile as it is gaining headway is a variable. The price of a stock may change from day to day and is expressed by a variable. The velocity of a falling body changes from instant to instant and is expressed by a variable. In fact, it is difficult to mention any material thing whose measure does not vary as a result of changing conditions. For instance, the length of a steel rod subject to a change in temperature, the weight of a rock exposed to the weather, and the height of a growing cornstalk.

In algebra variables are usually represented by the later letters of the alphabet. In other subjects, as physics, geometry, and electricity, a variable is often represented by the initial letter of the name of the quantity, as b for base, w for work, v for voltage.

EXERCISES

1. Mention several material things, and tell whether their measures, such as the measure of length, weight, volume, etc., are constants or variables.

2. Could the Congress of the United States determine by law a constant relating the meter and the inch? The kilogram and the pound? The circumference and the diameter of a circle?

315. Direct variation.—The idea of variation is a very common one. Nearly everything is affected by its surroundings; that is, things vary according as something else varies.

The growth of a tree depends upon the amount of light it receives; the more light it receives the faster it grows, if other conditions are favorable. In such a case we say that its growth varies **directly** as the amount of light.

The amount of pay that a man receives varies directly as the time he works; that is, the longer he works the more pay he receives.

Definition.—If two numbers are so related that their ratio is constant—that is, if either increases, the other increases; or if either decreases, the other decreases—the two numbers are said to **vary directly** as each other.

316. Mathematical statement for direct variation.—Just as with many other ideas, there is a mathematical way of expressing the idea of variation. When the ideas are so expressed, they can be combined and handled according to the rules of mathematics. In this manner, new relations are seen and new results obtained.

When y varies directly as x, the definition states that $\frac{y}{x} = k$ or $y = kx$, where k is a constant.

The constant k is called the **constant of variation** or the factor of proportionality.

Each of the following expressions is used with a meaning practically the same as the foregoing; "y varies as x," "y is directly proportional to x," "y is proportional to x." The notation $y \propto x$ is sometimes used for y varies as x.

Example 1.—If a train is moving away from a station at a uniform rate, express the relation between its distance d from the station and the time t since it left the station.

Here evidently the distance d varies directly as the time t.

$$\therefore\ d = kt$$

The student should consider very carefully the meaning of the constant k in the different examples taken up. Here the k evidently represents the uniform rate per unit of time. If the time is in minutes, k stands for the rate per minute. This rate may be given in feet, rods, miles, or any other unit of length. The k then depends for its value upon the kind of units used, but this is not the only thing that may change the value of k.

Example 2.—If two numbers x and y vary directly as each other, and when $x = 10$, $y = 4$, find x when $y = 25$.

Solution.—Since the relation between x and y is direct, $x = ky$.

Substitute the given values of x and y in $x = ky$, and

$$10 = 4k$$

Solving for k,

$$k = 2\tfrac{1}{2}$$

Therefore $x = 2\tfrac{1}{2}y$ is the relation between the variables; and if $y = 25$, we have $x = 2\tfrac{1}{2} \cdot 25 = 62\tfrac{1}{2}$. *Ans.*

Such a relation as $x = 2\tfrac{1}{2}y$ is often spoken of as a **law.**

Example 3.—The space passed through by a body falling freely from a distance above the ground varies as the square of the time. If $s = $ the space in feet and $t = $ time in seconds, write the law. Find the value of k, if the body will fall 402.5 ft. in 5 sec.

Solution.—Since the variation is directly as the square of the time, $s = kt^2$. Substituting values of s and t,

$$402.5 = k \cdot 5^2$$

Solving for k, $\qquad k = 16.1$ *Ans.*

Hence the law or formula to find the distance in feet that a body will fall in t sec. is $s = 16.1t^2$. This is usually written $s = \tfrac{1}{2}gt^2$, where $g = 32.2$.

317. Inverse variation.—Consider a horizontal beam, resting at each end on a support and having a weight at its midpoint. The size of the weight that it will support depends upon its length; but here the *longer* the beam the *less* it will support. In such a case the variation is said to be **inverse.**

The resistance to an electric current is less in a large wire than in a small one of the same material; the resistance varies inversely as the size of the wire in cross section.

The intensity of the light from a lamp decreases as we go away from it. Here the variation is an inverse one, but the intensity of illumination is not one-half so much when the distance is doubled. It varies inversely as the square of the distance; that is, the intensity is one-fourth as much at twice the distance.

Definition.—One number **varies inversely** as another when their product is constant. That is, if either increases, the other decreases; or if either decreases, the other increases.

318. Mathematical statement for inverse variation.—If x and y are two variables that vary inversely as each other, and k is a constant, then the mathematical statement for this is

$$xy = k, \ x = \frac{k}{y}, \ y = \frac{k}{x}$$

The equation $x = \frac{k}{y}$ is read x varies inversely as y; likewise, $y = \frac{k}{x}$ is read y varies inversely as x.

As has been stated, the illumination due to a source of light varies inversely as the square of the distance from the source. If I stands for the illumination, d for the distance, and k for the constant, then

$$I = \frac{k}{d^2} \text{ or } Id^2 = k$$

Example 1.—If x varies inversely as y, state the law and find the value of the constant if $x = 10$ when $y = \frac{1}{2}$.

Solution: xy = k is the mathematical statement of the variation.

Substituting, $10 \cdot \frac{1}{2} = k.$ $\therefore$ $k = 5.$

If this value of k is used, the law, or equation, becomes

$$xy = 5 \quad Ans.$$

Example 2.—If $x = \frac{1}{100}$, find y from the law of Example 1.

Substituting in the law, $\frac{1}{100}y = 5.$

$$\therefore \ y = 500 \quad Ans.$$

319. Joint variation.—One number **varies jointly** as two or more other numbers when it varies directly as the product of the others.   Thus, x varies jointly as u and v when $x = kuv$.

A number may vary directly as one number and inversely as another.   It then varies as the quotient of the first divided by the second.   Thus, if x varies directly as y and inversely as z, it is written $x = k\dfrac{y}{z}.$

EXERCISES

Answer the first twelve exercises orally.

1. State in the language of variation the relation between the area of a square and its side.

2. State the relation between the distance that a man walks at a uniform rate and the time that he is walking.

3. State the relation between the volume of a rectangular solid and its three dimensions.

4. State the relation between the amount of reading matter in a book and the thickness of the book and the distance between the lines.

5. Does the amount of gasoline used in driving an automobile 100 miles vary directly as the rate per hour?

6. Does the weight that a man can lift vary directly as the weight of the man?

7. Give several examples of variation different from those already given.

8. Express each of the following relations in the language of variations:

$S = 4\pi r^2$; $S = \pi r^2 h$; $V = 4\pi r^3$; $W \propto \dfrac{bd^2}{l}$; $z \propto \dfrac{\sqrt{x}}{y^2}$; $v \propto \dfrac{1}{p}$; $e = \dfrac{kwl^3}{bd^3}$;

$A = \dfrac{kq}{\sqrt{h}}$

Express the following in the algebraic language of variation:

9. The volume V of a circular cone varies as the altitude h and as the square of the radius r.

10. The weight of a body above the surface of the earth varies inversely as the square of the distance d of the body from the center of the earth.

11. The pressure of the wind on an exposed surface varies as the area of the surface and the square of the velocity of the wind.

12. Newton's law of gravitation states that the force F with which each of the two masses m_1 and m_2 attracts the other varies directly as the product of the masses and inversely as the square of the distance d between the masses.

13. In $R = \dfrac{xy}{u+v}$, how does R vary with x? With u? Does R become larger or smaller when v becomes smaller?

14. In $\dfrac{x}{a} = \dfrac{b}{y}$, where a and b are constants, how does y vary with x?

15. If $x \propto y$ and when $x = 10$, $y = 60$, write the equation between x and y.   *Ans.* $y = 6x$.

16. If $b \propto d$ and when $b = 20$, $d = 15$, find b when $d = 80$.
                                                                Ans. $106\frac{2}{3}$.

17. If x varies jointly as y and z, and when $y = 6$ and $z = 3$, $x = 120$; find the constant. Find y when $x = 200$ and $z = 15$.   *Ans.* $6\frac{2}{3}$; 2.

18. The area A of a triangle varies jointly as the base b and the altitude a. Write the law if, when $a = 6$ in. and $b = 4$ in., $A = 12$ sq. in. What will be the area when the base is 25 in. and the altitude is 40 in.?
                                            Ans. $A = \frac{1}{2}ab$; 500 sq. in.

Remark.—The law here is the well-known formula for the area of a triangle, but we have not supposed that we knew anything about the formula in working the example.

19. Similar solids vary in volumes as the cubes of their like dimensions. A water pail that is 10 in. across the top holds 12 qt. Find the volume of a similar pail that is 16 in. across the top.   *Ans.* $49+$ qt.

20. The volume of a sphere varies as the cube of its radius, and the volume of a sphere of radius 2 ft. is 33.5104 cu. ft. Find the volume of a sphere of radius 8 ft.   *Ans.* 2144.6656 cu. ft.

21. If a steamer travels at a uniform rate, the amount of coal consumed varies as the distance and as the square of the rate. It is found that a certain steamer traveling 150 miles at a rate of 18 miles per hour uses 80 tons of coal. Find the amount of coal used by the same steamer in going 200 miles at 24 miles per hour.   *Ans.* $189.62-$ tons.

22. A ball starts from rest and rolls down an incline of uniform slope. The distance s that the ball moves varies as the square of the time t.

If the ball rolls 10 ft. from rest in 6 sec., find the distance that it will roll in 12 sec. Find the time that it will take to roll 40 ft. from rest.

Ans. 40 ft.; 12 sec.

23. The number of vibrations made by a pendulum varies inversely as the square root of its length. A pendulum 39.1 in. long makes 1 vibration per second? How long must a pendulum be to make 4 vibrations per second? To make 1 vibration in 10 sec.?

Solution.—The law is $n = \dfrac{k}{\sqrt{l}}$, where n = number of vibrations per second and l = length of pendulum in inches.

To find k, put $n = 1$ and $l = 39.1$.

$$\therefore 1 = \frac{k}{\sqrt{39.1}} \text{ and } k = \sqrt{39.1}$$

To find the length of a pendulum to vibrate four times per second, put $n = 4$.

$$\therefore 4 = \frac{\sqrt{39.1}}{\sqrt{l}} \text{ and } l = \frac{39.1}{16} = 2.44 + \text{ in.}$$

To find the length of a pendulum to vibrate once in 10 sec., put $n = \frac{1}{10}$.

$$\therefore \frac{1}{10} = \frac{\sqrt{39.1}}{\sqrt{l}} \text{ and } l = 100 \times 39.1 = 3910 \text{ in.} = 325 \text{ ft. } 10 \text{ in.}$$

24. If $p \propto \dfrac{1}{v}$ and $v \propto \dfrac{1}{p'}$, show that $p \propto p'$.

25. If $a \propto s$ and $b \propto s$, show that $a^2 - b^2 \propto s^2$.

26. If the illumination of an object varies inversely as the square of the distance d from the source of light, and the illumination of an object at the distance 8 ft. from the source of light is 3, find the illumination of an object at 40 ft. from the source of light; at the distance of 4 ft. from the source of light. *Ans.* 0.12; 12.

27. The number of units of heat H generated by an electric current of I amperes in a circuit varies as the square of the current I, as the resistance R, and as the time t in seconds during which the current passes. Write the law in the two forms. *Ans.* $H \propto I^2 Rt$; $H = kI^2 Rt$.

28. By trial in the preceding formula it is found that $H = 388,800$ if $I = 10$, $R = 9$, and $t = 30$ min. Find H when $I = 30$, $R = 50$, and $t = 40$ min. *Ans.* 25,920,000.

29. A circular sheet of steel 2 ft. in diameter increases in diameter by $\frac{1}{200}$, when the temperature is increased by a certain amount. Find the increase in area of the sheet. *Ans.* $\frac{1}{100}$ approx.

30. A wire rope 1 in. in diameter will lift 10,000 lb.   What will one $\frac{5}{8}$ in. in diameter lift?   *Ans.* 3906.25.

31. A cone of cast iron 8 in. high weighs 50 lb.   What will be the weight of a cone of the same shape and material 6 in. high?

Ans. 21+ lb.

32. Two persons of the same "build" are similar in shape.   A man $5\frac{1}{2}$ ft. tall weighs 150 lb.   Find weight of a man of the same build and 6 ft. tall.   *Ans.* 194.74+ lb.

33. A man 5 ft. 5 in. tall weighs 140 lb., and one 6 ft. 2 in. tall weighs 216 lb.   Which is of the stouter "build"?   *Ans.* 216-lb. man.

34. The electrical resistance of a substance varies directly as the length L and inversely as the area A of the cross section.   If the resistance of a bar of annealed aluminum 1 in. long and 1 sq. in. in cross section is 0.000001144 ohm at 32 deg. F., find the resistance of a wire of the same material 1 ft. long and 0.002 in. in diameter.

Note that you have in this exercise the law of Art. 290.

Ans. 4.37− ohms.

35. Find the resistance of 1 mile of wire $\frac{1}{32}$ in. in diameter of aforementioned material and at 32 deg. F.   *Ans.* 94.5+ ohms.

36. If the resistance of a coil of wire of the foregoing material at 32 deg. F. is 27.3 ohms, and the wire is 0.05 in. in diameter, find the length.

Ans. 3904.7 ft.

37. If the resistance of a wire 9363 ft. long is 21.6 ohms, what would be the resistance if its length were reduced to 5732 ft. and its cross section made half again as large?   *Ans.* 8.816− ohms.

38. The *quantity* Q of electricity that will flow into a radio condenser varies jointly as the *capacity* C and the *voltage* E.   The constant of variation is 10^{-6} if Q is in *coulombs*, C in *microfarads*, and E in *volts*. If $C = 15$ microfarads, and $E = 820$ volts, find Q.

Ans. 0.0033 coulomb.

39. The amount of energy in *joules* stored by a condenser varies jointly as the capacity and the voltage squared.   The constant of variation is $\frac{1}{2}(10)^{-6}$ if C is in microfarads and E in volts.   What is the energy stored in a 2-microfarad condenser with 1000 volts applied?

Ans. 1 joule.

40. What is the capacity of a condenser that is charged to 0.0036 coulomb when 110 volts is applied?   *Ans.* 32.727 microfarads.

41. What energy goes into a condenser in a transmitting station if this condenser has a capacity of 0.001 microfarad and is charged with a 20,000-volt source?   *Ans.* 0.2 joule.

42. The size of a stone carried by a swiftly flowing stream varies as the sixth power of the velocity of the water.   If the velocity of a stream is doubled, what effect does it have on its carrying power? What effect if changed from 5 miles per hour to 15 miles per hour?

Ans. Multiplies by 64; multiplies by **729**.

320. Transverse strength of wooden beams.—Other things being equal, the strength of a beam, rectangular in cross section and supported at each end, varies (1) inversely as the length in feet, (2) directly as the breadth in inches, and (3) directly as the square of the depth in inches.

That the strength varies inversely as the length in feet means that if a beam, supported horizontally as in Fig. 245, has its length increased and everything else unchanged, the weight that it will support is decreased in the same ratio as the length

Fig. 245.

was increased. That is, if the length is doubled, it will support one-half as great a weight. If W is the weight and L the length, in the language of variation this fact is stated thus:

$$W \propto \frac{1}{L}, \text{ or } W = \frac{k_1}{L}$$

The length L is the distance between the points of support.

That the strength varies directly as the breadth in inches means that if the breadth b is **increased** in a certain ratio and everything else is unchanged, the weight that it will support is **increased** in the same ratio. That is, if the breadth is doubled, the weight that it will support will be doubled. This law is expressed in symbols thus:

$$W \propto b, \text{ or } W = k_2 b$$

That the strength varies directly as the square of the depth in inches means that if the depth d is **increased** in a certain ratio while other things remain the same, the weight that it will support is **increased** by the square of the ratio of that increase. That is, if the depth is doubled, the weight that it will support is four times as great. In symbols this is expressed thus:

$$W \propto d^2, \text{ or } W = k_3 d^2$$

Finally, if the length, breadth, and depth are all changed, we have a combination of all these laws, and it may be expressed thus (see Art. 319):

$$W \propto \frac{bd^2}{L}, \text{ or } W = \frac{Kbd^2}{L}$$

By the expression "other things being equal" is meant that the material must be the same and the beams must be similarly supported and similarly loaded. The nature of the timber is an important factor, since timber, even of the same kind, varies in strength to a considerable extent. Each beam therefore has what is called a natural **constant,** the K of the formula, which must be considered in the calculation of its carrying capacity. This constant is the same for beams when these "other things" are equal, that is, for beams of exactly the same material, supported the same and weighted the same.

321. The constant.—To find this constant, it is usual to take a bar of similar material, 1 in. square in cross section and long enough to allow of its being placed on supports 1 ft. apart. The constant to be used with beams weighted in the middle is the weight of the central load, which is just sufficient to break the bar. The constant may be expressed in pounds, hundredweight, tons, etc., and the carrying capacity of the beam to which it is applied will always be in the same units.

322. Factor of safety.—For the man who wishes to apply these facts, another important consideration is the ratio that the *breaking load* bears to the *safe load*. This ratio is called the **factor of safety.** Its value depends upon whether the load is a **live load,** that is, a moving load, or a **dead load,** that is, a stationary load.

The factor of safety for a dead load is usually taken as 5, which means that the safe load upon a beam must not be more than one-fifth of the breaking load. The factor of safety for a live load is often taken as 10.

EXERCISES

1. Solve the formula $W = \dfrac{Kbd^2}{L}$ for each letter used.

$$Ans.\ L = \frac{Kbd^2}{W};\ b = \frac{WL}{Kd^2};\ d = \sqrt{\frac{WL}{Kb}};\ K = \frac{WL}{bd^2}.$$

2. The constant for white pine is 300 lb. Find the weight that a beam of this material, centrally loaded and 10 ft. long, 3 in. broad, and 7 in. deep, will support. How much is the safe load if the factor of safety is 5? *Ans.* 4410 lb.; 882 lb.

3. How long may a beam of white pine, centrally loaded, be between supports if it is to have a safe load if 750 lb. and is 3 by 8 in. set on edge?
Ans. 15.36 ft.

4. By experiment we find that a beam of pine 40 ft. long, 1 ft. broad, and 1 ft. deep will carry a load of 4500 lb. Find the depth of a beam of the same wood similarly loaded to carry a load of 1200 lb., when the length is 6 ft. and the breadth is 2 in. *Ans.* 5.88 − in.

Solution.—Use the formula $W = \dfrac{Kbd^2}{L}$, and substitute $W = 4500$,

$L = 40$, $b = 12$, and $d = 12$. This gives $4500 = \dfrac{K \cdot 12 \cdot 12^2}{40}$. $\therefore K = \dfrac{625}{6}$.

Substituting, $W = 1200$, $L = 6$, $b = 2$, and $K = \dfrac{625}{6}$ in the same

formula, $1200 = \dfrac{625 \cdot 2d^2}{6 \cdot 6}$.

Solving for d, $d = 5.88 -$.

5. In the preceding exercise find the depth if we allow a factor of safety of 10. *Ans.* 18.6 − in.

6. In beams having the load uniformly distributed, the constant is twice as large as when the load is centrally located. Solve Exercise 2 if the beam is uniformly loaded. *Ans.* 8820 lb.; 1764 lb.

7. Find the breadth of a beam of oak, resting upon supports 18 ft. apart, the beam being 12 in. deep, to carry safely a uniformly distributed load of 5 tons.   The constant is 500 lb. if loaded in center, and the factor of safety is 5.   *Ans.* $6\frac{1}{4}$ in.

8. A hall 16 ft. wide has the floor supported by joists of pine 3 by 12 in. set on edge; using the constant 300 lb. and a factor of safety of 5, find how far the joists must be placed from center to center to support a load of 140 lb. per square foot of floor surface.   *Ans.* $17\frac{3}{8}$ in. nearly.

9. O'Connor gives the following formula to calculate the dead distributed safe load on timber, supported at both ends, and of rectangular cross section (this includes floor joists):

$$W = \frac{4bd^2K}{2L}$$

where

W = the load in pounds.

b = the breadth in inches.

d = the depth in inches.

L = the length of span in inches.

K = 1900 for oak and 1100 for fir.

(Notice how this formula differs from the one previously given.)   What safe weight distributed will an oak beam 6 by 10 in., set on edge, support if the span is 16 ft.?   *Ans.* 11,875 lb.

10. The joists in a room 14 ft. wide and 26 ft. long are fir 3 by 10 in. How far should their centers be placed apart if the floor is to support a crowd of men?   (A crowd of men closely packed averages 140 lb. per square foot.)   *Ans.* 2 ft. nearly.

11. From another source the following is taken: For white pine beams the formula $W = \frac{2000}{3} \times \frac{bd^2}{L}$ gives the safe load when the beam is supported at both ends and loaded in the middle.

W = the safe load in pounds, less weight of beam.

L = the length of beam in inches.

d = the depth of beam in inches.

b = the breadth of beam in inches

(1) Given L = 12 ft., b = 3 in. and d = 8 in., find W.

(2) Given L = 12 ft., b = 8 in. and d = 3 in., find W.

(3) Given L = 16 ft., b = 4 in. and W = 1900, find d.

(4) Given b = 6 in., d = 10 in. and W = 4100, find L.

        Ans. (1) 889 lb.; (2) $333\frac{1}{3}$ lb.; (3) 11.7 − in.; (4) 8 ft.

12. The following are the results of experiments on the strength of timbers when loaded in the middle.   In each case find the strength of a stick of the same material 1 ft. long, 1 in. in breadth, and 1 in. in depth This value is called K in the list.

Name of wood	Length in feet	Breadth in inches	Depth in inches	Breaking weight in pounds	K
White pine.............	2	2	2	1,430	$357\frac{1}{2}$
Yellow pine.............	$10\frac{3}{4}$	14	15	68,000	$232+$
Pitch pine.............	$10\frac{3}{4}$	14	15	118,500	404.4
Ash...................	2	2	2	2,052	513
Pitch pine.............	7	2	2	622	$544\frac{1}{4}$
Ash...................	7	2	2	772	$675\frac{1}{2}$
Fir...................	7	2	2	420	$367\frac{1}{2}$

13. Suppose that there are three pieces of timber of the following dimensions:

(1) 12 ft. long, 6 in. deep, and 3 in. thick.

(2) 8 ft. long, 5 in. deep, and 4 in. thick.

(3) 15 ft. long, 9 in. deep, and 8 in. thick.

Compare their strengths. *Ans.* In the ratio of 9:12.5:43.2.

14. Given a stick of timber 14 ft. long, 8 in. deep, and 3 in. thick; find the depth of another piece of the same material 18 ft. long and 4 in. thick that will support five times as much as the first. *Ans.* 17.6− in.

Solution.—Let W = the weight that the first stick will support. Then

$$W = \frac{Kbd^2}{L} = \frac{K \cdot 3 \cdot 8^2}{14} = \frac{96K}{7}$$

In the case of the second stick d is to be found when $5W = \dfrac{480K}{7}$ is the weight.

$$\therefore \frac{480K}{7} = \frac{K \cdot 4 \cdot d^2}{18}$$

Solving, $d = 17.6-$.

15. Given a piece of timber 12 ft. long, 6 in. deep, and 4 in. thick, find the thickness of another stick of the same material 16 ft. long and 8 in. deep that will support twice as much as the first. *Ans.* 6 in.

16. Given a stick of timber 12 ft. long, 5 in. deep, and 3 in. thick, find the thickness of another stick of the same material 14 ft. long and 6 in. deep that will support four times as much as the first.

Ans. 9.72+ in.

17. Given a stick of timber 12 ft. long, 6 in. deep, and 4 in. thick, find the depth of a stick of the same material 20 ft. long and 5 in. thick that will support twice the weight of the first. *Ans.* 9.8−˙ in.

CHAPTER XXXII

GRAPHICAL METHODS AND FUNCTIONS

323. The graph.—The temperatures read each hour during a certain day in March were as given in the following table:

Hour, A.M.	12	1	2	3	4	5	6	7	8	9	10	11	12
Temperature	45	45	45	45	43	42	41	40	42	51	57	59	62
Hour, P.M.	1	2	3	4	5	6	7	8	9	10	11	12	
Temperature	66	70	74	76	76	75	74	73	72	70	69	68	

The change in temperature is quite easily seen from a study of this table, but it may be seen at a glance if we put the facts into a diagram as shown in Fig. 246. Here the hours are located on a horizontal line, and the degrees on a line perpendicular to it. The reading for any hour is located so as to be above the hour and to the right of the degree of temperature. In this manner we can locate 24 points.

Evidently if the temperature reading had been taken each minute instead of each hour, 60 points would be determined in the same space in which we now have one. If we suppose no sudden change in temperature between the hourly readings, we may connect the points representing these by a line, and any point on this line will indicate the temperature for the corresponding time. Of course, if there had been a sudden rise and fall in temperature between the hours, it is not shown by this line. The oftener then we take the readings the truer will the line indicate the changes.*

* Cross-ruled paper, or paper ruled into squares of various sizes, can be obtained cheaply; and by using this paper, the points can be located with greater accuracy than on plain paper.

The representation, made as in Fig. 246, is called a **graph,** and such a method of representing relations between numbers is called a **graphical method.**

The use of the graph is of very wide application. At the weather bureaus there are thermometers with an attachment that automatically traces the graph of the temperature and

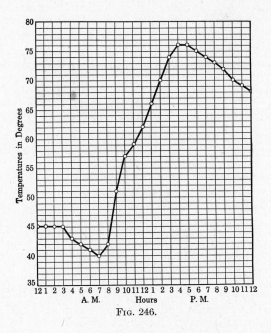

Fig. 246.

time. Engineers make constant use of the graph in their work. Laboratory data are put in the form of a graph. Graphs can be made for algebraic equations, and relations are thus clearly shown that otherwise would be difficult to see.

Making the graph is often spoken of as **plotting.**

324. Definitions and terms used.—Since we often wish to plot negative as well as positive numbers, it is necessary to give certain definitions and make certain assumptions that will now be explained.

If in Fig. 247 *OX* and *OY* are drawn at right angles to each other, the position of any point, as *P*, may be located by measuring its distance from *OY* and from *OX*. These lengths, which in the figure are *OA* and *OB*, are called the **coordinates** of the point *P*. The length *OA* is called the **x-coordinate**; and *OB*, the **y-coordinate**.

The two lines *OX* and *OY* are called the **x-axis** and the **y-axis**, respectively. Together they are spoken of as the

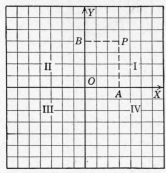

coordinate axes. The point *O* where the two axes cross is called the **origin**.

The *x*-axis is called the **axis of abscissas**, and the *y*-axis, the **axis** of **ordinates**. The *x*-coordinate and the *y*-coordinate are also called the **abscissa** and **ordinate**, respectively, of the point.

The coordinates are always measured from the origin. Any abscissa measured toward the right is **positive** and measured toward the left is **negative**. Any ordinate measured upward is **positive** and downward is **negative**.

Fig. 247.

The four parts into which the axes divide the plane are called **quadrants**. These are called the **first, second, third,** and **fourth quadrants** and are numbered in Fig. 247 by the numerals, I, II, III, IV.

Quadrant......................	I	II	III	IV
Abscissa........................	+	−	−	+
Ordinate........................	+	+	−	−

It is evident that in the first quadrant, both coordinates are positive; in the second quadrant, the abscissa is negative and the ordinate positive; in the third quadrant, both coordinates are negative; in the fourth quadrant, the abscissa is positive and the ordinate is negative. This is shown in the table on page 476.

325. Plotting points.—To plot a point is to locate it with reference to a set of coordinate axes. To plot a point whose x-coordinate is 3 and y-coordinate 4, first draw the axes (see Fig. 248), then choose a unit of measure and lay off OA 3 units to the right of O. Through A draw a line parallel to the

y-axis. Now lay off OB, 4 units above O, and through B draw a line parallel to the x-axis. The required point is located where these two lines meet. In the figure it is located as $P(3, 4)$, which is the usual manner of writing the coordinates of a point. The abscissa is placed first; they are separated by a comma and enclosed in parentheses. It is read: "The point P whose coordinates are 3 and 4."

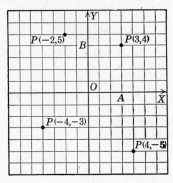

FIG. 248.

In a similar manner the following points are located as given in the figure: $P(-2, 5)$, $P(-4, -3)$, $P(4, -5)$.

EXERCISES

1. On a sheet of square-ruled paper draw a pair of coordinate axes, OX and OY, perpendicular to each other, and plot the following points: $(3, 4)$, $(10, 12)$, $(-2, 8)$, $(-6, 12)$, $(-4, -3)$, $(-8, -9)$, $(7, -4)$, $(10, -3)$, $(0, 9)$, $(0, -8)$, $(7, 0)$, $(-10, 0)$, $(0, 0)$.

2. The temperatures read each hour for the 24 hr., beginning at 3 P.M., Jan. 31, 1929, were as follows: 12, 10, 9, 6, 6, 5, 4, 3, 2, 1, 1, 0, -2, -2, -2, -2, -2, -2, 1, 5, 8, 11, 13, 14, 15. The minus numbers indicate temperatures below zero. Plot these using the hours as abscissas and the temperatures as ordinates, and connect the points by a smooth curve. From the drawing tell when the temperature was rising most rapidly; falling most rapidly.

3. The population of a town in 1850 was 16,000; in 1860, 16,300; in 1870, 16,850; in 1880, 17,800; in 1890, 19,100; and in 1900, 20,700.

Plot a curve showing the variation in population, and estimate the probable population in 1875 and 1907.

Discussion.—Draw the axes; lay off the years, beginning with 1850 at the origin, along the x-axis; and lay off the population in thousands along the y-axis, beginning with 16,000 at the origin. The curve will then be as in Fig. 249.

The population for any year is estimated by locating the year on the x-axis; drawing a perpendicular to the x-axis; and from the intersection of this with the curve, drawing a parallel to the x-axis. The point where this parallel intersects the y-axis determines the population.

The process by which we determine the coordinates of any point on the curve is called **interpolating.**

4. The appropriations in billions of dollars by Congress for each year from 1929 to 1939 were as follows: 4.6, 4.0, 5.1, 5.7, 7.6, 7.5, 9.5, 10.3, 9.3, 11.3, and 13.3. Plot a curve showing the yearly change in our national appropriations.

5. The population of the United States by decades is given in the following table. Plot and estimate the population for 1915; for 1925; for 1935; for 1945.

Year	Population	Year	Population
1790	3,929,200	1870	38,558,400
1800	5,308,400	1880	50,155,800
1810	7,229,900	1890	62,669,800
1820	9,663,800	1900	76,295,200
1830	12,806,000	1910	91,972,300
1840	17,096,500	1920	105,710,600
1850	23,191,900	1930	122,775,000
1860	31,443,300	1937	126,361,300

6. Make a graph from which can be read the product of any number from −225 to 225 multiplied by 0.25.

Suggestion.—Plot the numbers from −225 to 225 as abscissas and the products as ordinates.

7. Make a graph from which can be read the quotient of any number less in absolute value than 500 divided by 8.33.

8. A stone falling from rest falls through 4 ft. in $\frac{1}{2}$ sec., 16 ft. in 1 sec., 36 ft. in $1\frac{1}{2}$ sec., 64 ft. in 2 sec., 100 ft. in $2\frac{1}{2}$ sec., and 144 ft. in 3 sec. Find, by plotting a curve, how long a stone would be in falling 80 ft. and also how far it falls in $2\frac{3}{4}$ sec.

Suggestion.—The graph is shown in Fig. 250. To find how long the stone would be in falling 80 ft., locate 80 ft. on the *x*-axis, draw a perpendicular line *AB*, and through the point *B* on the curve draw a line parallel to the *x*-axis to intersect the *y*-axis. This point of intersection *C* determines the number of seconds that it will take the stone to fall

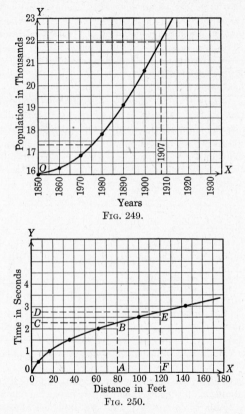

Fig. 249.

Fig. 250.

80 ft. To find how far the stone will fall in $2\frac{3}{4}$ sec., proceed in a similar manner, starting on the *y*-axis.

9. The number *W* of grams of potassium iodide that will dissolve in 100 g. of water depends upon the temperature *T* of the water in the following manner: When $T = 10, 20, 30, 40, 50$, it is found that $W = 135, 141, 144, 149, 152, 161, 169$, respectively. Choose the units on the *T*-axis ten times as great as the units on the *W*-axis and plot.

Estimate W when $T = 60$; when $T = 70$; when $T = 80$. Can you be certain of these estimated values of W?

10. The assets of a company were as follows: 1868, $1,000,000: 1878, $4,000,000; 1888, $10,000,000; 1898, $25,000,000; 1908, $64,000,000; 1918, $148,000,000; 1928, $554,000,000; 1938, $975,000,000. Plot these values, and estimate the assets for 1948. Can you be certain of this estimated value?

11. The table of redemption values of an $18.75 U.S. Savings Bond is as follows:

Beginning of year........	2	3	4	5	6	7	8	9	10	11
Redemption value.......	19.	19.50	20.	20.50	21.	21.50	22.	23.	24.	25.

Plot these values and note the difference for the last three years.

12. In order to print a certain pamphlet, it was found that the cost C varies with the number N of copies in accordance with the following:

N	1000	2000	3000	4000	5000
C	60	65	70	75	80

Plot these values, and determine the cost for printing 10,000 copies.

13. The number of stockholders for a large company at the end of each year was as follows:

Year.............................	1919	1924	1929	1934	1939
Number in thousands............	15	53	198	350	388

Plot these values, and estimate the number of stockholders for 1944. Can you be certain of the estimated number?

14. If T is the tensile strength in tons per square inch of cross section of steel containing $X\%$ of carbon, and we are given the following values, plot a curve to show, as accurately as the data will allow, the tensile strength of steel containing any percentage of carbon from 0.1 to 1%. What strength would you expect for 0.4% of carbon?

X	0.14	0.46	0.57	0.66	0.78	0.80	0.87	0.96
T	28.1	33.8	35.6	40	41.1	45.9	46.7	52.7

15. Plot the Fahrenheit thermometer scale on the *x*-axis and the centigrade scale on the *y*-axis. Draw the line any point of which has as coordinates equivalent temperatures on the two scales. How can this graph be used to reduce from one scale to the other? Read from the graph the centigrade temperatures for the following Fahrenheit readings: 25 deg.; 90 deg.; 367 deg.; −40 deg.; 15 deg. Give in Fahrenheit the following centigrade readings: 33 deg.; 76 deg.; 15 deg.; −46 deg.; −9 deg.

16. In an experiment on the stretching of an iron rod the linear extension *L* in inches for a load *W* in pounds was found to be as follows:

W	600	1100	1600	2100	2600	3100	3600	4100	4600	5100
L	0.005	0.009	0.013	0.018	0.022	0.027	0.032	0.037	0.043	0.050

Plot, choosing suitable distances on the *x*-axis for *W* and on the *y*-axis for *L*. Up to how great a load is the extension proportional to the load, that is, where does the curve begin to change direction rapidly?

Remark.—While the curve is a straight line, the relation between *L* and *W* can be expressed in the language of variation by the equation $W = kL$. Or we may say that the straight line is the graph of a direct variation where the ratio is constant.

17. A stick of white pine 1 in. broad and 0.5 in. thick is supported at points 24 in. apart and loaded in the middle. The deflection *d* in inches for a load *W* in pounds is as follows:

W	0	5	8	18	28	38	48	58	63	68	69	70
d	0	0.088	0.14	0.35	0.56	0.77	0.99	1.22	1.35	1.685	1.765	1.85

Plot so as to show that the deflection is proportional to the weight up to a certain point.

18. The value in millions of dollars of aircraft exports from the United States was as follows:

Year.............	1926	1929	1931	1933	1935	1937	1938
Value.............	1.	9.1	4.9	9.2	14.3	39.4	68.2

Plot these values and connect with a curve.

19. A rifle sighted to 1000 yd. rests upon a support 5 ft. from the ground and is fired. The height of the bullet above the support at the various distances is given in the following table:

Distance from firing point in yards......	100	200	300	400	500	600	700	800	900	1000
Vertical height above support in feet.....	7.3	11.2	15.0	18.5	21.0	23.3	25.0	22.5	16.0	0

Plot a representation of the path of the bullet. Show the ground level and the height of the support. Where does the bullet reach a height of 20 ft.?

20. Plot the relation between centimeters and inches.

Suggestion.—Take the numbers of centimeters on the x-axis and the inches on the y-axis. Any point on the curve has as coordinates a number of centimeters and a number of inches that are equivalent in length.

21. Plot a curve showing the relation between yards and meters. Does the number of yards vary directly as the number of meters?

22. Plot a curve showing the relation between pounds and kilograms? Is the variation direct?

23. The atmospheric pressure p in inches at various heights h in thousands of feet is as follows:

h	0	5	10	15	20	25	30
p	30	25	20	17	14	11.6	9.6

Plot these values, and connect with a curve. Estimate the pressure for 40,000 ft.

24. The speed s of a special chemical reaction is related to the temperature T in accordance with the following table of values:

s	5	7.6	11.4	17	25.4	38
T	0	1	2	3	4	5

CURVES OF EQUATIONS

326. Graph of an equation.—If we have an equation in two unknowns, as $3x + 4y = 12$, we can determine a number of pairs of values for x and y that will satisfy the equation. (See Art. 291.) If we consider each of these pairs as the coordinates of a point, the value of x for the abscissa and y for the ordinate, then the graph determined by these points is called the **graph of the equation** or the **curve of the equation.**

To plot the curve of $3x + 4y = 12$, determine the pairs of values: $(0, 3)$, $(4, 0)$, $(2, 1\frac{1}{2})$, $(3, \frac{3}{4})$, $(5, -\frac{3}{4})$, $(8, -3)$, $(-8, 9)$, $(-4, 6)$, $(12, -6)$ that satisfy the equation. Plot these points, and connect with a smooth line. The curve is shown in Fig. 251 and is the graph of the equation $3x + 4y = 12$.

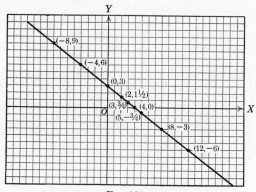

Fig. 251.

Here the graph appears to be a straight line; in fact it is a straight line, and this is true of any such equation of the first degree. For this reason an equation of the first degree is often called a **linear equation.**

Since a straight line is determined by knowing two points on it, the graph can be drawn when two points only have been plotted. Usually the most convenient points to take are those where the line crosses the two axes. These two points are found by putting $x = 0$ and finding y and then putting $y = 0$ and finding x. The two values thus found for x and y are called the **intercepts** on the axes. If the line goes through the origin, another point will be necessary.

If the two points are near together, the line will not be well determined unless the work is very accurate.

327. Slope of the curve of an equation.—As a point moves along the curve of an equation, the coordinates of the point in any particular position are a pair of values of x and y that satisfy the equation. Or we may think of x as taking different values and so causing y to take certain values; that is, x and y are variables that are related in a definite manner by the equation.

In the equation $y = x$, any change in x produces the same change in y. The curve of $y = x$ is plotted in Fig. 252 and is

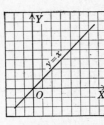

FIG. 252.

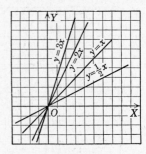

FIG. 253.

seen to bisect the angle in the first quadrant. As a point passes along the curve, which here is a straight line, any change in x produces an equal change in y.

The ratio of the change in y, produced by a change in x, to the change in x is called the **slope of the curve.**

The slope of the curve of $y = x$ is 1.

In the equation $y = 2x$, any change in x causes twice as large a change in y. Therefore the slope of the curve of $y = 2x$ is 2.

The slope of the curve of $y = \frac{1}{2}x$ is $\frac{1}{2}$; that of $y = 3x$ is 3; and, in general, the slope of the curve $y = mx$ is m. Note that here we have the form of a direct variation, where m is the constant ratio between the variables. (See Art. 316.)

The equations discussed are plotted in Fig. 253. They all pass through the origin and rise toward the right. It is true that they always rise toward the right when m is a positive number. When m is greater than 1, y increases faster than x; and when m is less than 1, y increases more slowly than x.

If m is negative, y will be negative when x is positive for such straight lines as pass through the origin, and the curve will slope downward as it extends toward the right. The curve of $y = -\frac{1}{2}x$ is shown in Fig. 254.

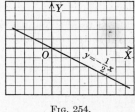

Fig. 254.   Fig. 255.

328. The curve of y = mx + b.—The curve of $y = \frac{1}{2}x + 3$ is shown in Fig. 255. When $x = 0$, $y = 3$; but the slope is still $\frac{1}{2}$, for any change in x produces $\frac{1}{2}$ as great a change in y. The effect of the constant 3 is to lift the curve of $y = \frac{1}{2}x$ vertically a distance 3. The curve crosses the y-axis 3 units above the origin. The point where a curve crosses the y-axis is called the y-intercept of the curve.

In general, the curve of the equation $y = mx + b$ has a slope m and a y-intercept equal to b. In this equation, m and b may be either positive or negative, integral or fractional. This amounts to saying that all values of y in $y = mx + b$ are equal to the corresponding values in $y = mx$ plus the constant b.

329. Slope of curve of any first-degree equation.—If the equation $2x - y = 4$ is solved for y, we have $y = 2x - 4$, from which we see at once that the slope of the curve is 2 and the y-intercept is -4.

The equation $3x + 4y = 12$ was plotted in Art. 326. Solving this for y, we have $y = -\frac{3}{4}x + 3$. Here the slope is $-\frac{3}{4}$ and the y-intercept is 3.

In general, any first-degree equation in two variables, x and y, can be solved for y and thus put into a form that shows immediately the slope and the y-intercept.

330. Equations of lines parallel to an axis.—In the equation $x = 2$, x is always equal to 2, and the graph of this equation must have only those points whose abscissas are 2. The curve of the equation is then a straight line parallel to the y-axis and having its x-intercept 2. Similarly, $y = 3$ is the equation of a straight line parallel to the x-axis and with a y-intercept 0. In general, $x = a$ is a straight line parallel to the y-axis; and $y = b$ is a line parallel to the x-axis. It

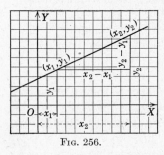

FIG. 256.

follows that $x = 0$ is the equation of the y-axis and $y = 0$ is the equation of the x-axis.

331. The equation of any straight line.—If the slope and the y-intercept of a straight line are known, its equation can be written at once by putting these values for m and b in the equation $y = mx + b$, which is known as the **slope-intercept form** of the equation of a straight line.

If two points through which the line passes are known, the equation of the line can be found as follows: Let (x_1, y_1) and (x_2, y_2) be the two points. Then the change in y from y_1 to y_2 is $y_2 - y_1$, and the change in x from x_1 to x_2 is $x_2 - x_1$. Hence the slope of the line through these points is $\dfrac{y_2 - y_1}{x_2 - x_1}$, which is the ratio of these changes. This is shown in Fig. 256. Now by the definition of a straight line it has the same direction throughout; that is, the slope is always the same.

Then let (x, y) be any other point on the line, and find the slope using one of the given points and the point (x, y). This gives the slope $\dfrac{y - y_1}{x - x_1}$. Since these two slopes are equal, the equation of the line is

$$\frac{y - y_1}{x - x_1} = \frac{y_2 - y_1}{x_2 - x_1}$$

This is known as the **two-point form** of the equation of a straight line.

The point (x_2, y_2) could as well be used with (x, y) in finding the slope.

If one point through which the line passes and the slope are known, the equation of the line can be found as follows: Let (x_1, y_1) be the point, and let m be the slope. If (x, y) is any point on the line, the slope of the line is $\dfrac{y - y_1}{x - x_1}$. But m is also the slope, and therefore the equation of the line is

$$\frac{y - y_1}{x - x_1} = m$$

This is known as the **point-slope form** of the equation of a straight line.

Example 1.—Find the equation of the straight line having a slope of $\frac{2}{3}$ and a y-intercept 2.

Solution.—Substituting in the equation $y = mx + b$,

$$y = \tfrac{2}{3}x + 2$$

Simplifying, $\qquad 2x - 3y + 6 = 0$

Example 2.—Find the equation of the straight line passing through the points $(3, 4)$ and $(-1, -2)$.

Solution.—Here we use the two-point form of the equation of a straight line, where $x_1 = 3$, $y_1 = 4$, $x_2 = -1$, $y_2 = -2$. Substituting these values,

$$\frac{y - 4}{x - 3} = \frac{-2 - 4}{-1 - 3}$$

Simplifying, $\qquad 3x - 2y - 1 = 0$

Example 3.—Find the equation of a line through $(4, -2)$ with a slope $\frac{1}{2}$.

Solution.—Substituting in the point slope form of the equation of a straight line,

$$\frac{y+2}{x-4} = \frac{1}{2}$$

Simplifying, $\qquad x - 2y - 8 = 0$

EXERCISES

1. Plot the following equations all on the same set of coordinate axes: (1) $y = \frac{1}{4}x$, (2) $y = \frac{1}{2}x$, (3) $y = 4x$, (4) $y = -2x$.

2. Plot the following equations on the same set of axes: (1) $y = 3$, (2) $y = x + 3$, (3) $y = 3x + 3$, (4) $y = -3x + 3$.

3. Plot the following equations on the same set of axes: (1) $y = \frac{1}{2}x + 6$, (2) $y = \frac{1}{2}x + 4$, (3) $y = \frac{1}{2}x - 4$, (4) $y = \frac{1}{2}x$.

Change the following equations to the slope intercept form and plot:

4. $2x - 3y = 6$.

5. $7x + 6y = 42$.

6. $3x - 2y - 6 = 0$.

7. $2x - 6y + 24 = 0$.

8. Plot the following equations on the same set of axes: (1) $x = 0$, (2) $x = 5$, (3) $x = -6$, (4) $y = 0$, (5) $y = -4$, (6) $y = 2\frac{1}{2}$.

Find the equations of straight lines determined as follows:

9. Through point $(0, 6)$ with slope $\frac{2}{3}$.   *Ans.* $2x - 3y + 18 = 0$.

10. Through $(0, -2)$ with slope $-\frac{2}{3}$.   *Ans.* $3x + 2y + 4 = 0$.

11. Through points $(2, 3)$ and $(4, 6)$.   *Ans.* $3x - 2y = 0$.

12. Through points $(6, 2)$ and $(-1, 3)$.   *Ans.* $x + 7y - 20 = 0$.

13. Through points $(0, 2)$ and $(7, 0)$.   *Ans.* $2x + 7y - 14 = 0$.

14. Through points $(-4, -2)$ and $(-1, 0)$.   *Ans.* $2x - 3y + 2 = 0$.

15. Through point $(3, 2)$ with slope -6.   *Ans.* $6x + y - 20 = 0$.

16. Through point $(-4, -1)$ with slope $\frac{3}{2}$.   *Ans.* $3x - 2y + 10 = 0$.

332. Simultaneous equations.—In Art. 292, a pair of first-degree equations in two variables x and y were classified under three headings, independent, inconsistent, and equivalent. The reason for this classification can now be made clear.

(1) A pair of equations like

$$3x + 2y = 4$$

and

$$x + 4y = 3$$

when plotted, give two *intersecting* straight lines as shown in Fig. 257.

Now two intersecting straight lines can intersect in just one point, and the coordinates of this point are the only pair of values that satisfy *both* equations. There is, therefore, one and only one pair of values in the solution of two such equations.

Such equations are **independent simultaneous equations** and are the kind that can be solved. We can determine that two equations are of this class by changing them to the slope-intercept form and noting that their slopes are different.

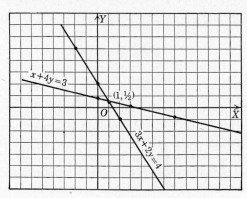

Fig. 257.

This depends upon the fact that two straight lines having different directions and lying in the same plane must intersect in just one point.

(2) A pair of equations like

$$x + 2y = 7$$

and

$$3x + 6y = 15$$

when plotted, give two *parallel* lines. Since parallel lines have no points in common, two such equations have no common pair of values satisfying each equation.

Such equations are **inconsistent** and cannot be solved. Since parallel lines have the same slope, we can determine that two equations are of this class by finding that their slopes are equal and their y-intercepts different.

Changing each of the equations $x + 2y = 7$ and $3x + 6y = 15$ to the slope-intercept form, we have

$$y = -\tfrac{1}{2}x + \tfrac{7}{2}$$

and

$$y = -\tfrac{1}{2}x + \tfrac{5}{2}$$

Here the slope is $-\tfrac{1}{2}$ in each case, and the y-intercepts are $\tfrac{7}{2}$ and $\tfrac{5}{2}$.

(3) A pair of equations like

$$2x + y = 10$$

and

$$6x + 3y = 30$$

when plotted, give two lines that lie together. Since all points that lie in one of these lines also lie in the other, any pair of values that satisfy one equation also satisfy the other.

Such equations are **equivalent** and cannot be solved for definite values of the unknowns. We can determine that two equations are of this class by changing them to the slope-intercept form and noting that the slopes are equal and the intercepts the same; that is, the two equations will be exactly alike when changed to the slope intercept form.

EXERCISES

Classify the following pairs of equations as independent, inconsistent, or equivalent; solve when possible; and in each case, plot the equations.

1. $x + y = 5$ and $3x + 2y = 12$.　　　　*Ans.* $x = 2,\ y = 3$.
2. $3x + 5y = 11$ and $4x + 7y = 15$.　　*Ans.* $x = 2,\ y = 1$.
3. $5x + 4y = 6$ and $7x + 6y = 10$.　*Ans.* $x = -2,\ y = 4$.
4. $2x + 3y = 4$ and $4x - 6y = 8$.　　*Ans.* $x = 2,\ y = 0$.
5. $6x + y = 6$ and $4x + 3y = 11$.　*Ans.* $x = \tfrac{1}{2},\ y = 3$.
6. $3x + 4y = 24$ and $5x - 6y = 2$.　　*Ans.* $x = 4,\ y = 3$.
7. $5x + 9y = 28$ and $7x + 3y = 20$.　*Ans.* $x = 2,\ y = 2$.
8. $5x - 2y = 1$ and $4x + 5y = 47$.　　*Ans.* $x = 3,\ y = 7$.
9. $3x - y = 2$ and $6x - 2y = 4$.　　　*Ans.* Equivalent.
10. $3x + y = 16$ and $6x + 10y = 5$.　*Ans.* $x = 6\tfrac{11}{24},\ y = -3\tfrac{3}{8}$.

11. $2x + y = 5$ and $3x + 2y = 10$.   *Ans.* $x = 0$, $y = 5$.

12. $x - 2y = 6$ and $2x - 4y = 5$.   *Ans.* Inconsistent.

13. $2x - 6y = 1$ and $x - 3y = 4$.   *Ans.* Inconsistent.

14. $5x - 2 = 3y$ and $10x - 6y = 4$.   *Ans.* Equivalent.

FUNCTIONS

333. In various places as we have proceeded in our study it has been pointed out that we were endeavoring to express common ideas in the language of mathematics. The machinery of mathematics has continually been used to handle these ideas effectively and obtain desired results.

One of the most common thoughts in everyday life is to think of the relations of things and how one event or happening depends upon others. One of the most common statements in speaking of things is to say that one depends upon another. The statement of these relations and their consideration, when carried into the field of mathematics, are the source of a great deal of trouble, which can be avoided if the ideas are thoroughly understood.

We have already studied how to state many relations in mathematical language. For instance, in the language of direct and inverse variation, we are able to state certain relations; but it will be remembered that these relations were such as could be expressed by a ratio. That is, the relation that one of the variables had to the other was always expressed by the help of a constant multiplier. It must be apparent to anyone who stops to think that there must be other relations between variables. When we wish to speak of any relation that may exist between variables, that is, when we wish to speak of how one thing depends upon another thing or other things, we use the word *function*. The following will illustrate this.

(1) The distance that an automobile will go at a given rate depends upon the time; that is, the distance is a *function* of the time.

(2) The area of a circle depends upon the length of its radius; that is, the area is a *function* of the radius.

(3) The pay that a man, working at a certain rate an hour, receives depends upon the number of hours that he works; that is, the pay is a *function* of the number of hours.

In each of these three illustrations, one magnitude depends upon one other magnitude. It is often the case, however, that one magnitude depends upon several others. One of the big problems of mathematics is endeavoring to express these relations in exact mathematical equations. This is not always easy or even possible. For instance, the temperature on a certain day is a function of the latitude, altitude, season of the year, direction of the wind, and many other factors. It would seem impossible to write a mathematical equation stating this relation.

334. Definitions.—If two variables are so related that for every value of one there is a corresponding value of the other, then the second is said to be a **function** of the first.

If two variables are represented by x and y, y is a function of x if for every value of x there is a corresponding value for y.

The variable supposed to depend upon the other variable is called the **dependent variable.** The variable that it depends upon is called the **independent variable.**

335. Functional notation.—Before one can deal with variables in their relations with each other by means of the machinery of mathematics, it is necessary to know how to express these relations in mathematical language. Since the relations are very numerous, it is to be expected that there are many different forms when they are written in mathematical language. Some will be found to be very simple; others are more complicated.

If a man works for \$1.50 an hour, and A and h are, respectively, the total number of dollars that he receives and the number of hours that he works, then

$$A = 1.50h$$

Here we say that A is a function of h, and the statement is an equation. It may also be called a formula.

In the formula $s = \frac{1}{2}gt^2$, where s is the distance that a body near the earth's surface will fall in time t sec. and g is the constant acceleration of gravity, s is evidently a function of t.

Likewise, $A = \pi r^2$ states the relation between the area A of a circle and its radius r.

Numerous such functional relations can be written from the facts learned in geometry, physics, and other sciences.

When one does not know the exact relation between the variables or for any reason does not wish to state the exact relation, a general form is used. Thus, $A = f(h)$ states that A is a function of h but does not give the exact relation. It is read "A equals a function of h" or "A equals the f-function of h."

Other letters than f are used in writing functions. Thus, $y = F(x)$, read "y equals capital F-function of x," $y = g(x)$, $s = f'(x)$, etc. It should be carefully noted that $f(x)$ does not mean f times x; in fact, f does not represent a number. The different letters are used to represent the functions when different relations exist between the variables. The same letter is used as a functional symbol when the same relation exists though the variables are different, or a constant is substituted for the variable.

If $y = f(x)$, then for each value of x, y has a value. For instance, if $f(x)$ is $x^2 + 2x + 1$, then when $x = 2$, $y = 2^2 + 2 \cdot 2 + 1 = 9$; and similarly for any value of x. The following are other illustrations:

If
$$f(x) = 3x^2 + 2x - 3$$
$$f(3) = 3 \cdot 3^2 + 2 \cdot 3 - 3 = 30$$
and
$$f(a) = 3a^2 + 2a - 3$$
If
$$F(x) = x^3 - 3x^2 + 2x - 1$$
$$F(4) = 4^3 - 3 \cdot 4^2 + 2 \cdot 4 - 1 = 23$$

The form $f(x, y)$ expresses a function of two variables x and y. Thus, the volume V of a right circular cylinder with r for radius of base and h for altitude is expressed by $V = f(r, h)$ when the exact relation is not stated and by $V = \pi r^2 h$ when the exact relation is stated.   Here the value of the function, which is the same as that of V, depends upon the values of r and h; that is, V is the dependent variable, and r and h are independent variables.

Note.—In the definition of a function of one variable (see Art. 334) it is important to understand that every value of one of the variables must be chosen from a particular *range* of values, say from a to b.   Then there is a determined corresponding value of the other variable on its particular range, say from c to d.

In particular, if the range of a variable is from a to a, that is, it does not change, it is called a *constant*.   (See Art. 314.)

EXERCISES

Express the following exercises in algebraic language, and give the exact functional relations.   State the range of the variables used. Answer the first 17 exercises orally.

1. The distance s that a man can drive in t hr. at the rate of 30 miles per hour.

2. The cost of 10 books at x dollars per book and 4 pencils at c cents per pencil.   Let C be the total cost.

3. The cost C for 4 years of education if the tuition is t dollars per year and other expense is p dollars per year.

Can all functional relations be expressed in mathematical language showing the exact relations?   Try to express the following in algebraic language, and tell why there is difficulty:

4. The cost of an automobile depends upon the country in which it is bought.

5. The height to which a gun will shoot depends upon the gun used.

6. The number of strokes that a man takes in playing 18 holes of golf depends upon the man.

7. The age at which a boy graduates from school depends upon the school.

8. The value of a book depends upon the number of pages that it contains.

9. In each of the five preceding exercises state other independent variables.

10. Express the simple interest on $100 at 6 % as a function of the time t in years.

11. Express the simple interest on $100 for 5 years as a function of the rate r.

12. Express the simple interest on p dollars for 5 years at 6 % as a function of p.

13. Express the amount at simple interest of p dollars at 6 % as a function of p and the time t in years.

14. Express the simple interest on p dollars at r % for t years as a function of p, r, and t.

15. Express the amount at compound interest of p dollars at r % for t years as a function of p, r, and t.

16. Express the area A of a right triangle as a function of the base b and the altitude a.

17. Express the hypotenuse c of a right triangle as a function of the base b and the altitude a.

18. In the formula for the horsepower of a steam engine, $H = \dfrac{PLAN}{33,000}$, there are five variables. Express each as a function of the four remaining variables.

19. State in words five functional relations, not already given, that you can also state in exact mathematical language.

20. State five functional relations, not already given, that you cannot state in exact mathematical language.

21. If $f(x) = mx + b$, write $f(t); f(u); f(t + u)$.
$$Ans. \ f(t) = mt + b.$$

22. If $f(A) = 10 + 5A$, find $f(0); f(5); f(-2)$.
$$Ans. \ f(0) = 10; f(5) = 35; f(-2) = 0.$$

23. If $g(x) = 2p(x - h)$, find $g(0); g(x + h); g(h + x^2)$.
$$Ans. \ g(0) = -2ph; g(x + h) = 2px; g(h + x^2) = 2px^2.$$

24. If $F(t) = v + at + 16t^2$, find $F(0); F(4); F(x - v)$.
Ans. $F(0) = v; \quad F(4) = v + 4a + 256; \quad F(x - V) = V + ax - av$
$$+ \ 16x^2 - 32xv + 16v^2.$$

25. If $V(x) = (x^2 - 2x + 1)^2$, find $V(1); V(0); V(2); V(-1)$.
$$Ans. \ V(1) = 0; \ V(0) = 1; \ V(-1) = 16.$$

26. If $V(x,y) = (x - 2)(x - 3)y$, write $V(0,1); \ V(u,4); \ V(a,b);$ $V(-x,y); V(x,-y); V(-x,-y); V(y,x)$.
Ans. $V(0,1) = 6; \ V(u,4) = 4u^2 - 20u + 24; \ V(a,b) = a^2b - 5ab + 6b; V(-x,y) = x^2y + 5xy + 6y; V(x,-y) = -x^2y + 5xy - 6y;$
$$V(-x,-y) = -x^2y - 5xy - 6y; V(y,x) = xy^2 - 5xy + 6x.$$

27. If A is a man's annual income and x dollars is the amount that he desires to give to a community fund, a reasonable amount to give is given by the formula $x = A \div 300$. (A between \$1200 and \$3600.)

Here $f(A) = A \div 300$, find $F(1200); F(1500); F(1800); F(3600)$.

If A is between \$4000 and \$6500, then $f(A) = A \div 200$.

If A is between \$7000 and \$9500, then $f(A) = 0.75(A \div 100)$.

If A is over \$10,000, then $f(A) = A \div 100$.

Find several values of $F(A)$ in the last three cases.

Ans. $F(1200) = 4$; $F(1500) = 5$; $F(1800) = 6$; $F(3600) = 12$; $F(4000)$
$\qquad = 20$; $F(8,000) = 60$; $F(10,000) = 100$.

336. Plotting functions.—The graphical representation of a function is much used in many everyday affairs, and especially in the sciences and engineering, as it represents vividly to the eye changes of the function. Such representations of functions are found in the newspapers and magazines, and their meaning is common knowledge of the reading public. Thus, the rise and fall of the price of a certain stock may be shown graphically by using the price each day as the ordinate of a point of which the date is the abscissa. The curve drawn through these points shows at a glance the fluctuations of this particular stock. In the same manner, the changes in the prices of food and clothing and the general cost of living from year to year are shown. It is evident that the changes in many functions can be shown graphically, even though they cannot be translated into exact mathematical forms.

Example 1.—Draw the graph of the function $\frac{2}{3}x + 3$.

For convenience represent $\frac{2}{3}x + 3$ by $f(x)$.

Form a table of values of x, chosen arbitrarily, and the corresponding values of $f(x)$.

x	-9	-6	$-4\frac{1}{2}$	-3	-1	0	2	3	6	9	12
$f(x)$	-3	-1	0	1	$2\frac{1}{3}$	3	$4\frac{1}{3}$	5	7	9	11

In Fig. 258, the points $(x, f(x))$ for each pair of values given in the table are plotted. A smooth line connecting these points is the graph of the function. The ordinate of any point is, of course, the value of the function corresponding to the value of x which is the abscissa of the point. For instance, it is seen at once from the plotting that the value of the function is 3 when $x = 0$, 7 when $x = 6$, and -1 when $x = -6$.

If y is used in place of $f(x)$, we have the equation

$$y = \frac{2}{3}x + 3$$

which is a first-degree equation in the slope-intercept form. The graph of this equation is a straight line with a slope of $\frac{2}{3}$ and crossing the y-axis at the point $(0, 3)$. This agrees with the plotting in Fig. 258. If a point is thought to move along the straight line from left to right, the point will rise two-thirds

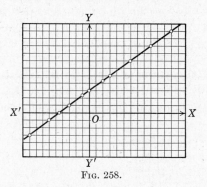

Fig. 258.

as fast as it moves to the right; that is, there is a rise of 2 units in going 3 units to the right.

Example 2.—Draw the graph of the function

$$x^2 - 3x - 10$$

Represent $x^2 - 3x - 10$ by $f(x)$, and form a table of corresponding values of x and $f(x)$. Here values of x less than -4 or greater than 7 are not chosen, for they would give values of $f(x)$ that would be too large to plot conveniently.

x	-4	-3	$-2\frac{1}{2}$	-2	-1	0	1	$1\frac{1}{2}$	2	3	4	5	6	7
$f(x)$	18	8	$3\frac{3}{4}$	0	-6	-10	-12	$-12\frac{1}{4}$	-12	-10	-6	0	8	18

In Fig. 259, the points $(x, f(x))$ are plotted and a smooth curve drawn connecting them. An inspection of the graph shows that a point moving along the curve from the left would fall rapidly at first, then more slowly, cease falling at

$(1\frac{1}{2}, -12\frac{1}{4})$, then begin to rise, slowly at first but more rapidly as x increases. The curve shown in the graph is a parabola.

Example 3.—Draw the graph of the function

$$x^3 - 21x + 20$$

x	-6	-5	-4	-3	-2	-1	0	$\frac{1}{2}$	1	$1\frac{1}{2}$	2	3	4	$4\frac{1}{2}$	5
$f(x)$	-70	0	40	56	54	40	20	$9\frac{5}{8}$	0	$-8\frac{1}{8}$	-14	-16	0	$16\frac{5}{8}$	40

In plotting the points $(x, f(x))$ in Fig. 260, it is convenient to use the side of a square as one unit on the x-axis and as five units on the y-axis. An inspection of the graph shows

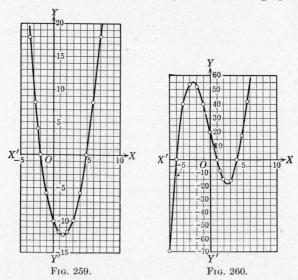

FIG. 259.   FIG. 260.

that a point moving along the curve from the left would rise rapidly, then more slowly, cease rising at about where $x = -2.6$, then fall to about where $x = 2.6$, and rise for greater values of x.

The point where the curve ceases to rise and afterward falls is called a **maximum point** of the curve, and the value of

the function at that point is a **maximum value of the function.**
Here the maximum value of the function is about 57.

The point where the curve ceases to fall and afterward
rises is called a **minimum point** of the curve, and the value of
the function at that point is a **minimum value of the function.**
Here the minimum value of the function is about -17.

EXERCISES

Use the first three exercises for oral work.

1. From Fig. 258, tell the value of x that makes $\frac{2}{3}x + 3 = 0$; that
makes $\frac{2}{3}x + 3 = -3$; that makes $\frac{2}{3}x + 3 = 9$.

2. From Fig. 259, tell the values of x that make $x^2 - 3x - 10 = 0$;
that makes $x^2 - 3x - 10 = -12$. What is the value of the function
when x is -3? 3? $3\frac{1}{2}$? What value of x makes $f(x) = -16$?

3. From Fig. 260, tell the values of x that make $f(x) = 0$; $f(x) = 40$;
$f(x) = -17$ (about); $f(x) = -20$. What is the value of $f(x)$ when
$x = 4\frac{1}{2}$? When $x = \frac{1}{2}$?

4. Plot the graphs of the following functions on the same set of
coordinate axes: (1) $2x - 3$; (2) $2x - 5$; (3) $2x + 3$; (4) $2x + 5$.

5. Plot on the same set of coordinate axes: (1) x^2; (2) $-x^2$.

6. Plot on the same set of coordinate axes: (1) $(x - 1)^2$; (2)
$-(x - 1)^2$.

7. Plot on the same set of coordinate axes: (1) $y = x^2 - 4x + 5$, or
what is the same graph, $y = x^2 - 4x + 4 + 1$, or $y - 1 = (x - 2)^2$.
(See Art. 310.) [Notice that the point $(2, 1)$ is the *minimum point* on
the graph.] (2) $y = -(x^2 - 4x + 3)$, or what is the same graph,
$y = -(x - 2)^2 + 1$, or $y - 1 = -(x - 2)^2$. [Notice that the point
$(2, 1)$ is the *maximum point* on the graph.]

8. Plot each of the following on different coordinate axes, and note
the maximum (minimum) point on each. Also note the points where the
graph cuts the x-axis; these points are found by setting $y = 0$ and then
solving the quadratic equation for its two roots. (1) $y = x^2 - 2x$;
(2) $y = x^2 + 2x$; (3) $y = x^2 - 6x + 8$; (4) $y = x^2 + 6x + 8$.

9. Given two numbers x and $x - 2$, find x so that their product is a
minimum. Draw a graph of their product. Find the minimum product.
Ans. 1; -1.

10. Two numbers differ by 4. Find them so that their product will
be a minimum. Draw a graph of their product. Find the minimum
product. *Ans.* 2; -4.

11. Find the area of the greatest rectangle that can be bounded by a
line 20 in. long.

Suggestion.—Let $x =$ the length of one side.

Then
$$10 - x = \text{length of other side}$$
$$\therefore \text{area} = x(10 - x)$$

Plot, and find the value of x that makes the area a maximum.

12. Find the area of the greatest rectangle that can be bounded by a line 24 in. long. See suggestions under Exercise 11. *Ans.* 36 sq. in.

13. A rectangular sheet of tin 24 in. wide is to be made into a gutter by turning up strips vertically along the sides. Find the width of the strip turned up in order to get the maximum cross-sectional area. Also find the maximum cross-sectional area. *Ans.* 6 in.; 72 sq. in.

14. The sum of two numbers is S. Find the maximum value of their product. Show that the result may be used to prove that when the perimeter of a rectangle is given, the area enclosed will be a maximum when the rectangle is a square.

Ans. Maximum product $\dfrac{S^2}{4}$, when the two numbers are $\dfrac{S}{2}$ and $\dfrac{S}{2}$.

15. A window has the form of a rectangle surmounted by a semicircle. If the perimeter is 40 ft., find the dimensions so that the greatest amount of light may be admitted.

Ans. A square, the side of which $= \dfrac{40}{4 + \pi}$ ft.

16. A street and a railroad track are straight and intersect at right angles. An automobile on the street is 2 miles away from the intersection and is approaching it at 60 miles per hour. An engine is on the track 1 mile from the intersection and is approaching it at 40 miles per hour. Find when the engine and the automobile are nearest to each other. *Ans.* $\frac{2}{65}$ hr.; $[S^2 = (2 - 60t)^2 + (1 - 40t)^2]$.

Hint.—They will be nearest to each other when the distance (or the square of the distance) between them is a minimum.

17. Divide 20 into two parts so that the double of one part added to the square of the other part gives a minimum sum. *Ans.* 1 and 19.

18. By observation over a long period of time insurance companies have discovered that in a group of 100,000 persons living at the age of ten, deaths occur on the average in accordance with the table selected from the American Experience Table of Mortality, shown in the following table.

Let 5 years represent one space on the x-axis and 5000 people represent one space on the y-axis, and draw a smooth curve for this functional relation.

Discuss this curve as to (1) the rate at which people die at certain ages and (2) what age the mortality rate appears to be the highest and what age the lowest.

Age	Number living	Age	Number living
10	100,000	70	38,569
20	92,637	75	26,237
30	85,441	80	14,474
40	78,106	85	5,485
50	69,804	90	847
60	57,917	95	3
65	49,341		

19. Many schemes have been suggested for drafting the wealth of the United States. Illustrate graphically the scheme indicated by the following table of values:

Wealth	Tax	Wealth	Tax
$ 1,500	$ 25	$ 500,000	$ 81,950
5,000	200	1,000,000	206,950
10,000	450	10,000,000	4,331,950
100,000	9,450	100,000,000	64,456,950

Estimate the tax for $3000; for $20,000; for $50,000; for $50,000,000.

20. A square sheet of tin 18 in. on a side has a small square cut out of each corner so that the sides may be turned up to form an open box. Find the sides of the small squares so that the box shall have the greatest volume.

Suggestion.—Let x = side of a small square in inches. The volume is evidently a function of x; for as x is changed, the volume will change. Show that volume = $x(18 - 2x)^2$. Plot the graph of this function, and note the value of x where the curve has a maximum point. This value of x is the side of the square to be cut out of each corner to make the open box of greatest volume.

CHAPTER XXXIII

LOGARITHMS

337. The invention of logarithms was one of the great inventions of all times for the saving of time and labor. Cajori, in his "A History of Elementary Mathematics," says: "The miraculous powers of modern calculations are due to three inventions: the Hindu Notation, Decimal Fractions, and Logarithms."

Logarithms were invented by John Napier, Baron of Merchiston of Scotland, who lived from 1550 to 1617. They were described by him in 1614. Burgi, a Swiss (1552–1632), was an independent inventor of logarithms, though his work was more crude than that of Napier. He published his work in 1620.

By the use of logarithms, the processes of multiplication, division, raising to a power, and extracting a root of arithmetical numbers are usually much simplified. The process of multiplication is replaced by one of addition, that of division by one of subtraction, that of raising to a power by a simple multiplication, and that of extracting a root by a division.

Many calculations that are difficult or impossible by other methods are readily carried out by means of logarithms. It was said by the great French astronomer Laplace that the method of logarithms, by reducing to a few days the labor of many months, doubled, as it were, the life of an astronomer, besides freeing him from the errors and disgust inseparable from long calculations. Of course, these same advantages are shared by others who find it necessary to perform numerical calculations. For instance, by the help of logarithms a square root is more readily found than by ordinary methods, and any other root is found as easily as a square root. The value

502

of a number affected with any exponent, as $2.34^{\frac{17}{16}}$, can be computed easily by logarithms.

338. Exponents.—For convenience the definitions and laws of exponents previously given are repeated here.

Definitions

(1) $a^n = a \cdot a \cdot a \cdots$ to n factors (n an integer)

(2) $a^{-n} = \dfrac{1}{a^n}. \quad (a \neq 0)$

(3) $a^0 = 1. \quad (a \neq 0)$

(4) $a^{\frac{n}{m}} = \sqrt[m]{a^n} = (\sqrt[m]{a})^n$ (a not negative)

Laws

(1) $a^n \cdot a^m = a^{n+m}$

(2) $a^n \div a^m = a^{n-m} \ (a \neq 0)$

(3) $(a \cdot b \cdot c \cdots)^n = a^n b^n c^n \cdots$

(4) $\left(\dfrac{a}{b}\right)^n = \dfrac{a^n}{b^n}. \quad (b \neq 0)$

(5) $(a^n)^m = a^{nm}$

A careful review should be made of these definitions and laws so that the principles of exponents may be fresh in mind; for logarithms are exponents, and the principles of logarithms depend upon those of exponents.

339. Definition of logarithm.—If 5 is taken as a base and 2 as an exponent, $5^2 = 25$. The exponent 2 is the logarithm of 25 when the base is 5. Similarly, since $4^3 = 64$, 3 is the logarithm of 64 when the base is 4. Evidently other numbers may be chosen as bases, and logarithms of numbers can be found. The following is given as a definition:

The logarithm of a number to a given base is the **exponent** *by which the base must be affected to produce that number.*

In symbols the definition may be stated as follows: If three numbers, N, b, and x, have such values that

$$N = b^x$$

then x is called the **logarithm of N to the base b.**

Thus, if $b = 4$ is selected as a base, some values of N and their logarithms are arranged in the following:

N	1	2	4	8	16	32	64	128	256	512	1024
x	0	$\frac{1}{2}$	1	$\frac{3}{2}$	2	$\frac{5}{2}$	3	$\frac{7}{2}$	4	$\frac{9}{2}$	5

The logarithms of all the positive numbers to a given base are called a **system of logarithms,** and the base is called the base of the system.

Any base except 0 and 1 may be used in a system of logarithms; but the base 10 is commonly used because, as will be seen later, it makes a very convenient system of logarithms to work with.

As invented by Napier, logarithms were arranged somewhat differently from the way that they are at present. Napier practically made use of the number 2.71828 . . . as a base. This base is still used in mathematics.   (See Art. 354.)

Henry Briggs (1556 to 1631), professor at Gresham College, London, modified the new invention by using the base 10 and so made it more convenient for practical purposes.

340. Notation.—If we take 2 as a base, we may write in the language of exponents, $2^4 = 16$.   In the language of logarithms, we may express the same idea by saying that the logarithm of 16 to the base 2 is 4.   This is abbreviated and written thus: $\log_2 16 = 4$.

Similarly, we have the following expressed in the language of exponents and in the language of logarithms.   One should practice reading these correctly.

Exponent notation	*Logarithmic notation*
$2^5 = 32.$	$\log_2 32 = 5.$
$3^4 = 81.$	$\log_3 81 = 4.$
$5^4 = 625.$	$\log_5 625 = 4.$
$8^3 = 512.$	$\log_8 512 = 3.$
$4^{0.5} = 2.$	$\log_4 2 = 0.5.$
$8^{\frac{2}{3}} = 4.$	$\log_8 4 = \frac{2}{3}.$
$64^{\frac{1}{3}} = 4.$	$\log_{64} 4 = \frac{1}{3}.$
$10^3 = 1000.$	$\log_{10} 1000 = 3.$
$\left(\frac{1}{3}\right)^3 = \frac{1}{27}.$	$\log_{\frac{1}{3}} \left(\frac{1}{27}\right) = 3.$

EXERCISES

1. Construct a table of partial system of logarithms to the base 3. (See Art. 339 where the base used was 4.)

In the following exercises read the first 49 correctly and answer the first 25 orally.

Express the following in logarithmic notation:

2. $2^0 = 1$.　　　　**5.** $32^{0.2} = 2$.　　　　**8.** $10^2 = 100$.

3. $1^4 = 1$.　　　　**6.** $100^{0.5} = 10$.　　　　**9.** $10^{0.5} = 3.16+$.

4. $2^7 = 128$.　　　　**7.** $625^{\frac{1}{2}} = 25$.　　　**10.** $10^{0.4997} = 3.16$.

Discuss Exercises 2, 3, 9, and 10.

Express the following in exponential notation:

11. $\log_{15} 225 = 2$.　*Ans.* $15^2 = 225$.

12. $\log_{64} 4 = \frac{1}{3}$.　*Ans.* $64^{\frac{1}{3}} = 4$.

13. $\log_{\frac{1}{2}} \frac{1}{16} = 4$.　*Ans.* $(\frac{1}{2})^4 = \frac{1}{16}$.

14. $\log_2 64 = 6$.　　　　**15.** $\log_{10} 64 = 1.8062$.

16. $\log_{12} 64 = x$.　*Ans.* $12^x = 64$.

Find the logarithms of the following:

17. $\log_9 81$.　*Ans.* 2.　　　　**21.** $\log_7 343$.　*Ans.* 3.

18. $\log_5 125$.　*Ans.* 3.　　　　**22.** $\log_{20} 8,000$.　*Ans.* 3.

19. $\log_{\frac{1}{2}} \frac{1}{16}$.　*Ans.* 4.　　　**23.** $\log_{10} 0.1$.　*Ans.* -1.

20. $\log_{10} 1,000$.　*Ans.* 3.　　　**24.** $\log_{10} 0.01$.　*Ans.* -2.

25. $\log_b N$.

Find the value of x in the following:

26. $\log_4 x = 3$.　*Ans.* 64.　　　**31.** $\log_3 x = -2$.　*Ans.* $\frac{1}{9}$.

27. $\log_5 x = 4$.　*Ans.* 625.　　**32.** $\log_8 x = -\frac{4}{3}$.　*Ans.* $\frac{1}{16}$.

28. $\log_4 x = 5$.　*Ans.* 1025.　**33.** $\log_b x = 1$.　*Ans.* b.

29. $\log_8 x = \frac{2}{3}$.　*Ans.* 4.　　**34.** $\log_1 x = b$.　*Ans.* 1.

30. $\log_2 x = -3$.　*Ans.* $\frac{1}{8}$.

35. $\log_0 x = b(b = 0)$.　*Ans.* $0(b$ greater than $0)$.

36. $\log_{169} x = 0.5$.　*Ans.* 13.　　**37.** $\log_{169} x = -0.5$.

Find the value of x in the following:

38. $\log_x 10 = 1$.　*Ans.* 10.　　**39.** $\log_x 64 = 6$.　*Ans.* 2.

40. $\log_x 49 = 2$.　*Ans.* 7.　　　**41.** $\log_x 81 = 4$.　*Ans.* 3.

42. $\log_x 1 = 0$.   *Ans.* Any number not zero.

43. $\log_x 100 = \frac{2}{3}$.   *Ans.* 1,000.   **44.** $\log_x 1,000 = \frac{3}{2}$.   *Ans.* 100.

45. $\log_x 2 = \frac{1}{8}$.   *Ans.* 256.   **46.** $\log_x 11 = 0.5$.   *Ans.* 121.

47. $\log_x 32 = \frac{5}{4}$.   *Ans.* 16.   **48.** $\log_{x+1} 4 = 2$.   *Ans.* 1.

49. $\log_{x+2} 10,000 = 4$.   *Ans.* 8.

50. What are the logarithms of 2, 4, 8, 16, 32, 64, 128, 256, to the base 2?   To the base 8?   *Ans.* $\log_2 2 = 1$; $\log_2 4 = 2$; $\log_2 8 = 3$; etc.

51. What are the logarithms of 2, 1, $\frac{1}{2}$, $\frac{1}{4}$, $\frac{1}{8}$, $\frac{1}{16}$, $\frac{1}{32}$, $\frac{1}{64}$, $\frac{1}{128}$, to the base 2?   To the base 8?

Ans. $\log_2 1 = 0$; $\log_2 \frac{1}{2} = -1$; $\log_2 \frac{1}{4} = -2$; etc.

341. Illustrative computations by means of exponents.

—It is very important that the fundamental ideas of logarithms shall be well understood.   In this article are given examples illustrative of the use of exponents, or logarithms, in making computations in multiplication, division, raising to powers, and extracting roots.   These computations are made by the help of the following table in which 2 is the base.   The work is kept in the language of exponents but can be easily translated into the language of logarithms.

$2^{-6} = \frac{1}{64}$	$2^1 = 2$	$2^8 = 256$
$2^{-5} = \frac{1}{32}$	$2^2 = 4$	$2^9 = 512$
$2^{-4} = \frac{1}{16}$	$2^3 = 8$	$2^{10} = 1024$
$2^{-3} = \frac{1}{8}$	$2^4 = 16$	$2^{11} = 2048$
$2^{-2} = \frac{1}{4}$	$2^5 = 32$	$2^{12} = 4096$
$2^{-1} = \frac{1}{2}$	$2^6 = 64$	$2^{13} = 8192$
$2^0 = 1$	$2^7 = 128$	$2^{14} = 16,384$

Multiplication.—Multiply 512 by 32.

From the table, $512 = 2^9$, and $32 = 2^5$.

$$\therefore 512 \times 32 = 2^9 \times 2^5 = 2^{14}$$

From the table, $2^{14} = 16,384$.

$$\therefore 512 \times 32 = 16,384$$

Division.—Divide 512 by 4096.

From the table, $512 = 2^9$, and $4096 = 2^{12}$.

$$\therefore 512 \div 4096 = 2^9 \div 2^{12} = 2^{-3}$$

From the table, $2^{-3} = \frac{1}{8}$.

$$\therefore\ 512 \times 4096 = \frac{1}{8}$$

Raising to a power.—Find the value of 16^3.
From the table, $16 = 2^4$.

$$\therefore\ 16^3 = (2^4)^3 = 2^{12}$$

From the table, $2^{12} = 4096$.

$$\therefore\ 16^3 = 4096$$

Extraction of a root.—Find the value of $\sqrt[4]{4096}$.
From the table, $4096 = 2^{12}$.

$$\therefore\ \sqrt[4]{4096} = \sqrt[4]{2^{12}} = 2^3$$

From the table, $2^3 = 8$.

$$\therefore\ \sqrt[4]{4096} = 8$$

EXERCISES

By help of the table of 2's solve the following exercises:

1. An agent bought 256 tires at $16 per tire. What was the total amount paid for the tires?

2. In Exercise 1 what would the tires cost at $32 per tire?

3. A man received $16,384 for 512 suits. What did he receive per suit?

4. A man drove 8192 miles and used 512 gal. of gas. How many miles per gallon of gas did he get?

5. The government bought a farm of 512 acres at $32 per acre. How much was paid for the farm?

6. If 128 radios cost $16,384, find the cost per radio.

7. $8192 \div 256$.

8. $2048 \div 1024$.

9. $16 \div 2048$.

10. $4 \div 512$.

11. 16^4.

12. 64^2.

13. $\sqrt{16,384}$.

14. $\sqrt[6]{4096}$.

15. $\sqrt[7]{16,384}$.

16. $\dfrac{32 \times 2048}{512}$.

17. $\dfrac{16,384 \times 512}{2048}$.

18. $\dfrac{32 \times 64}{512 \times 8}$.

22. $\dfrac{1024 \times 64}{512 \times 16,384}$.

19. $(4096)^{\frac{2}{3}}$.

23. $\left(\dfrac{512 \times 256}{1024 \times 8192}\right)^{\frac{1}{4}}$.

20. $(32 \times 128)^{\frac{1}{4}}$.

21. $(8192 \times 32)^{\frac{2}{3}}$.

24. $\sqrt[3]{\dfrac{256 \times 1024}{4096^2}}$.

342. Logarithms of any number.—It is readily seen that in the exercises of the last article, the numbers considered were all integral powers of 2. It is also readily seen that many numbers cannot be expressed as integral powers of 2. The same thing is true for any base. Thus, for the base 3, we have as integral powers the numbers 3, 9, 27, 81, 243, etc., and no numbers except these between 3 and 243.

We can, therefore, with any given base write integral logarithms for only a small part of all possible numbers. That is, the logarithms of numbers to any given base are usually not integral. Thus, the logarithm of 95 to the base 3 is 4 and a fraction, because 95 is between 3^4 and 3^5. What this fraction is cannot easily be determined.

343. Logarithms to the base 10.—We will now study, in particular, logarithms to the base 10 and how to compute with them. Much depends upon understanding the principles involved and attaining as high a degree of accuracy in numerical work as possible.

When the base is 10, we evidently have the following:

$$
\begin{array}{lll}
10^5 & = 100,000 & \text{or} \qquad \log 100,000 = 5. \\
10^4 & = 10,000 & \text{or} \qquad \log 10,000 = 4. \\
10^3 & = 1000 & \text{or} \qquad \log 1000 = 3. \\
10^2 & = 100 & \text{or} \qquad \log 100 = 2. \\
10^1 & = 10 & \text{or} \qquad \log 10 = 1. \\
10^0 & = 1 & \text{or} \qquad \log 1 = 0. \\
10^{-1} & = 0.1 & \text{or} \qquad \log 0.1 = -1. \\
10^{-2} & = 0.01 & \text{or} \qquad \log 0.01 = -2. \\
10^{-3} & = 0.001 & \text{or} \qquad \log 0.001 = -3. \\
10^{-4} & = 0.0001 & \text{or} \qquad \log 0.0001 = -4. \\
10^{-5} & = 0.00001 & \text{or} \qquad \log 0.00001 = -5.
\end{array}
$$

Two things are evident: (1) This range of numbers from
).00001 to 100,000 includes nearly all numbers used in com-
)utations; and (2) the eleven numbers given in the table are
,he only numbers from 0.00001 to 100,000 that have integers
or logarithms. Every other number in this range has, then,
or a logarithm an integer plus or minus a fraction. This
raction is put in the form of a decimal correct to as many
)laces as desired.

Thus, the logarithm of any number between 1000 and 10,000 is between
3 and 4, or it is 3 and a fraction. Between 100 and 1000 the logarithm
s 2 plus a fraction. Between 0.01 and 0.1 the logarithm is −2 plus a
raction or −1 minus a fraction.

In order that the fractional part of the logarithm may
ilways be positive, *we shall agree to take the logarithm so that
he integral part only is negative.*

Usually, then, the logarithm of a number consists of two
)arts, an *integer* and a *fraction*, the fraction being written
ipproximately as a decimal.

The integral part is called the **characteristic.**

The fractional part is called the **mantissa.**

The logarithm is the characteristic plus the mantissa.

Thus, the logarithm of 3467 consists of the characteristic 3 and a man-
issa, because 3467 lies between 1000 and 10,000. The logarithm of
;9,436 is 4 plus a fraction because 59,436 lies between 10,000 and 100,000.
The log 0.0236 is −2 plus a fraction because 0.0236 lies between 0.01 and
).1.

The mantissas for the positive numbers arranged in order
ire called a **table of logarithms.** A four-place table has
he mantissas given to four decimal places. The larger the
iumber of places in a table the more nearly accurate are the
:omputations when using the table. In any particular com-
)utation, one uses a table that will give the desired accuracy.

344. Effect of changing decimal point in number.—Since
nultiplying a number by 10 moves the decimal point one

place to the right, and dividing a number by 10 moves the decimal point one place to the left, it is evident that the logarithm of a number is increased by 1 for each place that the decimal point is moved to the right and the logarithm is decreased by 1 for each place that the decimal point is moved to the left.

This means that a change in the position of the decimal point in the number changes the characteristic of the logarithm but does not change the mantissa.

Thus, if we know that log 325 = 2.5119, then

log 32.5 = 1.5119, log 3250 = 3.5119,
log 3.25 = 0.5119, log 32500 = 4.5119.

345. Rules for determining the characteristic.—The advantages in using the base 10 are that the characteristic can be determined by inspection, and that the mantissa remains unchanged for the same figures in the same order. The rules for determining the characteristic follow at once from a study of the following table:

Number greater than 1	No. of digits to left of decimal point	Logarithm	Characteristic
3.765	1	0 + a decimal	0
49.37	2	1 + a decimal	1
823.7	3	2 + a decimal	2
4937	4	3 + a decimal	3
84376	5	4 + a decimal	4
Number less than 1	No. of zeros to right of decimal point		
0.564	0	−1 + a decimal	−1 or 9 − 10
0.027	1	−2 + a decimal	−2 or 8 − 10
0.00378	2	−3 + a decimal	−3 or 7 − 10

I. *When the number is greater than* 1, *the characteristic is positive and is* **one less** *than the number of digits to the left of the decimal point.*

II. *When the number is less than* 1 *and expressed decimally, the characteristic is negative and is* **one more** *than the number of zeros immediately at the right of the decimal point.*

When the characteristic is negative, the minus sign is placed above the characteristic to show that it alone is negative.

Thus, in log $0.009347 = \bar{3}.9707$, the form $\bar{3}.9797$ means $-3 + 0.9707$ and should not be written -3.9707, for then the minus sign would indicate that both characteristic and mantissa were negative. Do not misunderstand this; of course, the logarithm of a number may be written entirely as a negative number, but then it would not fit the mantissas as given in a table of logarithms, where the mantissas are always positive.

For instance, since $\bar{3}.9707 = -3 + 0.9707 = -2.0293;$
$\quad$ log $0.009347 = \bar{3}.9707$, or log $0.009347 = -2.0293;$

but the first form only can be used with a table.

In computations involving negative characteristics, to avoid the use of the negative, 10 may be added to the characteristic and subtracted at the right of the mantissa. In writing logarithms in this form, *the characteristic, when* 10 *is added, is* 9 *minus the number of zeros immediately at the right of the decimal point.*

Thus in the foregoing, log $0.009347 = 7.9707 - 10$.

The following are examples of characteristics:

Number	Characteristic	Rule
3426	0	I
3.2364	0	I
0.00639	-3 or $7 - 10$	II
2.04	0	I
0.000067	-5 or $5 - 10$	II

EXERCISES

In each of the following state the characteristic to base 10:

1. 38.8.	**6.** 5432.9.	**11.** 1564.90.	**16.** $65.5(10)^2$.
2. 9683.	**7.** 0.0045.	**12.** 5.5.	**17.** $65.5(10)^3$.
3. 1.05.	**8.** 464.9.	**13.** 0.000404.	**18.** $1000.4(10)^{-3}$.
4. 58.397.	**9.** 0.0404.	**14.** 0.0065.	**19.** 0.01(1000).
5. 10.101.	**10.** 404.04.	**15.** 625.26.	**20.** 10(100)0.1.

If log 364 = 2.5611, give
21. log 36,400.   *Ans.* 4.5611.
22. log 36.40.   *Ans.* 1.5611.
23. log 3.640.   *Ans.* 0.5611.
24. log 0.364.   *Ans.* −1. + 0.5611 or 9.5611 − 10.
25. log 0.00364.   *Ans.* −3. + 0.5611 or 7.5611 − 10.

26. log 0.0000364.   **27.** log (3.64)10.
28. log $36.4(10)^4$.   **29.** log $364,000(10)^{-7}$.

Write each of the following logarithms in the form where the decimal part is positive, that is, in a form that can be referred to a table of logarithms.

Illustration: log $x = -2.3456 = -3 + ? = -3 + 0.6544 = 7.6544 - 10$.

$$\begin{array}{r} 10.0000 - 10 \\ 2.3456 \\ \hline 7.6544 - 10. \end{array}$$

30. −2.0345.	**32.** −4.9093.	**34.** −4.4567.	**36.** −0.0456.
31. −0.9462.	**33.** −0.0104.	**35.** −7.0076.	**37.** −9.0000.

If N lies between the numbers as given below, find the characteristic of $\log_{10} N$.
38. $1 \leqq N < 10$.
39. $10 \leqq N < 100$.
40. $0.001 \leqq N < 0.01$.
41. $0.000001 \leqq N < 0.00001$.

346. The Mantissa.—The determination of the mantissa is more difficult than the determination of the characteristic. The mantissa is found from a table of logarithms.

Tables of logarithms are made only by a great deal of labor. They are spoken of as three-place tables, four-place tables, ten-place tables, etc., according to the number of decimal places given in the mantissas. The degree of accuracy in computations made by logarithms depends upon the number of places in the table used, the more places in the table the greater the degree of accuracy. The tables generally used are those having from four to six places.

Upon examining a four-place table of logarithms (see Table X), it is noticed that the first column on a page has the letter N at the top and bottom. This is an abbreviation for number. The other columns have at their tops and bottoms the numbers 0, 1, 2, 3, . . . , 9. Any number consisting of three figures has its first two figures in the column headed N and its third figure at the top or bottom of another column. For instance, take the number 456; 45 is found in the column headed N and 6 at the top of another column.

The columns, after the first, are made up of numbers consisting of four figures. These numbers are decimals and are the mantissas of the logarithms of the numbers made up of the figures in the column headed N together with a figure from the top or bottom of another column.

It will be noticed that the mantissas increase in size as we progress from the beginning of the table.

The difference between two consecutive mantissas is called the **tabular difference,** that is, the table difference.

Thus, at the right of 35 found in the N column, we find 5465 and 5478 in the columns headed 2 and 3, respectively. Then $5478 - 5465 = 13$, the tabular difference. Of course, these are decimals and the tabular difference really is 0.0013.

347. Rules for finding mantissa.—The method of finding the mantissa of the logarithm of a number will be readily mastered if one will make himself realize that the tables are arranged in the simplest manner possible, and will then think through the illustrations in the following examples. Here the illustrations are for a four-place table but they can readily be applied to tables of more places.

(1) *When the number has three significant figures.*

Examples.—Find the mantissa of 463.

From the manner in which the table is formed, the first two digits of 463 are found in the N column and the third digit at the top or bottom of the page. The mantissa of 463 is then read at the right of 46 and in the column headed 3. It is 0.6656. The mantissa of 4.63, 46,300, or any number having these significant figures is 0.6656.

Likewise the mantissa of 7.32 is 0.8645; the mantissa of 928 is 0.9675; and the mantissa of 23,700 is 0.3747.

(2) *When the number has one or two significant figures.*

Examples.—The mantissa of 47 is found at the right of 47 in the N column and in the column headed 0. It is 0.6721.

The mantissa of 6 is found at the right of 60 in the N column and in the column headed 0. It is 0.7782.

Likewise the mantissa of 2.7 is 0.4314; the mantissa of 0.025 is 0.3979; and the mantissa of 8700 is 0.9395.

(3) *When the number has four or more significant figures.*

Example 1.—Find the mantissa of 7586.

Since 7586 lies between 7580 and 7590, its mantissa must lie between the mantissas of 7580 and 7590.

$$\text{Mantissa of } 7580 = 0.8797$$
$$\text{Mantissa of } 7590 = 0.8802$$

The difference between these mantissas is 0.0005, which is the *tabular difference*. Since an increase of 10 in the number increases the mantissa 0.0005, an increase of 6 in the number will increase the mantissa 0.6 as much, or the increase is $0.0005 \times 0.6 = 0.0003$. Hence,

$$\text{Mantissa of } 7586 = 0.8797 + 0.0003 = 0.8800$$

The process of finding the mantissa as here is called **interpolation.** As carried out it is assumed that *the increase in the logarithm is proportional to the increase in the number.*

Example 2.—Find the mantissa of 43,286.

Mantissa of 43,200 = 0.6355
Mantissa of 43,300 = 0.6365

Hence the tabular difference = 0.0010.

Since an increase of 100 in the number increases the mantissa 0.0010, an increase of 86 in the number increases the mantissa 0.0010 × 0.86 = 0.0009 to the nearest fourth decimal place.

Hence, the mantissa of 43,286 = 0.6355 + 0.0009 = 0.6364.

The following rules for finding mantissas give the methods illustrated in the examples:

I. *For a number having three significant figures, find the first two digits of the number in the N column and the third at the head of a column; then read the mantissa at the right of the first two digits and in the column headed by the third digit.*

II. *For a number having one or two significant figures, find the digits in the N column and read the mantissa at the right in the column headed 0.*

III. *For a number having more than three significant figures, find the mantissa for the first three figures by Rule I and add to this the product of the tabular difference by the remaining figures of the number considered as decimals.*

348. Finding the logarithm of a number.—In finding the logarithm of a number, it is best *to determine the characteristic first and then look up the mantissa.* Perform all the interpolations without the use of a pencil if possible.

Example 1.—Find logarithm of 746.
Rule I for characteristic gives 2.
Rule I for mantissa gives 0.8727.

$$\therefore \ \log 746 = 2.8727$$

Example 2.—Find logarithm of 47.26.
Rule I for characteristic gives 1.
Rule III for mantissa gives 0.6745.

$$\therefore \ \log 47.26 = 1.6745$$

Example 3.—Find logarithm of 0.00037.

Rule II for characteristic gives −4.

Rule II for mantissa gives 0.5682.

$$\therefore \log 0.00037 = \bar{4}.5682 \text{ or } 6.5682 - 10$$

EXERCISES

1. Study the following to fix in mind the meaning of logarithms:

log 4580 = 3.6609; that is, 4580 = $10^{3.6609}$.

log 458.0 = 2.6609; that is, 458.0 = $10^{2.6609}$.

log 45.80 = 1.6609; that is, 45.80 = $10^{1.6609}$.

log 4.580 = 0.6609; that is, 4.580 = $10^{0.6609}$.

log 0.4580 = $\bar{1}$.6609; that is, 0.4580 = $10^{\bar{1}.6609}$ = $10^{-1+0.6609}$.

log 0.0458 = $\bar{2}$.6609; that is, 0.0458 = $10^{\bar{2}.6609}$ = $10^{-2+0.6609}$.

log 0.00458 = $\bar{3}$.6609; that is, 0.00458 = $10^{\bar{3}.6609}$ = $10^{-3+0.6609}$.

Verify the following logarithms, using the table where necessary:

2. log 2.71 = 0.4330.

3. log 505 = 2.7033.

4. log 432.3 = 2.6358.

5. log 0.101 = 9.0043 − 10.

6. log 5924 = 3.7726.

7. log 0.01 = 8.0000 − 10.

8. log 0.0001 = $\bar{4}$.0000.

9. log 0.0089 = $\bar{3}$.9494.

10. log 9278 = 3.9674.

11. log 0.00005 = $\bar{5}$.6990.

12. log 271 = 2.4330.

13. log 12.214 = 1.0869.

14. log 1005 = 3.0022.

15. log 0.7854 = 9.8951 − 10.

16. log 52.80 = 1.7226.

17. log 3.1416 = 0.4971.

18. log 1941 = 3.2879.

19. log 0.031 = 8.4914 − 10.

20. log 0.00273 = 7.4362 − 10.

21. log 0.0003 = 6.4771 − 10.

349. To find a number when its logarithm is given.—If log N = L, then N is the number corresponding to the logarithm L. The number N is also called the **antilogarithm** of L and written $N = \log^{-1} L$.

Thus, since log 542 = 2.7340, 542 is the number corresponding to the logarithm 2.7340.

In nearly every problem involving logarithms, it is necessary
not only to find the logarithms of numbers but also to use the
inverse process, that of finding the number corresponding to a
logarithm.

Since the position of the decimal point in a number in no
way affects the mantissa of its logarithm, we should expect
to determine only the sequence of the figures in the number
from the mantissa. And since a change in the position of the
decimal point increases or decreases the characteristic, the
decimal point in the number should be located by knowing
the characteristic. The following examples will illustrate the
methods for finding a number corresponding to a given
logarithm. These illustrations are for a four-place table but
can readily be extended to tables of five or more places.

(1) *When the mantissa of the logarithm is given exactly in the
table.*

Example.—Find the number having 1.5977 for its logarithm.

In the table find the mantissa 0.5977. To the left of this
mantissa, in the *N* column, find the first two figures, 39,
of the number, and at the head of the page find the third
figure, 6. The number then consists of the sequence of figures
396, but we do not know where to place the decimal point
until we consider the characteristic, 1, which shows that
there are two whole number figures.

$$\therefore \ 1.5977 \ = \ \log 39.6, \text{ or } 39.6 \ = \ \log^{-1} 1.5977$$

(2) *When the mantissa of the logarithm is not given exactly
in the table.* In this case, interpolation is necessary to approximate the number.

Example.—Find the number corresponding to the logarithm
3.4689.

Find the mantissas 0.4683 and 0.4698, between which the
given mantissa lies. Thinking only of the sequence of figures
in the numbers,

$$0.4698 = \text{mantissa of log } 295$$
$$\underline{0.4683} = \text{mantissa of log } \underline{294}$$
$$0.0015 \qquad\qquad\qquad 1$$

That is, an increase in the mantissa of 0.0015 makes an increase of 1 in the corresponding number. The given mantissa is 0.0006 larger than the mantissa 0.4683. Then the required number is $\dfrac{0.0006}{0.0015} \times 1 = 0.4$ larger than 294. Hence the sequence of figure is 2944.

$$\therefore \; 3.4689 = \log 2944$$

For convenience, in dealing with the tabular difference, it is best to drop the decimal point. Then the foregoing would be $\frac{6}{15} \times 1 = 0.4$. In working with a four-place table, *restrict the number of significant figures to four.*

The methods illustrated in the preceding examples are stated in the following rules:

I. *When the mantissa of the given logarithm is found exactly in the table, the first two figures of the number are found to the left of the mantissa in the N column, and the third figure is at the head of the column in which the mantissa is found.*

II. *When the mantissa of the given logarithm is not found exactly in the table, find the mantissa nearest the given mantissa but smaller. The first three figures of the number are those corresponding to this mantissa and are found by Rule I. For another figure, divide the difference between the mantissa found and the given mantissa by the tabular difference.*

In both I and II, place the decimal point so that when the rules for determining the characteristic are applied, they produce the characteristic of the original logarithm.

Example.—Find the number whose logarithm is 1.7624.

Mantissa nearest 0.7624 is 0.7619 = mantissa of log 578.

Tabular difference = 8.

Difference between mantissas = 5.

$$5 \div 8 = 0.6 \text{ to nearest tenth}$$
$$\therefore \; 1.7624 = \log 57.86.$$

The interpolation should always be done without a pencil if possible.

EXERCISES

Verify the following:

1. 0.0000 = log 1.
2. 0.3010 = log 2.
3. 0.4771 = log 3.
4. 0.6990 = log 5.
5. 0.8451 = log 7.
6. 1.7882 = log 61.4.
7. 2.8601 = log 724.6.
8. 1.6304 = log 42.7.

9. 1.3762 = log 23.78.
10. 9.9525 − 10 = log 0.8964.
11. 8.4683 − 10 = log 0.0294.
12. 7.5894 − 10 = log 0.003885.
13. 7.5156 − 10 = log 0.003278.
14. $\overline{5}$.6399 = log 0.000043641.
15. $\overline{1}$.6028 = log 0.4007.
16. $\overline{2}$.8840 = log 0.076553.

Find the value of x in the following:
17. log x = 9.3424 − 10.   *Ans.* 0.220.
18. log x = 2.3444.   *Ans.* 221.
19. log x = 8.3493 − 10.   *Ans.* 0.02236−.
20. log $10N$ = x, N = 1, 2, 3. . . .
21. log $\dfrac{1}{10N}$ = x, N = 1, 2, 3. . . .
22. $\log^{-1}$ 0.9200 = x.   *Ans.* 8.318.
23. $\log^{-1}$ 6.0917 = x.
24. $\log^{-1}$ $\overline{3}$.5032 = x.   *Ans.* 0.003186.

COMPUTATIONS BY LOGARITHMS

350. To multiply by means of logarithms.—The law of exponents in multiplication, $a^n \cdot a^m = a^{n+m}$, gives the following:

RULE.—*To find the product of two or more factors, find the sum of the logarithms of the factors; the product is the number corresponding to this sum.*

Example 1.—Find the product of 4.53 × 0.036 × 68.42.

$$
\begin{aligned}
\log\ 4.53 &=\ 0.6561 \\
\log 0.036 &=\ 8.5563 - 10 \\
\log 68.42 &=\ \underline{1.8352} \\
\log \text{ of product} &=\ \overline{1.0476} \\
\text{product} &=\ 11.16
\end{aligned}
$$

That this is an application of the law of exponents in multiplication is seen from the following form:

$$4.53 = 10^{0.6561}, \ 0.036 = 10^{\bar{2}.5563}, \ 68.42 = 10^{1.8352}$$
$$\therefore \ 4.53 \times 0.036 \times 68.42 = 10^{0.6561} \times 10^{\bar{2}.5563} \times 10^{1.8352}$$
$$= 10^{0.6561 + \bar{2}.5563 + 1.8352}$$
$$= 10^{1.0476} = 11.16$$

Example 2.—Find product of $3.276 \times (-4.624) \times (-0.00468)$.

$$
\begin{aligned}
\log 3.276 &= 0.5153 \\
\log 4.624 &= 0.6650n \\
\log 0.00468 &= \bar{3}.6702n \\
\log \text{ of product} &= \bar{2}.8505 \\
\text{product} &= 0.07088 \quad .
\end{aligned}
$$

NOTE.—Since the logarithms cannot take into account the negative numbers, an easy way to keep account of the negative factors is to place a letter n after their logarithms. In finding a sum or difference of logarithms, write an n after the result only if the number of the several logarithms followed by an n is odd. This method was introduced by the mathematician Gauss (1777–1855).

351. To divide by means of logarithms.—The law of exponents in division, $a^n \div a^m = a^{n-m}$, gives the following:

RULE.—*To find the quotient of two numbers, subtract the logarithm of the divisor from the logarithm of the dividend; the quotient is the number corresponding to this difference.*

Example 1.—Divide 38.76 by 7.923.

$$
\begin{aligned}
\log 38.76 &= 1.5884 \\
\log 7.923 &= 0.8989 \\
\log \text{ of quotient} &= 0.6895 \\
\text{quotient} &= 4.892
\end{aligned}
$$

Example 2.—Evaluate $\dfrac{9.337 \times 0.876 \times 6.458}{4.756 \times 389.2 \times 0.0456}$.

$$\log 9.337 = 0.9702$$
$$\log 0.876 = 9.9425 - 10$$
$$\log 6.458 = \underline{0.8101}$$
$$\log \text{ of numerator} = 1.7228$$
$$\log 4.756 = 0.6772$$
$$\log 389.2 = 2.5901$$
$$\log 0.0456 = \underline{8.6590 - 10}$$
$$\log \text{ of denominator} = 1.9263$$
$$\log \text{ of quotient} = \log \text{ of numerator} - \log \text{ of denominator}$$
$$= 9.7965 - 10$$
$$\text{quotient} = 0.6259$$

EXERCISES

Multiply the following by logarithms, and check by actual multiplication:

1. 10×100.

2. 100×64.

3. 25×500.

4. 0.1×200.

5. 0.02×50.

6. 0.005×6.

7. 4.56×11.

8. 0.841×66.6.

9. 0.0075×0.12.

10. 32.32×1002.

11. 845.9×9.287.

12. 1034×0.02406.

Divide the following by logarithms, and check by actual division:

13. $10 \div 100$.

14. $100 \div 10$.

15. $200 \div 25$.

16. $225 \div 15$.

17. $0.05 \div 25$.

18. $0.0064 \div 400$.

19. $5280 \div 12$.

20. $3.1416 \div 40$.

21. $0.15 \div 0.30$.

22. $0.1008 \div 0.8001$.

23. $1.414 \div 7000$.

24. $70 \div 1.4146$.

Evaluate the following by use of logarithms:

25. $\dfrac{23.7 \times 1.42}{1.093}$. *Ans.* $30.79-$.

26. $\dfrac{12.4 \times 5.76}{0.798}$. *Ans.* 89.5.

27. $\dfrac{2.13 \times 43.2}{1.67 \times 48.9}$. *Ans.* $1.127-$.

28. $\dfrac{0.06547 \times 1000}{0.05938 \times 74.938 \times 100}$. *Ans.* 0.1471+.

29. $\dfrac{0.03467 \times 46.57}{39.08 \times 0.07189}$. *Ans.* 0.5746+.

30. $\dfrac{93.14 \times 1.414 \times 1.732}{12 \times 2.718 \times 60}$. *Ans.* 0.1165−.

352. To find the power of a number by logarithms.—The law of exponents, $(a^n)^m = a^{nm}$, gives the following:

RULE.—*To find the power of a number, multiply the logarithm of the number by the exponent of the power. This gives the logarithm of the power. The number corresponding to this logarithm is the required power.*

Example 1.—Find the value of $(1.756)^7$.

$$\log 1.756 = 0.2445$$
$$7 \times \log 1.756 = 1.7115 = \log (1.756)^7$$
$$\therefore (1.756)^7 = 51.46$$

Example 2.—Find the value of $(9.876)^{\frac{3}{4}}$.

$$\log 9.876 = 0.9946$$
$$\tfrac{3}{4} \times \log 9.876 = 0.7460 = \log (9.876)^{\frac{3}{4}}$$
$$\therefore (9.876)^{\frac{3}{4}} = 5.571$$

353. To find the root of a number by logarithms.—From the definitions of exponents we have $\sqrt[m]{a^n} = a^{\frac{n}{m}}$, which gives the following:

RULE.—*To find the root of a number, divide the logarithm of the number by the index of the root. This gives the logarithm of the root. The number corresponding to this logarithm is the required root.*

Example 1.—Evaluate $\sqrt[5]{237.68}$.

$$\log 237.68 = 2.3760$$
$$\tfrac{1}{5} \text{ of } \log 237.68 = 0.4752 = \log \sqrt[5]{237.68}$$
$$\therefore \sqrt[5]{237.68} = 2.987$$

Example 2.—Evaluate $\sqrt[6]{0.008673}$.

$$\log 0.008673 = 7.9382 - 10$$
$$\log \sqrt[6]{0.008673} = \tfrac{1}{6} \text{ of } (7.9382 - 10)$$
$$= \tfrac{1}{6} \text{ of } (57.9382 - 60)$$
$$= 9.6564 - 10$$
$$\therefore \sqrt[6]{0.008673} = 0.4533$$

NOTE.—When a logarithm with a negative characteristic is to be divided by a number not exactly contained in the characteristic, it is best first to add and subtract such a multiple of 10 that, after dividing, there will be a minus 10 at the right. In Example 2, before dividing (7.9382 − 10) by 6, 50 was added and subtracted. If, however, the divisor had been 3, the division could have been performed by writing the logarithm in the form $\overline{3}.9382$ and dividing at once by 3.

EXERCISES

Evaluate the following by use of logarithms:

1. $(3.1416)^2$. *Ans.* 9.868.

2. $(0.707)^3$. *Ans.* 0.3533.

3. $(0.886)^2$. *Ans.* 0.7848.

4. $(1.732)^5$. *Ans.* 15.58.

5. $(\tfrac{22}{7})^2$. *Ans.* 9.876.

6. $\sqrt{5288}$. *Ans.* 72.72.

7. $\sqrt{0.224}$. *Ans.* 0.4732.

8. $\sqrt[3]{0.0025}$. *Ans.* 0.1357.

9. $\sqrt[4]{1.014}$. *Ans.* 1.003.

10. $\sqrt[3]{0.00027}$. *Ans.* 0.0646.

11. $(4.4)^{\frac{3}{4}}$. *Ans.* 3.038.

12. $(0.059)^{\frac{2}{3}}$. *Ans.* 0.1516.

13. $(958)^{0.2}$. *Ans.* 3.947.

14. $(803.5)^{-0.11}$. *Ans.* 0.4791.

15. $(296)^{-6.1}$. *Ans.* $8.42(10^{-16})$.

16. $\sqrt[n]{2}$, $n = 1, 2, 3, 4, 5, \ldots$

17. $\sqrt[r]{r}$, $r = 2, 3, 4, 5, \ldots$

354. Natural logarithms.—Although in making computations, logarithms to the base 10 are almost always used, there are many formulas in electricity, physics, chemistry, and other sciences in which another base occurs. This base is a number that cannot be exactly expressed by figures. To seven decimal places it is 2.7182818. It is usually represented by the letter e, just as the ratio of the circumference of a circle to its diameter is represented by the Greek letter π.   Logarithms to this base are called **natural logarithms, hyperbolic logarithms,** or **Napierian logarithms.**

Tables of natural logarithms are published; but for purposes of computation, it is necessary to remember only that the natural logarithm of a number is approximately 2.3026 times the common logarithm of the same number.   Or the common logarithm of a number is 0.4343 times the natural logarithm.

The relations between common logarithms and natural logarithms are stated in the following formulas, where N is any number:

$$\log_e N = 2.3026 \log_{10} N$$
$$\log_{10} N = 0.4343 \log_e N$$

Thus,

$$\log_e 100 = 2.3026 \log_{10} 100$$
$$= 2.3026 \times 2 = 4.6052$$

The following examples give actual formulas in which logarithms to the base e occur:

Example 1.—In finding the insulation resistance by the leakage method, the resistance R is found from the formula

$$R = 10^6 \cdot \frac{t}{C} \cdot \frac{1}{\log_e \left(\dfrac{V_0}{V} \right)}$$

where

t = the time in seconds.

C = the capacity.

V = the voltage.

Compute the value of R if $t = 120$, $V_0 = 123$, $V = 115.8$, and $C = 0.082$.

Solution.—In order that we may use the table of common logarithms, the formula may be written

$$R = 10^6 \cdot \frac{t}{C} \cdot \frac{1}{2.3026 \log_{10} \left(\dfrac{V_0}{V} \right)}$$

Substituting values,

$$R = 10^6 \times \frac{120}{0.082} \times \frac{1}{2.3026(\log 123 - \log 115.8)}$$

$$\therefore R = 2.426 \times 10^{10}$$

As another example where the base of the natural system of logarithms occurs, consider the following:

Example 2.—In an alternating-current circuit, the current i at any instant is given by the formula

$$i = I \left(1 - e^{-\frac{Rt}{L}}\right)$$

where

I = the maximum current.

R = the resistance.

L = the coefficient of self-induction.

t = the time in seconds.

e = the base of the natural system of logarithms.

Example 3.—The work W done by a volume of gas, expanding at a constant temperature from a volume V_0 to a volume V_1, is given by the following formula:

$$W = p_0 V_0 \log_e \left(\frac{V_1}{V_0}\right)$$

355. Suggestions on computing by logarithms.—In computing by means of logarithms, accuracy is of the utmost importance. In all interpolations, do the computations the second time to avoid errors.

In interpolating, do not carry logarithms beyond the number of decimal places given in the table used.

The results obtained by means of logarithms are approximate and are correct to about as many significant figures as the number of places in the table used. A table should be used that will give the desired number of significant figures.

In writing numbers correct to a certain number of figures, take as the last figure the one nearest the true result when this is possible.   If the next figure after the last one to be taken is 5 followed only by zeros, most computers take the nearest even figure for the last one.   Thus, if the number is 0.02467500, it would be taken 0.02468 to four figures; and if 0.02468500, it would also be taken 0.02468.

In working with tables, use the pencil as little as possible. Work for accuracy first and then for speed.

Write out a scheme for all logarithmic work before referring to the table.   Be sure that your work is arranged so that it could be followed at any time by yourself or another person.

Example.—Write out a scheme for finding the value of x in

$$x = \frac{9.46 \times (4.16)^2 \times \sqrt{9.462}}{276.2 \times 3.4675}$$

$$\log x = (\log 9.46 + 2 \log 4.16 + \tfrac{1}{2} \log 9.462) -$$
$$(\log 276.2 + \log 3.4675)$$

$$= \log \text{numerator} - \log \text{denominator}$$
$$\log 9.46 =$$
$$2 \log 41.6 =$$
$$\tfrac{1}{2} \log 9.462 = \underline{\hspace{2cm}}$$
$$\log \text{of numerator} =$$
$$\log 276.2 =$$
$$\log 3.4675 = \underline{\hspace{2cm}}$$
$$\log \text{of denominator} =$$
$$\log \text{of numerator} =$$
$$\log \text{of denominator} = \underline{\hspace{2cm}}$$
$$\log x =$$
$$x =$$

EXERCISES

Solve the following by logarithms:

1. A man drives his car 417 miles in one day.   If he averages 15.8 miles per gallon of gas and pays 16.6 cents per gallon, find his daily expense for gas.   *Ans.* $4.38.

2. On the day that his son was born, a man placed $873.50 at compound interest at 3.5%.   On the son's twenty-first birthday how much would the original deposit be worth? Use $A = P(1 + r)^n$. Also solve with a five-place table. (See Exercise 25, Art. 356.) *Ans.* $1795.

3. A factory employs 3562 people at $0.66 per hour for 8 hr. per day for $5\frac{1}{2}$ days per week. What was the factory's weekly pay roll? NOTE. —Five-place tables would be better here. *Ans.* $103,440.48.

4. Find the radius of the inscribed circle of a triangle whose sides are $a = 3.41$, $b = 2.60$, $c = 1.58$, if

$$r = \sqrt{\frac{(s - a)(s - b)(s - c)}{s}}, \quad 2s = a + b + c \quad Ans. \ 0.5182.$$

5. It is estimated that the United States will spend 15 billion dollars for the year 1941. How much would this average per person if there are 150 million people in the United States and possessions.

6. $\dfrac{585 \times 79.9 \times 0.063}{1.56 \times 4580 \times 0.029}$. *Ans.* 14.21.

7. $\dfrac{0.654 \times 0.004683 \times 192,700}{0.0329 \times 10.28 \times 162.4}$. *Ans.* 10.74.

8. $\sqrt{687 \times 3274 \times 0.0325}$. *Ans.* 270.4.

9. $(5.235)^3$. *Ans.* 143.5.

10. $(-0.09337) \times 23.6$. *Ans.* -2.204.

11. $(-23.74) \times (-8.143)$. *Ans.* 193.4.

12. $(-8.271) \div 3.142$. *Ans.* -2.633.

13. $3.249 \times 8.342 \div (-246.7)$. *Ans.* -0.1099.

14. $0.8764 \times (-0.0439) \div (-8.273)$. *Ans.* 4.65×10^{-3}).

15. $0.9286 \times 10^7 \div (-9567)$. *Ans.* -970.5.

16. $\dfrac{100^2}{49 \times 64 \times 11}$. *Ans.* 0.2959.

17. $\dfrac{52^2 \times 300}{12 \times 0.31225 \times 400,000}$. *Ans.* 0.5411.

18. $\sqrt{\dfrac{400}{55 \times 3.1416}}$. *Ans.* 1.522.

19. $-(7)^{-\frac{1}{3}}(8)^{\frac{1}{2}}$. *Ans.* -0.1479.

20. $50 \times \dfrac{2^{1.5}}{8^{1.63}}$. *Ans.* 4.769.

21. $\left(\dfrac{6.89}{0.009}\right)^{\frac{1}{3}}$. *Ans.* 9.148.

22. $\left(\dfrac{7.1 \times 0.09}{0.123}\right)^{\frac{4}{5}}$. *Ans.* 3.737.

23. $\left(\dfrac{4.56}{0.025}\right)^{\frac{2}{3}}$. *Ans.* 32.16.

24. $\left(\dfrac{211 \times 0.07}{0.054}\right)^{\frac{1}{5}}$. *Ans.* 3.072.

25. $\left(\dfrac{31.4 \times 5.2}{7.8 \times 0.091}\right)^{\frac{1}{3}}$. *Ans.* 1410.

26. $\sqrt{\dfrac{0.434 \times 96^4}{64 \times 1500}}$. *Ans.* 19.60.

27. $\sqrt{\dfrac{3500}{(1.06)^5}}$. *Ans.* 51.14.

28. $\dfrac{3.8961 \times 0.6945 \times 0.01382}{4694 \times 0.00457}$. *Ans.* 0.001743.

29. $\sqrt[4]{0.0009657} \div \sqrt[3]{0.0044784}$. *Ans.* 1.070.

30. $\left(\dfrac{7.61 \times 0.0593}{1.307}\right)^{\frac{3}{4}}$. *Ans.* 0.4504.

31. $\sqrt[8]{5106.5 \times 0.00003109}$. *Ans.* 0.7945.

32. $\left(\dfrac{4400}{69.37}\right)^{\frac{2}{3}}$. *Ans.* 5.259.

33. $(837.5 \times 0.0094325)^{\frac{2}{3}}$. *Ans.* 1.805.

34. $(0.01)^{\frac{3}{2}} \div \sqrt[3]{7}$. *Ans.* 0.0005228.

35. $\dfrac{0.0005616 \times \sqrt[7]{424.65}}{(6.73)^4 \times (0.03194)^{\frac{3}{8}}}$. *Ans.* 0.00001146.

36. $\dfrac{\sqrt{3929} \times \sqrt[4]{6548}}{\sqrt[6]{721.83}}$. *Ans.* 188.2

37. $\dfrac{\sqrt[5]{0.05287}}{\sqrt[3]{0.374} \times \sqrt[9]{0.078359}}$. *Ans.* 1.023.

38. $\left[\left(\dfrac{0.42 \times 21.3}{2.34 \times 2.09}\right)^{\frac{3}{2}}\right]^{\frac{2}{5}}$. *Ans.* 2.064.

39. $\dfrac{\sqrt{3} \times \sqrt{7} \times \sqrt{1.1}}{\sqrt[3]{0.024}}$. *Ans.* 16.66.

40. $\dfrac{\sqrt{2} \times 2\sqrt{3}}{8.4 \times 2.13}$. *Ans.* 0.2738.

41. $\dfrac{\sqrt{5} \times \sqrt{12.5}}{7.2 \times \sqrt{3.26}}$. *Ans.* 0.6082.

42. $4.2^{0.12} \times 3.9^{0.16}$. *Ans.* 1.477.

43. $36^{7.2} \times 9.3^{3.9}$. *Ans.* $96.05(10)^{13}$.

44. $9.4^{4.9} \div 4.9^{9.4}$. *Ans.* 0.01907.

45. $\left[\left(\dfrac{24^{0.5} - 2\sqrt{3}}{729}\right)^{\frac{1}{5}}\right]^{\frac{2}{3}}$. *Ans.* 0.1542.

NOTE.—Find the value of $24^{0.5}$ and $2\sqrt{3}$ as two separate exercises; then substitute the difference of these two values in the exercise and continue as for all the preceding problems.

356. Actual formulas and logarithms.—The following list of exercises involves formulas actually occurring in various fields of endeavor. Such selections as desired can be made from these. Some of the exercises will review ideas previously discussed in proportion and variation; others require the solution of equations. Logarithms should be used when they can be employed to advantage.

EXERCISES

1. How long will it take money to double if the compound interest rate is 3 % annually? Use $2 = 1(1.03)^n$.   *Ans.* 23+ years.

2. The most economical proportions for a tin can with a given capacity, making allowance for waste, is given by the formula: height $= \dfrac{2\sqrt{3}}{\pi}$ times the diameter of the base, or

$$H = (2\sqrt{3} \div \pi)D$$

(1) Find H if D = one unit.   *Ans.* 1.103.
(2) Find D if H = one unit.   *Ans.* 0.907.

3. Cylindrical steam boilers are to be constructed having a given capacity of V cu. ft. If the material for the sides costs $2 per square foot and for the ends $3 per square foot, the most economical proportions are given by the formula

$$R = \sqrt[3]{\frac{V}{3\pi}} \quad (R \text{ is the radius of the base})$$

(1) Find R if $V = 1$ qt. (231 cu. in. in 1 gal.)   *Ans.* 1.83 in.
(2) Find V if $R = 2$ in.   *Ans.* 75.4 cu. in.
(3) Find the height H in (1) and (2) if $V = \pi R^2 H$.

     Ans. 5.49 in.; 6 in.

4. For $6350 cash an FHA approved house can be bought. The buyer agrees to pay $39.60 per month. If the rate of interest is 0.4 % per month, how many years will it take to pay for the house? Use the formula

$$n = \frac{\log R - \log (R - Ar)}{\log (1 + r)}$$

where
A = the cash value of the house.
r = the rate per cent per month.
n = the number of months.
R = the amount of each monthly payment.

     Ans. 21 years, 10 months.

5. A loan company will lend $100 cash. It is to be paid back in 20 months at $6.43 per month. Find the annual rate of interest. Twelve times the monthly rate is approximately correct. Use the formula given in Exercise 4. Solve by choosing r as 1%, 2%, 3%, . . . until an approximate result is found.

6. Given $W = 0.0033 \times 10^{-7}n$, find W when $n = 75,000$.

Ans. 0.00002475.

7. If E = E. M. F. in volts in moving conductor, L = length of conductor in centimeters, V = velocity in centimeters per second, B = the number of lines of force per square centimeter, we have the formula $E = LVB10^{-8}$. Given $V = \dfrac{9 \times 100}{60}$, $B = 8000$, and $L = 0.6 \times 100$, find E.

Ans. 0.0720.

8. Find the value of P from the formula

$$P = \sqrt[3]{\frac{ABC}{1.4\left(B + \dfrac{A^2}{C^2}\right)}}$$

when $A = 11$, $B = 1.71$, and $C = 1.3$. *Ans.* 0.6199.

Suggestion.—First find the logarithm of the expression under the radical, and then divide by 3. This will give the log P.

9. In measuring electrical resistance by a Wheatstone's bridge, the following data were taken:

(1) $R = 8$, $a_1 = 539.7$, $a_2 = 459$.
(2) $R = 9$, $a_1 = 510.1$, $a_2 = 488.4$.

Find the values of x from (1) and (2) by the formula

$$\frac{x}{R} = \frac{1000 + (a_1 - a_2)}{1000 - (a_1 - a_2)} \qquad Ans.\ 9.404;\ 9.400.$$

10. In finding the diameter of a wrought-iron shaft that will transmit 90 hp. when the number of revolutions is 100 per minute, using a factor of safety of 8, we have to find the diameter d from the formula

$$d = 68.5 \sqrt[3]{\frac{90}{100 \times \dfrac{50,000}{8}}}$$

Find d. *Ans.* 3.591.

11. Find the value of M from the formula

$$M = \frac{Wgl^3}{4bd^3B}$$

when $g = 980$, $W = 75$, $l = 50$, $b = 0.98178$, $d = 0.5680$, and $B = 0.01093$.

Solution

log W	=	1.8751	log 4	= 0.6021
log g	=	2.9912	log b	= $\overline{1}$.9920
log l^3	=	5.0970	log d^3	= $\overline{1}$.2629
log numerator	=	9.9633	log B	= $\overline{2}$.0386
log denominator	=	$\overline{3}$.8956	log denominator	= $\overline{3}$.8956
log M	=	12.0677		

$$\therefore M = 1{,}169{,}000{,}000{,}000 = 11.69 \times 10^{11}$$

12. Find the value of n from the formula

$$n = \frac{360Lmgl}{\pi^2\theta r^4}$$

when $g = 980$, $l = 28$, $\theta = 0.857$, $r = 0.477$, $L = 109.7$, and $m = 100$.
Ans. 24.76×10^{10}.

13. Use the same formula as in Exercise 12, and find the value of n when $L = 69.6$, $m = 10$, $g = 980$, $l = 28$, $\theta = 1.1955$, and $r = 0.317$.
Ans. 5.77×10^{10}.

14. If $m = ar^{-1.16}$, find r when $m = 2.263$ and $a = 0.4086$.

Solution.—Solving for r, we have

$$r = \sqrt[1.16]{\frac{a}{m}} = \left(\frac{a}{m}\right)^{\frac{1}{1.16}} = \left(\frac{a}{m}\right)^{0.862}$$

$$\text{log } a = \overline{1}.6113$$
$$\text{log } m = 0.3547$$
$$\text{log } \frac{a}{m} = \overline{1}.2566$$

It is now best to unite the characteristic and mantissa by algebraic addition.
Thus,

$$\overline{1}.2566 = -1 + 0.2566 = -0.7434$$

Now multiply by the exponent 0.862, and we get

$$-0.7434 \times 0.862 = -0.6408$$

This is next changed to the form of a logarithm as given in the table, that is, to a form where the mantissa is not negative.

$$-0.6408 = \overline{1}.3592.$$
$$\therefore \text{log } \left(\frac{a}{m}\right)^{0.862} = \overline{1}.3592$$
$$\therefore \left(\frac{a}{m}\right)^{0.862} = 0.2287$$

15. Given

$$p = p_0 \left(\frac{2}{\gamma + 1} \right)^{\frac{\gamma}{\gamma - 1}}$$

find the value of p in terms of p_0 if $\gamma = 1.41$. *Ans. $p = 5.27p_0$.*

16. Evaluate $\sqrt{\dfrac{s(s - b)(s - c)}{s - a}}$, where $2s = a + b + c$ and $a = 47.236$, $b = 82.798$, and $c = 75.643$. *Ans. 31.75.*

17. Evaluate $\sqrt{s(s - a)(s - b)(s - c)}$, where $2s = a + b + c$ and $a = 4.2763$, $b = 9.9264$, and $c = 8.4399$. *Ans. 17.90.*

18. The work W done by a volume of gas, expanding at a constant temperature from volume V_0 to a volume V_1, is given by the formula

$$W = p_0 V_0 \log_e \left(\frac{V_1}{V_0} \right)$$

Find the value of W if $p_0 = 87.5$, $V_0 = 246$, and $V_1 = 472$.

Ans. 14,030.

19. If an open tank kept full of water has a rectangular notch cut on one side, as shown in Fig. 261, the number of cubic feet of water that will

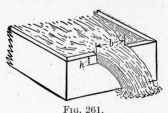

Fig. 261.

flow through this notch per second is given by the formula

$$Q = \tfrac{2}{3} c b h^{\frac{3}{2}} \sqrt{2g}$$

where

Q = the amount of flow in cubic feet.

c = a constant found by experiment.

b = the width of the notch in feet.

h = the depth of the notch in feet.

$g = 32.2$.

Find Q when $h = 1\frac{1}{3}$, $b = 2$, and $c = 0.586$. *Ans. 9.654.*

20. Using the formula of the preceding exercise, find Q when $h = \frac{5}{6}$, $b = 2.5$, and $c = 0.589$.

21. If Q is the number of cubic feet that will flow through a V-shaped notch per second and h the height in feet of the water above the bottom of the notch, then $Q \propto h^{\frac{3}{2}}$. If $Q = 7.26$ when $h = 1.5$, find h when $Q = 5.68$.

Suggestion.—If $Q \propto h^{\frac{3}{2}}$, then $Q = Kh^{\frac{3}{2}}$.

Substituting values,

$$7.26 = K1.5^{\frac{3}{2}}$$
$$\therefore K = 7.26 \div 1.5^{\frac{3}{2}}$$

Using this value of K with $Q = 5.68$, gives

$$5.68 = (7.26 \div 1.5^{\frac{3}{2}})h^{\frac{3}{2}}$$
$$\therefore h^{\frac{3}{2}} = \frac{5.68 \times 1.5^{\frac{3}{2}}}{7.26}$$

22. The following is an approximate formula for determining the number of wires that can be enclosed in a pipe.

$$N = 0.907 \left(\frac{D}{d} - 0.94\right)^2 + 3.7$$

where

$N =$ the number of wires.

$D =$ the diameter of the enclosing pipe.

$d =$ the diameter of the wires.

Solve this formula for D, and find

$$D = d \left(0.94 + \sqrt{\frac{N - 3.7}{0.907}}\right)$$

23. Use the formula of the preceding exercise, and find the diameter of a casing to hold 100 wires each having a diameter of $\frac{1}{8}$ in.

24. The amount of a principal at compound interest for a certain time is given by the following formula

$$A = P(1 + r)^n$$

where

$A =$ the amount.

$P =$ the principal.

$r =$ the rate per cent.

$n =$ the time in years.

Find the amount of \$236 at compound interest for 14 years at 3 %.

Ans. \$356.50.

25. Find the amount of \$3764 at compound interest for 21 years at $4\frac{1}{2}$ %. *Ans.* \$9478.

Note.—It should be noted that in such problems as those of Exercises 24, 25, and the following, a four-place table of logarithms will not give results that can be relied upon when the exponent is large. For instance, if Exercise 24 is computed by a six-place table of logarithms, the amount is \$356.97, and that of Exercise 25 is \$9486.07. Of course, all that is necessary to secure a desired degree of accuracy is to use a table of logarithms that has a sufficiently large number of decimal places. In life insurance computations a ten-place table is used.

26. In biology where the science of heredity is studied the important formula

$$y = \frac{e^{-x^2}}{\sqrt{\pi}}$$

is fundamental. Solve this formula for x.

$$Ans.\ x^2 = -\left(\frac{\log y + \frac{1}{2}\log \pi}{\log e}\right).$$

27. In the theory of machine designing the formula

$$\frac{P}{A} = \frac{\pi E}{\left(\frac{l}{r}\right)^2}$$

is important. Solve this formula for $\log r$.

$$Ans.\ \frac{\log P - \log A - \log E - \log \pi + 2 \log l}{2}.$$

28. In computing shearing stress the formula

$$d = 4 \sqrt[3]{\frac{h}{N}}$$

is used. Solve this formula for $\log N$.

$$Ans.\ 3(\log 4 - \log d) + \log h.$$

29. Find the radius of a sphere that contains 5263 cu. ft.

$$Ans.\ 10.79\ \text{ft.}$$

Suggestion.—Take the formula for the volume of a sphere

$$V = \tfrac{4}{3}\pi r^3$$

and solve it for r. This gives

$$r = \sqrt[3]{\frac{3V}{4\pi}}$$

30. In the equation $y = \log x$, find the values of y corresponding to the values 0.5, 1, 2, 5, 10, 25, 50, and 100 of x. Choose a pair of coordinate axes, and plot these pairs of points. This will give a curve that shows the relation between a number and its logarithm. (It will be best to choose a unit on the y-axis five or ten times the length of the unit on the x-axis.)

31. If the mixture in a gas engine expands without gain or loss of heat, it is found that the law of expansion is given by the equation $pv^{1.37} = C$. Given that $p = 188.2$ when $v = 11$, find the value of C, then plot the curve of the equation using this value of C. This curve shows the pressure at any volume as the gas expands. Consider values of v from 11 to 23.

Solution.—Given $pv^{1.37} = C$.

Substituting $p = 188.2$ and $v = 11$ gives $C = 188.2 \times 11^{1.37}$.

Computing by logarithms,

$$
\begin{aligned}
\log 188.2 &= 2.2747 \\
1.37 \log 11 &= 1.4267 \\
\log C &= 3.7014 \\
C &= 5028
\end{aligned}
$$

The formula is then $pv^{1.37} = 5028$.

$$\therefore p = \frac{5028}{v^{1.37}}$$

Now choose, say, six values of v, as given in the table, from 11 to 23 and compute the corresponding values of p.

v	11	13	15	17	20	23
p	188.2	149.7	123.1	103.7	82.98	68.53

These values are plotted in Fig. 262, and a smooth curve is drawn through the points. From this curve any value of p corresponding to values of v from 11 to 23 can be read. Such curves when accurately plotted are of great value in engineering.

32. D is the diameter of a wrought-iron shaft to transmit an indicated horsepower H at N R. P. M. Given

$$D = \sqrt[3]{\frac{65H}{N}}$$

plot a curve showing the relation between D and H, from $H = 10$ to $H = 80$, when N is 100 R. P. M. From the curve find the diameters for horsepowers 35, 47, and 72.

33. The tractive power of a locomotive is found by the formula

$$T = \frac{D^2 PL}{W}$$

where

D = the diameter of the cylinder in inches.

P = the mean pressure of the steam in the cylinder in pounds per square inch

L = the length of the piston stroke in inches.

W = the diameter of the driving wheel in inches.

T = the tractive force upon the rails in pounds.

Find the tractive force for the following data:
(1) $D = 16$ in., $P = 90$ lb., $L = 45$ in., $W = 78$ in.;
(2) $D = 20$ in., $P = 100$ lb., $L = 54$ in., $W = 84$ in.

Ans. 13,290 lb.; 25,710 lb.

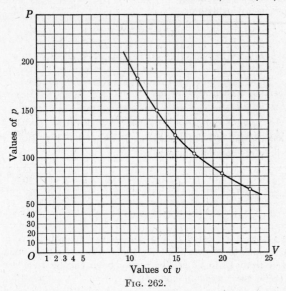

Fig. 262.

34. To find the weight that a column of soft steel, with square bearings, will support per square inch of cross section we use the following formula:

$$P = \frac{45,000}{1 + \frac{(12L)^2}{36,000r^2}}$$

where
P = the weight in pounds.
L = the length in feet.
r = the radius of gyration in inches.

Find P if $\dfrac{L}{r} = 5$.   *Ans.* 40,910 lb.

Suggestion.—$P = \dfrac{45,000}{1 + \dfrac{(12L)^2}{36,000r^2}} = \dfrac{45,000}{1 + \dfrac{144}{36,000}\left(\dfrac{L}{r}\right)^2} = \dfrac{45,000}{1 + \dfrac{144 \times 5^2}{36,000}}.$

35. In a column that is solid and circular in cross section, $r = \dfrac{d}{4}$, where d is the diameter of the cross section in inches. Find the weight that such a column of soft steel will support per square inch of cross section if $L = 16$ ft. and $d = 6$ in. Find the total weight that this column will support. *Ans.* 30,920 lb.; 874,400 lb.

36. In a hollow cylindrical column,

$$r = \frac{\sqrt{d^2 + d_1^2}}{4}$$

where d and d_1 are the outer and inner diameters of the column, respectively, in inches. Find the weight that the column in the preceding exercise will support per square inch of cross section and the total, if it is hollow and the shell is 1 in. thick. *Ans.* 34,200 lb.; 537,500 lb.

37. For a column whose cross section is a regular hexagon, $r = 0.264d$, where d is the diameter of the circle inscribed in the hexagon. Find the weight that a solid hexagonal pillar of soft steel and square bearings will support if the length is 12 ft. and the edge of the base is 2 in.

Ans. 276,900 lb.

NOTE.—The safe load for the preceding columns is one-fourth or one-fifth of the value given. The formula used is Gordon's formula. For medium steel the 45,000 of the formula is changed to 50,000.

38. In any class of turbine, P is power of the waterfall; H, the height of the fall; and n, the rate of revolution. It is known that for a particular class of turbines of all sizes, $n \propto H^{1.25} P^{-0.5}$. In the list of a certain maker, when the fall equals 6 ft. and horsepower 100, the number of R. P. M. is 50. Calculate n for a fall of 20 ft. and 75 hp.

Ans. 260 approx.

39. In transmitting power by means of a belt and pulley, if the belt embraces 180° of the pulley, the number of horsepower transmitted is given by the formula

$$H = \frac{tws}{33,000}$$

where

H = the horsepower.

t = the tension in pounds per inch width of belt.

w = the width of belt in inches.

s = the speed of belt in feet per minute.

Solve for values of t, w, and s in terms of the remaining letters.

40. Using the formula of the preceding exercise, find t when $H = 50$, $w = 10$ in., and $s = 4000$ ft. per minute. *Ans.* 41.25 lb.

41. To determine the elevation of the outer rail in a curve in a railroad track, the following formula is used:

$$e = \frac{GV^2}{32.2R}$$

where

    e = the elevation in feet.

    G = the gage of the track in feet.

    V = the velocity of train in feet per second.

    R = the radius of curvature of the curve in feet.

Find e for the following data, if G is 4 ft. $8\frac{1}{2}$ in., the standard gage:

  (1) R = 5730 ft., (a) V = 20 miles per hour, and (b) V = 50 miles per hour.

  (2) R = 2865 ft., (a) V = 15 miles per hour, and (b) V = 40 miles per hour.

  (3) R = 716.8 ft., (a) V = 25 miles per hour, and (b) V = 50 miles per hour.   *Ans.* 0.02 ft., 0.14 ft.; 0.02 ft., 0.18 ft., 0.27 ft., 1.10 ft.

42. In long water pipes, when the diameter and length of the pipes are constant, that is, do not change, the amount of discharge varies as the square root of the head. How many times must the head H be increased to double the amount of discharge G? To make the discharge five times as much?   *Ans.* 4; 25.

Definition.—The **head** is the distance of the source of supply above the point of discharge.

43. If the pipe is of such length and diameter that the discharge is 20 gal. per minute, what will it be if the head is doubled?

    Ans. 28.28 gal.

44. If, when the head is 10 ft., the discharge through a certain pipe is 50 gal. per minute, what must be the head so that the same pipe may discharge 210 bbl. per hour?   *Ans.* 48.62 ft.

45. In long water pipes, when the lengths of the pipes are the same and when the head does not change, the amount of discharge varies directly as the square root of the fifth power of the diameter. Using D and d for the diameters and G and g for the amounts of discharge, write this relation in the form of a proportion.

    Ans. $G : g = \sqrt{D^5} : \sqrt{d^5}$.

46. Write the preceding relation in the variation form both with and without the constant. What does the constant include in it? Would there be a different constant for each length of pipe? For each head?

    Ans. $G = K\sqrt{D^5}$; $G \propto \sqrt{D^5}$.

47. If the length and the head remain constant, what change in the discharge will be caused by a change in diameter from 3 to 4 in.?

    Ans. 2.05 times as great.

Suggestion.—Increased in the ratio $\sqrt{3^5} : \sqrt{4^5}$.

48. A 3-in. pipe 100 ft. in length with a certain head discharges 110 gal. per minute; find the discharge from a 5-in. pipe of the same length and head.

Suggestion: $110 : x = \sqrt{3^5} : \sqrt{5^5}$.   *Ans.* 394.5 gal. per minute.

49. How many 1-in. pipes will it take to discharge the same amount as one 6-in. pipe?   Here we are considering long pipes, so use the formula

$$N = \frac{\sqrt{D^5}}{\sqrt{d^5}}$$

where N = the number of small pipes, and D and d are the diameters of the large and the small pipes, respectively.   *Ans.* 88.2.

50. In long water pipes, when the discharge and the length are constant, the head will be inversely as the fifth power of the diameter. Using H and h for heads and D and d for the diameters, respectively, write this relation in the proportion form.   *Ans.* $H:h = d^5:D^5$.

51. With a head of 4.1 ft. and a length of 100 ft. a 3-in. pipe will discharge 95.4 gal. per minute.   Find the head so that a 2-in. pipe of the same length will discharge an equal amount.   *Ans.* 31.13 ft.

52. Using H and D for head and diameter, respectively, write the relation given in Exercise 50 in the variation form.   Using this formula solve Exercise 51.   *Ans.* $H = \dfrac{K}{D^5}$.

53. In long water pipes when the head and the diameter are constant, the discharge will be inversely as the square roots of the lengths.   Using G for discharge and L for length, state this in the variation form.   In the proportion form.   *Ans.* $G = \dfrac{K}{\sqrt{L}}; G:g = \sqrt{l}:\sqrt{L}$.

54. In a long water pipe of a certain diameter and head, the discharge is 2000 gal. per minute.   How many gallons will be discharged per minute under the same head and the same size of pipe if the length is doubled?   If six times as long?   *Ans.* 1,414 gal.; 816.5 gal.

55. In long water pipes, when the discharge and the diameter are constant, the head varies directly as the length.   Using the letters given in the preceding exercises, state this in the form of a proportion, and in the variation form.   *Ans.* $H:h = L:l, H = KL$.

56. The square of the initial velocity of a projectile in feet per second varies as the number of pounds of powder in the charge and inversely as the weight of the projectile.   If 5 lb. of a certain kind of powder will give a projectile weighing 10 lb. an initial velocity of 1850 ft. per second, how great a velocity will 50 lb. of powder give an 80-lb. projectile?

Solution.—Let p = number of pounds of powder in charge, w = weight of projectile, and v = velocity in feet per second.
Then

$$v^2 = k\,\frac{p}{w}$$

When $p = 5$ and $w = 10$, $v = 1850$.

$$\therefore 1850^2 = k\,\frac{5}{10}$$

and

$$k = 2 \times 1850^2$$

When $p = 50$ and $w = 80$,

$$v = \sqrt{2 \times 1850^2 \times \frac{50}{80}} = 2068$$

57. Using the same quality of powder as in the last, find the charge necessary to give a 1200-lb. projectile an initial velocity of 2100 ft. per second.   *Ans.* 733 lb.

PART FOUR

Trigonometry

CHAPTER XXXIV

INTRODUCTION, ANGLES

357. Introductory.—Each advance step in mathematics is an attempt to do something more easily than it could have been done before or to accomplish something that was before impossible. We have seen that many problems could be worked more easily by algebra than by arithmetic and that many other problems could be solved by algebra that could not be solved by methods of arithmetic.

It was found that the area of a segment of a circle could not be obtained by geometry except in a few special cases; by methods of trigonometry, this area can be found in all cases where there are sufficient facts to do it by any means. By geometry, one side of a right triangle can be found if the two other sides are known; but there is no way by geometry of finding the acute angles when only the sides are known. By trigonometry, the angles as well as the sides can be found. Many such illustrations could be given in which trigonometry is a more powerful tool than either algebra or geometry. Trigonometry is based upon geometry but makes use of the methods and machinery of algebra.

While trigonometry can be applied at once to the solution of various practical problems, it is also of great assistance in other more advanced branches of mathematics.

To pursue the subject of trigonometry successfully, the student should know the subjects usually treated in algebra up to and including quadratic equations and be familiar with plane geometry, especially the theorems on triangles and circles.

Frequent use is made of the protractor, compasses, and the straightedge.

358. Meaning and history.—The word trigonometry is derived from two Greek words, τριγωνον (trigonon), meaning triangle, and μετρια (metria), meaning measurement. Although the derivation of the word would seem to confine the subject to triangles, the measurement of triangles is merely a part of the general subject which includes many other investigations involving angles.

Trigonometry is both geometric and algebraic in nature. Historically, trigonometry developed in connection with astronomy, where distances that could not be measured directly were computed by means of angles and lines that could be measured. The beginning of these methods may be traced to Babylon and ancient Egypt.

The noted Greek astronomer Hipparchus is often called the founder of trigonometry. He did his chief work between 146 and 126 B.C. and developed trigonometry as an aid in measuring angles and lines in connection with astronomy. The subject of trigonometry was separated from astronomy and established as a distinct branch of mathematics by the great mathematician Leonhard Euler, who lived from 1707 to 1783.

359. Angles.—Because trigonometry deals primarily with angles, it is necessary that one should have a very clear conception of the meaning and the measurement of angles.

The definition of an angle as given in Art. 106 admits of a clear conception of small positive angles only. In trigonometry we wish to deal with *negative* as well as *positive* angles, and these of any size whatever. We therefore need a more comprehensive definition of an angle.

If a line is turned about a fixed point in the line and kept in the same plane, it is said to **generate** or **sweep out** an **angle**.

The hand of a clock may be thought of as the line that is revolving and generating the angle.

The *size* of the angle is determined by the *amount of turning* made by the line.

If the line turns in a **counterclockwise direction,** that is, opposite in direction to the hands of a clock, the angle described is called a **positive angle.** If the line turns in a **clockwise direction,** the angle described is called a **negative angle.**

The position of the line at the start is called the **initial line** or **side,** and the final position is called the **terminal line** or **side.**

A circular arrow drawn between the two lines and having its head in the terminal line shows the *direction of turning* and the *size of* the angle.

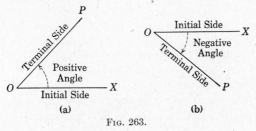

Fɪɢ. 263.

In Fig. 263(*a*), the line *OX* is imagined pinned at *O* and turning in a counterclockwise direction to the position *OP*. The angle described is positive and is read angle *XOP*. Notice that the initial line is read first.

In Fig. 263(*b*), the line *OX* is thought of as turning in a clockwise direction and so describing the negative angle *XOP*.

It is evident that the idea of an angle given in this article allows it to be of any value whatever, positive or negative.

Thus, an angle of 467° is one complete turn and 107°. It is shown in Fig. 264(*a*).

An angle of −229° is a turn of 229° in the negative, clockwise, direction. It is shown in Fig. 264(*b*).

An angle of 720° is two complete turns of the initial line. An angle of 3760° is ten complete turns and 160° more.

360. Location of angles, quadrants.—For convenience in locating the angles, the agreement is made as for plotting.

(See Art. 324.) Two lines, $X'X$ and $Y'Y$ of Fig. 265, are drawn at right angles to each other. The directions of the lines and the location of the quadrants are as in the article referred to.

Since the size and sense of an angle are unchanged when it is moved about into different positions in a plane, any angle

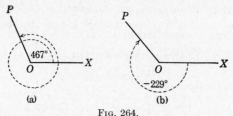

FIG. 264.

may be moved so that its vertex is at the origin and its initial side on the positive part of the x-axis. When an angle is placed in this position, it gives a very convenient way for determining its size and sense.

If the positive direction of the x-axis is taken as the initial side, the angle is said to be in the **first quadrant** if its terminal

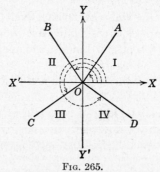

FIG. 265.

side lies between OX and OY. It does not matter how many turns are made. Thus the angles of 40°, 400°, and 760° all lie in the first quadrant.

Similarly, if the terminal side lies between OY and OX', the angle is said to be in the **second quadrant**. If the terminal side lies between OX' and OY', the angle is said to be in the **third quadrant.** If the terminal side lies between OY' and OX, the angle is said to be in the **fourth quadrant.**

Thus, angle XOA is in the first quadrant.
Angle XOB is in the second quadrant.
Angle XOC is in the third quadrant.
Angle XOD is in the fourth quadrant.

If the terminal side falls on OX, OY, OX', or OY', the angle is said to lie **between** two quadrants.

EXERCISES

In the following exercises the initial side is to be taken on the positive part of the x-axis. Show the sense and size of all angles by circular arrows. Use the protractor in drawing angles where the size is given in degrees.

1. Draw positive angles, one in each quadrant and one between each quadrant.

2. Draw negative angles, one in each quadrant and one between each quadrant.

3. Draw the following angles and tell in which quadrant or between which quadrants each one's terminal side lies:

$65°$	$375°$	$1020°$	$-1200°$
$240°$	$210°$	$630°$	$-145°$
$374°$	$15°$	$-100°$	$-225°$
$180°$	$790°$	$-315°$	$-800°$

4. Select two angles from Exercise 3 whose sum is an angle in (1) the first quadrant; (2) the second quadrant; (3) the third quadrant; and (4) the fourth quadrant.

NOTE.—The sum of $210°$ and $-100°$ is an angle in the second quadrant.

5. Draw the terminal side of $60°$. Give four other positive angles that have the same terminal side. Draw four negative angles that have the same terminal side as $60°$. Give their values.

6. Draw $-215°$. What is the smallest positive angle having the same terminal side as this? How many angles are there having the same terminal side as $-215°$?

7. Draw the following pairs of angles, using the same initial side for each pair: $170°$ and $-190°$; $-40°$ and $320°$; $150°$ and $-210°$.

8. Draw the following angles and their complements: $30°$; $210°$; $-45°$; $-300°$; $0°$.

9. Show by a drawing the position of the revolving line when it has generated each of the following: 2 right angles; $2\frac{1}{2}$ right angles; $1\frac{1}{3}$ right angles; $4\frac{1}{3}$ right angles.

· **361. Units for measuring angles.**—In measuring any magnitude, a unit of measure is necessary. In measuring length, there are the units, inch, foot, etc., and meter. Likewise in the measurement of angles, in use as units are the **right angle,** the **degree,** and the **radian.**

(1) *The right angle as a unit.*—When using the right angle as a unit, we speak of an angle as such a part of or as so many times a right angle.

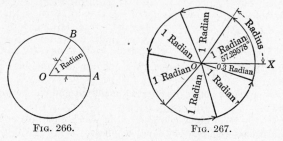

Fig. 266.   Fig. 267.

(2) *The degree as a unit.*—The degree as a unit for measuring angles has been defined as the value of the angle formed by dividing a right angle into 90 equal parts. The degree is also used as a unit for measuring arcs. It is then defined as $\frac{1}{360}$ part of a circumference. In either case the degree is divided into 60 parts called minutes, and the minute into 60 parts called seconds. Degrees, minutes, and seconds of angle or arc are indicated by the signs °, ′, and ″. For example, a measurement of 27 degrees, 47 minutes, 35 seconds is written thus: 27° 47′ 35″. The measurement of angles by means of the protractor has already been explained in Art. 108.

As already defined, if an angle has its vertex at the center of a circle and its sides formed by radii of the circle, it is spoken of as an angle at the center of a circle. The number of degrees in the angle so placed is equal to the number of degrees in the arc of the circle intercepted between the sides of the angle.

Thus, in Fig. 266, *AOB* is an angle at the center. The number of degrees in this angle equals the number of degrees in the arc *AB*.

The angle *AOB* is said to be measured by the arc *AB*.

(3) *Circular measure, radian.*—The unit of circular measure of angles is the **radian**. The **radian** is defined as the angle at the center of a circle and measured by an arc equal in length to the radius of the circle.

In Fig. 266, arc *AB* = radius *OA*; hence angle, *AOB* is one radian.

362. Radian and degree compared.—In Fig. 267 are shown roughly the number of radians in 1 revolution of the line generating the angle, or in 360°. To find more exactly the relation between the number of degrees and the number of radians in an angle, we may proceed as follows:

Since the circumference of a circle is 2π times the radius,

$$2\pi \text{ radians} = 1 \text{ revolution}$$

Also $\qquad\qquad 360° = 1 \text{ revolution}$

Then $\qquad 2\pi \text{ radians} = 360°$

$$\therefore 1 \text{ radian} = \frac{360°}{2\pi} = \frac{180°}{\pi} = \frac{180°}{3.14159} = 57.29578° -$$

$$= 206264.8'' + \; = 57° \; 17' \; 44.8'' +$$

For less accurate work, 1 radian is taken as 57.3°.
Conversely, $180° = \pi$ radians.

$$\therefore 1° = \frac{\pi}{180} = 0.017543 + \text{ radian}$$

To convert radians to degrees, multiply the number of radians by $\frac{180}{\pi}$, *or* 57.29578 −.

To convert degrees to radians, multiply the number of degrees by $\frac{\pi}{180}$, *or* 0.017453 +.

Example 1.—Reduce 2.5 radians to degrees, minutes, and seconds.

Solution: 1 radian = 57.29578°

$\therefore$ 2.5 radians = 2.5 × 57.29578° = 143.2394°

To find the number of minutes, multiply the decimal part of the number of degrees by 60,

$\therefore$ 0.2394° = 60 × 0.2394 = 14.364′

Likewise,   0.364′ = 60 × 0.364 = 21.8″

$\therefore$ 2.5 radians = 143° 14′ 22″. *Ans.*

Example 2.—Reduce 22° 36′ 30″ to radians.

Solution.—First, change to degrees and decimals of degrees,

22° 36′ 30″ = 22.6083°+

1° = 0.017453+ radians

$\therefore$ 22.6083°+ = 22.6083 × 0.017453 = 0.3946− radian.

Ans.

The measurement of an angle by the radian unit is often called **circular measure** or **π-measure.**

Many of the most frequently used angles are conveniently expressed in radian measure by using π. In this manner the values are expressed accurately and long decimals are avoided. Since 2π radians = 360°, π radians = 180°. Whenever the number of degrees is a simple fractional part of 180°, π can be used to advantage.

Thus, 90° = $\frac{1}{2}\pi$ radians, 60° = $\frac{1}{3}\pi$ radians, 270° = $\frac{3}{2}\pi$ radians, etc.   (See table on page 560.)

In using circular measure, the word radian is usually omitted. Thus, we write π, $\frac{1}{2}\pi$, $\frac{1}{4}\pi$, 3, 0.5, meaning in each case so many radians.

EXERCISES

1. Express the following angles as some multiple of π radius (thus: 54° = $\frac{54}{180}\pi$ radius = $\frac{3}{10}\pi$ radians): 18°, 20°, 30°, 36°, 45°, 60°, 72°, 90°, 120°, 135°, 180°, 210°, 225°, 270°, 300°, 315°, 330°, 360°, 540°, 720°, 1080°. Reduce the following to radians:

2. 18°.   *Ans.* 0.3141.

3. 147°.   *Ans.* 2.566.

4. 130°.   *Ans.* 2.269.

5. 185°.   *Ans.* 3.229.

6. 62°40′.   *Ans.* 1.094.

7. 75°30′.   *Ans.* 1.318.

8. 16°43′10″.   *Ans.* 0.292.

9. 95°10′10″.   *Ans.* 1.661.

10. 125°46′30″.   *Ans.* 2.195.

11. 127°41′50″.   *Ans.* 2.229.

The following are angles expressed in radians. Reduce them (1) to degrees and decimals of degrees to four places; (2) to degrees, minutes, and seconds.

12. $\frac{1}{10}\pi$.   *Ans.* 18°.   **14.** $\frac{1}{3}\pi$.   *Ans.* 60°.   **16.** $\frac{3}{4}\pi$.   *Ans.* 135°.

13. $\frac{1}{6}\pi$.   *Ans.* 30°.   **15.** $\frac{2}{3}\pi$.   *Ans.* 120°.   **17.** 3π.   *Ans.* 540°.

18. 2.236.   *Ans.* 128.1133°+; 128°6′48″.

19. 4.23.   *Ans.* 242.361°+; 242°21′40″.

20. 0.125.   *Ans.* 7.1619°; 7°9′43″.

21. Express the angles of the following regular polygons in both degrees and radians: (1) three sides, (2) four sides, (3) five sides, (4) six sides, (5) eight sides, (6) twelve sides.

$$Ans. \ (1) \ 60°; \ \frac{\pi}{3}. \quad (2) \ 90°; \ \frac{\pi}{2}. \quad (3) \ 108°; \ \frac{3\pi}{5}.$$

22. If a man walks completely around a circle, through how many π radians does he turn? If the radius is 10 ft., how far does he walk?

$$Ans. \ 2\pi; \ 20\pi \text{ ft.}$$

23. In 3 hr., through how many radians has the minute hand of a clock turned? The hour hand? The second hand?

$$Ans. \ 6\pi.; \ \frac{\pi}{2}; \ 360\pi.$$

24. How many radians are in each of the angles of a right triangle if one of the acute angles is 36°47′?   *Ans.* $\frac{1}{2}\pi$; 0.642−; 0.929−.

25. How many degrees are there in each of the angles of an isosceles triangle if the angle at the vertex is $\frac{1}{6}\pi$ radians?   *Ans.* 30° 75°, 75°.

26. Two of the angles of a triangle are respectively $\frac{2}{3}$ and $\frac{2}{5}$ radian. Find the number of radians and degrees in the third angle.

$$Ans. \ 2.074926 \text{ radians} = 118°53′4″.$$

CHAPTER XXXV

TRIGONOMETRIC FUNCTIONS

363. All the computations of trigonometry are based upon certain ratios, six in number, and formed by using certain lines connected with an angle. It is now necessary to define and become perfectly familiar with these ratios, or *trigonometric functions* as they are called.

In geometry, we learn of the relations between the sides of a few triangles. We have the Pythagorean proposition for the right triangle; we know very definitely the relations between the sides and angles in the 45° isosceles triangle and the 30–60° right triangle; but on the whole, in geometry very little attention is paid to the relations of the sides and angles in a triangle. In trigonometry, the ratios mentioned give exact relations between sides and angles in any triangle. These relations make it possible to solve a great variety of problems that cannot be solved by geometry.

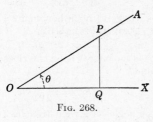

Fig. 268.

In the present chapter, these ratios are defined in such a manner as to show that they have to do with an angle and not with a triangle. The student should make certain that he thoroughly comprehends the definitions, as all trigonometry is based on these ratios.

364. The three most important ratios.—If an acute angle *XOA*, Fig. 268, is taken, and from *P*, any point in *OA*, a perpendicular *QP* is drawn to *OX*, a right triangle *QOP* is formed. It is evident because of similar triangles (see Art.

550

128) that the following ratios will not change no matter where the perpendicular QP may be drawn, so long as the angle XOA, or θ, does not change.

The ratio $\dfrac{QP}{OP}$ is called the **sine** of angle θ, written **sin θ**.

The ratio $\dfrac{OQ}{OP}$ is called the **cosine** of angle θ, written **cos θ**.

The ratio $\dfrac{QP}{OQ}$ is called the **tangent** of angle θ, written **tan θ**.

These lines can be measured, say, in inches, and numerical values of these ratios can then be found.

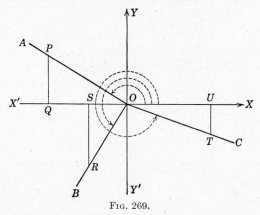

Fig. 269.

365. Ratios for any angle.—The same ratios may be written for an angle in any quadrant. Thus, in Fig. 269, angle XOA is in the second quadrant. QP is the perpendicular drawn from any point in the terminal side to the x-axis. The ratios are

$$\sin XOA = \frac{QP}{OP}, \cos XOA = \frac{OQ}{OP}, \tan XOA = \frac{QP}{OQ}$$

As an exercise the student may write these ratios for the angles XOB and XOC.

As will be seen in the next article, some of the ratios are positive and some are negative numbers.

366. General form for ratios.—Draw any four angles, one in each quadrant, as shown in Fig. 270. On the terminal sides of these angles locate the points P_1, P_2, P_3, and P_4 at any convenient distances from O, and draw the four perpendiculars to the x-axis. Let the distance from O along the terminal side of any angle to the point chosen be called the **distance,** represented by r, and *always* considered *positive*. The perpendicular to the x-axis is the **ordinate** of the point, *positive* if extending above and *negative* if below the x-axis, and is represented by y. The line segment from O to the foot of the

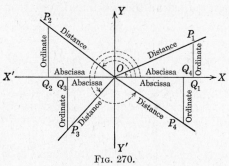

Fig. 270.

perpendicular is the **abscissa** of the point, *positive* if extending to the right of the origin and *negative* if to the left, and is represented by x. The ratios for any angle θ (see Fig. 270) may then be written as follows:

$$\sin \theta = \frac{\text{ordinate}}{\text{distance}} = \frac{y}{r}$$

$$\cos \theta = \frac{\text{abscissa}}{\text{distance}} = \frac{x}{r}$$

$$\tan \theta = \frac{\text{ordinate}}{\text{abscissa}} = \frac{y}{x}$$

The *reciprocals* of these ratios are often used and are named as follows:

cosecant θ, abbreviated **csc θ** $= \dfrac{1}{\sin \theta} = \dfrac{r}{y}$

secant θ, abbreviated **sec θ** $= \dfrac{1}{\cos \theta} = \dfrac{r}{x}$ ·

cotangent θ, abbreviated **cot θ** $= \dfrac{1}{\tan \theta} = \dfrac{x}{y}$

These six ratios are called **trigonometric functions.** They are of the greatest importance in trigonometry and must be learned so thoroughly that they can be given at any time without hesitation.

The first three of these ratios, the sine, cosine, and tangent, are the ratios most frequently used and are the ones that should receive the chief attention. In fact, if they are carefully learned, the others can be readily remembered, as they are the reciprocals of these.

That these ratios are truly functions of the angle is evident, for each angle has these six ratios connected with it. Also any change in the size of the angle will change the values of the ratios. If the angle is considered the independent variable, the lines and the ratios are dependent variables. (See Art. 333.)

367. Signs of the trigonometric functions.—The sine of an angle θ has been defined as the ratio of the ordinate to the distance of any point in the terminal side of the angle. Since the distance r is always positive, sin θ will have the same algebraic sign as the ordinate of the point. Therefore sin θ is positive when the angle is in the first or second quadrant and negative when the angle is in the third or fourth quadrant.

In a similar manner the algebraic signs of the remaining functions of θ are determined. The student should verify the following table:

Quadrant	sin θ	cos θ	tan θ	cot θ	sec θ	csc θ
I	+	+	+	+	+	+
II	+	−	−	−	−	+
III	−	−	+	+	−	−
IV	−	+	−	−	+	−

EXERCISES

Remember that the trigonometric ratios are real numbers and hence are positive, negative, or zero depending upon which quadrant the terminal side of the angle lies.

Give the quadrant or quadrants in which the terminal side of the angle lies, and draw the graph, in each of the following exercises:

1. When sin θ is positive.   *Ans.* First and second.

2. When sin θ is negative.

3. When sin θ is zero.   *Ans.* Between first and fourth, etc.

4. When cos θ is positive.

5. When cos θ is negative.

6. When cos θ is zero.

7. When tan θ is (1) positive, (2) negative, (3) zero.

8. Answer the three questions as in Exercise 7 for sec θ, csc θ, and cot θ.

9. When all functions are positive. (How about all negative?)

10. What two functions are positive in the second quadrant?

11. What four functions are negative in the fourth quadrant?

12. In what quadrant is sin θ positive and cos θ negative?

13. In what quadrant is sin θ negative and cos θ positive?

14. In what quadrant is cos θ positive and tan θ negative?

15. In what quadrant is sec θ negative and csc θ positive?

16. In what quadrant is cot θ positive and sec θ positive?

17. When the terminal side lies along the x-axis, what functions are zero? What functions are unity? What functions are not defined? *Suggestion.*—Division by zero is not defined.

18. When the terminal side lies along the y-axis, what functions are zero? What functions are unity? What functions are not defined?

19. What functions are equal in value when the terminal side lies along the 45° line? The 225° line?

Give the algebraic signs of each of the trigonometric functions of the following angles (draw the graph):

20. 30°.	**23.** 315°	**26.** −45°.	**29.** $\frac{1}{4}\pi$.
21. 120°.	**24.** 420°.	**27.** −150°.	**30.** $-\frac{5}{6}\pi$.
22. 225°.	**25.** 750°.	**28.** −300°.	**31.** $\frac{2}{3}\pi$.

32. Show that neither the sine nor the cosine of an angle can be greater than $+1$ nor less than -1.

33. Show that neither the secant nor the cosecant of an angle can have a value between -1 and $+1$.

34. Show that the tangent and the cotangent of an angle may have any value whatever.

35. Is there an angle whose tangent is positive and whose cotangent is negative? Whose secant is positive and whose cosine is negative? Whose secant is positive and whose cosecant is negative?

36. Draw a pair of coordinate axes, and locate an angle of 60°. Locate a point in the terminal side 2 in. from the origin, and find the abscissa and ordinate of this point. Finally, tabulate the trigonometric functions of 60°.

Suggestion.—The distance is 2; the abscissa is 1; and the ordinate is $\sqrt{3}$.

37. Follow the same directions for 120°, noting that the abscissa is −1. (See page 556.)

COMPUTATION OF TRIGONOMETRIC FUNCTIONS

368. There are two right triangles for which geometry gives definite relations between sides and angles. These are the right isosceles triangle, whose acute angles are each 45°, and the right triangle, whose acute angles are 30 and 60°. (See Arts. 127, 136.) The functions of any angle, for which the abscissa, ordinate, and distance form one of these triangles, can readily be computed to any desired degree of accuracy. All such angles, together with 0°, 90°, 180°, 270°, and 360°, with their functions are tabulated on page 560. They are very important for future use.

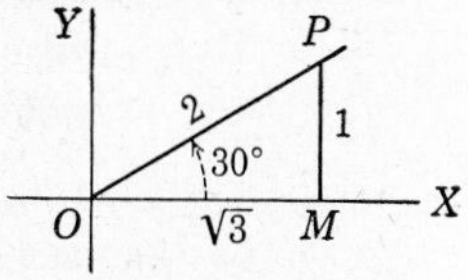

369. Trigonometric functions of 30°. Draw angle $XOP = 30°$ as in Fig. 271. Choose P in the terminal side, and draw

Fig. 271.

PM perpendicular to OX. By geometry, MP, the side opposite the 30° angle, is one-half the hypotenuse OP. Take $y = MP = 1$ unit and $r = OP = 2$ units; then $x = OM = \sqrt{3}$. By definition then we have

$$\sin 30° = \frac{y}{r} = \frac{1}{2}$$

$$\cos 30° = \frac{x}{r} = \frac{\sqrt{3}}{2} = \frac{1}{2}\sqrt{3}$$

$$\tan 30° = \frac{y}{x} = \frac{1}{\sqrt{3}} = \frac{\sqrt{3}}{3} = \frac{1}{3}\sqrt{3}$$

$$\cot 30° = \frac{x}{y} = \frac{\sqrt{3}}{1} = \sqrt{3}$$

$$\sec 30° = \frac{r}{x} = \frac{2}{\sqrt{3}} = \frac{2}{3}\sqrt{3}$$

$$\csc 30° = \frac{r}{y} = \frac{2}{1} = 2$$

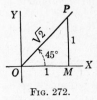

Fig. 272.

370. Trigonometric functions of 45°.— Draw angle $XOP = 45°$ as in Fig. 272. Choose the point P in the terminal side, and draw its coordinates OM and MP, which are necessarily equal. Then the coordinates of P may be taken as $(1, 1)$, and $r = \sqrt{2}$. By definition then we have

$$\sin 45° = \frac{y}{r} = \frac{1}{\sqrt{2}} = \frac{1}{2}\sqrt{2}$$

$$\cos 45° = \frac{x}{r} = \frac{1}{\sqrt{2}} = \frac{1}{2}\sqrt{2}$$

$$\tan 45° = \frac{y}{x} = \frac{1}{1} = 1$$

$$\cot 45° = \frac{x}{y} = \frac{1}{1} = 1$$

$$\sec 45° = \frac{r}{x} = \frac{\sqrt{2}}{1} = \sqrt{2}$$

$$\csc 45° = \frac{r}{y} = \frac{\sqrt{2}}{1} = \sqrt{2}$$

371. Trigonometric functions of 120°.—Draw angle $XOP = $ 120° as in Fig. 273. Choose any point P in the terminal side, and draw its coordinates OM and MP. Triangle MOP is a right triangle with $\angle MOP = 60°$. Then, as in computing the functions of 30°, we may take $OP = 2$, $MO = 1$, and $MP = \sqrt{3}$. But the abscissa of P is $OM = -1$. Then the coordinates of P are $(-1, \sqrt{3})$, and $r = 2$. By definition then we have

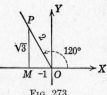

Fig. 273.

$$\sin 120° = \frac{y}{r} = \frac{\sqrt{3}}{2} = \frac{1}{2}\sqrt{3}$$

$$\cos 120° = \frac{x}{r} = \frac{-1}{2} = -\frac{1}{2}$$

$$\tan 120° = \frac{y}{x} = \frac{\sqrt{3}}{-1} = -\sqrt{3}$$

$$\cot 120° = \frac{x}{y} = \frac{-1}{\sqrt{3}} = -\frac{1}{3}\sqrt{3}$$

$$\sec 120° = \frac{r}{x} = \frac{2}{-1} = -2$$

$$\csc 120° = \frac{r}{y} = \frac{2}{\sqrt{3}} = \frac{2}{3}\sqrt{3}$$

372. Trigonometric functions of 0°.—In forming the ratios for the angles whose terminal sides lie on the lines between the quadrants, such as 0°, 90°, 180°, 270°, and 360°, the denominator is frequently zero. Strictly speaking, this gives rise to an impossibility, for division by zero is meaningless. In all such cases we say that the function has become infinite.

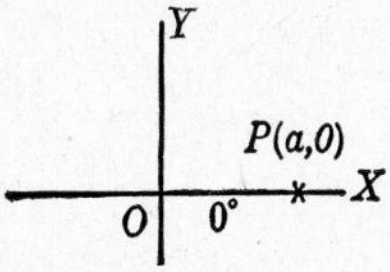

The initial and terminal sides of 0° are both on OX. Choose the point P on OX, as in Fig. 274, at the distance of a from O.

Fig. 274.

Then the coordinates of P are $(a, 0)$ and $r = a$. By definition then we have

$$\sin 0° = \frac{y}{r} = \frac{0}{a} = 0 \qquad \cot 0° = \frac{x}{y} = \frac{a}{0} \text{ (not defined)}$$

$$\cos 0° = \frac{x}{r} = \frac{a}{a} = 1 \qquad \sec 0° = \frac{r}{x} = \frac{a}{a} = 1$$

$$\tan 0° = \frac{y}{x} = \frac{0}{a} = 0 \qquad \csc 0° = \frac{r}{y} = \frac{a}{0} \text{ (not defined)}$$

By the expression $\frac{a}{0} = \infty$, as used by some writers, is understood the value of $\frac{a}{x}$ as x approaches zero as a limit. For example, we have $\dfrac{a}{1} = a$; $\dfrac{a}{0.1} = 10\ a$; $\dfrac{a}{0.01} = 100\ a$; $\dfrac{a}{0.001}$

$= 1000\ a$; $\dfrac{a}{0.0000001} = 10,000,000\ a$; etc. That is, as x gets

nearer and nearer to zero, $\dfrac{a}{x}$ gets larger and larger and can be

made to become larger than any number N. The value of $\dfrac{a}{x}$ is

then said to become infinite as x approaches zero. The symbol

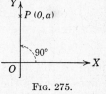

FIG. 275.

∞ is usually read "infinity." It should be carefully noted that a is not divided by 0, for division by 0 is meaningless.

373. Trigonometric functions of 90°.— Draw angle $XOY = 90°$ as in Fig. 275. Choose any point P in the terminal side at the distance a from the origin. Then the coordinates of P are $(0, a)$ and $r = a$. By definition, then, we have

$$\sin 90° = \frac{y}{r} = \frac{a}{a} = 1$$

$$\cos 90° = \frac{x}{r} = \frac{0}{a} = 0$$

$$\tan 90° = \frac{y}{x} = \frac{a}{0} \text{ (not defined)}$$

$$\cot 90° = \frac{x}{y} = \frac{0}{a} = 0$$

$$\sec 90° = \frac{r}{x} = \frac{a}{0} \text{ (not defined)}$$

$$\csc 90° = \frac{r}{y} = \frac{a}{a} = 1$$

That the values of the functions are as given will readily be seen if one draws an angle XOP, Fig. 276, nearly equal to 90° and considers the values of the ratios as the angle changes to 90°.

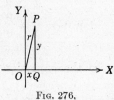

FIG. 276.

EXERCISES

Construct the figure and compute the functions for each of the following angles. These functions together with those computed in the text are tabulated on page 560.

1. 60°.	**4.** 180°.	**7.** 240°.	**10.** 315°.
2. 135°.	**5.** 210°.	**8.** 270°.	**11.** 330°.
3. 150°.	**6.** 225°.	**9.** 300°.	**12.** 360°.

APPLICATIONS TO RIGHT TRIANGLES

374. When the angle θ is acute, the abscissa, ordinate, and distance for any point in the terminal side form a right triangle, in which the given angle θ is one of the acute angles. On account of the many applications of the right triangle in trigonometry, the definitions of the trigonometric functions will be stated with special reference to the right triangle. These definitions are very important and are frequently the first ones taught, but it should be carefully noted that they are not general because they apply only to *acute* angles.

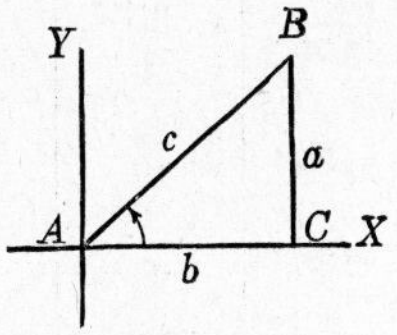

Draw the right triangle ABC, Fig. 277, with the vertex A at the origin and with AC on the initial line. Then AC and CB are the coordinates of B in the terminal side AB. Let $AC = b$, $CB = a$, and $AB = c$.

Fig. 277.

By definition (when either a, b, or c appears as a denominator, it is not to be zero)

$$\sin A = \frac{\text{ordinate}}{\text{distance}} = \frac{a}{c} = \frac{\text{side opposite}}{\text{hypotenuse}}$$

$$\cos A = \frac{\text{abscissa}}{\text{distance}} = \frac{b}{c} = \frac{\text{side adjacent}}{\text{hypotenuse}}$$

$$\tan A = \frac{\text{ordinate}}{\text{abscissa}} = \frac{a}{b} = \frac{\text{side opposite}}{\text{side adjacent}}$$

$$\cot A = \frac{\text{abscissa}}{\text{ordinate}} = \frac{b}{a} = \frac{\text{side adjacent}}{\text{side opposite}}$$

$$\sec A = \frac{\text{distance}}{\text{abscissa}} = \frac{c}{b} = \frac{\text{hypotenuse}}{\text{side adjacent}}$$

$$\csc A = \frac{\text{distance}}{\text{ordinate}} = \frac{c}{a} = \frac{\text{hypotenuse}}{\text{side opposite}}$$

FREQUENTLY USED ANGLES AND THEIR FUNCTIONS

$\theta°$	θ in radians	$\sin \theta$	$\cos \theta$	$\tan \theta$	$\cot \theta$	$\sec \theta$	$\csc \theta$
0°	0	0	1	0	Not defined	1	Not defined
30°	$\frac{\pi}{6}$	$\frac{1}{2}$	$\frac{\sqrt{3}}{2}$	$\frac{\sqrt{3}}{3}$	$\sqrt{3}$	$\frac{2\sqrt{3}}{3}$	2
45°	$\frac{\pi}{4}$	$\frac{\sqrt{2}}{2}$	$\frac{\sqrt{2}}{2}$	1	1	$\sqrt{2}$	$\sqrt{2}$
60°	$\frac{\pi}{3}$	$\frac{\sqrt{3}}{2}$	$\frac{1}{2}$	$\sqrt{3}$	$\frac{\sqrt{3}}{3}$	2	$\frac{2\sqrt{3}}{3}$
90°	$\frac{\pi}{2}$	1	0	Not defined	0	Not defined	1
120°	$\frac{2\pi}{3}$	$\frac{\sqrt{3}}{2}$	$-\frac{1}{2}$	$-\sqrt{3}$	$-\frac{\sqrt{3}}{3}$	-2	$\frac{2\sqrt{3}}{3}$
135°	$\frac{3\pi}{4}$	$\frac{\sqrt{2}}{2}$	$-\frac{\sqrt{2}}{2}$	-1	-1	$-\sqrt{2}$	$\sqrt{2}$
150°	$\frac{5\pi}{6}$	$\frac{1}{2}$	$-\frac{\sqrt{3}}{2}$	$-\frac{\sqrt{3}}{3}$	$-\sqrt{3}$	$-\frac{2\sqrt{3}}{3}$	2
180°	π	0	-1	0	Not defined	-1	Not defined
210°	$\frac{7\pi}{6}$	$-\frac{1}{2}$	$-\frac{\sqrt{3}}{2}$	$\frac{\sqrt{3}}{3}$	$\sqrt{3}$	$-\frac{2\sqrt{3}}{3}$	-2
225°	$\frac{5\pi}{4}$	$-\frac{\sqrt{2}}{2}$	$-\frac{\sqrt{2}}{2}$	1	1	$-\sqrt{2}$	$-\sqrt{2}$
240°	$\frac{4\pi}{3}$	$-\frac{\sqrt{3}}{2}$	$-\frac{1}{2}$	$\sqrt{3}$	$\frac{\sqrt{3}}{3}$	-2	$-\frac{2\sqrt{3}}{3}$
270°	$\frac{3\pi}{2}$	-1	0	Not defined	0	Not defined	-1
300°	$\frac{5\pi}{3}$	$-\frac{\sqrt{3}}{2}$	$\frac{1}{2}$	$-\sqrt{3}$	$-\frac{\sqrt{3}}{3}$	2	$-\frac{2\sqrt{3}}{3}$
315°	$\frac{7\pi}{4}$	$-\frac{\sqrt{2}}{2}$	$\frac{\sqrt{2}}{2}$	-1	-1	$\sqrt{2}$	$-\sqrt{2}$
330°	$\frac{11\pi}{6}$	$-\frac{1}{2}$	$\frac{\sqrt{3}}{2}$	$-\frac{\sqrt{3}}{3}$	$-\sqrt{3}$	$\frac{2\sqrt{3}}{3}$	-2
360°	2π	0	1	0	Not defined	1	Not defined

Again, suppose the triangle ABC placed so that angle B has its vertex at the origin, BC for the initial side, and BA for the terminal side, as in Fig. 278. The coordinates of A are $BC = a$ and $CA = b$.

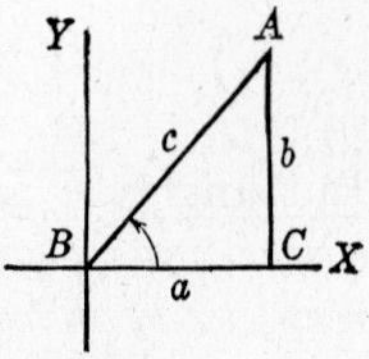

By definition (when either a, b, or c appears as a denominator, it is not to be zero)

Fig. 278.

$$\sin B = \frac{b}{c} = \frac{\text{side opposite}}{\text{hypotenuse}}$$

$$\cos B = \frac{a}{c} = \frac{\text{side adjacent}}{\text{hypotenuse}}$$

$$\tan B = \frac{b}{a} = \frac{\text{side opposite}}{\text{side adjacent}}$$

$$\cot B = \frac{a}{b} = \frac{\text{side adjacent}}{\text{side opposite}}$$

$$\sec B = \frac{c}{a} = \frac{\text{hypotenuse}}{\text{side adjacent}}$$

$$\csc B = \frac{c}{b} = \frac{\text{hypotenuse}}{\text{side opposite}}$$

Then, no matter where the right triangle is found, the functions of the acute angles may be written in terms of the legs and the hypotenuse of the right triangle.

375. Relations between the functions of complementary angles.—From the formulas of Art. 374, the following relations are evident:

$$\sin A = \cos B = \frac{a}{c}$$

$$\cos A = \sin B = \frac{b}{c}$$

$$\tan A = \cot B = \frac{a}{b}$$

$$\cot A = \tan B = \frac{b}{a}$$

$$\sec A = \csc B = \frac{c}{b}$$

$$\csc A = \sec B = \frac{c}{a}$$

But angles A and B are complementary; therefore, *the sine, cosine, tangent, cotangent, secant, and cosecant of an angle are, respectively, the cosine, sine, cotangent, tangent, cosecant, and secant of the complement of the angle. They are also called cofunctions.*

For example,

$$\cos 75° = \sin (90° - 75°) = \sin 15°$$
$$\tan 80° = \cot (90° - 80°) = \cot 10°$$

The term "cosine" was not used until the beginning of the seventeenth century. Before that time the expression "sine of the complement" (Latin, *complementi sinus*) was used instead. Cosine is a contraction of this. Similarly, cotangent and cosecant are contractions of *complementi tangens* and *complementi secans*, respectively.

The abbreviations, sin, cos, tan, cot, sec, and csc did not come into general use until the middle of the eighteenth century.

EXERCISES

1. Give orally the six trigonometric ratios of each of the acute angles of the right triangles in Fig. 279.

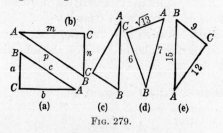

Fig. 279.

2. In a right triangle find a if $\sin A = \frac{2}{5}$ and $c = 3.45$.
Solution.—Substituting in the formula

$$\sin A = \frac{a}{c}$$

we have $\dfrac{2}{5} = \dfrac{a}{3.45}$; and solving for a, $a = 1.38$. *Ans.*

3. In a right triangle find a if $\sin A = \frac{3}{4}$, and $c = 1$.   *Ans.* $\frac{3}{4}$.

4. In a right triangle find b if $\cos A = \frac{2}{3}$, and $c = 2$.   *Ans.* $\frac{4}{3}$.

5. In a right triangle find a if $\tan A = 2$, and $b = 4$.   *Ans.* 8.

6. In a right triangle find c if $\sin A = \frac{5}{16}$, and $a = 8$.   *Ans.* $\frac{128}{5}$.

7. In a right triangle find b if $\sin B = \frac{3}{7}$, and $c = 16$.   *Ans.* $\frac{48}{7}$.

8. In a right triangle find a and c if $\sin B = \frac{2}{3}$, and $b = 48$.

                                         Ans. $24\sqrt{5}$; 72.

9. In a right triangle find a and b if $\sin A = 0.245$, and $c = 100$.

                                    Ans. 24.5; 96.95+.

10. Express the following functions as functions of the complements of these angles: $\sin 60°$; $\sin 20°$; $\cos 45°$; $\tan 70°$; $\sec 27°$; $\csc 42°$; $\sin \theta$: $\cot (90° - \theta)$.

11. If $\sin \theta = \cos 2\theta$, what is the sum of θ and 2θ?   *Ans.* 90°.

12. If $\sin \theta = \cos 60°$, find θ.   *Ans.* 30°.

13. If $\tan 20° = \cot \frac{1}{2}\theta$, find θ.   *Ans.* 140°.

14. If $\tan 40° = \cot \theta$, find θ.   *Ans.* 50°.

15. If $\tan \theta = \cot 3\theta$, find θ.   *Ans.* 22°30′.

16. If $\cos \frac{1}{2}\theta = \sin \frac{3}{4}\theta$, find θ.   *Ans.* 72°.

17. Express each of the following functions as functions of angles less than 45°: $\cos 70°$; $\sin 80°$; $\cot 82°26′$; $\tan 61°42′56″$.

376. Trigonometric functions by construction and measurement.—In the table on page 560 are arranged the functions of certain angles. These functions may be accurately expressed in decimals to as many places as desired, because they were determined from exact geometrical relations between the sides of the triangles involved. For most other angles such relations cannot be found, but approximate values can be found by measurement.

Let it be required to find the sine, cosine, and tangent of 40°.

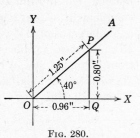

Fig. 280.

Draw an angle $XOA = 40°$, Fig. 280. Take a convenient distance OP on the terminal side, and draw the perpendicular QP. Then by measuring the lines (or Table XI may be used for a check; see Art. 380) we have the following:

$$\sin 40° = \frac{QP}{OP} = \frac{0.80}{1.25} = 0.64$$

$$\cos 40° = \frac{OQ}{OP} = \frac{0.96}{1.25} = 0.77$$

$$\tan 40° = \frac{QP}{OQ} = \frac{0.80}{0.96} = 0.84$$

As an exercise draw the angles and fill out the following table. Carry the results to two places of decimals.

Angle	sin	cos	tan	Angle	sin	cos	tan
10°				50°			
15°				55°			
20°				60°			
25°				65°			
30°				70°			
35°				75°			
40°				80°			
45°				85°			

In the table above, compare the sine and cosine of 10° and 80°, 15° and 75°, 20° and 70°, etc. As in Art. 375, it will be noticed that any function of any angle is the cofunction of the complement of that angle. It follows that any function of an angle larger than 45° is a function of an angle that is less than 45°. If, then, a table is made for the functions of all the angles from 0° to 45°, it can be used for finding the functions of the angles from 45° to 90° as well. Table XI, page 685, is arranged in exactly this way. It includes the angles for every 10′ from 0° to 90°.

377. Use of functions in constructing angles.

Example 1.—Construct an angle of 40°.

Construction: sin 40° = 0.64, by Table XI. By the help of this, the angle may be drawn as follows: Draw a straight line *AB*, Fig. 281. At a point *Q*, erect a perpendicular *QP*, 0.64 in. in length.

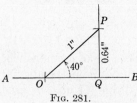

Fig. 281.

With P as a center draw an arc with a radius of 1 in. cutting AB at O. Draw OP. Angle QOP is 40°, for sin $QOP = 0.64 =$ sin 40°.

In constructing an angle of 40°, all that is necessary is to make the sides QP and OP of such lengths that the ratio shall be 0.64. For this 1.28 and 2 in. could be used conveniently. Usually it is most convenient to make one of the sides unity.

In making the construction, another function of 40° could be used as well as the sine.

Example 2.—Construct an angle of 35° by using tan 35°.

Construction: tan 35° = 0.70, by Table XI. Draw a straight line

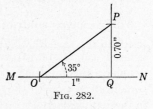

Fig. 282.

MN, Fig. 282. At a point Q erect a perpendicular QP to MN, 0.70 in. in length. Locate O making $OQ = 1$ in. Draw OP. Angle QOP is 35°, for tan $QOP = 0.70 =$ tan 35°.

EXERCISES

In the following exercises use Table XI when necessary.

1. Use sines and construct angles of 15°, 50°, 54°30′, and 75°50′.

2. Use tangents and construct angles of 20°, 40°40′, and 69°10′.

3. Construct an angle whose cosine is 0.4. Find the other functions of this angle.

4. Construct an angle whose tangent is 4. Find the other functions of this angle. Check by Table XI.

5. Construct θ when (1) sec $\theta = 4$; (2) csc $\theta = 5$; (3) cot $\theta = 6$.

CHAPTER XXXVI

TABLES AND THEIR USES

378. From our study of trigonometric functions in the previous chapter, it is seen that they are abstract numbers and, in general, cannot be expressed exactly as decimals. For convenience in computing, these functions are arranged in tables somewhat similar to the tables of logarithms. The functions in these tables may be carried to any number of decimal places. The larger the number of decimal places the more nearly accurate the computations with the tables will be.

The ratios themselves are called **natural** sines, cosines, etc.; and the logarithms of these ratios are called **logarithmic** sines, cosines, etc.

379. Table of functions.—In Table XI are arranged the natural and logarithmic functions of angles for every 10' from 0° to 90°. The logarithms have 10 added when the characteristics are negative to avoid the writing of negative signs in the table. These logarithms are simply the logarithms of the natural functions that are in the adjoining columns and are placed here for convenience.

Since, as stated in Art. 376, each acute angle above 45° has as a function the *cofunction* of an angle less than 45°, each number in the table serves as the function of two different angles whose sum is 90°.

The angles less than 45° are found at the *left* of the page, and the names of the functions at the *top* of the page. The angles greater than 45° are found at the *right* of the page, and the names of the functions at the *bottom* of the page.

380. To find the function of an angle from the table.—To find the function of an angle from the table we proceed much the same as with the table of logarithms. It can best be illustrated by examples.

(*A*) *When the angle is given in the table.*

Example 1.—Find the tangent of 23°20′.

Find the angle of 23°20′ at the left of the page, and read 0.4314 in the column headed Natural Tangent.

$$\therefore \tan 23°20′ = 0.4314 \quad Ans.$$

Example 2.—Find the cosine of 86°40′.

Find 86°40′ at the right of the page, and read 0.0581 in the column with natural cosine at the bottom.

$$\therefore \cos 86°40′ = 0.0581 \quad Ans.$$

(*B*) *When the angle is not given in the table.*

Example 3.—Find sin 17°27′.

Find sin 17°20′ = 0.2979. Find the tabular difference between 0.2979 and the next ratio below. This difference is 0.0028. Since this difference is for 10′, the difference for 7′ is 0.7 × 0.0028 = 0.0020,

$$\therefore \sin 17°27′ = 0.2979 + 0.0020 = 0.2999 \quad Ans.$$

Note that the interpolation is very similar to that in logarithms and, in general, gives approximate results only.

Example 4.—Find tan 69°43.6′.

Find tan 69°40′ = 2.6985.

Tabular difference for 10′ = 0.0243.

Difference for 3.6′ = 0.0243 × 0.36 = 0.0087.

$$\therefore \tan 69°43.6′ = 2.7072 \quad Ans.$$

Example 5.—Find cos 37°57.3′.

Find cos 37°50′ = 0.7898.

Tabular difference for 10′ = 0.0018.

Difference for 7.3′ = 0.0018 × 0.73 = 0.0013.

$$\therefore \cos 37°57.3′ = 0.7898 - 0.0013 = 0.7885 \quad Ans.$$

It is to be noted that a *subtraction* is to be made when interpolating in finding a cosine or a cotangent of an angle; whereas in finding a sine or a tangent, an *addition* is performed. This is because as the angle *increases* from 0° to 90°, the sine and the tangent *increase* but the cosine and the cotangent *decrease*.

Example 6.—Find log sin 34° 16′.

Find log sin 34° 10′ = 9.7494.

Tabular difference for 10′ = 0.0019.

Difference for 6′ = 0.0019 × 0.6 = 0.0011.

$$\therefore \text{ log sin } 34° 16′ = 9.7494 + 0.0011 = 9.7505 \quad Ans.$$

The same result would be arrived at by finding sin 34° 16′ = 0.5630; and then, by the table of logarithms, finding log 0.5630 = 9.7505 − 10.

381. To find the angle corresponding to a function.

(*A*) *When the function is given in the table.*

Example 1.—Find x if sin x = 0.2728.

Find 0.2728 in the column labeled Natural Sine, and read 15°50′ in the column labeled angle.

$$\therefore \quad x = 15°50′ \quad Ans.$$

(*B*) *When the function is not given in the table.*

Example 2.—Find x if tan x = 1.5725.

In the column labeled Natural Tangent, find the ratio nearest 1.5725 and smaller. This is 1.5697 and is the tangent of 57°30′. The tabular difference is 0.0101. The difference between 1.5697 and 1.5725 is 0.0028. Since a difference of 10′ gives a difference in the ratio of 0.0101, it will take a difference of as many minutes to give a difference in the ratio of 0.0028 as $\frac{28}{101} \times 10′ = 2.8′$.

$$\therefore \quad x = 57°30′ + 2.8′ = 57°32.8′ \quad Ans.$$

Note again how similar the interpolating is to that in logarithms.

Example 3.—Find x if cos x = 0.7396.

Since the cosine decreases as the angle increases, find the cosine nearest to 0.7396 but larger. This is cos 42°10′ = 0.7412.

Tabular difference = 0.0020.
Difference of 0.7412 − 0.7396 = 0.0016.

$$\tfrac{16}{20} \times 10 = 8'$$
$$\therefore \; x = 42°10' + 8' = 42°18' \quad Ans.$$

Example 4.—Find x if log sin $x = 9.3762 - 10$.

From the table, log sin $13°40' = 9.3734$. (9.3734 − 10 understood.)

$$9.3762 - 9.3734 = 0.0028$$

Tabular difference $\qquad\qquad = 0.0052.$
$$\tfrac{28}{52} \times 10' = 5.4'$$
$$\therefore \; 13°40' + 5.4' = 13°45.4' \quad Ans.$$

EXERCISES

1. Find the sine, cosine, and tangent of 40° 10′, 59° 50′, 76° 30′, and 5° 40′.

2. Find the sine, cosine, and tangent of (*a*) 17° 36′, (*b*) 29° 29′, (*c*) 76° 14′, (*d*) 83° 33′, (*e*) 63° 47′.

Ans. (*a*) $\begin{cases} 0.3024 \\ 0.9532 \\ 0.3172 \end{cases}$ (*b*) $\begin{cases} 0.4922 \\ 0.8705 \\ 0.5654 \end{cases}$ (*c*) $\begin{cases} 0.9713 \\ 0.2380 \\ 4.0817 \end{cases}$ (*d*) $\begin{cases} 0.9937 \\ 0.1123 \\ 8.8468 \end{cases}$ (*e*) $\begin{cases} 0.8971 \\ 2.4418 \\ 2.0308 \end{cases}$

3. Find the angles having the following as sines: 0.5807, 0.2725, 0.4986, 0.9127, 0.0276.

Ans. 35° 30′, 15° 48.9′, 29° 54.4′, 65° 52.7′, 1° 34.8′.

4. Find the angles having cosines as follows: 0.3764, 0.8642, 0.9091, 0.4848, 0.0986. *Ans.* 67° 53.3′, 30° 12.7′, 24° 37.5′, 61°, 84° 20.3′.

5. Find the angles having tangents as follows: 0.2256, 1.7624, 2.8427, 0.1111, 3, 0.6666.

Ans. 12° 42.9′, 60° 25.7′, 70° 37.1′, 6° 20.3′, 71° 33.9′, 33° 41.2′.

6. Find sin 34° 40′, and find the logarithm of this result from Table X. Find log sin 34° 40′ from Table XI and compare results.

7. Verify the following by the tables:

log sin 56° 35′ = 9.9215; log tan 34° 15.6′ = 9.8332;
log cos 27° 55′ = 9.9462; log cos 19° 53.4′ = 9.9733;
log sin 17° 9′ = 9.4696; log tan 75° 56.8′ = 0.6015.

8. Find x in each of the following:

(*a*) log cos x = 9.8236;   (*c*) log tan x = 0.4293;
(*b*) log sin x = 9.4737;   (*d*) log cot x = 9.4236.

Ans. (*a*) 48° 13.6′; (*b*) 17° 19′; (*c*) 69° 35.3′; (*d*) 75°8.8′.

382. Evaluation of formulas.—Formulas in various lines of work often contain trigonometric functions. As with other formulas, these can usually be evaluated with or without logarithms. Since logarithms are a very convenient and useful tool, they should be used whenever they can be employed to advantage.

To indicate the power of a trigonometric function the exponent is placed before the symbol for the angle.

Thus, $\sin^2 30°$ means the square of $\sin 30°$.

The logarithms of trigonometric functions are found in Table XI, and those of numbers in Table X.

Example 1.—Find $\sqrt[3]{\sin 47° + \tan^3 36°}$.

Solution:

$$\sin 47° = 0.7314, \text{ from Table XI}$$
$$\log \tan 36° = 9.8613 - 10$$
$$\therefore \log \tan^3 36° = 9.5839 - 10 \ (= 3 \log \tan 36°)$$
$$\therefore \tan^3 36° = 0.3836, \text{ from Table X}$$
$$\therefore \sin 47° + \tan^3 36° = 0.7314 + 0.3836 = 1.1150$$
$$\log 1.1150 = 0.0473$$
$$\log \sqrt[3]{1.1150} = 0.0158 = \tfrac{1}{3} \log 1.1150$$
$$\therefore \sqrt[3]{1.1150} = 1.037$$
$$\therefore \sqrt[3]{\sin 47° + \tan^3 36°} = 1.037 \quad Ans.$$

Example 2.—Given $x = \dfrac{\tan 72° \ 34'}{69° \ 40'}$, find the value of x to two decimal places.

In an example like this it is agreed that $69° \ 40'$ shall be changed to radians to give the number to divide by.

Solution:

$$\tan 72° \ 34' = 3.1846$$
$$69° \ 40' = 69\tfrac{2}{3}° = 69\tfrac{2}{3} \times 0.01745 \text{ radian} = 1.216 \text{ radians}$$
$$3.1846 \div 1.216 = 2.62$$
$$\therefore x = 2.62 \quad Ans.$$

Logarithms could be used in solving this example.

EXERCISES

In the theory of curvature the following formulas are important:

1. Given $R = 0.75a \sin^2 \frac{1}{3}x$, find R if $a = 4$ and $x = 66° 30'$.

Ans. 0.427.

2. Given $R = 2a \div \cos^3 0.5x$, find R if $a = 16$ and $x = 16°20'$.

Ans. 33 −.

3. Given $R = 3a \sin x \cos x$, find R if $a = 2$ and $x = 15°$.

Ans. 1.5.

4. Given $R = \dfrac{a(5 - 4 \cos x)^{1.5}}{9 - 6 \cos x}$, find R if $a = 100$ and $x = 18°$.

Ans. 39.7.

5. Given $R = \dfrac{a(1 - e^2)(1 - 2e \cos x + e^2)^{1.5}}{(1 - e \cos x)^3}$, find R if $a = 5$, $e = 0.4$, and $x = 4°40'$. *Ans.* 52.9.

6. Find the numerical value of $r^{\frac{2}{3}}(s^2 - t^2) \tan \theta$, where $r = 25.2$, $s = 90$, $t = 49.6$, and $\theta = 31°52'$. *Ans.* 30,140.

7. Find the value of $ae^{-bt} \sin (ct + \theta)$ if $a = 5$, $b = 200$, $c = 600$, $\theta = -0.1745$ radian, $e = 2.718$, and $t = 0.001$. *Ans.* 1.69.

Suggestion: $(ct + \theta) = 0.6 + (-0.1745) = 0.4255$ radian

$$0.4255 \times 57.296° = 24.379° = 24°22.7'$$

8. Given $x = \dfrac{\sin 45°56'20''}{36°20'}$, find the value of x to three decimal places. *Ans.* 1.133.

Suggestion.—First change $36°20'$ to radians.

9. Given $x = \dfrac{\tan 1.3788}{\sqrt{3} + \frac{4}{3}\pi}$, find x to four decimal places.

Ans. 0.8689.

Suggestion.—Here the angle is expressed in radians, and it is first necessary to reduce 1.3788 radians to degrees and minutes in order to find the tangent.

10. If the two sides a and b and the included angle C of a triangle are given, then the third side c is given by the formula

$$c = \sqrt{a^2 + b^2 - 2ab \cos C}$$

Find c if $a = 748$, $b = 375$, and $C = 63°35.5'$. *Ans.* 671+.

11. In constructing lenses the formula

$$n = \sin \frac{A + D}{2} \div \sin \frac{A}{2}$$

is used. Find n if $A = 41°8'$ and $D = 34°52'$. *Ans.* 1.752.

12. In order to determine the heights of objects such as that of an airplane, the formula

$$h = s \div (\cot A - \cot B)$$

may be used.   Find h if $A = 69°40'$, $B = 80°$, and $s = 1$ mile.

Ans. 5.15 miles.

13. Find the value of each of the following:

(1) $\sin^2 33° + \cos^2 33°$.

(2) $\sin^2 41° + \cos^2 41°$.

(3) $\sin^2 68°10' + \cos^2 68°10'$.

(4) $\sin^2 83°40' + \cos^2 83°40'$.

Compare the results in the above and state conclusions.

14. The velocity v of a body sliding a distance s down a smooth plane, Fig. 283, inclined at an angle φ with the horizontal is given by the formula

$$v = \sqrt{2gs \sin \varphi}$$

where $g = 32$.   Find v when $s = 50$ ft. and $\varphi = 27°16'$.

Ans. 38.3 ft. per second.

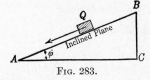

FIG. 283.

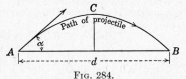

FIG. 284.

15. If the resistance of the air is disregarded, the distance along a horizontal plane, Fig. 284, that a projectile will go is given by the formula

$$d = \frac{v^2 \sin 2\alpha}{g}$$

where

$v =$ the velocity at which the body is projected in feet per second.

$\alpha =$ the angle that the initial direction makes with the horizontal.

$d =$ the distance along the horizontal.

The value of g may be taken as 32.   Find d if v is 800 ft. per second and α is 5°.   Using the same velocity find d when α is 20°, 30°, 40°, and 45°. Notice that the distance is the greatest when the angle is 45°.

Ans. 3472 ft.; 12,860 ft.; 17,320 ft.; 19,700 ft.; 20,000 ft.

16. Disregarding the resistance of the air, the highest point reached by a projectile is given by the formula

$$y = \frac{v^2 \sin^2 \alpha}{2g}$$

Find the greatest height above the starting point reached by a projectile having an initial velocity of 2000 ft. per second and having successive values for α of 5°, 10°, 20°, 30°, 45°, 60°, and 90°.

Ans. 474.8 ft.; 1885 ft.; 7312 ft.; 15,630 ft.; 31,250 ft.; 46,860 ft.; 62,500 ft.

17. The height y reached by a projectile after traversing a horizonal distance x, when projected with a velocity v in a direction making an angle α with the horizontal, is given by the following formula

$$y = x \tan \alpha - \frac{gx^2}{2v^2 \cos^2 \alpha}$$

Find y when $x = 1000$ yd., $v = 2000$ ft. per second, $\alpha = 5°$, and $g = 32$.
Ans. 226.2 ft.

18. If the resistance of the air is disregarded, the greatest horizontal distance that a projectile will go is found by making the initial direction at an angle of 45° with the horizontal. Find the greatest horizontal distance that a shell having an initial velocity of 2200 ft. per second can reach. *Ans.* 28.6 miles.

19. If F is the force required to move a weight W up a plane inclined to the horizontal at an angle α, and μ (Greek letter mu) the coefficient of friction, then

$$F = W \frac{\sin \alpha + \mu \cos \alpha}{\cos \alpha - \mu \sin \alpha}$$

Calculate F if $W = 200$ lb., $\alpha = 30°$, and $\mu = 0.2$ *Ans.* 175.75.

20. In computing the illumination on a surface when the surface is not perpendicular to the rays of light from a source of light, Fig. 285, the following formula is used:

$$E = \frac{I}{d^2} \times \cos \varphi$$

where

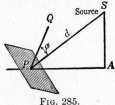

Fig. 285.

   E = the illumination at the point on the surface in foot-candles.
   I = the luminous intensity of the source in candles.
   d = the distance in feet from the source of light.
   φ = the angle between the incident ray and a line perpendicular to the surface.

Solve this formula for d and I, and obtain the following formulas:

$$d = \sqrt{\frac{I \cos \varphi}{E}}, \quad I = \frac{Ed^2}{\cos \varphi}$$

21. By means of the preceding formulas compute
(1) E when $I = 50$, $d = 10$, and $\varphi = 75°$.
(2) d when $I = 60$, $E = 0.25$, and $\varphi = 65°$.
(3) I when $E = 4$, $d = 8$, and $\varphi = 45°$

Ans. (1) 0.1294; (2) 10 ft.; (3) 362.

22. What do the formulas in Exercise 20 become if $\varphi = 0°$, that is, if the rays are normal (perpendicular) to the surface.

23. To compute the illumination on a horizontal surface from a source of light at a given vertical distance from the surface, Fig. 286, the follow-

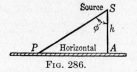

Fig. 286.

ing formula is used:

$$E_h = \frac{I}{h^2} \times \cos^3 \varphi$$

where

E_h = the illumination in foot-candles at a point on the horizontal surface.

I = the luminous intensity of the source in candles.

h = the vertical distance in feet from the horizontal surface to the source of light.

φ = the angle between the incident ray and a vertical line.

Solve this formula for h and I and obtain the following formulas:

$$h = \sqrt{\frac{I \cos^3 \varphi}{E_h}}$$

$$I = \frac{E_h h^2}{\cos^3 \varphi}$$

24. By means of the preceding formulas compute
(1) E_h when $I = 250$, $h = 12$, and $\varphi = 55°$.
(2) h when $I = 100$, $E_h = 65$, and $\varphi = 12°$.
(3) I when $E_h = 0.85$, $h = 8$, and $\varphi = 37°$.

Ans. (1) 0.3276; (2) 1.2 ft.; (3) 106.8.

CHAPTER XXXVII

RIGHT TRIANGLES

383. One of the direct applications of trigonometry is the solution of triangles both right and oblique.   In this way the surveyor determines heights and distances that cannot be measured directly, for instance, the height of a mountain or the distance from one point to another where a lake or a mountain prevents direct measurement.

It is a recognized fact in all walks of life, and it is certainly ingrained in mathematical science, that every real advance goes hand in hand with the invention of sharper tools and simpler methods.   Practical geometry was developed in Egypt to help redetermine boundaries of the land after an overflow of the Nile.   As has been stated before, astronomy, at an early date, gave the main incentive for the development of trigonometry.

In attacking the triangle, trigonometry, in many ways, is a more powerful tool than geometry, since the latter makes little use of the angles whereas trigonometry makes use of the angles as well as of the sides of a triangle.

Any triangle has three sides and three angles; these are called the six **elements** of the triangle.

The angles are usually represented by the capital letters A, B, and C; the sides, by the small letters a, b, and c.   The side a is opposite angle A; side b, opposite angle B; and side c, opposite angle C.

To **solve** a triangle is to find the values of the remaining elements when some of them are given.

384. Solving.—A triangle may be solved in two ways:

(1) By constructing the triangle from the known elements and measuring the remaining elements with the ruler and the protractor.

(2) By computing the remaining elements from those which are known.

The first has already been done to some extent in Chap. XIII. The second has been done for special triangles, such as the right triangle, the isosceles triangle, and the equilateral triangle, in Chap. XI, but only for some of the elements, not including the angles.

By trigonometry a triangle can always be solved when the facts given are sufficient for its construction; and not only can the sides be found, but the angles also. Before attempting to solve triangles by computation, it is well for the learner to construct carefully a number of triangles using a variety of data. The following exercises are for this purpose.

EXERCISES

If A, B, and C represent the angles of a triangle, and a, b, and c, respectively, the sides opposite these angles, construct carefully the following triangles, to scale if necessary, and measure the other elements. It is important that the student should carry out these carefully, for it will help him to see when there are sufficient data for solution.

1. Given one side and two angles:

$$A = 20°, B = 50°, \text{ and } c = 3 \text{ units}$$

2. Given two sides and an angle opposite one of them:

$$A = 25°, a = 4 \text{ units, and } c = 6 \text{ units.}$$

Can more than one triangle be constructed from these data?

3. Given two sides and the included angle:

$$C = 40°, a = 10 \text{ units, and } b = 9 \text{ units}$$

4. Given the three sides:

$$a = 4 \text{ units, } b = 5 \text{ units, and } c = 6 \text{ units}$$

5. Given the three angles $A = 50°$, $B = 70°$, and $C = 60°$. (At least two solutions.)

Construct the following right triangles and find the other elements. C is to be a right angle.

6. $A = 44°$, $b = 4$ units.

7. $B = 68°$, $b = 10$ units.

8. $A = 15°$, $a = 8$ units.

9. $a = 3$ units, $b = 4$ units.
10. $a = 6$ units, $c = 10$ units.

385. The right triangle.—The right triangle has already been solved when any two sides are known, but the angles were not found. The previous exercises from 6 to 10 should lead us to expect that we could find the other elements when any two are given, other than the right angle, and including at least one side. Geometry does not do this, but trigonometry does.

It is well to recall the following facts concerning the right triangle:

(1) *The hypotenuse is greater than either of the two other sides and less than their sum.*

(2) *The square of the hypotenuse is equal to the sum of the squares of the two other sides.*

(3) *The sum of the two acute angles is 90°; that is, the acute angles are complements of each other.*

(4) *The greater side is opposite the greater angle, and the greater angle is opposite the greater side.*

An inspection of the problems of construction will show that all the possible sets of two given parts for the right triangle are included in the following cases:

CASE I. *Given an acute angle and a side not the hypotenuse.*

CASE II. *Given an acute angle and the hypotenuse.*

CASE III. *Given the hypotenuse and one other side.*

CASE IV. *Given the two sides not the hypotenuse.*

386. Directions for solving.—To solve a right triangle, two elements must be given, at least one of which is a side.

Each equation of Art. 374 involving a trigonometric ratio, as $\sin A = \dfrac{a}{c}$, contains three quantities. When two of these are given, the third can be found. These equations together with the facts from geometry—(1) that the square of the hypotenuse equals the sum of the squares of the two other sides and (2) that the sum of the two acute angles equals 90°—enable one to solve any right triangle.

These equations may be written thus (see Fig. 287):

(1) $\sin A = \dfrac{a}{c}$

(6) $\cos B = \dfrac{a}{c}$

(2) $\cos A = \dfrac{b}{c}$

(7) $\tan B = \dfrac{b}{a}$

(3) $\tan A = \dfrac{a}{b}$

(8) $\cot B = \dfrac{a}{b}$

(4) $\cot A = \dfrac{b}{a}$

(9) $c^2 = a^2 + b^2$

(5) $\sin B = \dfrac{b}{c}$

(10) $A + B = 90°$

Notice that all these except (9) and (10) are simply the definitions of the trigonometric ratios.

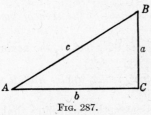

Fig. 287.

387. Case I. Given A and b, A and a, B and a, or B and b.

Example.—In a right triangle $A = 32°\ 20'$ and $b = 10$ ft.; find B, a, and c. (See Fig. 288.)

Solution.—(1) construct the triangle carefully; (2) write equations using two of the known elements and one of the unknown in each. These equations will be from the list given in the previous article.

Equations

(1) $A + B = 90°$, this gives B

(2) $\cos A = \dfrac{b}{c}$, this gives c

(3) $\tan A = \dfrac{a}{b}$, this gives a

Construction

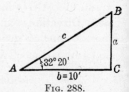

Fig. 288.

Substituting in (1), $32°\ 20' + B = 90°$.

$\therefore B = 90° - 32°\ 20' = 57°\ 40'$ *Ans.*

Substituting in (2), $\cos 32°\ 20' = \dfrac{10}{c}$.

$\therefore c = 10 \div \cos 32°\ 20' = 10 \div 0.8450 = 11.83$ ft. *Ans.*

Substituting in (3), $\tan 32° 20' = \dfrac{a}{10}$.

$\therefore a = 10 \times \tan 32° 20' = 10 \times 0.6330 = 6.33$ ft. *Ans.*

This may be checked (a) by measuring the elements in the triangle constructed; (b) by using another equation than the ones used in solving.

Thus, substitute values in $c^2 = a^2 + b^2$.

$$11.83^2 = 6.33^2 + 10^2$$
$$139.95 = 39.97 + 100 = 139.97$$

This agrees closely with the expected check.

The check can be carried out with less work if the formula $c^2 = a^2 + b^2$ is written

$$b^2 = c^2 - a^2 = (c + a)(c - a)$$

Then
$$10^2 = (11.83 + 6.33)(11.83 - 6.33)$$
$$100 = 18.16 \times 5.5 = 99.88$$

This solution has been carried through with natural functions. Logarithms could be used to advantage in performing the multiplications and divisions.

Thus, in (2),

$$c = \frac{b}{\cos A}$$

$$\therefore \log c = \log b - \log \cos A$$
$$\log 10 = 1.0000 \ (11.0000 - 10)$$
$$\log \cos 32° 20' = 9.9268 - 10$$
$$\overline{\quad\log c = 1.0732\quad}$$
$$\therefore c = 11.83 + \text{ft}$$

This agrees with the result obtained before.

388. Directions for solution of triangles.—(1) *Construct the triangle as accurately as possible with instruments.* This gives a clear idea of the relations of the parts and will detect any serious blunder in computation.

(2) *Write down all the equations necessary to find the elements wanted.*

(3) *Compute the elements by natural or logarithmic functions.*

(4) *Check the work.*

(5) *Strive for neatness and clearness in the work.*

389. Case II.—Given A and c or B and c.

Example.—Given $A = 67°42.8'$ and $c = 23.47$ ft., find B, a, and b.

Formulas

(1) $A + B = 90°$ $\quad \therefore B = 90° - A$

(2) $\sin A = \dfrac{a}{c}$ $\quad \therefore a = c \sin A$

(3) $\cos A = \dfrac{b}{c}$ $\quad \therefore b = c \cos A$

Construction

Fig. 289.

Computation by logarithms

By (1), $B = 90° - 67°42.8' = 22°17.2'$ *Ans.*

By (2), $a = 23.47 \sin 67°42.8'$

By (3), $b = 23.47 \cos 67°42.8'$

$$\log 23.47 = 11.3705 - 10$$
$$\log \sin 67°42.8' = \underline{\;\;9.9663 - 10}$$
$$\log a = \overline{\;\;1.3368}$$
$$\therefore a = 21.72 \quad Ans.$$

$$\log 23.47 = 11.3705 - 10$$
$$\log \cos 67°42.8' = \underline{\;\;9.5789 - 10}$$
$$\log b = \overline{\;\;0.9494}$$
$$\therefore b = 8.90 \quad Ans.$$

Check.—Use $a^2 = c^2 - b^2 = (c + b)(c - b)$.

$$\log (c + b) = 1.5101$$
$$\log (c - b) = 1.1635$$
$$\log (c^2 - b^2) = 2.6736 = \log a^2 = 2 \log a$$

390. Case III.—Given c and a or c and b.

Example.—Given $c = 35.62$ ft. and $a = 23.85$ ft., find b, A, B.

Formulas	*Construction*

(1) $\sin A = \dfrac{a}{c}$

$\therefore A = \sin^{-1} \dfrac{a}{c}$ (See Art. 391.)

(2) $\cos B = \dfrac{a}{c}$

$\therefore B = \cos^{-1} \dfrac{a}{c}$

(3) $\tan A = \dfrac{a}{b}$

$\therefore b = a \div \tan A$

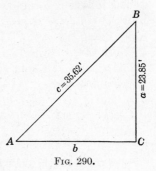

FIG. 290.

Computation: $\log 23.85 = 1.3775$

$\quad\quad\quad\quad\quad \log 35.62 = 1.5517$

$\quad\quad\quad\quad \log \sin A = 9.8258 - 10 = \log \cos B$

$\therefore A = 42°2.1'$ *Ans.* and $B = 47°57.9'$ *Ans.*

$\quad\quad\quad\quad\quad \log 23.85 = 11.3775 - 10$

$\quad\quad\quad\quad \log \tan A = 9.9549 - 10$

$\quad\quad\quad\quad\quad\; \log b = 1.4226$

$\quad\quad\quad\quad\quad\quad \therefore b = 26.46$ ft. *Ans.*

Check: $\quad \log (c + b) = 1.7930$

$\quad\quad\quad\; \log (c - b) = 0.9619$

$\quad\quad \log (c^2 - b^2) = 2.7549 = \log a^2 = 2 \log a$

391. Remark on inverse functions.—The form $A = \sin^{-1} \dfrac{a}{c}$

is read "A = the angle whose sine is $\dfrac{a}{c}$." This is a convenient

way of expressing the fact and allows the angle symbol to
stand alone. The -1 that is in the position of an exponent
is not a negative exponent in meaning.

The form $\sin^{-1} \dfrac{a}{c}$ is called an **inverse trigonometric function.**

It is also written $\arcsin \dfrac{a}{c}$ and $\text{invsin } \dfrac{a}{c}$. These forms are also

read "antisine $\dfrac{a}{c}$," "arcsine $\dfrac{a}{c}$," and "inverse sine $\dfrac{a}{c}$."

392. Case IV.—Given a and b.

The following formulas are used:

(1) $c^2 = a^2 + b^2$ $\qquad$ $\therefore$ $c = \sqrt{a^2 + b^2}$

(2) $\tan A = \dfrac{a}{b}$ $\qquad$ $\therefore$ $A = \tan^{-1} \dfrac{a}{b}$

(3) $\tan B = \dfrac{b}{a}$ $\qquad$ $\therefore$ $B = \tan^{-1} \dfrac{b}{a}$

Check: $\qquad$ $\sin A = \dfrac{a}{c}$, and $\cos A = \dfrac{b}{c}$

EXERCISES

Solve the following right triangles, and check each by making an accurate construction and by substituting in a formula not used in solving.

1. Given $A = 68°13'$, $c = 200$ ft.; find B, a, and b.

Ans. 21°47'; 185.7 ft.; 74.22 ft.

2. Given $B = 66°30'$, $b = 575$ ft.; find A, a, and c.

Ans. 23°30'; 250 ft.; 627 ft.

3. Given $A = 13°41'$, $a = 992$ ft.; find B, b, and c.

Ans. 76°19'; 4075 ft.; 4194 ft.

4. Given $B = 52°4'$, $b = 4$ ft.; find A, a, and c.

Ans. 37°56'; 3.117 ft.; 5.071 ft.

5. Given $A = 53°30'$, $c = 30.69$ ft.; find B, a, and b.

Ans. 36°30'; 24.67 ft.; 18.25 ft.

6. Given $A = 63°$, $c = 43$ ft.; find B, a, and b.

Ans. 27°; 38.31 ft.; 19.52 ft.

7. Given $B = 36°45'$, $a = 1758$ ft.; find A, B, and c.

Ans. 53°15'; 1313 ft.; 2194 ft.

8. Given $B = 85°25'$, $a = 637$ ft.; find A, b, and c.

9. Given $A = 86°$, $a = 0.0008$ mile; find B, b, and c.

Ans. 4°; 0.0000559 miles; 0.000802 miles.

10. Given $A = 21°8'$, $a = 73$ ft.; find B, b, and c.

11. Given $a = 2$ ft., $b = 2$ ft.; find A, B, and c.

Ans. $A = B = 45°$; $c = 2.828$ ft.

12. Given $c = 8$ ft., $b = 4$ ft.; find A, B, and a.

13. Given $a = 8.49$ ft.; $c = 9.35$ ft.; find A, B, and b.

Ans. $A = 65°14'$; $B = 24°46'$; $b = 3.917$ ft.

14. Given $b = 16.926$ ft.; $a = 13.690$ ft.; find A, B, and c.

15. Given $a = 2.19$ ft., $c = 91.92$ ft.; find A, B, and b.

16. Given $c = 2194$ ft., $b = 1312.7$ ft.; find A, B, and a.

17. Given $b = \sqrt[3]{2}$ ft., $c = \sqrt{3}$ ft.; find A, B, and a.

RIGHT TRIANGLES APPLIED TO PROBLEMS

393. Direction of one point from another.—The direction from one point to another may be given in a variety of ways involving some angle. The meaning will usually be understood from the statement of the problem without any special explanation.

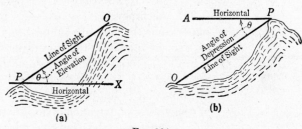

FIG. 291.

The **angle of elevation** is the angle between the line of sight and the horizontal plane through the eye when the object observed is above that horizontal plane. When the object observed is below this horizontal plane, the angle is called the **angle of depression.**

Thus, in Fig. 291 (a), an object O is seen from the point P. The angle θ between the line PO and the horizontal PX is the angle of elevation. In (b) an object O is seen from the point of observation P. The angle θ between the line PO and the horizontal AP is called the angle of depression.

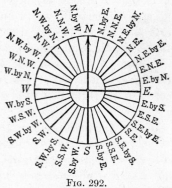

FIG. 292.

Directions on the surface of the earth are often given by directions as located on the **mariner's compass.** As seen from Fig. 292, these directions are located with reference to the four cardinal points, north, south, east, and west. The directions are often spoken of as **bearings.** Present practice, however, gives the bearing of a line in degrees. The bearing of a line is defined to be the acute angle that the line makes with the north-and-south line.

Thus, in Fig. 293, if O is the point of observation, the bearing of OA is north, 20° east, written N 20° E. The bearing of

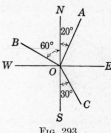

Fig. 293.

OB is N 60° W, and that of OC is S 30° E.

394. Accuracy.—It is of very great importance that one should bear in mind as far as possible the limitations as regards accuracy. The degree of accuracy that can be depended upon in a computation is limited by the accuracy of the tables of trigonometric functions and logarithms used and by the data involved in the computation.

The greater the number of decimal places in the table the more accurately, in general, can the angles be determined from the natural or logarithmic functions; but in a given table, the accuracy is greater the more rapidly the function is changing. Since the cosine of the angle changes slowly when the angle is near 0°, small angles should not be determined from the cosine. For instance, if the cosine of an angle is 0.9997, the angle may be taken as 88° 30′ or 88° 40′ from Table XI. For a like reason, the sines should not be used when the angle is near 90°. The tangent and cotangent change more rapidly throughout the quadrant and so can be used for any angle.

Most of the data used in problems are obtained from measurements made with instruments devised to determine those data more or less accurately. The inability to be precise in the data depends not only upon the instruments used but upon the person making the measurements and upon the thing measured.

A man in practical work uses instruments of such accuracy as to secure results suitable for his purpose. The data given in problems for practice are supposed to be of such accuracy as the instruments used in such measurements would warrant.

In the solution of a problem it is useless to carry out the computations with a greater degree of accuracy than that of the data. That is, if the data are correct only to, say, four significant figures, there is no necessity to compute to more figures than this. If the measuring instrument can be read only to minutes of angle, in the computation, there is no object in carrying the work to seconds of angle.

In general, the following is the agreement between the measurement of distances and the related angles:

(1) Distances to two significant figures, angles to the nearest 0.5°.

(2) Distances to three significant figures, angles to the nearest 5'.

(3) Distances to four significant figures, angles to the nearest 1'.

(4) Distances to five significant figures, angles to the nearest 0.1'.

In drill problems, the angles are often expressed as if accurate to a higher degree than they really are. This gives variety in interpolating, but one should not be misled by the implied accuracy.

The United States Coast and Geodetic Survey sets the following standards for its finest surveys: A line 1 mile long may turn to the one side or the other not more than $\frac{1}{8}$ in. The average closing error in leveling work must be less than 1 in. in 100 miles. The first gives a variation in the angle of 0.4″ to each side, or a total of 0.8″. In making such accurate computations, a 10-place table is used.

395. Tests of accuracy.—The practical man endeavors in one way or another to check both his measurements and his computations. In our work here we are interested in checks on the computation.

(1) Often a graphical construction to scale will give results that will check the numerical work. If the construction is

made free hand, only the gross mistakes in computation will be discovered; but if the construction is made carefully with accurate instruments, results may be obtained as accurate as the data will warrant. This, then, may be considered a graphical solution of the problem.

(2) Mistakes in the computations may be found by making another computation using a different set of data or by recomputing, using the same data but a different set of formulas. Many ways will present themselves to the thoughtful student.

EXERCISES

1. If a man 6 ft. tall stands on level ground, and if the elevation of the sun is 64°, how long will his shadow be?   *Ans.* 2.9+ ft.

Suggestion: $\cot 64° = \dfrac{x}{6}$.

2. If the man in Exercise 1 casts a shadow 4 ft. long, find the elevation of the sun.   *Ans.* 56° 19′ −.

3. A building 600 ft. tall stands on level ground, and the angle of elevation of the top is observed to be 5°. Find the distance from the point of observation to the foot of the building.   *Ans.* 6858 ft.

4. If the building in Exercise 3 is the Empire State Building, which is 1248 ft. high, solve the problem.   *Ans.* 14,263+ ft.

5. The bottom of a picture on the wall is level with the eye of the observer. If the picture is 8 ft. across from top to bottom, and if the elevation of the top is 20°, find how far the observer's eye is from the bottom of the picture.   *Ans.* 21.98 ft.

6. What is the inclination from the vertical of the face of a wall having a batter of $\frac{1}{8}$? A batter of $\frac{1}{8}$ means that the wall inclines 1 ft. from the vertical in a rise of 8 ft.   *Ans.* 7°7.6′.

7. What is the angle of inclination of a stairway with the floor if the steps have a tread of 8 in. and a rise of $6\frac{1}{2}$ in.?   *Ans.* 39°5.6′.

8. What angle does a rafter make with the horizontal if it has a rise of 6 ft. in a run of 12 ft.?   *Ans.* 26°33.9′.

9. Find the angle between the rafters and the horizontal in roofs of the following pitches: two-thirds, one-half, one-third, one-fourth.
    Ans. 53°7.8′.; 45°; 33°41.4′; 26°33.9′.

NOTE.—By the pitch of a roof is meant the ratio of the rise of the rafters to twice the run; or in a V-shape roof (Fig. 294), it is the ratio of the distance from the plate to the ridge to the width of the building.

10. One of the equal sides of an isosceles triangle is 4.2 in., and one of the base angles is 27° 15′; find the altitude and the base.
    Ans. 1.923 in.; 7.468 in.

11. The base of an isosceles triangle is 60 ft., and the vertex angle is 58°30′; find the equal sides and the base angles. *Ans.* 61.47 ft.

12. If it is 1000 yd. to the foot of an object 1 yd. high, what angle does this object subtend? This is approximately the *mil*, which is used as the unit of angle in artillery practice. (Use the tangent. Notice the inadequacy of the four-place table.) *Ans.* 0°3′+.

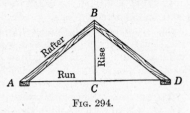

FIG. 294.

13. A mountain road has a rise of 1 mile for every 6 miles along the road. What is the angle of rise? *Ans.* 9°36′−.

14. A grade of 1% in a roadbed is a rise of 1 ft. in a horizontal distance of 100 ft., and proportionately for other grades. What is the angle of slope of a roadbed that has a grade of 5%? One with a grade of 0.25%? *Ans.* 2°51.7′; 8.6′.

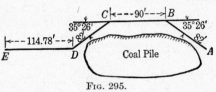

FIG. 295.

15. A road rises 400 ft. in a horizontal distance of 2600 ft. Find the per cent of grade and the inclination of the roadbed with the horizontal. *Ans.* $15\frac{5}{13}$%; 8°44.7′.

16. A man whose eyes are 5 ft. 6 in. above the ground is on a level with and 150 ft. distant from the foot of a flagstaff 72 ft. high. What angle does his line of sight make with the horizontal line from his eyes to the pole when he is looking at the top of the staff? *Ans.* 23°54.6′.

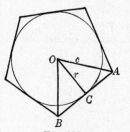

FIG. 296.

17. In surveying on the Lake Front in Chicago, measurements were taken as shown in Fig. 295. Find the distance on a straight line from A to E. *Ans.* 338.4 ft.

18. The side of a regular pentagon (five-sided figure) is 12 in. Find the radius of the inscribed circle and the area of the pentagon. *Suggestion.*—Draw the pentagon, and inscribe a circle as in Fig. 296. Angle $AOB = 72°$. Triangle AOB is isosceles. We have $\tan 36° = \dfrac{6}{r}$.

$$\therefore r = 6 \div \tan 36°$$

Could this problem be solved as easily by geometry?

Ans. 8.258 in.; 247.8 sq. in.

19. Find a side of the regular octagon circumscribed about a circle 20 ft. in diameter.   *Ans.* 8.284 ft.

20. A building stands on level ground.   At a point A on the ground the elevation of the second-floor window sill, which is 20 ft. from the ground, is 40°.   When viewed from A, the angle of elevation of the top of the building is 70°.   Find the height of the building.

Ans. 20(cot 40°) (tan 70°) ft.

21. An observation balloon was attached to a point on the ground at A.   On a level with A and in the same straight line the points B and C were chosen so that BC equaled 300 ft.   From the points B and C the angle of elevation of the balloon was 40° and 30°, respectively.   Find the height of the balloon.   *Ans.* 555 ft.

Suggestion.—Form two equations in two unknowns.

22. Find the shorter altitude and area of a parallelogram whose sides are 10 and 25 ft. and whose angle between the sides is 75°.

Ans. 9.659 ft.; 241.5 sq. ft.

23. Two points C and B are on opposite banks of a river.   A line AC at right angles to CB is measured 40 rods long, and the angle CAB is measured and found to be 41° 40′.   Find the width of the stream.

Ans. 35.60 rods.

24. A ship is sailing due east at 16 miles per hour.   A lighthouse is observed due south at 8:30 A.M.   At 9:45 A.M. the bearing of the same lighthouse is S 38°30′ W.   Find the distance from the ship to the lighthouse at the time of the first observation.   *Ans.* 25.14 mi.

25. In order to locate accurately holes that are to be drilled in a piece of work, the piece is clamped to the table of a milling machine.   The

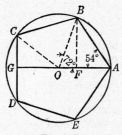

Fig. 297.

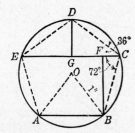

Fig. 298.

table is so constructed that it can be moved in two directions at right angles to each other.   In order to drill five holes accurately spaced at the vertices of a regular pentagon inscribed in a circle of radius 1 in., it is desired to determine the lengths of *OF*, *FB*, *OG*, and *GC* of Fig. 297. Find these to the nearest 0.001 in.

Ans. 0.309 in.; 0.951 in.; 0.809 in.; 0.588 in.

26. Locate the holes in the same piece by determining the lengths of *AB*, *BF*, *FC*, *EC*, *EG*, and *GD* of Fig. 298, to the nearest 0.001 in.

Ans. 1.175 in.; 1.118 in.; 0.363 in.; 1.902 in.; 0.951 in.; 0.691 in.

27. Locate the centers of the holes *B* and *C*, Fig. 299, by finding the distance each is to the right of and above the center *O*. The radius of the circle is 1.5 in. Compute correctly to three decimal places.

Ans. B 1.214 in., 0.882 in.; *C* 0.464 in., 1.427 in.

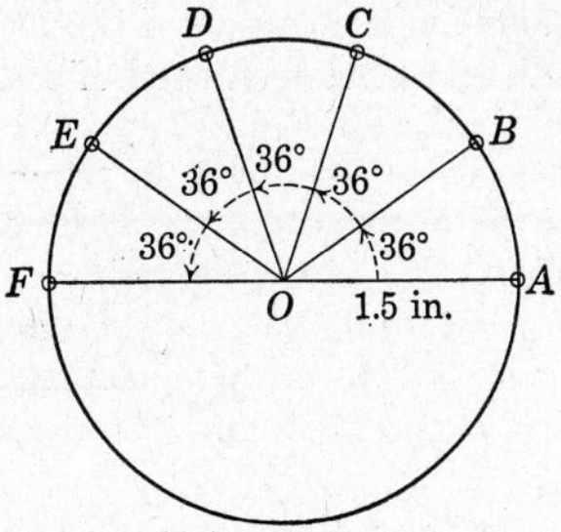

28. To drill holes accurately at *A*, *B*, and *C*, it is necessary to determine *AC* and *CB* in Fig. 300. Find them to the nearest 0.001 in.

Ans. 3.955 in.; 2.147 in.

29. Determine the lengths *AD*, *DC*, and *DB* to the nearest 0.001 in., for drilling holes at *A*, *B*, and *C* in Fig. 301.

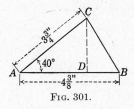

Fig. 299.

Ans. 2.873 in.; 2.411 in.; 1.502 in.

30. One side of a regular pentagon inscribed in a circle is 8 in.; find the radius of the circle. *Ans.* 6.807 in.

31. One side of a regular octagon inscribed in a circle is 10 in.; find the radius of the circle. *Ans.* 13.07 in.

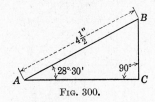

Fig. 300.

Fig. 301.

32. A man surveying a mine measures a length *AB* = 220 ft. due east with a dip of 6°15′, then a length *BC* = 325 ft. due south with a dip 10°45′. How much deeper is *C* than *A*? *Ans.* 84.57 ft.

33. In the side of a hill that slopes upward at an angle of 32°, a tunnel is bored sloping downward at an angle of 12°15′ with the horizontal. How far below the surface of the hill is a point 115 ft. down the tunnel?

Ans. 94.63 ft.

34. The angle of elevation of a balloon from a point due south of it is 60°, and from another point 1 mile due west of the former the angle of elevation is 45°. Find the height of the balloon.   *Ans.* 1.225 miles.

35. In Exercise 34 let the 60° angle be *A*; the 45° angle, *B*; the 1 mile due west, *s*; and the height of the balloon, *h*. Find *h* as a function of *A*, *B*, and *s*. Check the answer of Exercise 34.

36. From the top of a mountain 1050 ft. high, two buildings are seen on a level plane and in a direct line from the foot of the mountain. The angle of depression of the first is 35° and of the second is 24°. Find the distance between the buildings.   *Ans.* 858.8 ft.

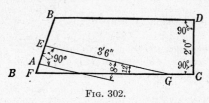

Fig. 302.

37. Using Fig. 302, with the dimensions as given, find *AB*.

Ans. 23.61 in.

38. A chord of 2 ft. is in a circle of radius 3 ft. Find the length of the arc subtended by the chord and the number of degrees in it.

Ans. 2.038 ft.; 38°56.3′.

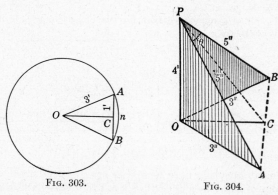

Fig. 303.

Fig. 304.

Suggestion.—In Fig. 303 the chord *AB* = 2 ft. and the radius *OA* = 3 ft. Triangle *AOC* is a right triangle. Angle *AOC* = ½ angle *AOB*, and the central angle *AOB* has the same measure as the arc *AnB*.

39. Find the angle between the diagonal of a cube and one of the diagonals of a face that meets it.   *Ans.* 35°15.9′.

40. Two set squares, whose sides are 3, 4, and 5 in., are placed as in Fig. 304 so as to form a tetrahedron. The angle AOB between the 3-in. sides is 50°. Find the angle θ, which is APB, between the longest sides. *Ans.* 29°22.5′.

41. What size target at 30 ft. from the eye subtends the same angle as a target 4 ft. in diameter at 1000 yd.? Find the angle that it subtends.
Ans. 0.48 in.; 4.6′.

42. The description in a deed runs as follows: "Beginning at a stone A at the NW corner of a lot 401; thence east 112 ft. to a stone B; thence S $36\frac{1}{2}$° W 100 ft.; thence west parallel with AB to the west line of said lot 401; thence north on west line of said lot to the place of beginning." Find the area of the land described. *Ans.* 6612.9 sq. ft.

43. An observation balloon has an angle of elevation of 42°30′ from point A on a level ground and an elevation of 36°45′ from a point B directly above A. If AB is 66 ft., find the height of the balloon and the distance from A to a point directly under it.
Ans. 356.6 ft.; 389 ft.

44. A ship sailing due north observes two lighthouses in a line due west; after an hour's sailing, the bearings of the lighthouses are observed to the southwest and south-southwest. If the distance between the lighthouses is 8 miles, at what rate is the ship sailing?
Ans. 13.66 miles per hour.

45. Wishing to determine the width of a river, I observed a tree standing directly across on the bank. The angle of elevation of the top of the tree was 32°; at 150 ft. back from this point and in the same

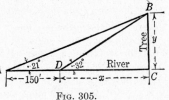

FIG. 305.

direction from the tree the angle of elevation of the top of the tree was 21°. Find the width of the river. *Ans.* 239 ft. approx.

Suggestion.—Let x = width of river and y = height of tree. The relations of the parts are as given in Fig. 305.

$$(1) \qquad \tan 32° = \frac{y}{x}$$

$$(2) \qquad \tan 21° = \frac{y}{150 + x}$$

Here are two equations and two unknown numbers. The solution of them will give the values of x and y.

46. At a certain point the angle of elevation of a mountain peak is 44°30′; at a distance of 3 miles farther away in the same horizontal plane, its angle of elevation is 29°45′. Find the distance of the top of the mountain above the horizontal plane and the horizontal distance from the first point of observation to the peak.   *Ans.* 4098 miles; 4171 miles.

47. At a certain point A the angle of elevation of a mountain peak is α; at a point B that is a miles farther away in the same horizontal plane its angle of elevation is β. If h represents the distance of the peak above the plane and x the horizontal distance of the peak from A, derive the following formulas:

$$h = \frac{a \tan \alpha \tan \beta}{\tan \alpha - \tan \beta}$$

$$x = \frac{a \tan \beta}{\tan \alpha - \tan \beta}$$

Note.—In using these formulas, it is convenient to use natural functions. In Art. 436, Exercise 32, a solution of the same problem is given, obtaining formulas adapted to logarithms.

48. Find the height of a tree if the angle of elevation of its top changes from 35° to 64° 30′ on walking toward it 150 ft. in a horizontal line through its base.   *Ans.* 157.7 ft.

49. A man walking on a level plain toward a tower observes that at a certain point the angle of elevation of the top of the tower is 28° and that on walking 250 ft. directly toward the tower, the angle of elevation of the top is 48°. Find the height of the tower if the point of observation each time is 5 ft. above the ground.   *Ans.* 260 ft.

50. The length of a degree of longitude on the equator is 69.16 miles. Find the length of a degree of longitude on the parallel of 45° north latitude, on the parallel of 30° south latitude. Find the length of a degree of longitude for any latitude.

Ans. 48.90 miles; 59.89 miles; 69.16 × cosine of latitude.

51. In Whitworth's English Standard screw threads, Fig. 306, the angle between the sides of the threads is 55°. If the top of a thread is

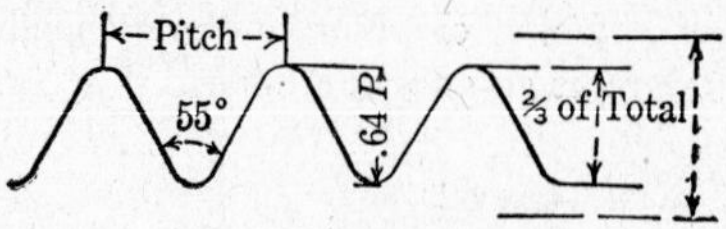

Fig. 306.

rounded off one-sixth of the height and the bottom filled in the same amount, find the depth to four decimal places of the threads of the following pitches: 1, 8, 14, and 26.

Ans. 0.6403 in.; 0.0800 in.; 0.0457 in.; 0.0246 in.

52. In an acme thread, the angle between the sides of the threads is 29°. When the pitch is P, the depth and the other dimensions are as shown in Fig. 307. (1) Suppose that the top dimensions and the depth are given; find the dimensions at the bottom. (2) Find the dimensions at the top and bottom and the depth for an 8-pitch acme thread.

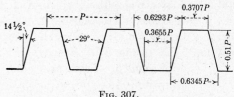

Fig. 307.

53. In a worm thread, the angle between the sides is 29°. The dimensions are as shown in Fig. 308. (1) Suppose that the top dimensions and the depth are given; find the bottom dimensions. (2) Find the

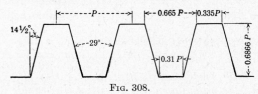

Fig. 308.

dimensions in a 7-pitch thread. (The foregoing are the Brown and Sharpe proportions.) What are the differences between a worm thread and an acme thread?

APPLICATION OF RIGHT TRIANGLES TO VECTORS

396. Orthogonal projection.—If from a point P, Fig. 309 (a), a perpendicular PQ is drawn to any straight line RS, then the

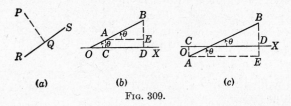

Fig. 309.

foot of the perpendicular Q is said to be the **orthogonal projection** or simply the **projection** of P upon RS.

The **projection of a line segment** upon a given straight line is the portion of the given line lying between the projections of the ends of the segment.

In Fig. 309 (*b*) and (*c*), *CD* is the projection of *AB* on *OX*. In each case *AE* = *CD* and *AE* = *AB* cos θ.

The projections usually made are upon a horizontal line *OX* and a vertical line *OY* as in Fig. 310.   Hence, if *l* is the length

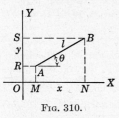

Fig. 310.

of segment of line projected, *x* the projection upon *OX*, *y* the projection upon *OY*, and θ the angle of inclination, that is, the angle that the line segment makes with the *x*-axis, then

x = 1 cos θ

y = 1 sin θ

This may be stated in words as follows:

The projection of any line segment upon a horizontal line equals the length of the segment multiplied by the cosine of the angle of inclination; the projection upon a vertical line equals the length of the segment multiplied by the sine of the angle of inclination.

397. Vectors.—In physics and engineering, line segments are often used to represent quantities that have direction as well as magnitude. Velocities, accelerations, and forces are such quantities.

For instance, a force of 100 lb. acting in a northeasterly direction may be represented by a line, say, 10 in. long drawn in a northeasterly direction. The line is drawn so as to represent the force to some scale; here it is 10 lb. to the inch. An arrowhead is put on one end of the line to show its direction.

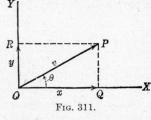

Fig. 311.

In Fig. 311, *OP* = *v* is a line representing a directed quantity. Such a line is called a **vector.**   *O* is the **beginning** of the vector, and *P* is the **terminal.**   *OQ* = *x* is the **projection of the vector upon the horizontal** *OX*; *OR* = *y* is the **projection upon the** vertical OY; and θ is the **inclination** of the vector. The vectors x and y are called **components** of the vector v. As before,

$$x = v \cos \theta$$
$$y = v \sin \theta$$

Suppose that the vectors OQ and OP, Fig. 312, represent the magnitude and direction of two forces acting at the point O and having any angle φ between their lines of action. If the parallelogram $OQRP$ is completed, then the diagonal OR represents in magnitude and direction a force that will produce the same effect as the two given forces.

The vector OR is called the **resultant** of the vectors OQ and OP. The process of finding the resultant of two or more given forces is called **composition of forces.**

Conversely, the vectors OQ and OP are **components** of OR.

Since QR is equal and parallel to OP, it follows that the two components and their resultant form a closed triangle OQR. The relations between forces and their resultant may then be found by solving a triangle that is, in general, an oblique triangle.

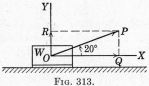

Fig. 313.

Example 1.—Suppose that a weight W is resting on a rough horizontal table as shown in Fig. 313. Suppose that a force of 40 lb. is acting on the weight and in the direction OP, making an angle of 20° with the horizontal; then the horizontal pull on the weight is $OQ = 40 \cos 20° = 37.588$ lb., and the vertical lift on the weight is $OR = 40 \sin 20° = 13.68$ lb.

Example 2.—A car is moving up an incline, making an angle of 35° with the horizontal, at the rate of 26 ft. per second. What is its horizontal velocity? Its vertical velocity?

Solution.—Horizontal velocity $= 26 \cos 35° = 21.3$ ft. per second. Vertical velocity $= 26 \sin 35° = 14.9$ ft. per second.

EXERCISES

1. Two lines OX and OY are perpendicular at O. A line segment PQ is 10 in. long and lies in the plane of OX and OY. If PQ makes an angle of 67° with OX, find its projection on OX. Find its projection on OY. *Ans.* 3.907 in.; 9.205 in.

2. In Exercise 1 find the projection of PQ on a line that makes an angle of 45° with OX. [Projection = 10 cos (67° − 45°). Why?]

3. A car is moving north at the rate of 60 miles per hour. How fast is it moving east? How fast is it moving southeast?

4. A golf ball is hit at an angle of 15° with the horizontal with a force of p lb. What is the force that drives it forward? What force causes it to rise if gravity is neglected? *Ans.* 0.9659p lb.; 0.2588 p lb.

5. The eastward and northward components of the velocity of a ship are, respectively, 5.5 and 10.6 miles. Find the direction and the rate at which the ship is sailing.
Ans. 11.94 miles per hour, N 27° 25.4′ E.

6. A roof is inclined at an angle of 33° 30′. The wind strikes this horizontally with a force of 1800 lb. Find the pressure perpendicular to the roof. *Ans.* 993.4 lb.

7. A roof 20 by 25 ft. and inclined at an angle of 27° 25′ with the horizontal will shelter how large an area? *Ans.* 443.85 sq. ft.

8. A force of 300 lb. is acting on a body lying on a horizontal plane, in a direction that makes an angle of 20° with the horizontal. What is the force tending to lift the body from the plane, and what is the force tending to move the body along the plane?
Ans. 102.6 lb.; 281.9 lb.

9. A body weighing 45 lb. rests on a horizontal table and is acted on by a force of 50 lb. acting at an angle of 25° 15′ with the surface of the table. What is the pressure on the table? *Ans.* 23.67 lb.

10. A body weighing 75 lb. rests on a horizontal table and is acted on by a force of 100 lb. acting at an angle of −36° 30′ with the surface of the table. What is the pressure on the table? *Ans.* 134.5 lb.

11. The horizontal and vertical components of a force are, respectively, 245.8 and 325.6 lb. What is the magnitude of the force, and what angle does its line of action make with the horizontal?
Ans. 408.0 lb.; 52° 57′.

12. The horizontal and vertical components of a force are, respectively, 125.5 and −189.6 lb. What is the magnitude of the force, and what angle does its line of action make with the horizontal?
Ans. 227.4 lb.; −56° 29.9′.

13. A river runs directly south at 4 miles an hour. A man starts at the west bank and rows directly across at the rate of 3 miles an hour. In what direction does his boat move? *Ans.* 36° 52.2′ with bank.

14. A ferryboat at a point on one bank of a river $\frac{1}{2}$ mile wide must reach a point directly across the river. If the river flows 3.5 miles an hour and the ferryboat can steam 7.6 miles an hour, in what direction should the boat be pointed? *Ans.* 27° 25.3′ upstream.

15. Two men are lifting a stone by means of ropes running over a pulley and acting in the same vertical plane. One man pulls 85 lb. in a direction 23° from the vertical, and the other 125 lb. in a direction 42° from the vertical. Determine the weight of the stone.

Ans. 171.1 lb.

16. Two forces of 240 and 180 lb. act in the same vertical plane on a heavy body, the first at an angle of 40° with the horizontal and the second at an angle of 65°. Find the total force tending to move the body horizontally, to lift it vertically. *Ans.* 259.9 lb.; 317.4 lb.

CHAPTER XXXVIII

USEFUL AND MORE DIFFICULT PROBLEMS

398. Relations between angle, arc, and radius.—From the definition of the radian, Art. 361, it is evident that the number of radians in an angle at the center of a circle can be found by dividing the length of the arc its sides intercept by the length of the radius; that is,

$$\textbf{Number of radians in angle} = \frac{\textbf{arc}}{\textbf{radius}}$$

In Fig. 314, angle AOB (in radians) $= \dfrac{\text{arc } AB}{\text{radius } OA}.$

If θ stands for the number of radians in an angle; r for the

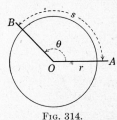

FIG. 314.

length of the radius of a circle, having its center at the vertex of the angle; and s for the length of the arc between the sides of the angle, then

$$\theta = s \div r, \ s = r\theta, \ \text{or } r = s \div \theta$$

These relations are important, as they may be used in solving many practical problems.

Example 1.—In a circle an angle of 3.5 radians has an arc of 10.5 ft.; find the radius.

Solution.—Substituting in the formula $s = r\theta$,

$$10.5 = 3.5r$$

Solving for r, $r = 10.5 \div 3.5 = 3$.
Hence the radius is 3 ft. *Ans.*

Example 2.—The diameter of a graduated circumference is 10 ft., and the graduations are 5' of arc apart; find the distance, length of arc, between the graduations in fractions of an inch to three decimal places.

Solution.—By formula, $s = r\theta$.

From the example,

$$r = 12 \times 5 = 60 = \text{length in inches}$$

and $\qquad \theta = 0.01745 \times \tfrac{5}{60} = 0.00145+$

Substituting in the formula,

$$s = 60 \times 0.00145+ = 0.087+$$

∴ length of 5′ of arc is 0.087+ in. *Ans.*

399. Railroad curves.—In the United States it is customary to express the curvature of railroad tracks in *degrees*. The degree of a curve is determined by the central angle which is subtended by a chord of 100 ft. Thus, in a circle, a **5° curve** is one in which a 100-ft. chord subtends a central angle of 5°.

In curves commonly used, the error is slight if the arc is taken in place of the chord. Then, assuming that 1 radian = 57.30°, the radius of a 1° curve is found from the formula of the preceding article. Thus,

$$r = s \div \theta = 100 \div \frac{1}{57.30} = 5730 \text{ ft.}$$

Hence, 1° of curvature gives a radius of 5730 ft. It follows that 5730 divided by the number of degrees in the curve gives the radius of the curve and 5730 divided by the number of feet in the radius gives the number of degrees in the curve.

EXERCISES

1. If an angle of 126° at the center has an arc of 226 ft., find the radius of the circle.

Solution.—Use the formula $r = s \div \theta$.

$$\theta = 126 \times 0.017453 = 2.199$$
$$r = 226 \times 2.199 = 102.77$$
$$\therefore \text{radius is } 102.77 \text{ ft. } \textit{Ans.}$$

2. A flywheel 20 ft. in diameter has an angular velocity of 3π per second. Find the rim velocity. *Ans.* 94.25 ft. per second.

3. The circumferential speed generally advised by makers of emery wheels is 5500 ft. per minute. Find the angular velocity per second in radians for a 10-in. wheel.   *Ans.* 220 radians per second.

Suggestion.—Use the formula $\theta = s \div r$.

4. Solve similar problems for the velocities of the following:

(a) Ohio grindstones, advised speed 2500 ft. per minute.

(b) Huron grindstones, advised speed 3500 ft. per minute.

(c) Wood, leather-covered, polishing wheels, 7000 ft. per minute.

(d) Walrus hide polishing wheels, 8000 ft. per minute.

(e) Rag wheels, 7000 ft. per minute.

(f) Hairbrush wheels, 12,000 ft. per minute.

5. A flywheel of 4-ft. radius is revolving counterclockwise with a circumferential velocity of 75 ft. per second. Find the angular velocity in radians per second.   *Ans.* $18\frac{3}{4}$ radians.

Solution: $$\frac{75 \times 2\pi}{8\pi} = 18\frac{3}{4}$$

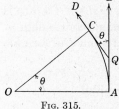

Fig. 315.

6. A train is traveling on a curve of half a mile radius at the rate of 30 miles per hour. Through what angle does it turn in 45 sec.? Express the answer in both radians and degrees.

Solution.—Let the train run from A to C in Fig. 315 in 45 sec. At A it is moving in the direction AB; and at C, in the direction CD. The change in direction is BQD, which equals AOC or θ.

In 45 sec. the train travels $\frac{3}{8}$ mile.

To find θ use formula $\theta = s \div r$.

$\therefore \theta = \frac{3}{8} \div \frac{1}{2} = 0.75$ radian $= 42° 58' 19''$. *Ans.*

7. Find the radius of a circle in which an arc of 20 ft. measures an angle of 2.3 radians at the center. In this circle, find the angle at the center measured by an arc of 3 ft. 8 in.
Ans. 8.70 − ft.; 0.421 + radian.

8. Find the angular velocity per minute of the minute hand of a watch. Express in degrees and radians.   *Ans.* $6° = 0.1047+$ radian.

9. A train of cars is going at the rate of 15 miles per hour on a curve of 600-ft. radius; find its angular velocity in radians per minute.
Ans. 2.2 radians.

10. A flywheel 22 ft. in diameter is revolving with an angular velocity of 9 radians per second. Find the rate per minute that a point on the circumference is traveling.   *Ans.* 5940 ft. per minute.

11. Find the length of arc that, at the distance of 1 mile, will subtend an angle of 10' at the eye; an angle of 1''.   *Ans.* 15.36 ft.; 0.0256 ft.

12. The radius of the earth's orbit, which is about 92,700,000 miles, subtends at the star Sirius an angle of about 0.4″. Find the approximate distance of Sirius from the earth. *Ans.* 478 × 10¹¹ miles.

13. What radius has a 5° curve in a railroad track? A curve of 3° 15′? If the radius of curvature is 4550 ft., what is the degree of curve?

Ans. 1146 ft.; 1763 + ft.; $1\frac{1}{4}$° nearly.

400. Lengths of belts.—The length of a belt required to connect two pulleys may usually be found by measurement. An approximate rule often used for finding the length of an

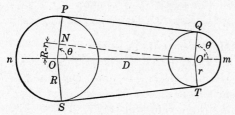

Fig. 316.

uncrossed belt is: Add twice the distance between the centers of the shafts to half the sum of the circumferences of the two pulleys.

The lengths of belts can be computed accurately as follows:

(1) *Length of uncrossed, or open, belt.*

In Fig. 316, R and r, respectively, are the radii of the two pulleys, and D the distance between their centers.

Let L = number of units in length of belt.

(1) L = arc PnS + $2PQ$ + arc QmT

But arc $PnS = 2R(\pi - \theta)$, arc $QmT = 2r\theta$, and $PQ = NO' = D \sin \theta$.

Substituting these values in (1),

$$L = 2R(\pi - \theta) + 2D \sin \theta + 2r\theta$$
$$\therefore L = 2[R(\pi - \theta) + r\theta + D \sin \theta]$$

To find θ, we have $\cos \theta = \dfrac{R - r}{D}$.

In using the formula for L, in the parts $R(\pi - \theta)$ and $r\theta$, π and θ must be in radians.

(2) *Length of crossed belt.*

In Fig. 317, R and r, respectively, are the radii of the two pulleys, and D the distance between their centers.

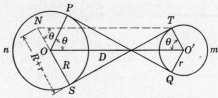

Fig. 317.

Let L = number of units in length of belt.

(1) $L = $ arc $PnS + 2ST + $ arc QmT

But arc $PnS = 2R(\pi - \theta)$, arc $QmT = 2r(\pi - \theta)$, and $ST = NT \sin \theta = D \sin \theta$.

Substituting these values in (1),

$$L = 2R(\pi - \theta) + 2D \sin \theta + 2r(\pi - \theta)$$
$$\therefore L = 2[(R + r)(\pi - \theta) + D \sin \theta]$$

To find θ, we have $\cos \theta = \dfrac{R + r}{NT} = \dfrac{R + r}{D}.$

In using the formula for L, $\pi - \theta$ must be taken in radians.

EXERCISES

1. Two pulleys 4 and 2 ft. in diameter, respectively, have their centers 12 ft. apart.   Find the length of an open belt connecting them.

Ans. 33 ft. 6 in.

Suggestion.—Here $R = 2$, $r = 1$, and $D = 12$.

$$\cos \theta = \frac{R - r}{D} = \frac{2 - 1}{12} = \frac{1}{12} = 0.0833$$

$$\therefore \theta = 85° \ 13' = 1.487 \text{ radians}$$
$$\therefore L = 2[2(3.1416 - 1.487) + 1 \cdot 1.487 + 12 \sin 85° \ 13']$$

2. Find the length of a crossed belt connecting the pulleys of Exercise 1.   *Ans.* 34 ft. 2 in.

3. Given $R = 18$ in., $r = 8$ in., $D = 12$ ft., find the length of an open belt by the formula.   Find the length by the approximate rule.

Ans. 30 ft. $10\frac{1}{2}$ in.; 30 ft. $9\frac{3}{4}$ in.

4. Two pulleys, of diameters 7 and 2 ft., respectively, are connected by a crossed belt. If the centers of the pulleys are 16 ft. apart, find the length of the belt. *Ans.* 47 ft. 5 in.

5. Show that any two pulleys with their centers the same distance apart have the same length for a crossed belt if the sum of the diameters is the same.

401. Areas of sector and segment of circle.—These areas are discussed in Arts. 153 and 154, and it is stated there that trigonometry is required in general to find the area of a segment.

In Fig. 318, let it be required to find the area of the segment XAn.

Let G stand for the area of the segment XAn, and let S stand for area of sector $XOAn$.

Evidently, $G = S -$ area of triangle XOA.

By formula [**29(b)**], $S = \frac{1}{2}$ arc $\cdot r$.

But by formula, $S = r\theta$, Art. 398, arc $= r\theta$.

$$\therefore S = \tfrac{1}{2}r^2\theta$$

Area of triangle $XOA = \frac{1}{2}r \cdot BA$.

But, in triangle BOA, $BA = r \sin \theta$.

$$\therefore \text{ area } XOA = \tfrac{1}{2}r^2 \sin \theta$$

Substituting in (1), $G = \frac{1}{2}r^2\theta - \frac{1}{2}r^2 \sin \theta$.

$$\therefore \mathbf{G} = \tfrac{1}{2}\mathbf{r}^2(\boldsymbol\theta - \sin \boldsymbol\theta)$$

Here θ is taken acute. The student may later show that the formula holds when θ is not acute.

This formula is the simplest accurate formula for finding the area of a segment of a circle. It is of frequent use in many practical problems.

If θ is not given, but the radius and chord are given, the value of θ can be readily found.

Example.—Find the area of the segment in a circle of radius 16 in. and having a central angle of 78° 30′.

Solution: 78° 30′ = 78.5° = 78.5 × 0.017453 = 1.3701 radians.

$$\sin 78° 30′ = 0.9799$$

Substituting in formula, $G = \frac{1}{2}r^2(\theta - \sin\theta)$,

$$G = \frac{1}{2} \times 16^2(1.3701 - 0.9799) = 49.94$$

∴ area of segment = 49.94 sq. in.   *Ans.*

EXERCISES

1. Find the area of a sector in a circle of radius 8 ft. and having a central angle of 60°. Find the area of the segment.

Ans. 33.51 sq. ft.; 5.798 sq. ft.

2. Find the area of the segment whose chord is 4 ft. in a circle of 10 ft. diameter.   *Ans.* 1.124 sq. ft.

3. Find the area of a segment whose chord is 12 ft. and height 2 ft.

Ans. 16.35 sq. ft.

4. In a circle of 60 in. radius, find the area of a segment having an angle of 63° 15′. Find the length of the chord and the height of the segment; take $\frac{2}{3}$ of their product; and compare with the area found.

Ans. 379 sq. in.

5. A cylindrical tank resting in a horizontal position is filled with water to within 10 in. of the top. Find the number of cubic feet of water in the tank. The tank is 10 ft. long and 4 ft. in diameter.

Ans. 106.7 cu. ft.

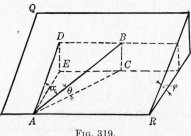

Fig. 319.

402. Slope of a line making a given angle with the line of greatest slope.—In laying out a roadbed over a steep hill, it is often necessary to determine the direction of the road so that it will have a given grade.

Example.—The plane RQ in Fig. 319 is inclined at an angle φ with the horizontal. AD is a line of greatest slope and therefore makes an angle φ with the horizontal. AB, lying in the plane RQ, makes an angle φ with AD. Find the angle θ that AB makes with the horizontal AC.

Solution: $\sin \theta = \dfrac{CB}{AB}$

$$\cos \alpha = \frac{AD}{AB}, \text{ or } AB = \frac{AD}{\cos \alpha}$$

$$\sin \varphi = \frac{ED}{AD}, \text{ or } ED = CB = AD \sin \varphi$$

Substituting, $\sin \theta = AD \sin \varphi \div \dfrac{AD}{\cos \alpha}$.

$$\therefore \sin \theta = \sin \varphi \cos \alpha \quad Ans.$$

This gives θ when φ and α are known.

The formula can also be used to find either φ or α when the two other angles are known.

EXERCISES

1. The slope of a roof is 30°. Find the angle θ that is the inclination to the horizontal of the line AB, drawn in the roof and making an angle of 35° with the line of greatest slope. *Ans.* 24° 11.1′.

2. A hill has a slope of 32°. A path leads up it, making an angle of 45° with the line of greatest slope. Find the slope of the path.

Ans. 22° 0.3′.

3. Two roofs have their ridges at right angles, and each is inclined to the horizontal at an angle of 30°. Find the inclination of their line of intersection to the horizontal. *Ans.* 22° 12.5′.

4. A mountain side has a slope of 30°. A road ascending the mountain is to be built and is to have a grade of 6%. Find the angle that the road will make with the line of greatest slope. *Ans.* 83° 7.2′.

5. A road making an angle of 7° with the horizontal is on a mountain side that makes an angle of 20° with the horizontal. Find the angle that the road makes with the line of greatest slope. *Ans.* 69° 8.1′.

6. A road of 6% grade is on a mountain side having a slope of 35%. Find the angle that the road makes with the line of greatest slope.

Ans. 75°2.1′.

403. Distance and dip of the horizon.—The question often arises as to how far one can see on the surface of the earth from an elevated position, as on a cliff or from an airplane.

In Fig. 320, let O be the center of the earth, r the radius of the earth, and h the height of the point P above the surface; it is required to find the distance from the point P to the horizon at A.

$$(PA)^2 = (PO)^2 - (OA)^2 = (r + h)^2 - r^2 = 2rh + h^2$$
$$\therefore \mathbf{PA} = \sqrt{\mathbf{2rh + h^2}}$$

For points above the surface that are reached by man, h^2 is very small as compared with $2rh$.

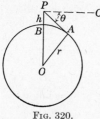

$$\therefore \mathbf{PA} = \sqrt{\mathbf{2rh}}, \text{ approx.}$$

Here PA, r, and h are in the same units. Now let h be in feet and r and PA be in miles. Also let $r = 3960$ miles. Then

Fig. 320.

$$PA = \sqrt{2 \times 3960 \times \frac{h}{5280}} = \sqrt{\frac{3}{2}} h \text{ miles}$$

We may then state the following approximate rules:

The distance of the horizon in miles is approximately equal to the square root of $\frac{3}{2}$ times the height of the point of observation in feet.

The height of the point of observation in feet is $\frac{2}{3}$ times the square of the distance of the horizon in miles.

Definition.—The angle $APC = \theta$ is called the **dip of the horizon.**

Evidently, $$\tan \theta = \frac{PA}{r}$$

EXERCISES

1. A cliff 2000 ft. high is on the seashore; how far away is the horizon? What is the dip of the horizon? *Ans.* 54.8 miles; 47′.

2. Find the greatest distance at which the lamp of a lighthouse can be seen from the deck of a ship. The lamp is 85 ft. above the surface of the water, and the deck of the ship 30 ft. above the surface.

Ans. 18 miles.

3. Find the radius of one's horizon if located 1250 ft. above the surface of the earth. How large when located 3 miles above the earth?

Ans. 43.3 miles; 154 miles.

4. How high above the earth must one be to see a point on the surface 40 miles away?   *Ans.* 1067 ft.

5. Two lighthouses, one 95 ft. high and the other 80 ft., are just visible from each other over the water.   Find how far they are apart

Ans. 23 miles, approx.

404. Widening of pavement on curves.—The tendency of a motorist to "cut the corners" is due to his unconscious desire to give the path of his car around a turn the longest possible radius.   Many highway engineers recognize this tendency by widening the pavement on the inside of the curve as shown in Fig. 321.   The practice adds much to the attractive appear-

ance of the highway.   If the pavement is the same width around the
curve as on the tangents, the curved
section appears narrower than the
normal width; wherea if the curved
section is widened gradually to the
mid-point G of the turn, the pavement appears to have a uniform
width all the way around.

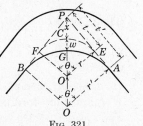

Fig. 321.

In order that the part added may fit the curve properly, it is necessary to have the curve of the inner edge a true arc of a circle, tangent to the edge of the straightaway sections; and therefore it must start before the point E of the curve is reached.   The part added may be easily staked out on the ground with transit and tape, by means of data derived from the radius r, the central angle θ of the curve, and the width w. In practice the width w is taken from 2 to 8 ft. according to the value of r.   The area added can be readily computed when values of r, w, and θ are given.

Referring to the figure, derive the following formulas:

(1)
$$x = r \sec \frac{1}{2}\theta - r = \frac{r}{\cos \frac{1}{2}\theta} - r$$

$$x + w = r' \sec \frac{1}{2}\theta - r' = \frac{r'}{\cos \frac{1}{2}\theta} - r'$$

(2) $$\therefore r' = \frac{x + w}{\sec \frac{1}{2}\theta - 1} = \frac{(x + w) \cos \frac{1}{2}\theta}{1 - \cos \frac{1}{2}\theta}$$

(3) $$t = r \tan \tfrac{1}{2}\theta$$

(4) $$t' = r' \tan \tfrac{1}{2}\theta$$

Area added $= BFCEAG = BPAO' - FPEC - BGAO'$. But $BPAO' = r't'$,

$$FPEC = FPEO - FCEO = rt - \frac{\theta}{360}\pi r^2$$

and $$BGAO' = \frac{\theta}{360}\pi r'^2$$

Then   area $BFCEAG = r't' - \left(rt - \frac{\theta}{360}\pi r^2\right) - \frac{\theta}{360}\pi r'^2$

(5) $$\therefore \text{ area} = r't' - rt - \frac{\theta}{360}\pi(r' + r)(r' - r)$$

In applying formula (5), it is necessary to first compute x, r', t, and t' by formulas (1), (2), (3), and (4).

EXERCISES

1. Find the number of square feet in the area added in turning a right-angle corner if $w = 6$ ft. and $r = 100$ ft.   *Ans.* 666.6 sq. ft.

2. Find the area added if $r = 300$ ft., $w = 4$ ft. and $\theta = 100°$.
Ans. 1395 sq. ft.

405. Spirals.—If a line is drawn around a circular cylinder so that it advances a certain distance along the cylinder for each revolution, the curve thus formed is a **spiral** or a **helix.**

If a piece of paper is cut as shown in (a) Fig. 322, and lines AB and CD drawn, this piece of paper can be rolled into the cylinder (b) Fig. 322, where the lines AB and CD of (a) form the spiral running from A to D of (b).

The advance along the cylinder for each turn of the spiral is the **lead of the spiral,** or the spiral lead. In Fig. 322, AC is the lead. It is customary to give the lead of the spiral as so many inches per one turn. For instance, a spiral that advances 8 in. in one turn is called an 8-in. spiral.

The angle α that the spiral makes with an element of the cylinder is the angle of the spiral. It is seen that

$$\tan \alpha = \frac{circumference\ of\ cylinder}{lead\ of\ the\ spiral}$$

or, in (*a*) Fig. 322, $\tan \alpha = \dfrac{CB}{AC}$.

In setting milling machines for cutting spirals such as worms, spiral gears, counterbores, and twist drills, it is often necessary to know the angle of the spiral.

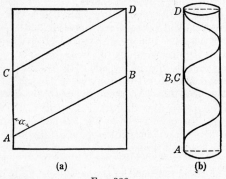

(a)　　　　**(b)**

Fig. 322.

To find the angle of a spiral or for the cutters in cutting a spiral, make a drawing as shown in Fig. 323, the angle C being a right angle; CB, the circumference; and AC, the lead. Angle A is the angle required and may be measured with a protractor, or it may be found by finding $\tan A = \dfrac{CB}{AC}$ and using the table of tangents.

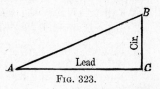

Fig. 323.

For ready reference the following rules are given:

Angle.—Divide the circumference of the spiral by the lead (advance to one turn), and the quotient is the tangent of the angle of the spiral.

Lead.—Divide the circumference of the spiral by the tangent of the angle, and the quotient is the lead of the spiral.

Circumference.—Multiply the tangent of the angle by the lead of the spiral, and the product will be the circumference.

When applying calculations to spiral gears, the angle is reckoned at the pitch circumference.

EXERCISES

1. Find the angle of the spirals in the following twist drills:
(1) Diameter of drill $\frac{5}{16}$ in., lead 2.92 in.   *Ans.* 18° 35′.
(2) Diameter of drill $1\frac{1}{8}$ in., lead 9.33 in.   *Ans.* 20° 44.8′.
(3) Diameter of drill $1\frac{3}{16}$ in., lead 7.29 in.   *Ans.* 19° 17.8′.

2. Find the angle of the spiral thread on a double-threaded worm of pitch diameter $3\frac{1}{2}$ in. and having three threads in 2 in.   *Ans.* 83° 5.1′.

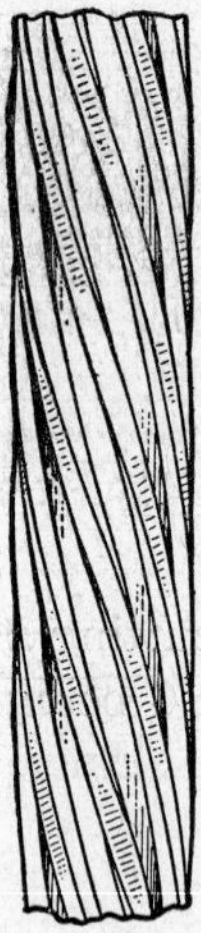

3. At the Illinois Institute of Technology a winding stairway has an outer diameter of 12 ft. The stairway makes one turn in ascending 10 ft.; find the angle of the spiral formed. If the steps are 4 ft. long, find the angle of the spiral formed by the inner ends of the steps.
                    Ans. 75°9′ − ; 51°9′ +.

4. The piece shown in Fig. 324 has a length of $3\frac{1}{2}$ in. and a diameter of $\frac{5}{8}$ in. If the spiral grooves make a half turn in the length of the piece, find the angle of the spiral.
                    Ans. 15° 40′.

5. Find the angle for setting cutters in cutting the following spirals: (1) diameter $\frac{1}{4}$ in. and lead 2.78 in.; (2) $\frac{3}{4}$ in. and 7.62 in.; (3) 2 in. and 10.37 in.; (4) $\frac{7}{8}$ in. and 22.5 in.
          Ans. 15° 46.7′; 17° 10.9′; 31° 13.1′; 6° 59.2′.

6. A cylinder 2 in. in diameter is to have spiral grooves making angles of 20° with the center line of the cylinder. What will be the lead of the spiral?   *Ans.* 17.26 in.

7. Find the length of one turn of a spiral around a cylinder 3 in. in diameter if the lead of the spiral is 9 in.

Fig. 324.

                    Ans. 13.03 in.

8. Show that the length of any spiral is given by formula

$$L = n \sqrt{C^2 + l^2}$$

where
  L = the length of spiral.
  n = the number of turns of the spiral.
  C = circumference of cylinder the spiral is on.
  l = lead of the spiral.

9. Find the length of a spiral making 20 turns in 8 in. on a cylinder 3.5 in. in diameter. *Ans.* 220.0 in.

406. Reflection and refraction of light.—The path of a ray of light in a homogeneous medium such as air is a straight line. But when a ray of light strikes a polished surface, it is **reflected** according to the well-known law that states that *the angle of incidence is equal to the angle of reflection.*

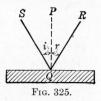

FIG. 325.

Thus, in Fig. 325, the incident ray SQ strikes the polished surface at Q and is reflected in the direction QR. The line QP is perpendicular to the surface at Q. The angle $SQP = i$ is the **angle of incidence,** and the angle $PQR = r$ is the **angle of reflection.** The law states that these two angles are equal.

When a ray of light passes from one transparent medium to another that is more or less dense, its direction is changed; that is, the ray of light is **refracted.**

Thus, in Fig. 326, a ray of light SQ, passing through air, meets the surface of a piece of glass at Q and is refracted toward the normal, or perpendicular, QP'. It continues in the direction QT until it meets the other surface of the glass at T, where it is again refracted, but this time away from the normal, and passes into the air in the direction TR. If the two surfaces of the glass are parallel, it has been found by experiment that the direction of TR is the same as that of SQ.

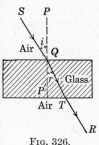

FIG. 326.

The lines QP and QP' are perpendicular to the surface at Q. The angle $SQP = i$ is the **angle of incidence,** and the angle $P'QT = r$ is the **angle of refraction.**

It has been found by experiment that for a given kind of glass, the ratio

$$\frac{\sin i}{\sin r} = \mu$$

is constant whatever the angle of incidence may be. This means that for a certain kind of glass, if the angle of incidence is changed, then the angle of refraction also changes in such a manner that the ratio of the sines is constant. This ratio for a ray of light passing from air to crown glass is very nearly $\frac{3}{2}$, and for water it is $\frac{4}{3}$.

The value of the ratio $\frac{\sin i}{\sin r} = u$ is called the **index of refraction** of the glass with respect to air.

It follows that the index of refraction of air with respect to glass is the reciprocal of that of glass with respect to air. That is, if the index of refraction of glass with respect to air is μ, then the index of refraction of air with respect to glass is $\frac{1}{\mu}$. The same may be stated for any other two transparent substances.

EXERCISES

1. If $\mu = 1.167$, find the angle of refractions in the following:

(1) Given: The angle of incidence is 9°15'.   *Ans.* 7°54.9'.

(2) Given: The angle of incidence is 18°30'.

Solution: $\sin r = \dfrac{\sin i}{\mu} = \dfrac{\sin 18° 30'}{1.167}$

$\log \sin r = \log \sin 18° 30' - \log 1.167$

       $= (9.5015 - 10) - 0.0671 = 9.4344 - 10$

$\therefore r = 15° 46.6'$.   *Ans.*

(3) Given: The angle of incidence is 37°.   *Ans.* 31° 2.9'.

2. The sine of the critical angle is equal to the reciprocal of the index of refraction. Find μ in the following:

(1) For water the critical angle is 48°28'.

(2) For crown glass it is 41°10'.

(3) For diamond it is 24°26'.

For jewels with regular facets the smaller the critical angle the larger the proportion of the light incident on it that is internally reflected. Hence the brilliancy of the diamond.

3. The eye is 25 in. in front of a mirror, and an object appears to be 20 in. back of the mirror, while the line of sight makes an angle of 32° 30' with the mirror. Find the distance and direction of the object from the eye.

Ans. 70.8 in. in a direction making an angle of 4° 3' with plane of mirror.

4. A ray of light travels the path $ABCD$, Fig. 327, in passing through the plate glass MN 0.525 in. thick. What is the displacement CE

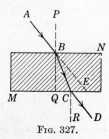

Fig. 327.

if the ray strikes the glass at an angle $ABP = 43° 15'$, the index of refraction being $\frac{3}{2}$?

Solution.—Here $\mu = \frac{3}{2} = 1.5$, and $i = 43° 15'$.

$$\therefore \sin r = \frac{\sin 43° 15'}{1.5} = 0.4568, \text{ and } r = 27° 10.1'$$

$$BC = \frac{BQ}{\cos r} = \frac{0.525}{\cos 27° 10.1'} = 0.590 \text{ in.}$$

Angle $CBE = 43° 15' - 27° 10.1' = 16° 4.9'$

$CE = BC \sin CBE = 0.590 \sin 16° 4.9' = 0.1634$ in.   *Ans.*

5. A source of light is under water. What is the greatest angle that a ray can make with the normal and pass into the air? For any greater angle the ray is totally reflected.

Suggestion.—As the ray passes into the air, it is refracted away from the normal. When the angle with the normal in air is 90°, the ray will not pass out of the water. When the ray in the water makes any greater angle with the normal than is necessary to make the angle in the air 90°, the ray is totally reflected at the surface of the water.

$$\frac{\sin i}{\sin 90°} = \frac{3}{4}$$

$$\therefore i = 48° 35.4'$$

6. If the eye is at a point under water, what is the greatest angle from the zenith that a star can appear to be?   *Ans.* 48° 35.4'.

7. A straight rod is partially immersed in water. The image in the water appears inclined at an angle of 40° with the surface. Find the inclination of the rod to the surface of the water if the index of refraction is $\frac{4}{3}$.   *Ans.* 58° 59.3'.

CHAPTER XXXIX

RELATIONS BETWEEN TRIGONOMETRIC FUNCTIONS

407. Many of the usual and direct applications of trigonometry involve the solutions of triangles; but in handling questions that occur further on in mathematics and in manipulating formulas used in physics, mechanics, and electricity, it is necessary to be familiar with relations existing among trigonometric functions. These relations are very numerous, and only a few of the most useful will be given here. The more important should be memorized, for they are quite as necessary in applying trigonometry as are the multiplication tables in arithmetic.

408. Fundamental relations between functions of one angle.

[62] $$\sin^2 \theta + \cos^2 \theta = 1$$

Proof.—By definition, $\sin \theta = \dfrac{y}{r}$, and $\cos \theta = \dfrac{x}{r}$.

Squaring and adding these,

$$\sin^2 \theta + \cos^2 \theta = \frac{y^2}{r^2} + \frac{x^2}{r^2} = \frac{y^2 + x^2}{r^2} = \frac{r^2}{r^2} = 1$$

$x^2 + y^2 = r^2$ because x, y, and r are the sides of a right triangle.

Therefore formula [62] is always true. This means that for *any angle* the square of the sine plus the square of the cosine equals 1.

[63] $$1 + \tan^2 \theta = \sec^2 \theta$$

Proof.—By definition, $\tan \theta = \dfrac{y}{x}$, and $\sec \theta = \dfrac{r}{x}$.

Then $1 + \tan^2 \theta = 1 + \dfrac{y^2}{x^2} = \dfrac{x^2 + y^2}{x^2} = \dfrac{r^2}{x^2} = \sec^2 \theta.$

Therefore formula [**63**] is always true.

As an exercise the student may prove the following formulas:

[**64**] $$1 + \cot^2 \theta = \csc^2 \theta$$

[**65**] $$\csc \theta = \frac{1}{\sin \theta}, \text{ and } \sin \theta = \frac{1}{\csc \theta}$$

[**66**] $$\sec \theta = \frac{1}{\cos \theta}, \text{ and } \cos \theta = \frac{1}{\sec \theta}$$

[**67**] $$\cot \theta = \frac{1}{\tan \theta}, \text{ and } \tan \theta = \frac{1}{\cot \theta}$$

[**68**] $$\tan \theta = \frac{\sin \theta}{\cos \theta}$$

[**69**] $$\cot \theta = \frac{\cos \theta}{\sin \theta}$$

Two functions sometimes met with are: versedsine θ, abbreviated vers θ, and defined to be

$$\text{vers } \theta = 1 - \cos \theta$$

and conversedsine θ, abbreviated covers θ, and defined to be

$$\text{covers } \theta = 1 - \sin \theta$$

The eight formulas of this article are **identities,** for they are true for any angle whatever. They are often spoken of as **fundamental identities,** or **formulas.** They should be carefully memorized, as they are frequently used.

Example 1.—Test formula [**63**] for $\theta = 30°$.

From table on page 560, $\tan 30° = \frac{1}{3} \sqrt{3}$, and $\sec 30° = \frac{2}{3} \sqrt{3}$.

Substituting these values in $1 + \tan^2 \theta = \sec^2 \theta$, we have

$$1 + \tfrac{3}{9} = \tfrac{12}{9}, \tfrac{4}{3} = \tfrac{4}{3}$$

Example 2.—Prove $(\tan \theta + \cot \theta) \sin \theta \cos \theta = 1$.

Proof by using definitions.—Substituting the definitions of the functions for the functions, we have

$$\left(\frac{y}{x} + \frac{x}{y}\right)\frac{y}{r} \cdot \frac{x}{r} = \frac{y^2 + x^2}{xy} \cdot \frac{xy}{r^2} = \frac{x^2 + y^2}{r^2} = \frac{r^2}{r^2} = 1$$

Proof by using formulas.—Substituting $\dfrac{\sin\theta}{\cos\theta}$ for tan θ and $\dfrac{\cos\theta}{\sin\theta}$ for cot θ, we have

$$\left(\frac{\sin\theta}{\cos\theta} + \frac{\cos\theta}{\sin\theta}\right)\sin\theta\cos\theta = \frac{\sin^2\theta + \cos^2\theta}{\sin\theta\cos\theta}\sin\theta\cos\theta$$
$$= \sin^2\theta + \cos^2\theta = 1$$

EXERCISES

1. Make the following tests:

(1) Formula [**62**] for $\theta = 30°$.

(2) Formula [**63**] for $\theta = 120°$.

(3) Formula [**64**] for $\theta = 225°$.

(4) Formulas [**62**], [**63**], and [**64**] for $\theta = 300°$.

2. Prove formula [**64**].

3. Solve formula [**62**] for sin θ; also for cos θ.

4. Solve formula [**63**] for sec θ; also for tan θ.

5. Solve formula [**64**] for csc θ; also for cot θ.

6. Divide formula [**62**] by $\cos^2\theta$, then use formulas [**68**] and [**66**] and thus obtain formula [**63**].

7. By using the formulas (fundamental relations) or the definitions of the trigonometric functions, show that the following identities are true:

(1) $\sin\theta\csc\theta = 1$.

(2) $\cos\theta\sec\theta = 1$.

(3) $\tan\theta\cot\theta = 1$.

(4) $\sec^2\theta - \tan^2\theta = 1$.

8. $\cos\theta\csc\theta \div \cot\theta = 1$.

9. $\sin\theta\sec\theta \div \tan\theta = 1$.

10. $\tan\theta = \sec\theta \div \csc\theta$.

11. $[(\sec\theta \div \sin\theta) - \tan\theta](\sin\theta) = \cos\theta$.

12. $(\tan\theta - \sin\theta)(\tan\theta + \sin\theta) = (\tan\theta\sin\theta)^2$.

13. $\sec^2\theta + \csc^2\theta = \sec^2\theta\csc^2\theta$.

409. To express all the functions of an angle in terms of any one function of the angle.—The scheme outlined in this article can be carried out rapidly and will be found of very great use.

Example 1.—Express all the functions of θ in terms of sin θ.

Solution.—Construction angle θ in the first quadrant, Fig. 328, and choose the point P in the terminal side with coordinates OM and MP. Then by definition, sin

$\theta = \dfrac{MP}{OP}$; and if OP is taken equal to 1, $MP =$ sin θ and

$$OM = \sqrt{\overline{OP^2} - \overline{MP}^2} = \sqrt{1 - \sin^2 \theta}.$$

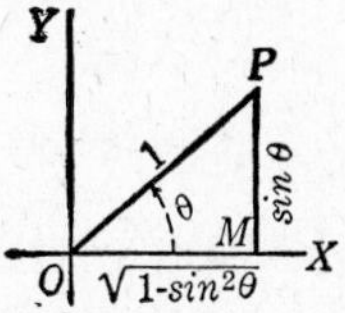

The remaining functions may then be written as follows:

Fig. 328.

$$\cos \theta = \frac{OM}{OP} = \sqrt{1 - \sin^2 \theta} \qquad \sec \theta = \frac{OP}{OM} = \frac{1}{\sqrt{1 - \sin^2 \theta}}$$

$$\tan \theta = \frac{MP}{OM} = \frac{\sin \theta}{\sqrt{1 - \sin^2 \theta}} \qquad \csc \theta = \frac{OP}{MP} = \frac{1}{\sin \theta}$$

$$\cot \theta = \frac{OM}{MP} = \frac{\sqrt{1 - \sin^2 \theta}}{\sin \theta}$$

Example 2.—Express all the functions in terms of cos θ.

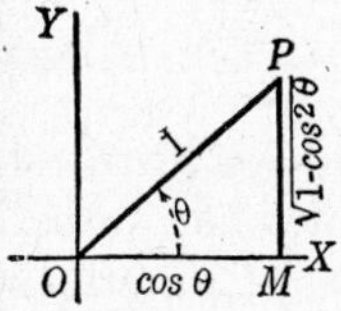

Solution.—Construct angle θ in the first quadrant, Fig. 329, and choose the point P in the terminal side with coordinates OM and MP. Then by definition, cos $\theta = \dfrac{OM}{OP}$; and if OP is taken equal to 1, $OM =$ cos θ and

Fig. 329.

$$MP = \sqrt{OP^2 - OM^2} = \sqrt{1 - \cos^2 \theta}.$$

The remaining functions may then be written as follows:

$$\sin \theta = \frac{MP}{OP} = \sqrt{1 - \cos^2 \theta} \qquad \cot \theta = \frac{OM}{MP} = \frac{\cos \theta}{\sqrt{1 - \cos^2 \theta}}$$

$$\tan \theta = \frac{MP}{OM} = \frac{\sqrt{1 - \cos^2 \theta}}{\cos \theta} \qquad \sec \theta = \frac{OP}{OM} = \frac{1}{\cos \theta}$$

$$\csc \theta = \frac{OP}{MP} = \frac{1}{\sqrt{1 - \cos^2 \theta}}$$

The formulas in terms of any desired function can as readily be found. All that is necessary in setting up the triangle in the figure is to place the function on the line that is the *numerator* in the definition and 1 on the line that is the *denominator*.

$\sin\theta$	$\sin\theta$	$\sqrt{1-\cos^2\theta}$	$\dfrac{\tan\theta}{\sqrt{1+\tan^2\theta}}$	$\dfrac{1}{\sqrt{1+\cot^2\theta}}$	$\dfrac{\sqrt{\sec^2\theta-1}}{\sec\theta}$	$\dfrac{1}{\csc\theta}$
$\cos\theta$	$\sqrt{1-\sin^2\theta}$	$\cos\theta$	$\dfrac{1}{\sqrt{1+\tan^2\theta}}$	$\dfrac{\cot\theta}{\sqrt{1+\cot^2\theta}}$	$\dfrac{1}{\sec\theta}$	$\dfrac{\sqrt{\csc^2\theta-1}}{\csc\theta}$
$\tan\theta$	$\dfrac{\sin\theta}{\sqrt{1-\sin^2\theta}}$	$\dfrac{\sqrt{1-\cos^2\theta}}{\cos\theta}$	$\tan\theta$	$\dfrac{1}{\cot\theta}$	$\sqrt{\sec^2\theta-1}$	$\dfrac{1}{\sqrt{\csc^2\theta-1}}$
$\cot\theta$	$\dfrac{\sqrt{1-\sin^2\theta}}{\sin\theta}$	$\dfrac{\cos\theta}{\sqrt{1-\cos^2\theta}}$	$\dfrac{1}{\tan\theta}$	$\cot\theta$	$\dfrac{1}{\sqrt{\sec^2\theta-1}}$	$\sqrt{\csc^2\theta-1}$
$\sec\theta$	$\dfrac{1}{\sqrt{1-\sin^2\theta}}$	$\dfrac{1}{\cos\theta}$	$\sqrt{1+\tan^2\theta}$	$\dfrac{\sqrt{1+\cot^2\theta}}{\cot\theta}$	$\sec\theta$	$\dfrac{\csc\theta}{\sqrt{\csc^2\theta-1}}$
$\csc\theta$	$\dfrac{1}{\sin\theta}$	$\dfrac{1}{\sqrt{1-\cos^2\theta}}$	$\dfrac{\sqrt{1+\tan^2\theta}}{\tan\theta}$	$\sqrt{1+\cot^2\theta}$	$\dfrac{\sec\theta}{\sqrt{\sec^2\theta-1}}$	$\csc\theta$

As an exercise carry out the remaining derivations and arrange as in the preceding table.

The table has been prepared under the assumption that θ is an acute angle. Should θ be in any other quadrant, the proper sign for each function may then be determined.

FUNCTIONS OF LARGE ANGLES

410. In Art. 376, it was pointed out that the *function* of an acute angle is equal to the *cofunction* of its complement. And because of this relation, each number in a table of functions was made to do double duty; for instance, $\sin 13°$ is also $\cos 77°$.

So far in the solution of triangles we have not used angles greater than 90°; but in oblique triangles, we may have angles greater than 90°; and in other problems, angles of any value may occur. It is therefore necessary to be able to find the functions of angles larger than 90°, and a method will now be developed for finding any of these from the table of functions for angles less than 90°.

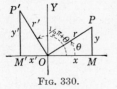

Fig. 330.

411. Functions of an angle in second quadrant: $90° + \theta$, where θ is an acute angle, is an angle in the second quadrant. In Fig. 330, let θ

be any acute angle. Lay off $90° + \theta$; take $OP' = OP$; and draw the abscissas and ordinates as shown. Evidently, right triangles OMP and $OM'P'$ are equal.

Then $y' = x$; $x' = -y$; and $r' = r$; and we have

$$\sin (90° + \theta) = \frac{y'}{r'} = \frac{x}{r} = \cos \theta$$

$$\cos (90° + \theta) = \frac{x'}{r'} = \frac{-y}{r} = -\frac{y}{r} = -\sin \theta$$

$$\tan (90° + \theta) = \frac{y'}{x'} = \frac{x}{-y} = -\frac{x}{y} = -\cot \theta$$

$$\cot (90° + \theta) = \frac{x'}{y'} = \frac{-y}{x} = -\frac{y}{x} = -\tan \theta$$

$$\sec (90° + \theta) = \frac{r'}{x'} = \frac{r}{-y} = -\frac{r}{y} = -\csc \theta$$

$$\csc (90° + \theta) = \frac{r'}{y'} = \frac{r}{x} = \sec \theta$$

Notice that here in each line, the *function* at the end is the cofunction of the one at the beginning.

Examples: $\sin 130° = \sin (90° + 40°) = \cos 40°$

$\cot 110° = \cot (90° + 20°) = -\tan 20°$

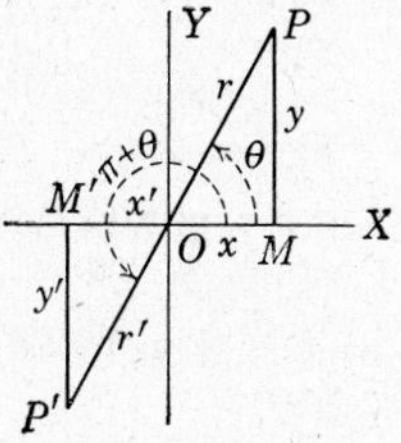

412. Functions of an angle in third quadrant: $180° + \theta$, where θ is an acute angle, is an angle in the third quadrant. In Fig. 331, let θ be an acute angle. Con-

Fig. 331.

struct $180° + \theta$; take $OP' = OP$; and represent the other parts as shown.

Then $x' = -x$; $y' = -y$; and $r' = r$; and we have:

$$\sin (180° + \theta) = \frac{y'}{r'} = \frac{-y}{r} = -\frac{y}{r} = -\sin \theta$$

$$\cos (180° + \theta) = \frac{x'}{r'} = \frac{-x}{r} = -\frac{x}{r} = -\cos \theta$$

$$\tan (180° + \theta) = \frac{y'}{x'} = \frac{-y}{-x} = \frac{y}{x} = \tan \theta$$

$$\cot (180° + \theta) = \frac{x'}{y'} = \frac{-x}{-y} = \frac{x}{y} = \cot \theta$$

$$\sec (180° + \theta) = \frac{r'}{x'} = \frac{r}{-x} = -\frac{r}{x} = -\sec \theta$$

$$\csc (180° + \theta) = \frac{r'}{y'} = \frac{r}{-y} = -\frac{r}{y} = -\csc \theta$$

Notice that here, in each line, the *function* at the end is the same *function* as the one at the beginning.

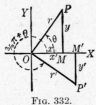

FIG. 332.

Examples: tan 230° = tan (180° + 50°) = tan 50°

cos 205° = cos (180° + 25°) = − cos 25°

413. Functions of an angle in fourth quadrant: 270° + θ, where θ is an acute angle, is an angle in the fourth quadrant.

In Fig. 332, let θ be an acute angle. Construct 270° + θ; take $OP' = OP$; and represent the other parts as shown.

Then $y' = -x$; $x' = y$; and $r' = r$; and we have

$$\sin (270° + \theta) = \frac{y'}{r'} = \frac{-x}{r} = -\frac{x}{r} = -\cos \theta$$

$$\cos (270° + \theta) = \frac{x'}{r'} = \frac{y}{r} = \sin \theta$$

$$\tan (270° + \theta) = \frac{y'}{x'} = \frac{-x}{y} = -\frac{x}{y} = -\cot \theta$$

$$\cot (270° + \theta) = \frac{x'}{y'} = \frac{y}{-x} = -\frac{y}{x} = -\tan \theta$$

$$\sec (270° + \theta) = \frac{r'}{x'} = \frac{r}{y} = \csc \theta$$

$$\csc (270° + \theta) = \frac{r'}{y'} = \frac{r}{-x} = -\frac{r}{x} = -\sec \theta$$

Notice that here, in each line, the *function* at the end is the *cofunction* of the one at the beginning.

Examples: cot 310° = cot (270° + 40°) = − tan 40°

sec 340° = sec (270° + 70°) = csc 70°

414. Functions of a negative angle.—It is also necessary to be able to find the function of a negative angle.
The following formulas are proved for θ an acute angle, but it can be shown that they hold for any value of $-\theta$.

Construct θ and $-\theta$ as in Fig. 333; take $OP' = OP$; and represent the other parts as shown.

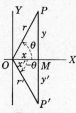

Fig. 333.

Then $x' = x$; $y' = -y$; and $r' = r$; and we have

$$\sin(-\theta) = \frac{y'}{r'} = \frac{-y}{r} = -\frac{y}{r} = -\sin\theta$$

$$\cos(-\theta) = \frac{x'}{r'} = \frac{x}{r} = \cos\theta$$

$$\tan(-\theta) = \frac{y'}{x'} = \frac{-y}{x} = -\frac{y}{x} = -\tan\theta$$

$$\cot(-\theta) = \frac{x'}{y'} = \frac{x}{-y} = -\frac{x}{y} = -\cot\theta$$

$$\sec(-\theta) = \frac{r'}{x'} = \frac{r}{x} = \sec\theta$$

$$\csc(-\theta) = \frac{r'}{y'} = \frac{r}{-y} = -\frac{r}{y} = -\csc\theta$$

These formulas can readily be remembered by noting that the functions of the negative angle are the same as those of the positive angle, but of opposite sign, except the cosine and the secant, which are of the same sign.

Examples: $\sin(-40°) = -\sin 40°$
$\cos(-145°) = \cos 145°$
$\tan(-240°) = -\tan 240°$

415. Summary of these reduction formulas.—In the second quadrant we could as well have used $180° - \theta$; in the third quadrant, $270° - \theta$; and in the fourth quadrant, $360° - \theta$. The functions of these together with those of $90° - \theta$ and the ones derived are arranged here for ready reference.

It will be well to memorize the last group, the one expressing the functions of negative angles as functions of positive angles.

$$\sin (90° − θ) = \cos θ \qquad \sin (90° + θ) = \cos θ$$
$$\cos (90° − θ) = \sin θ \qquad \cos (90° + θ) = − \sin θ$$
$$\tan (90° − θ) = \cot θ \qquad \tan (90° + θ) = − \cot θ$$
$$\cot (90° − θ) = \tan θ \qquad \cot (90° + θ) = − \tan θ$$
$$\sec (90° − θ) = \csc θ \qquad \sec (90° + θ) = − \csc θ$$
$$\csc (90° − θ) = \sec θ \qquad \csc (90° + θ) = \sec θ$$

$$\sin (180° − θ) = \sin θ \qquad \sin (180° + θ) = − \sin θ$$
$$\cos (180° − θ) = − \cos θ \qquad \cos (180° + θ) = − \cos θ$$
$$\tan (180° − θ) = − \tan θ \qquad \tan (180° + θ) = \tan θ$$
$$\cot (180° − θ) = − \cot θ \qquad \cot (180° + θ) = \cot θ$$
$$\sec (180° − θ) = − \sec θ \qquad \sec (180° + θ) = − \sec θ$$
$$\csc (180° − θ) = \csc θ \qquad \csc (180° + θ) = − \csc θ$$

$$\sin (270° − θ) = − \cos θ \qquad \sin (270° + θ) = − \cos θ$$
$$\cos (270° − θ) = − \sin θ \qquad \cos (270° + θ) = \sin θ$$
$$\tan (270° − θ) = \cot θ \qquad \tan (270° + θ) = − \cot θ$$
$$\cot (270° − θ) = \tan θ \qquad \cot (270° + θ) = − \tan θ$$
$$\sec (270° − θ) = − \csc θ \qquad \sec (270° + θ) = \csc θ$$
$$\csc (270° − θ) = − \sec θ \qquad \csc (270° + θ) = − \sec θ$$

$$\sin (360° − θ) = − \sin θ \qquad \sin (−θ) = − \sin θ$$
$$\cos (360° − θ) = \cos θ \qquad \cos (−θ) = \cos θ$$
$$\tan (360° − θ) = − \tan θ \qquad \tan (−θ) = − \tan θ$$
$$\cot (360° − θ) = − \cot θ \qquad \cot (−θ) = − \cot θ$$
$$\sec (360° − θ) = \sec θ \qquad \sec (−θ) = \sec θ$$
$$\csc (360° − θ) = − \csc θ \qquad \csc (−θ) = − \csc θ$$

Although the proofs of all these formulas have been based upon the assumption that $θ$ is an acute angle, they are true for all values of $θ$ and can be carried through for any value of $θ$ in exactly the same manner as for $θ$ an acute angle.

416. Functions of an angle greater than 360°.—Any angle $α$ greater than 360° has the same trigonometric functions as $α$ minus an integral multiple of 360°, because $α$ and $α − n \cdot 360°$

have the same initial and terminal sides. That is, the functions of α equal the same functions of $\alpha - n \cdot 360°$, where n is an integer. In other words, *a function of an angle that is larger than 360° can be found by dividing the angle by 360° and finding the required funrtion of the remainder.*

Example 1.—Find cos 1240°.

$$1240° = 3 \times 360° + 160°$$
$$\therefore \cos 1240° = \cos 160°$$
$$\cos 160° = \cos (90° + 70°) = - \sin 70° = -0.9397$$

Example 2.—Find tan $(-684°)$.

$$\tan (-684°) = - \tan 684° = - \tan 324°$$
$$= - \tan (270° + 54°) = -(- \cot 54°) = 0.7265$$

Almost every instructor has his method for a final summary of the preceding articles. Perhaps the following summary is as good as any:

(1) Construct the angle. Then from the quadrant in which its terminal side lies the algebraic sign of each particular function may be determined. If the angle is greater than 360°, apply the method as explained above and illustrated in Example 1.

(2) In order to reduce the angle to an angle less than 90°, it will be necessary to subtract 270°, 180°, or 90°. If 270° or 90° is necessarily subtracted, take the cofunction of the remainder instead of the given function as was indicated for the original angle.

However, if 180° is necessarily subtracted, take the same function of the remainder as was indicated for the original angle.

(3) If the original angle is negative, apply Art. 414 first and then proceed as in (1) and (2).

Study carefully the double algebraic signs as illustrated in Example 2, above.

EXERCISES

Use the tables of natural functions, and find the sine, cosine, and tangent of each of the following angles: [It will be necessary to apply the formulas of article 415 or else the summary given in (1), (2), and (3) of Art. 416.

1. 140°.

Ans. sin 140° = cos (140° − 90°) = cos 50°, or sin 140°
$$= \sin (180° - 140°) = \sin 40°.$$

2. 170°. **5.** 280°.

3. 190°. **6.** 340°.

4. 250°.

7. 460°. *Ans.* sin 460° = sin (460° − 360°) = sin 100° = cos 10°.

8. 1220°. **9.** 3890°.

10. −1190°.

Ans. sin (−1190°) = − sin 1190° = − sin (1190° − 1080°)
$$= - \sin 110° = - \cos 20°.$$

11. −915°. *Ans.* 0.2588; −0.9659; −0.2679.

12. −1420°40′.

Find the angle A less than 360° so that the following will be true:

13. sin 20° = sin A. *Ans.* 160°. **16.** sin 20° = cos A. *Ans.* 70°.

14. cos 130° = cos A. *Ans.* 230°. **17.** cos 130° = sin A. *Ans.* 220°.

15. tan 250° = tan A. *Ans.* 70°. **18.** tan 250° = cot A. *Ans.* 20°.

19. Prove that sin (180° − B) sin B − cos (180° − B) cos B = 1.

20. Prove that sec (360° − C) sec C − cot (270° − C) tan C = 1.

21. Find the value of $\frac{1}{2}x - \frac{1}{4}\sin 2x$ when $x = 2\pi$. *Ans.* π.

22. Find the value of $16(\frac{1}{2}x - \frac{1}{4}\sin 2x)$ when $x = 2$ radians.

Ans. 12.97.

23. Use formula for G, Art. 401, to find the area of a segment having a central angle of 140° in a circle of radius 10 in. *Ans.* 90.03 sq. in.

24. A cylindrical tank of length 30 ft. and diameter 8 ft. lies horizontally. Find the volume of oil in the tank when filled to a depth of 3 ft.

Ans. 516.5 cu. ft.

CHAPTER XL

GRAPHICAL REPRESENTATION OF TRIGONOMETRIC FUNCTIONS

417. Plotting the sine curve.—Algebraic functions were plotted in Chap. XXXII. In this manner the changes in the variables were shown graphically. As an angle increases from $0°$ to $360°$, the sine of the angle changes. For each value of the angle there is just one value of the sine of the angle. For $0°$ the sine is 0. As the angle increases toward $90°$, the sine increases and reaches 1 at $90°$. As the angle increases from $90°$ toward $180°$, the sine decreases and reaches 0 at $180°$. As the angle goes on from $180°$, the sine decreases to -1 for $270°$ and then increases to 0 for $360°$. From $360°$ to $720°$, these values of the sine are repeated. These relations between the values of the angle and their sines can be represented graphically by a curve.

Example.—Plot the curve for $y = \sin x$.

Choose suitable angles for values of x and take the values for y from the table on page 560 or from Table XI.

Values of x, $0°$ $30°$ $45°$ $60°$ $90°$ $120°$ $135°$ $150°$ $180°$
Values of y, 0 0.5 0.7 0.87 1 0.87 0.7 0.5 0
Values of x, $210°$ $225°$ $240°$ $270°$ $300°$ $315°$ $330°$ $360°$
Values of y, -0.5 -0.7 -0.87 -1 -0.87 -0.7 -0.5 0

Choose a convenient unit on the x-axis and y-axis, and plot the points as shown in Fig. 334, using the angle as abscissa and the sine as ordinate.

The curve in Fig. 334 is called the **sine curve**. It extends both ways indefinitely, repeating the part given. That is, if values between $360°$ and $720°$ are taken, the curve will be found to be of the same shape. The same will be true for values of the angle less than 0°.

Here the angle and the function are both plotted to the same unit or scale; that is, the unit on the *y*-axis is the same length as that to represent 1 radian on the *x*-axis. The curve so plotted may be called the **proper sine curve.** Often, however, for convenience when plotting on coordinate paper, the angles are plotted according to the divisions on the paper. For example, 1 space = 6 or 10° or some other convenient angle, depending on the size of the plot.

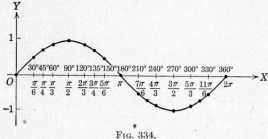

Fig. 334.

418. Periodic functions and periodic curves.—In nature there are many motions that are recurrent. Sound waves, light waves, and water waves are familiar examples. Motions in machines are repeated in a periodic manner. The vibration of a pendulum is a simple case, as is also the piston-rod motion in an engine. Other familiar illustrations are the vibration of a piano string, breathing movements, heartbeats, and the motion of tides. An alternating electric current has periodic changes. It increases to a maximum value in one direction, decreases to zero and on down to a minimum, that is, to a maximum value in the opposite direction, rises again and repeats these changes. It is thus an *alternating* current passing from a maximum in one direction to a maximum in the other direction, say, sixty times a second.

Before physical quantities that change in a periodic fashion can be dealt with mathematically, it is necessary to find a mathematical expression for such a periodic change.

Definitions.—A curve that repeats in form as illustrated by the sine curve is called a **periodic curve**. The function that gives rise to a periodic curve is called a **periodic function**. The least repeating part of a periodic curve is called a **cycle** of the curve. The change in value of the variable necessary for a cycle is called the **period** of the function. The greatest absolute value of the ordinates of a periodic function is called the **amplitude** of the function.

In Fig. 334 is shown one cycle of the sine curve. The period of $y = \sin x$ is 2π, for a change in x of 2π gives the complete curve of the figure. The amplitude of this curve is 1, the greatest value of an ordinate.

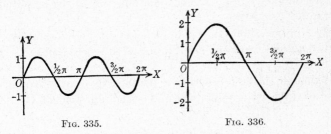

Fig. 335.   Fig. 336.

Example 1.—Find the period of $\sin n\theta$, and plot the curve of $y = \sin 2\theta$.

Since, in finding the value of $\sin n\theta$, the angle θ is multiplied by n before finding the sine, the period is $\dfrac{2\pi}{n}$. Here the radian is taken as the unit for the angle, which is customary.

The curve for $y = \sin 2\theta$ is shown in Fig. 335. The period of this function is π radians, and there are two cycles of the curve in 2π radians. If $n = 3$, there are three cycles in 2π radians and the period is $\frac{2}{3}\pi$. It is evident that $y = \sin n\theta$ can be made to have any period desired by giving proper values to n.

The number n in $n\theta$ is called the **periodicity factor.**

It should be noticed that in order to plot $y = \sin n\theta$, n must be given a definite value as 2.

Example 2.—Find the amplitude of $b \sin \theta$, and plot $y = 2 \sin \theta$.

Since, in finding the value of $b \sin \theta$, $\sin \theta$ is found and then multiplied by b, the amplitude of the function is b, for the greatest value of $\sin \theta$ is 1.

The curve for $y = 2 \sin \theta$ is shown in Fig. 336. The amplitude is 2.

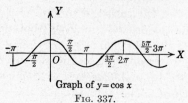

Graph of $y = \cos x$

Fig. 337.

The number b in $b \sin \theta$ is sometimes called the **amplitude factor.**

By a proper choice of a periodicity factor and an amplitude factor, a function of any amplitude and any period desired can be found.

Although the sine function is perhaps the most frequently used of the periodic functions, the cosine function can be used

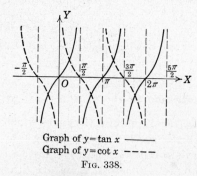

Graph of $y = \tan x$ ————
Graph of $y = \cot x$ — — — —

Fig. 338.

quite as readily. By a proper choice and combination of sines and cosines a function can be built up that will represent exactly or approximately any periodic phenomenon. Just how this can be done can hardly be explained here.

419. Curves for cosine, tangent, cotangent, secant, and cosecant.—By choosing suitable angles for values of x and determining the corresponding values of y, the coordinates of points are obtained that, when plotted, give the curves of Figs. 337, 338, and 339.

The tangent, cotangent, secant, and cosecant functions cannot be used to represent periodic happenings; for although these functions are periodic, they become infinite for certain values of the angle, and periodic motions do not have values that become infinite. It is always necessary to choose a mathematical expression that will truly represent the actual motion or happening. For periodic happenings the sine and cosine are chosen.

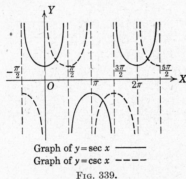

Graph of $y = \sec x$ ————
Graph of $y = \csc x$ ————

Fig. 339.

EXERCISES

Write equations of periodic curves using, first, sine and then cosine functions for the following:

1. Amplitude 1 and period 180°.

2. Amplitude 2 and period 180°.

3. Amplitude 4 and period 90°.

4. Amplitude $\frac{1}{2}$ and period $\frac{1}{3}\pi$.

5. Amplitude $\frac{2}{3}$ and period $\frac{2}{3}\pi$.

6. Plot $y = \sin \theta$, (1) using as a unit on the x-axis a length twice as great as that on the y-axis, (2) using as a unit on the x-axis a length one-half as great as that on the y-axis. Plot both curves on the same set of axes.

7. Plot $y = \cos \theta$. Give its period and amplitude.

8. Plot $y = \tan \theta$ and $y = \cot \theta$ on the same set of axes.

9. Plot $y = \sec \theta$ and $y = \csc \theta$ on the same set of axes.

10. Plot $y = \sin x + \cos x$.

Suggestion.—Plot $y_1 = \sin x$ and $y_2 = \cos x$ on the same set of axes. Then find the points on the curve $y = \sin x + \cos x$ from the relation $y = y_1 + y_2$, by adding the ordinates for various values of x.

11. Plot $y = \sin^2 x$ and $y = \cos^2 x$ on the same set of axes. Note that the curves never extend below the x-axis.

12. Plot $y = \frac{1}{2} \sin x$, $y = \sin x$, $y = 2 \sin x$, and $y = \frac{3}{2} \sin x$ on the same set of axes. Give the period and amplitude of each.

13. Plot $y = \sin \frac{1}{2}x$, $y = \sin x$, $y = \sin 2x$, and $y = \sin \frac{3}{2}x$ on the same set of axes. Give the period and amplitude of each.

420. Projection of a point having uniform circular motion.
Example 1.—A point P, Fig. 340, moves around a vertical

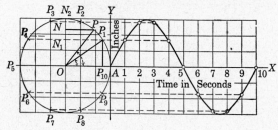

Fig. 340.

circle of radius 3 in. in a counterclockwise direction. It starts with the point at A and moves with an angular velocity of 1 revolution in 10 sec. Plot a curve showing the distance that the projection of P on the vertical diameter is from O at any time t, and find its equation.

Plotting.—Let OP be any position of the radius drawn to the moving point. OP starts from the position OA and at the end of 1 sec. is in position OP_1, having turned through an angle of $36° = 0.6283$ radian. At the end of 2 sec. it has turned to OP_2, through an angle of $72° = 1.2566$ radians, and so on to positions OP_3, OP_4, . . . , OP_{10}.

The points $N_1, N_2, \ldots$ are the projections of $P_1, P_2, \ldots$, respectively, on the vertical diameter.

Produce the horizontal diameter OA through A, and lay off the seconds on this to some scale, taking the origin at A.

For each second plot a point whose ordinate is the corresponding distance of N from O. These points determine a curve of which any ordinate y is the distance from the center O of the projection of P upon the vertical diameter at the time t represented by the abscissa of the point.

It is evident that for the second and each successive revolution, the curve repeats, that is, it is a periodic curve.

Since the radius OP turns through 0.6283 radian per second,

$$\text{Angle } AOP = 0.6283t \text{ radians}$$

and
$$ON = OP \cdot \sin 0.6283t$$

or $y = 3 \sin 0.6283t$ is the equation of the curve

In general, then, it is readily seen that if a straight line of length r starts in a horizontal position when time $t = 0$ and revolves in a vertical plane around one end at a uniform angular velocity ω per unit of time, the projection y of the moving end upon a vertical straight line has a motion represented by the equation

$$y = r \sin \omega t$$

Similarly, the projection of the moving point upon the horizontal is given by the ordinates of the curve whose equation is

$$y = r \cos \omega t$$

If the time is counted from an instant other than that from which the foregoing is counted, then the motion is represented by

$$y = r \sin (\omega t + \alpha)$$

where α is the angle that OP makes with the line OA at the instant from which t is counted. As an illustration of this consider the following:

Example 2.—A crank OP, Fig. 341, of length 2 ft. starts from a position making an angle $\alpha = 40° = \frac{2}{9}\pi$ radians with the horizontal line OA when $t = 0$. It rotates in a vertical plane in the positive direction at the rate of 2 revolutions per second. Plot a curve showing the projection of P on a vertical diameter.

Discussion.—As before, draw a circle of 2 ft. radius to some scale. Extend the horizontal axis to the right, and represent the part of a second necessary for 1 revolution to a suitable scale.

When $t = 0$, OP starts from the position OP_0, making an angle $AOP_0 = \alpha = 40°$. OP turns through 720° in 1 sec., or

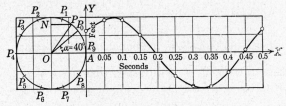

Fig. 341.

36° = 0.6283 radian in 0.05 sec. Here we plot a point for every 0.05 sec. Any other convenient fraction of a second could be chosen. The position of the free end of the crank for each 0.05 sec. until a complete revolution is made is located by $P_0, P_1, P_2, P_3, \ldots$. These are at intervals of 36° starting with 40°.

At any time t, the position of OP makes with OA an angle $AOP = \omega t + \alpha$. And the distance from O to the projection of P at N is

$$ON = OP \sin (\omega t + \alpha)$$

Since $\omega = 720° = 4\pi$ radians, and $\alpha = 40° = \frac{2}{9}\pi$ radians,

$$ON = 2 \sin (720t° + 40°), \text{ or } ON = 2 \sin (4\pi t + \tfrac{2}{9}\pi)$$

These are of the general form

$$y = r \sin (\omega t + \alpha)$$

The angle α is called the **angle of lag.**

The curve of this example is periodic. It repeats itself for each complete revolution of the crank.

421. Sine curves of different frequency.—The **frequency** refers to the number of *cycles* of the *periodic curve* in a unit of time. Thus, if a crank makes 4 revolutions in 1 sec., the curve showing the motion makes 4 cycles in 1 sec., whereas the curve for a crank that makes 2 revolutions in 1 sec. makes 2 cycles in 1 sec. The frequency of the first is 4; of the second, 2.

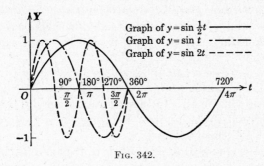

Fig. 342.

The angular velocity ω divided by 360° when measured in degrees, or by 2π when measured in radians, gives the frequency f;

$$\therefore f = \frac{\omega}{2\pi}$$

The time necessary for 1 cycle is called the **period.** It is evident that the period T is given by the formula

$$T = \frac{2\pi}{\omega}$$

Example.—Consider the motions represented by

(1) $y = r \sin \frac{1}{2}t$, (2) $y = r \sin t$, (3) $y = r \sin 2t$

Plot the curves, and determine the velocity, frequency, and period of each.

If r is taken as 1 and the three curves are plotted, they are as shown in Fig. 342.

The values of ω, f, and T are

For $y = r \sin \frac{1}{2}t$, $\omega t = \frac{1}{2}t$, $\omega = \frac{1}{2}$, $f = 0.0796$, $T = 12.566$
For $y = r \sin t$, $\;\;\omega t = t$, $\;\;\omega = 1$, $f = 0.1592$, $T = 6.283$
For $y = r \sin 2t$, $\omega t = 2t$, $\omega = 2$, $f = 0.3183$, $T = 3.1416$

It is to be noted that *the frequency of a sine curve varies directly as the value of ω, that is, as the coefficient of t in the angle ωt*. The number ω is sometimes called the **frequency factor**.

422. Summary.—In summary it may be noted again that the equation

$$y = a \sin (nx + \alpha)$$

gives a periodic curve. In this equation there are three arbitrary constants, a, n, and α. A change in any one of these constants will change the curve.

(1) If a is changed, the *amplitude* of the curve is changed.

(2) If n is changed, the *period* of the curve is changed.

(3) If α is changed, the curve is moved without change in shape from left to right or *vice versa*.

EXERCISES

Recall that in $y = a \sin (bx)$ or $y = a \cos (bx)$, the amplitude is a and the period is $2\pi \div b$ in each case. Then write equations of periodic curves by using (1) sine and (2) cosine for the following:

1. Amplitude 1 and period 2π. Plot (1) and (2) on the same set of axes. Remember that the units on the different axes may not be the same.

2. Amplitude 2 and period π. Plot as in Exercise 1.

3. Amplitude $\frac{1}{2}$ and period $\frac{1}{2}\pi$. Plot as in Exercise 1.

4. Amplitude π and period π. Plot as in Exercise 1.

5. Amplitude 10 and period $\frac{2}{3}\pi$. Plot as in Exercise 1.

6. Plot $y = \tan x$. **Notice** that a point on this curve may be as far from the x-axis as is desired; hence, it is said to have an **infinite amplitude.** What is the period of this graph?

7. Plot $y = \cot x$. What is the amplitude and period of this graph? (See Exercise 6.)

8. Graph the following functions, and state the period and amplitude in each (read the notice in Exercise 6):

(1) $2 \sin 4x$.   (2) $4 \cos \frac{1}{3}x$.   (3) $5 \sec 2x$.   (4) $2 \csc \frac{2}{3}x$.

9. A series of waves may be represented graphically by means of a periodic function. The length of the wave is then the period of the graph. State the wave length of the function sin $10x$.

10. A crank 18 in. long starts in a horizontal position and turns in a positive direction in a vertical plane at the rate of 0.7854 radian per second. The projection of the moving end of the crank upon a vertical line oscillates with a simple periodic motion. Construct a curve whose ordinates show the distance of the projection from the center of its path at any time.

11. Write the equation of the curve in the preceding exercise. Find the value of the ordinate when $t = 0.5$; when $t = 2.3$.

Ans. $y = 18 \sin (0.7854t)$; 6.89 in.; 17.50 in.

12. A crank 8 in. long starts in a position making an angle of 55° with the horizontal and rotates in a positive direction at the rate of 20 R. P. M. Draw a curve to show the projection of the moving end of the crank on a vertical line.

13. Write the equation of the curve in the preceding exercise. Find the value of y when $t = 1.5$ sec.

Ans. $y = 8 \sin (120t° + 55°)$; −6.55 in.

Plot the curves that represent the following motions:

14. $y = 3.5 \sin (35t° + 36°)$.

15. $y = 12 \sin (1.88t + 0.44)$.

16. $y = 2.5 \sin (\frac{1}{8}\pi t + \frac{1}{12}\pi)$.

17. Plot $y = r \sin \frac{1}{2}\pi t$ and $y = r \sin (\frac{1}{2}\pi t + \frac{1}{4}\pi)$ on the same axes. Notice that the highest points are separated by the constant angle $\frac{1}{4}\pi$. Such curves are said to be out of phase. The difference in phase is stated in time or as an angle; in the latter case it is called the phase angle.

18. Plot $y = r \sin \frac{1}{4}\pi t$, $y = r \sin (\frac{1}{4}\pi t - \frac{1}{2}\pi)$, and $y = r \cos \frac{1}{4}\pi t$, all on the same axes. What is the difference in phase between these?

19. Plot on the same axes: (1) $y = r \sin \pi t$, (2) $y = r \sin \frac{1}{2}\pi t$, (3) $y = r \sin \frac{1}{8}\pi t$.

20. Plot on the same axes: (1) $y = 40 \sin \theta$, (2) $y = 30 \sin \theta$, (3) $y = 20 \sin 2\theta$.

CHAPTER XLI

FUNCTIONS INVOLVING MORE THAN ONE ANGLE

423. In the previous chapters only functions of single angles are dealt with. In solving oblique triangles and in many of the applications of trigonometry, formulas are used that are derived from the functions of the sums or differences of angles.

In the present chapter will be considered a number of formulas involving sums or differences of angles. Many of these formulas are given for reference, and little attempt will be made here to prove them or to illustrate their uses.

424. Functions of the sum or difference of two angles.— The following formulas express the function of the sum or the difference of two angles in terms of the functions of the separate angles. These formulas are sometimes called the **addition** and **subtraction** formulas of trigonometry.

[70] $\qquad \sin (A + B) = \sin A \cos B + \cos A \sin B$

[71] $\qquad \sin (A - B) = \sin A \cos B - \cos A \sin B$

[72] $\qquad \cos (A + B) = \cos A \cos B - \sin A \sin B$

[73] $\qquad \cos (A - B) = \cos A \cos B + \sin A \sin B$

[74] $\qquad \tan (A + B) = \dfrac{\tan A + \tan B}{1 - \tan A \tan B}$

[75] $\qquad \tan (A - B) = \dfrac{\tan A - \tan B}{1 + \tan A \tan B}$

These six formulas should be memorized in the symbols as given here and should also be stated in words and memorized; thus, formula [70] stated in words is:

The sine of the sum of two angles is equal to the sine of the first angle times the cosine of the second angle plus the cosine of the first angle times the sine of the second angle.

Proof of formula [**70**] *for* $A < 90°$, $B < 90°$, *and* $(A + B) < 90°$.—In Fig. 343, angle $XOQ = A$ and angle $QOP = B$. Hence angle $XOP = A + B$.

Draw NP, QP, QR, and MQ perpendicular, respectively, to OX, OQ, NP, and OX. Then angle $RPQ = A$.

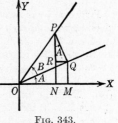

Fig. 343.

$$\sin (A + B) = \frac{NP}{OP} = \frac{MQ + RP}{OP} = \frac{MQ}{OP} + \frac{RP}{OP}$$

But $MQ = OQ \sin A$, and $RP = QP \cos A$, from the right triangles. Putting these values in place of MQ and RP,

$$\sin (A + B) = \frac{OQ \sin A}{OP} + \frac{QP \cos A}{OP}$$

But $\dfrac{OQ}{OP} = \cos B$, and $\dfrac{QP}{OP} = \sin B$.

$$\therefore \sin (A + B) = \sin A \cos B + \cos A \sin B$$

Formulas [**71**] to [**75**] may be proved in a similar manner.

Example 1.—Given the functions of 45° and 30°, find the value of sin 15°.

Solution: $\sin 15° = \sin (45° - 30°)$
$= \sin 45° \cos 30° - \cos 45° \sin 30°$
$= 0.7071 \times 0.8660 - 0.7071 \times 0.5$
$= 0.2588$ *Ans.*

Example 2.—Test formula [**74**] by using $A = 16°$ and $B = 27°$.

Substituting these values in the formula,

$$\tan (16° + 27°) = \frac{\tan 16° + \tan 27°}{1 - \tan 16° \tan 27°}$$

Putting in the values of tan 16° and tan 27° from Table XI,

$$\tan 43° = \frac{0.2867 + 0.5095}{1 - 0.2867 \times 0.5095} = 0.9325$$

This is tan 43° as given in Table XI.

EXERCISES

Find exact values of the following in terms of radicals, then express them approximately as decimals by Table IX, and check by Table XI.

1. $\sin 75° = \sin (45° + 30°) = \sin 45° \cos 30° + \cos 45° \sin 30° = ?$

2. $\cos 75° = \cos (45° + 30°) = ?$

3. $\tan 75° = ?$

4. Write $15° = 45° - 30°$ and by applying formulas [**71**], [**73**], and [**75**]. Find the exact and then the approximate values of (1) $\sin 15°$, (2) $\cos 15°$, (3) $\tan 15°$. Check by Table XI.

5. Show that the $\tan 105° = -2 - \sqrt{3}$.

6. Given $\sin A = \frac{3}{5}$, A between 90° and 180°, $\tan B = 2$, B between 0° and 90°, show that $\cos (A + B) = -\frac{2}{5} \sqrt{5}$.

7. Derive $\sin (90° + \theta) = \cos \theta$ by applying formula [**70**].

Derivation.—Applying formula [**70**] to $\sin (90° + \theta)$,

$\sin (90° + \theta) = \sin 90° \cos \theta + \cos 90° \sin \theta$

But $\sin 90° = 1$, and $\cos 90° = 0$

$\therefore \sin (90° + \theta) = 1 \cdot \cos \theta + 0 \cdot \sin \theta = \cos \theta$

8. Derive $\cos (90° - \theta) = -\cos \theta$ by applying formula [**73**].

9. Derive $\tan (180° + \theta) = \tan \theta$ by applying formula [**74**].

10. Show that $\sin 575° \cos 927° + \cos 575° \sin 927° = \sin 1502°$.

11. Show that $\dfrac{\tan 327° + \tan 846°}{1 - \tan 327° \tan 846°} = \tan 1173°$.

425. Functions of an angle in terms of functions of half the angle.—By putting $B = A$ in formula [**70**],

$$\sin (A + B) = \sin (A + A) = \sin A \cos A + \cos A \sin A$$
$$\therefore \sin 2A = 2 \sin A \cos A$$

By putting $B = A$ in formula [**72**],

$$\cos (A + B) = \cos (A + A) = \cos A \cos A - \sin A \sin A$$
$$\therefore \cos 2A = \cos^2 A - \sin^2 A$$

But from formula [**62**], $\cos^2 A = 1 - \sin^2 A$.

$$\therefore \cos 2A = 1 - 2 \sin^2 A$$

Also from formula [**62**], $\sin^2 A = 1 - \cos^2 A$.

$$\therefore \cos 2A = 2 \cos^2 A - 1$$

By putting $B = A$ in formula [**74**],

$$\tan (A + B) = \tan (A + A) = \frac{\tan A + \tan A}{1 - \tan A \tan A}$$

$$\therefore \tan 2A = \frac{2 \tan A}{1 - \tan^2 A}$$

The following formulas are then derived:

[**76**] **sin 2A = 2 sin A cos A**

[**77**] **cos 2A** $= \cos^2 A - \sin^2 A = 1 - 2\sin^2 A = 2\cos^2 A - 1$

[**78**] **tan 2A** $= \dfrac{2 \tan A}{1 - \tan^2 A}$

These formulas are used to express the function of any angle in terms of the functions of one-half that angle.

Examples: $\sin 60° = 2 \sin 30° \cos 30°$

$$\cos 60° = \cos^2 30° - \sin^2 30° = 1 - 2\sin^2 30° = 2\cos^2 30° - 1$$

$$\tan 60° = \frac{2 \tan 30°}{1 - \tan^2 30°}$$

EXERCISES

Use formulas [**76**], [**77**], and [**78**], and fill in the parentheses in the following:

1. Sin $(\quad) = 2 \sin x \cos x$.

2. $\sin x = 2(\qquad)$.

3. $\cos (\quad) = \cos^2 \dfrac{x}{2} - \sin^2 \dfrac{x}{2} = (\qquad) = (\qquad)$.

4. $\tan x = 2\left(\dfrac{\quad}{\quad} \right)$.

5. $\sin \pi = (\qquad)$.

6. $\cos 4x = (\qquad) = (\qquad) = (\qquad)$.

7. $\tan \frac{1}{2}\pi = (\qquad)$.

8. $\cos 90° = (\qquad) = (\qquad) = (\qquad)$.

9. $\tan 20° = (\qquad)$.

10. $\sin 15° \cos 15° = \frac{1}{2}(\qquad)$.

11. Show that if z stands for $\tan A$,

(1) $\sin 2A = 2z \div (1 + z^2)$.

(2) $\cos 2A = (1 - z^2) \div (1 + z^2)$.

(3) $\tan 2A = 2z \div (1 - z^2)$

12. Show that $\sin t = \cos 2t$ if $\sin t = \frac{1}{2}$.   Find two values of angle t less than 360°.

13. Using functions of 90°, find $\sin 180°$ and $\cos 180°$.

14. Using functions of 60°, find $\sin 120°$ and $\cos 120°$.

15. Take values from Table XI for the functions of 15°, and find $\sin 30°$, $\cos 30°$, and $\tan 30°$.

426. Functions of an angle in terms of functions of twice the angle.—From formula [**77**],

$$\cos 2A = 1 - 2 \sin^2 A$$

Solving for $\sin A$, $\sin A = \pm \sqrt{\dfrac{1 - \cos 2A}{2}}$

Also from formula [**77**], $\cos 2A = 2 \cos^2 A - 1$.

Solving for $\cos A$, $\cos A = \pm \sqrt{\dfrac{1 + \cos 2A}{2}}$.

By dividing, $\dfrac{\sin A}{\cos A} = \tan A = \pm \sqrt{\dfrac{1 - \cos 2A}{1 + \cos 2A}}$.

$$= \frac{\sin 2A}{1 + \cos 2A} = \frac{1 - \cos 2A}{\sin 2A}.$$

The following formulas are then derived:

[**79**] $\sin A = \pm \sqrt{\dfrac{1 - \cos 2A}{2}}$

[**80**] $\cos A = \pm \sqrt{\dfrac{1 + \cos 2A}{2}}$

[**81**] $\tan A = \pm \sqrt{\dfrac{1 - \cos 2A}{1 + \cos 2A}} = \dfrac{\sin 2A}{1 + \cos 2A} = \dfrac{1 - \cos 2A}{\sin 2A}$

These formulas are used to express the functions of any angle in terms of functions of twice that angle. The sign before the radical will be known when the value of A is known. For instance, the sign is $+$ if A is in the first quadrant.

Example.—Given $\cos 60° = \frac{1}{2}$, find $\sin 30°$.

By formula [**79**],

$$\sin 30° = \sqrt{\frac{1 - \cos 60°}{2}}$$

$$\therefore \sin 30° = \sqrt{\frac{1 - \frac{1}{2}}{2}} = \sqrt{\frac{1}{4}} = \frac{1}{2}$$

EXERCISES

Use formulas [**79**], [**80**], and [**81**], and fill in the parentheses in the following:

1. $\sin (\quad) = \pm \sqrt{\dfrac{1 - \cos A}{2}}$.

2. $\cos (\quad) = \pm \sqrt{\dfrac{1 + \cos A}{2}}$.

3. $\tan \frac{1}{2}A = \pm (\qquad) = (\qquad) = (\qquad)$.

4. $\sin (45° + \frac{1}{2}\theta) = \pm (\qquad) = \pm (\qquad)$.

5. $\cos (45° - \frac{1}{2}\theta) = \pm (\qquad) = \pm (\qquad)$.

6. $\tan (22\frac{1}{2}° + \frac{1}{2}\theta) = (\qquad) = (\qquad) = (\qquad)$.

7. Given $\cos 135° = -\frac{1}{2}\sqrt{2}$, find $\cos 67\frac{1}{2}$.

8. Using the functions of $45°$, find $\sin 22\frac{1}{2}°$ and $\cos 22\frac{1}{2}°$, $\tan 22\frac{1}{2}°$.

9. Given $\sin 2\theta = \frac{3}{5}$, find $\tan \theta$ and $\cos \theta$.

427. Formulas for changing products to sums or differences and sums and differences to products.—The following four formulas are convenient for expressing a product of two functions as the sum or difference of two functions.

[**82**] $\sin A \cos B = \frac{1}{2} \sin (A + B) + \frac{1}{2} \sin (A - B)$

[**83**] $\cos A \sin B = \frac{1}{2} \sin (A + B) - \frac{1}{2} \sin (A - B)$

[**84**] $\cos A \cos B = \frac{1}{2} \cos (A + B) + \frac{1}{2} \cos (A - B)$

[**85**] $\sin A \sin B = -\frac{1}{2} \cos (A + B) + \frac{1}{2} \cos (A - B)$

The following four formulas express a sum or a difference as a product. This is often convenient when working with logarithms.

[**86**] $\sin A + \sin B = 2 \sin \frac{1}{2}(A + B) \cos \frac{1}{2}(A - B)$

[**87**] $\sin A - \sin B = 2 \cos \frac{1}{2}(A + B) \sin \frac{1}{2}(A - B)$

[**88**] $\cos A + \cos B = 2 \cos \frac{1}{2}(A + B) \cos \frac{1}{2}(A - B)$

[**89**] $\cos A - \cos B = -2 \sin \frac{1}{2}(A + B) \sin \frac{1}{2}(A - B)$

Example 1.—Express sin 80° cos 60° as a sum of functions. By formula [**82**],

$$\sin 80° \cos 60° = \tfrac{1}{2} \sin (80° + 60°) + \tfrac{1}{2} \sin (80° - 60°)$$
$$= \tfrac{1}{2} \sin 140° + \tfrac{1}{2} \sin 20°$$

Example 2.—Express sin 80° + sin 60° as a product of functions.

By formula [**86**],

$$\sin 80° + \sin 60° = 2 \sin \tfrac{1}{2}(80° + 60°) \cos \tfrac{1}{2}(80° - 60°)$$
$$= 2 \sin 70° \cos 10°$$

EXERCISES

Use formulas [**82**] to [**85**] inclusive and fill in the following blanks:

1. sin 60° cos 30° = ( ) = ( ).
2. cos 60° sin 30° = ( ) = ( ).
3. cos 60° cos 30° = ( ) = ( ).
4. sin 60° sin 30° = ( ) = ( ).

Use formulas [**86**] to [**89**] inclusive, and factor the following sums and differences. (Note that these formulas are useful in factoring and thus important in solving trigonometric equations.) Answer orally.

5. sin 150° + sin 30°.
6. cos 150° − cos 30°.
7. sin 105° − sin 15°.

8. cos 105° + cos 15°.
9. sin 3θ − sin θ.
10. cos 5θ − cos 3θ.

11. sin 120° + cos 60° = sin 120° + sin 30°.
12. cos A − sin A = cos A − cos (90° − A).
13. Show that $\dfrac{\sin 150° + \sin 30°}{\cos 150° - \cos 30°} = -\tan 30°$.
14. Show that $\dfrac{\sin 47° + \sin 17°}{\cos 47° + \cos 17°} = 0.6249$.
15. Show that $\dfrac{\sin 3\alpha + \sin 5\alpha}{\cos 3\alpha - \cos 5\alpha} = \cot \alpha$.
16. Show that $\dfrac{\sin 67° - \sin 23°}{\cos 67° + \cos 23°} = 0.4040$.

REVIEW EXERCISES

1. Find (1) sin 105°, (2) cos 105° by writing 105° = 60° + 45°.
   Ans. (1) $\tfrac{1}{4}(\sqrt{2} + \sqrt{6})$; (2) $\tfrac{1}{4}(\sqrt{2} - \sqrt{6})$.
2. Show that cos 306° + cos 234° + cos 162° + cos 18° = 0,

(1) By using Chap. XXXIX.

(2) By using Art. 427.

3. If tan $A = m$, show that

(1) $\tan (45° + A) = \dfrac{1 + m}{1 - m}$.

(2) $\tan (45° - A) = \dfrac{1 - m}{1 + m}$.

4. Given the functions of 135°, find (1) the sine, cosine, and tangent of $67\frac{1}{2}°$.

(2) The functions of 30°, find the sine, cosine, and tangent of 15°. Check by Table XI.

5. Show that $\sin 3\theta = 3 \sin \theta - 4 \sin^3 \theta$.

Suggestion.—In formula [**70**], let $A = 2\theta$ and $B = \theta$.

6. Show that $\cos 3\theta = 4 \cos^3 \theta - 3 \cos \theta$.

7. Show that $\tan 3\theta = \dfrac{3 \tan \theta - \tan^2 \theta}{1 - 3 \tan^2 \theta}$.

8. If $\theta = \tan^{-1} a$ and $\phi = \tan^{-1} b$, construct these angles in the first quadrant and find

(1) $\tan (\theta + \phi)$.   *Ans.* $\dfrac{a + b}{1 - ab}$.

(2) $\tan (\theta - \phi)$.   *Ans.* $\dfrac{a - b}{1 + ab}$.

9. If $a = \frac{1}{2}$ and $b = \frac{1}{5}$ in Exercise 8, find the value of (1); of (2).

10. Find $\tan (\tan^{-1} \frac{1}{2} - \tan^{-1} \frac{1}{5})$.   *Ans.* $\frac{3}{11}$.

11. Find $\sin (\cos^{-1} \frac{1}{2} + \sin^{-1} \frac{1}{2})$.   *Ans.* 1.

12. Find $\cos (\sin^{-1} \frac{3}{5} - \tan^{-1} \frac{3}{4})$.   *Ans.* 1.

13. Find the value of $\sin \dfrac{11\pi}{6} \cos \dfrac{15\pi}{4} + \tan \dfrac{9\pi}{4} \cot \dfrac{5\pi}{2}$.

Solution.—Using table on page 560 and Art. 414,

$\sin \frac{11}{6}\pi = -\frac{1}{2}$, $\cos \frac{15}{4}\pi = \cos \frac{7}{8}\pi = \frac{1}{2} \sqrt{2}$, $\tan \frac{9}{4}\pi = \tan \frac{1}{4}\pi = 1$, $\cot \frac{5}{2}\pi = \cot \frac{1}{2}\pi = 0$.

$$\therefore \sin \tfrac{11}{6}\pi \cos \tfrac{15}{4}\pi + \tan \tfrac{9}{4}\pi \cot \tfrac{5}{2}\pi = -\tfrac{1}{2} \times \tfrac{1}{2} \sqrt{2} + 1 \times 0$$
$$= -\tfrac{1}{4} \sqrt{2} = -0.3536 \quad Ans.$$

14. Find the value of

$$\cos \left(-\frac{11\pi}{6} \right) \sin \frac{19\pi}{6} + \cos \left(-\frac{4\pi}{3} \right) \sin \left(-\frac{7\pi}{3} \right) \quad Ans.\ 0.$$

15. If $\sin \alpha = -\frac{1}{7}$ and α is in III quadrant, and $\cos \beta = \frac{3}{4}$ and β is in I quadrant, find the value of $\sin (\alpha + \beta)$, $\sin (\alpha - \beta)$, and $\tan (\alpha + \beta)$.

                     Ans. −0.7618; 0.5475; 1.1760.

16. In a right triangle $\cos A = \dfrac{b}{c}$ and $\cos B = \dfrac{a}{c}$. Show that $\sin \dfrac{1}{2} A = \sqrt{\dfrac{c - b}{2c}}$ and $\sin \dfrac{1}{2} B = \sqrt{\dfrac{c - a}{2c}}$.

17. If α is less than $360°$, in what quadrants may α be if $\sin \frac{1}{2}\alpha$ is negative? positive? $\tan \frac{1}{2}\alpha$ is negative? positive? $\cos \frac{1}{2}\alpha$ is negative? positive? $\sec \frac{1}{2}\alpha$ is negative? positive?

Solve the following equations for values of θ not greater than $90°$.

18. $\tan \theta = 1$.   *Ans.* $45°$.   **23.** $\sin \theta = \frac{2}{3}$.   *Ans.* $41° 48'$.

19. $\cos \theta = 1$.   *Ans.* $0°$.   **24.** $\cos \theta = \frac{1}{3}$.   *Ans.* $70° 32'$.

20. $\cot \theta = 1$.   *Ans.* $45°$.   **25.** $\tan \theta = 2$.   *Ans.* $63° 25$.

21. $\cos \theta = 0$.   *Ans.* $90°$.   **26.** $\sin \theta = \frac{3}{4}$.   *Ans.* $48° 35'$.

22. $\sin \theta = \frac{1}{2}$.   *Ans.* $30°$.   **27.** $\tan \theta = \frac{1}{2}$.   *Ans.* $26° 34'$.

28. $\sin \theta = 0.6085$.   *Ans.* $37° 29'$.

29. $\tan \theta = 1.6139$.   *Ans.* $58° 13'$.

30. $\sin \theta = 0.2251$.   *Ans.* $13° 0.4'$.

31. $\cos \theta = 0.6540$.   *Ans.* $49° 9.5'$.

32. $\tan \theta = 0.5680$.   *Ans.* $29° 36'$.

33. $2 \cos^2 \theta - 3 \cos \theta + 1 = 0$.

Solution.—This is a quadratic equation in $\cos \theta$ and may be solved for $\cos \theta$ by factoring.

This gives $(2 \cos \theta - 1)(\cos \theta - 1) = 0$.

Equating each factor to 0 (see Art. 270), and solving the resulting equations,

$$2 \cos \theta - 1 = 0 \qquad \cos \theta - 1 = 0$$
$$\cos \theta = \tfrac{1}{2} \qquad\qquad \cos \theta = 1$$
$$\theta = 60° \qquad\qquad\quad \theta = 0°$$

Check for $\theta = 60°$:

$$2 \cos^2 60° - 3 \cos 60° + 1 = 0$$
$$2 \times (\tfrac{1}{2})^2 - 3 \times \tfrac{1}{2} + 1 = 0$$
$$\tfrac{1}{2} - \tfrac{3}{2} + 1 = 0$$

34. $2 \sin^2 \theta + 3 \sin \theta - 2 = 0$.   *Ans.* $30°$.

35. $6 \sin^2 \theta - 5 \sin \theta + 1 = 0$.   *Ans.* $30°, 19° 28'$.

36. $8 \cos^2 \theta - 10 \cos \theta + 3$.   *Ans.* $60°, 41° 25'$.

37. $3 \tan \theta = 4 \sin \theta$.   *Ans.* $0°, 41° 25'$.

Suggestion.—Put $\tan \theta = \dfrac{\sin \theta}{\cos \theta}$; clear of fractions; and factor.

38. $4 \cos \theta = \sec \theta$.   *Ans.* $60°$.   **39.** $\tan \theta = 3 \cot \theta$.   *Ans.* $60°$

40. $\sin^2 \theta - \cos \theta - \frac{1}{4} = 0$.   *Ans.* $60°$.

Solve the following equations for values of θ less than $360°$.

41. $\cos \theta + \sin 2\theta = 0$.   *Ans.* 90°, 210°, 270°, 330°.

Suggestion.—By formula [**76**], $\sin 2\theta = 2 \sin \theta \cos \theta$.

Then
$$\cos \theta + 2 \sin \theta \cos = 0$$

Factoring
$$\cos \theta(1 + 2 \sin \theta) = 0$$

$$\therefore \cos \theta = 0, \text{ and } 1 + 2 \sin \theta = 0$$

42. $\cos \theta - \sin 2\theta = 0$.   *Ans.* 30°, 90°, 150°, 270°.

43. $\sin \theta + \sin 2\theta = 0$.   *Ans.* 0°, 120°, 180°, 240°.

44. $\sin \theta + \cos 2\theta = 0$.   *Ans.* 90°, 210°, 330°.

Suggestion.—By formula [**77**], $\cos 2\theta = 1 - 2 \sin^2 \theta$.

Then
$$\sin \theta + 1 - 2 \sin^2 \theta = 0$$
$$2 \sin^2 \theta - \sin \theta - 1 = 0$$

This is a quadratic equation in $\sin \theta$ and can be solved by factoring.

45. $\sin \theta - \cos 2\theta = 0$.   *Ans.* 30°, 150°, 270°.

46. $\sin \theta + \cos 2\theta = 1$.   *Ans.* 0°, 30°, 150°, 180°.

47. $\cos \theta + \cos 2\theta = 0$.   *Ans.* 60°, 180°, 300°.

48. $\cos \theta + \cos 2\theta = -1$.   *Ans.* 90°, 120°, 240°, 270°.

49. $2 \sin^2 \theta + 3 \sin \theta - 2 = 0$.   *Ans.* 30°, 150°.

50. $2 \sin^2 \theta + \sin \theta - 1 = 0$.   *Ans.* 30°, 150°, 270°.

CHAPTER XLII

SOLUTION OF OBLIQUE TRIANGLES

428. Remarks on solving triangles.—In the present chapter methods for solving any triangle will be developed. As pointed out in Art. 384, it is possible to solve a triangle whenever enough elements are given so that the triangle can be constructed. The constructions and, likewise, the solutions fall under four cases, depending upon the elements given and required. In each case *three of the six elements of a triangle must be given and at least one of these elements must be a side.* In the right triangle, one element, the right angle, is always given. Therefore two other elements must be given, and at least one of these must be a side.

There arise the four following cases:

Case I.—*When any side and any two angles are given.*

Case II.—*When any two sides and the angle opposite one of them are given.*

Case III.—*When any two sides and the angle included between them are given.*

Case IV.—*When the three sides are given.*

Since there are six elements to a triangle, and, in each of the four cases, three elements are given, then, in general, three unknown elements are to be found in solving a triangle.

The oblique triangle can be divided into right triangles by drawing a convenient altitude and so be solved by methods already given in the chapter on right triangles. It is, however, usually a saving of time to solve oblique triangles by means of formulas derived especially for that purpose. The simpler of these formulas will now be derived.

429. The law of sines.—The statement of the law is:

In any triangle, the sides are proportional to the sines of the opposite angles.

Proof.—Let ABC in Fig. 344 be any triangle. Draw the altitude h from B to the side AC. Because of the right triangles, in either (a) or (b) of the figure,

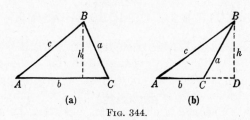

(a)   (b)

Fig. 344.

$$h = c \sin A, \text{ and } h = a \sin C$$
$$\therefore \ a \sin C = c \sin A$$

Dividing both members of this by $\sin C \sin A$,

$$\frac{a}{\sin A} = \frac{c}{\sin C}$$

Similarly by drawing an altitude from C to AB,

$$\frac{a}{\sin A} = \frac{b}{\sin B}$$

[90] $$\therefore \ \frac{a}{\sin A} = \frac{b}{\sin B} = \frac{c}{\sin C}$$

Formula [90] is the statement in symbols of the *law of sines*. From the law of sines may be written the three equations:

$$\frac{a}{\sin A} = \frac{b}{\sin B}$$

$$\frac{a}{\sin A} = \frac{c}{\sin C}$$

$$\frac{b}{\sin B} = \frac{c}{\sin C}$$

any one of which involves four elements of a triangle. It is evident that if any three of the elements involved in one of the equations are given, the remaining element can be found. Thus, if in $\dfrac{a}{\sin A} = \dfrac{b}{\sin B}$, A, B, and b are given, then solving for a,

$$a = \frac{b \sin A}{\sin B}$$

Likewise, if a, b, and B are given, solving for A gives

$$A = \sin^{-1} \frac{a \sin B}{b}$$

EXERCISES

1. Draw a figure, and derive $\dfrac{a}{\sin A} = \dfrac{b}{\sin B}$.

2. Solve $\dfrac{a}{\sin A} = \dfrac{c}{\sin C}$ for each element involved.

3. What does the law of sines become if angle C is a right angle?

430. The law of cosines.—The statement of the law is:

In any triangle, the square of any side equals the sum of the squares of the two other sides minus twice the product of these two sides times the cosine of the angle between them.

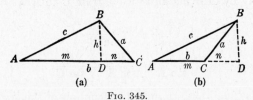

Fig. 345.

Proof.—In Fig. 345, either (a) or (b), draw the altitude h from B to the side AC. Let $AD = m$ and $DC = n$.

Because of the right triangles, in either (a) or (b),

$$(1) \qquad a^2 = h^2 + n^2$$

In (a), $n = b - m = b - c \cos A$.
In (b), $n = m - b = c \cos A - b$.

In either case, $n^2 = b^2 - 2bc \cos A + c^2 \cos^2 A$.

In either (*a*) or (*b*), $h^2 = c^2 \sin^2 A$.

Substituting these values for h^2 and n^2 in (1),

$$a^2 = c^2 \sin^2 A + b^2 - 2bc \cos A + c^2 \cos^2 A$$
$$\therefore a^2 = b^2 + c^2 (\sin^2 A + \cos^2 A) - 2bc \cos A$$

But $\sin^2 A + \cos^2 A = 1$ by [**5**].

[**91**] $$\therefore \mathbf{a^2 = b^2 + c^2 - 2bc \cos A}$$

Similarly there may be obtained

[**92**] $$\mathbf{b^2 = a^2 + c^2 - 2ac \cos B}$$
[**93**] $$\mathbf{c^2 = a^2 + b^2 - 2ab \cos C}$$

Any one of these three formulas involves four elements of a triangle; and if any three of these elements are given, the fourth can be found, but not easily in all cases.

Solving formulas [**91**], [**92**], and [**93**] for cos *A*, cos *B*, and cos *C*, respectively:

[**94**] $$\cos A = \frac{b^2 + c^2 - a^2}{2bc}$$

[**95**] $$\cos B = \frac{a^2 + c^2 - b^2}{2ac}$$

[**96**] $$\cos C = \frac{a^2 + b^2 - c^2}{2ab}$$

By these formulas the values of the angles of a triangle can be computed when the sides are known.

EXERCISES

1. Draw a figure, and derive formula [**92**].

2. Solve formula [**91**] for *b*.

3. What does the law of cosines as given in formula [**93**] become when *C* is a right angle?

4. Do the formulas of this article seem to be suited to work with logarithms? Why?

431. Directions for solving.—Since each of the formulas from the law of sines and the law of cosines involves four elements of the triangle, in order to find any required element by means of these formulas proceed as follows:

(1) *Select a formula that contains the required element together with three that are known.*

(2) *Solve this formula for the required element in terms of the others.*

(3) *Substitute the numerical values and compute.*

The work may be checked, (*a*) by making a careful construction and (*b*) by using a formula other than is used in solving.

Two particularly convenient equations for checking the accuracy of the numerical solutions of triangles are the following, known as Mollweide's equations.

$$[97] \qquad \frac{a - b}{c} = \frac{\sin \frac{1}{2}(A - B)}{\cos \frac{1}{2}C}$$

$$[98] \qquad \frac{a + b}{c} = \frac{\cos \frac{1}{2}(A - B)}{\sin \frac{1}{2}C}$$

The certainty of these equations as checks lies in the fact that each contains all six elements of a triangle.

In the solution of a triangle adhere to the directions given in Art. 388 for the solution of a right triangle. Draw the triangle; state the formulas; make out a careful scheme for all the work; and, *lastly*, fill in the numerical part by the use of the tables. Remember that in computations, *time* and *accuracy* are of very great importance. Time will be saved by carefully planning the arrangement of the work. Accuracy can be secured by checking the work at every step. Verify at every step the additions, subtractions, multiplications, and divisions. Check interpolations when using tables by repeating the work at each step.

432. Case I, a side and two angles given.—In this case it is evident that the third angle can always be found from the equation

$$A + B + C = 180°$$

The sides can then be found by using the relations stated in the law of sines; namely,

$$\frac{a}{\sin A} = \frac{b}{\sin B}, \frac{a}{\sin A} = \frac{c}{\sin C}, \text{ and } \frac{b}{\sin B} = \frac{c}{\sin C}$$

The work may be checked by using the law of cosines, though the work of checking may be tedious, or by using Mollweide's equations.

Example.—Given $a = 45$, $B = 36° 17'$, and $C = 83° 32'$; to find b, c, and A.

Solution

Given $\begin{cases} a = 45 \\ B = 36° 17' \\ C = 83° 32' \end{cases}$

To find* $\begin{cases} A = 60° 11' \\ b = 30.70 \\ c = 51.54 \end{cases}$

Construction

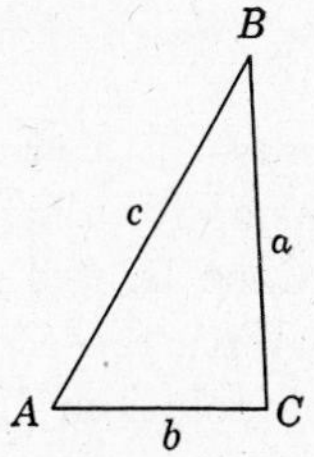

FIG. 346.

Formulas: (1) $A = 180° - (B + C)$

(2) $\dfrac{a}{\sin A} = \dfrac{b}{\sin B}, \quad \therefore b = \dfrac{a \sin B}{\sin A}$

(3) $\dfrac{a}{\sin A} = \dfrac{c}{\sin C}, \quad \therefore c = \dfrac{a \sin C}{\sin A}$

Logarithmic formulas: $\log b = \log a + \log \sin B - \log \sin A$
$\log c = \log a + \log \sin C - \log \sin A$

Computation by natural functions: $A = 180° - (36° 17' + 83° 32') = 60° 11'$

$$b = \frac{a \sin B}{\sin A} = \frac{45 \times 0.5918}{0.8676} = 30.70$$

$$c = \frac{a \sin C}{\sin A} = \frac{45 \times 0.9937}{0.8676} = 51.54$$

* These values are to be filled in after the computations are made.

Computation by logarithms

log 45 =	1.6532	log 45 =	1.6532
log sin 36° 17′ =	9.7722	log sin 83° 32′ =	9.9972
	11.4252		11.6504
log sin 60° 11′ =	9.9384	log sin 60° 11′ =	9.9384
log b =	1.4870	log c =	1.7120
∴ b =	30.69	∴ c =	51.53

Check by formula [97]: $\dfrac{a - b}{c} = \dfrac{\sin \frac{1}{2}(A - B)}{\cos \frac{1}{2}C}$

$$\frac{45 - 30.70}{51.54} = \frac{\sin 11° 57'}{\cos 41° 46'}$$

$$0.2775 = 0.2776$$

Of course it is not necessary to compute both by natural functions and by logarithms.

433. Case II, two sides and an angle opposite one of them given.—With these parts given it is possible (*a*) that there is only one solution, that is, only one triangle can be found; (*b*) that there are two solutions, that is, there are two different triangles that fulfill the conditions; (*c*) that there is no solution, that is, no triangle exists that will fulfill the conditions.

Whether there is one solution, two solutions, or no solution can be determined in most cases by making a careful construction of the triangle from the given parts.

Example 1.—Given $a = 15$, $c = 10$, and $A = 40° 30'$; to find *b*, *B*, and *C*.

From the construction it is seen that there is only one solution.

Formulas

(1) $\dfrac{a}{\sin A} = \dfrac{c}{\sin C}$

$\therefore \sin C = \dfrac{c \sin A}{a}$

(2) $B = 180° - (A + C)$

(3) $\dfrac{a}{\sin A} = \dfrac{b}{\sin B}$, $\therefore b = \dfrac{a \sin B}{\sin A}$

Construction

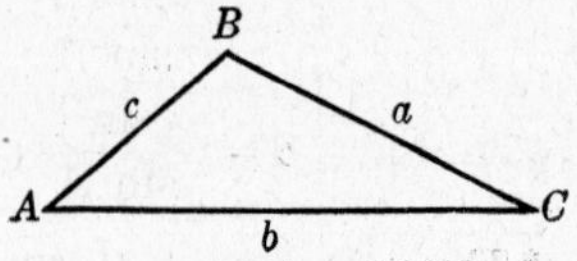

Fig. 347.

Example 2.—Given $a = 20$, $c = 25$, and $A = 52° 40'$; to find b, B and C.

From the construction, Fig. 348, it is seen that there are two triangles, ABC and ABC', that fulfill the conditions.

Formulas

(1) $\dfrac{a}{\sin A} = \dfrac{c}{\sin C}$

$\therefore \sin C = \dfrac{c \sin A}{a}$

(2) $C' = 180° - C$
(3) $B = ABC = 180° - (A + C)$
(4) $B' = ABC' = 180° - (A + C')$

(5) $\dfrac{a}{\sin A} = \dfrac{b}{\sin B}$

$\therefore b = \dfrac{a \sin B}{\sin A}$

(6) $\dfrac{a}{\sin A} = \dfrac{b'}{\sin B'}$, $\therefore b' = \dfrac{a \sin B'}{\sin A}$

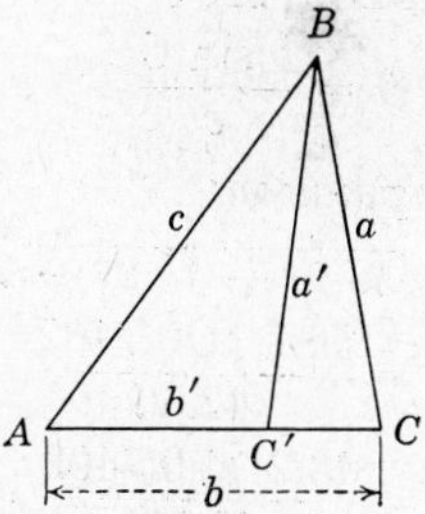

Construction

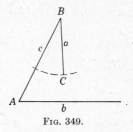

Fig. 348.

Example 3.—Given $a = 12$, $c = 20$, and $A = 62° 20'$; to find b, B, and C.

From the construction, Fig. 349, it is evident that the side a is not long enough to form a triangle. Hence, there is no solution.

Fig. 349.

434. Case III, two sides and the angle between them given.

Example.—Given $b = 45.2$, $a = 56.7$, and $C = 47° 45'$; to find c, A, and B.

Formulas   Construction

(1) $c = \sqrt{a^2 + b^2 - 2ab \cos C}$

(2) $\dfrac{a}{\sin A} = \dfrac{c}{\sin C}$

$\therefore \sin A = \dfrac{a \sin C}{c}$

(3) $\dfrac{b}{\sin B} = \dfrac{c}{\sin C}$

$\therefore \sin B = \dfrac{b \sin C}{c}$

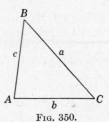

Fig. 350.

Computation:

$c = \sqrt{56.7^2 + 45.2^2 - 2 \times 56.7 \times 45.2 \times 0.6723} = 42.56$

$\sin A = \dfrac{56.7 \times 0.7402}{42.56} = 0.9861, \qquad \therefore A = 80° \; 26'$

$\sin B = \dfrac{45.2 \times 0.7402}{42.56} = 0.7861, \qquad \therefore B = 51° \; 49'$

Check: $A + B + C = 180°$

$$80° \; 26' + 51° \; 49' + 47° \; 45' = 180°$$

Logarithms cannot be used conveniently with formulas such as (1) above. Formulas in which logarithms can be used for the solution of examples under Case III can be derived from the law of sines.

435. Case IV, three sides given.

Example.—Given $a = 10$, $b = 12$, and $c = 15$; to find A, B, and C.

Formulas   Construction

(1) $\cos A = \dfrac{b^2 + c^2 - a^2}{2bc}$

(2) $\cos B = \dfrac{a^2 + c^2 - b^2}{2ac}$

(3) $\cos C = \dfrac{a^2 + b^2 - c^2}{2ab}$

Fig. 351.

Computation:

$\cos A = \dfrac{12^2 + 15^2 - 10^2}{2 \times 12 \times 15} = 0.7472, \qquad \therefore A = 41° \; 39'$

$$\cos B = \frac{10^2 + 15^2 - 12^2}{2 \times 10 \times 15} = 0.6033, \qquad \therefore B = 52° \ 53.5'$$

$$\cos C = \frac{10^2 + 12^2 - 15^2}{2 \times 10 \times 12} = 0.0792, \qquad \therefore C = 85° \ 27.6'$$

Check: $A + B + C = 180°$
$41° \ 39' + 52° \ 53.5' + 85° \ 27.6' = 180° \ 0.1'$

The preceding formulas are not suitable for work with logarithms; but from them formulas can be derived that lend themselves readily to logarithmic work. These formulas are given below without derivation, which is too complicated to be given here.*

In these formulas $s = \dfrac{a + b + c}{2}$, and

$$r = \sqrt{\frac{(s-a)(s-b)(s-c)}{s}}$$

$$[99] \qquad \sin \frac{1}{2} A = \sqrt{\frac{(s-b)(s-c)}{bc}}$$

$$[100] \qquad \sin \frac{1}{2} B = \sqrt{\frac{(s-a)(s-c)}{ac}}$$

$$[101] \qquad \sin \frac{1}{2} C = \sqrt{\frac{(s-a)(s-b)}{ab}}$$

$$[102] \qquad \cos \frac{1}{2} A = \sqrt{\frac{s(s-a)}{bc}}$$

$$[103] \qquad \cos \frac{1}{2} B = \sqrt{\frac{s(s-b)}{ac}}$$

$$[104] \qquad \cos \frac{1}{2} C = \sqrt{\frac{s(s-c)}{ab}}$$

$$[105] \qquad \tan \frac{1}{2} A = \frac{r}{s-a}$$

$$[106] \qquad \tan \frac{1}{2} B = \frac{r}{s-b}$$

$$[107] \qquad \tan \frac{1}{2} C = \frac{r}{s-c}$$

* For their derivation consult Palmer and Leigh, "Plane and Spherical Trigonometry."

The last three formulas are the best group to use in solving for the angles when the three sides are given.

436. Area of a triangle.—From the geometry the area of a triangle equals one-half the base times the altitude; that is,

$$K = \tfrac{1}{2}bh$$

where

K = the area.

b = any side.

h = the altitude drawn to that side.

The following are convenient formulas to use in finding the area of a triangle:

[108] $\mathbf{K = \tfrac{1}{2}ab \sin C = \tfrac{1}{2}ac \sin B = \tfrac{1}{2}bc \sin A}$

[109] $\mathbf{K = \sqrt{s(s - a)(s - b)\,(s - c)}}$

where $s = \dfrac{a + b + c}{2}$.

Formula [109] has already been given as formula [7] on page 160.

EXERCISES

1. Draw a figure for each, and derive the formulas in [108].

Solve the following, which are in Case I, and check by Mollweide's equation when results are not given:

2. Given $A = 33°$, $B = 72°30'$, $a = 10$; find C, c, b.
         Ans. $C = 74°30'$; $b = 17.51+$; $c = 17.69+$.

3. Given $A = 10°12'$, $B = 46°36'$, $a = 50$; find C, b, c.

4. Given $A = 12°49'$, $B = 141°59'$, $a = 82$; find C, b, c, K.
         Ans. $C = 25°12'$; $b = 227.7-$; $c = 157.4-$; $K = 3973.6$.

5. Given $B = 77°$, $C = 65°2'$, $b = 99.9$; find A, a, c, K.

6. Given $A = 99°55'$, $C = 35°4'$, $a = 80.4$; find B, b, c, K.
         Ans. $B = 45°1'$; $b = 57.7+$; $c = 46.9-$; $K = 1333$.

7. Given $B = 34°47.3'$, $C = 109°26.3'$, $a = 322.4$; find $b = 314.7$, $c = 520.1$, $A = 35°46.4'$, $K = 47,833$.

8. Given $A = 144°8.4'$, $B = 25°19.2'$, $b = 430.1$; find $a = 589.1$, $c = 184$, $C = 10°32.4'$, $K = 23,174$.

Solve the following, which are in Case II, and check when results are not given.

9. Given $a = 840$, $b = 485$, $A = 21°31'$; find B, C, c.

10. Given $A = 51°9.1'$, $a = 91.06$, $b = 77.04$; find B, C, c.

11. Given $b = 978.7$, $c = 871.6$, $C = 38°14.2'$; find $A = 97°44.3'$, $B = 44°1.5'$, $a = 1395$; and $A' = 5°47.3'$, $B' = 135°58.5'$, $a' = 142$.

12. Given $B = 16°15.6'$, $a = 75$ ft., $b = 29$ ft.; find the difference between the areas of the two corresponding triangles. *Ans.* 420 sq. ft.

Solve and check the following in Case III:

13. Given $a = 4$, $c = 6$, $B = 60°$; find b, A, C.

14. Given $a = 17$, $b = 12$, $C = 59°17'$; find A, B, c.

15. Given $A = 80°$, $b = 872.5$, $c = 632.7$; find $B = 60°45'$, $C = 39°15'$, $a = 984.8$.

16. Given that the two sides of a triangle are each equal to 6 and the included angle is 120°; find the third side. *Ans.* 10.392.

Solve the following exercise in Case IV, and check by using the formula $A + B + C = 180°$.

17. Given $a = 4$, $b = 6$, $c = 8$; find A, B, C.

18. Given $a = 19$, $b = 34$, $c = 49$; find A, B, C.

19. Given $a = 51$, $b = 65$, $c = 20$; find $A = 38°52.8'$, $B = 126°52.2'$, $C = 14°15$.

20. Given $a = 40$ ft., $b = 13$ ft., $c = 37$ ft.; find $K = 240$ sq. ft.

21. Given $a = 61.52$, $b = 81.74$, $c = 75.34$; find A, B, C. Use formulas [**105**], [**106**], [**107**].

22. Find the area of a triangle with sides 12.5 and 17.05 ft. and included angle 106°36.3'. *Ans.* 102.1 sq. ft.

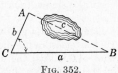

Fig. 352.

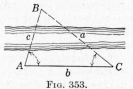

Fig. 353.

23. Find the area of a triangle with the three sides, respectively, 46.45, 27.3, and 32.75 ft. *Ans.* 438.9 sq. ft.

24. To find the distance AB through the swamp, Fig. 352, the following data were measured: $a = 748$ rods, $b = 375$ rods, and $C = 63°35.5'$. Compute the distance AB. *Ans.* 671.3 rods.

25. Compute the inaccessible distance AB, Fig. 353, from the measured data: $b = 1113.8$ ft., $A = 78°19'$, and $C = 47°14'$. *Ans.* 1005 ft.

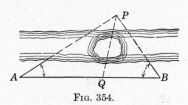

Fig. 354.

26. Two points, P and Q, Fig. 354, are on opposite sides of a stream and invisible from each other on account of an island in the stream. A straight line AB is run through Q, and the following measurements taken: AQ = 824 ft., QB = 662 ft., angle QAP = 42°34.4′, and angle QBP = 57°45′.   Compute QP.   *Ans.* 872.1 ft.

27. Two headlands P and Q are separated by water.   In order to find the distance between them a third point A is chosen from which both P and Q are visible, and the following measurements are made: AP = 1140 ft., AQ = 1846 ft., and angle PAQ = 58°30′.   Find the distance PQ.

Ans. 1584 ft.

28. Two highways intersect at a point A at an angle of 43°30′.   From A to B along one highway is a straighaway of 10 miles; from A to C along the other straightaway it is 15 miles.   Another straightaway connects B and C.   How long will it take a car averaging 50 miles per hour to go from A to B to C to A?   *Ans.* 40 min. approx.

29. A smokestack that stands vertical casts a shadow 80 ft. long on a hillside sloping so that the angle that it makes with the horizontal is 10°. If the angle of elevation of the sun is 49° find the length of the smokestack.

Ans. 104.5+ ft.

30. A triangular lot was offered for sale at $1000 per acre.   The sides of the lot were 5, 9, and 10 rods, respectively.   Find the sale price of the lot.   (160 square rods is an acre).   *Ans.* $140.31.

31. A tapestry hangs on a wall so that the angles of elevation, from a point on the floor, of the top and bottom (along a vertical line) are 60° and 30°, respectively.   Prove that the vertical distance from the top to the bottom of the tapestry is twice the vertical distance from the floor to the bottom of the tapestry.

32. An army officer wants to know the distance from a gun emplacement at A to a trench at D, Fig. 355.   He can measure the distance a and the angles α and β.   Find the distance AD.   Find the distances x and y, and then check the result found for AD by showing that $x^2 + y^2 = \overline{AD}^2$.

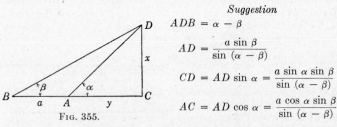

Suggestion

$$ADB = \alpha - \beta$$

$$AD = \frac{a \sin \beta}{\sin (\alpha - \beta)}$$

$$CD = AD \sin \alpha = \frac{a \sin \alpha \sin \beta}{\sin (\alpha - \beta)}$$

$$AC = AD \cos \alpha = \frac{a \cos \alpha \sin \beta}{\sin (\alpha - \beta)}$$

Fig. 355.

33. Two scouts stationed on the opposite sides of an observation balloon note its angles of elevation to be 44°56′ and 36°4′.   They find the distance between them to be 700 ft.   What is the height of the balloon?   *Ans.* 294.7 ft.

34. It is desired to find the distance DC across a lake as shown in Fig. 356. The distance AB and the angles CAB, DAC, ABD, and DBC may be measured. Derive two formulas for finding the distance DC. This problem is sometimes known as **Hansen's problem.**

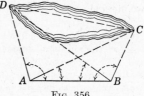

Suggestions

Find (1) DA and AC. Then find DC.

(2) DB and BC. Then find DC.

Fig. 356.

35. To find the distance between two inaccessible points A and B, a base line $CD = 800$ ft. is measured in the same plane as A and B, and the angles $DCA = 106°$, $DCB = 39°$, $CBD = 122°$, and $CDA = 41°$ are measured. Compute the distance AB. *Ans. 1924 ft.*

36. Show that the area of any quadrilateral is equal to one-half the product of its diagonals and the sine of the included angle.

37. From a point on a horizontal plane the angle of elevation of the top of a hill is $23°46'$; and a tower 45 ft. high standing on the top of a hill subtends an angle of $5°16'$. Find the height of the hill. *Ans. 173 ft.*

38. Two observers at A and B, 100 rods apart on a horizontal plane, observe at the same instant an aviator. His angle of elevation at A is $68°25$ and at B, $55°58.2'$. The angles in the horizontal plane made by the projections of the lines of sight with the line AB are $43°27'$ at A and $23°45'$ at B. Find the height of the aviator. *Ans. 1820 ft.*

39. B is 42 miles from A in a direction of N 68° W and C is 58 miles from A in a direction N 17° E. What is the position of C relative to B?
Ans. 68.6 miles N 54°38.9′ E.

40. From a point C two inaccessible points A and B were visible, but no other point could be found from which both A and B were visible.

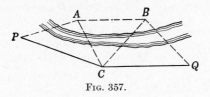

Fig. 357.

However, from a point P both A and C were visible, and from a point Q both B and C were visible. (See Fig. 357.) Find AB if $CP = 425.3$ ft., $CQ = 405.4$ ft., angle $APC = 37°15.4'$, angle $ACP = 42°35.3'$, angle $BQC = 53°14.8'$, angle $BCQ = 58°4.7'$, and angle $ACB = 65°10.5'$.
Ans. 336.8 ft.

41. From a point 300 ft. above the level of a lake and at some distance from one side, an observer finds the angles of depression of the two ends of the lake to be 4°15′ and 3°30′, respectively. The angle between the two lines of sight is 58°45′. Find the length of the lake.

Ans. 4460 ft.

42. A man is on a bluff 250 ft. above the surface of a lake. From his position the angles of depression of the two ends of the lake are 8°15′ and 4°45, respectively. The angle between the two lines of sight is 98°40′. Find the length of the lake. *Ans.* 3706 ft.

43. A ship *S* is 12 miles north of a ship *Q*. *S* sails 10 miles per hour, and *Q* 15 miles per hour. Find the distance and direction that *Q* should sail in order to intercept *S*, which is sailing in a northeasterly direction.

Ans. 29.23 miles N 28°7′ E.

44. A tug that can steam 11 miles per hour is at a point *P*. It must intercept a steamer as soon as possible that is due east at a point *Q* and

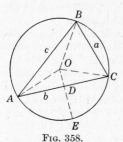

FIG. 358.

making 18 miles per hour in a direction S 58° W. Find the direction in which the tug must steam and the time that it will take if *Q* is 2 miles from *P*.

Ans. S 29°52.3′ E; 5 min. 47 sec.

437. Diameter of a circle circumscribed about a triangle.— Draw a triangle with a circumscribed circle as shown in Fig. 358.

Let the sides of the triangle be *a*, *b*, and *c*; and let *R* be the radius of the circumscribed circle.

Draw *OE* perpendicular to *AC*, and draw the radii *OA*, *OB*, and *OC*.

Then *OE* bisects *AC*, and angle *AOD* equals angle *B*.

In triangle *AOD*, $\dfrac{AD}{AO} = \sin AOD.$

But $AD = \frac{1}{2}b$, $AO = R$, and angle $AOD =$ angle B.

Substituting, $\dfrac{\frac{1}{2}b}{R} = \sin B$, or $R = \dfrac{\frac{1}{2}b}{\sin B}$.

$$\therefore 2R = \dfrac{b}{\sin B}$$

Therefore the diameter of a circle circumscribed about a triangle is equal to the ratio of any side to the sine of the opposite angle.

If the center of the circle did not lie within the triangle as in the figure used, the proof would be slightly different.

438. Radius of a circle inscribed in a triangle.—Draw a triangle with an inscribed circle as shown in Fig. 359.

Let the sides of the triangle be a, b, and c; and let r be the radius of inscribed circle.

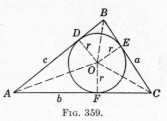

Draw the radii OD, OE, and OF and the lines OA, OB, and OC.

Fig. 359.

(1)   Area ABC = area BOC + area AOC + area AOB

But by geometry, area $ABC = \sqrt{s(s-a)(s-b)(s-c)}$, where $s = \frac{1}{2}(a + b + c)$.

Also, area $BOC = \frac{1}{2}ra$, area $AOC = \frac{1}{2}rb$, area $AOB = \frac{1}{2}rc$.

Substituting in (1),

$$\sqrt{s(s-a)(s-b)(s-c)} = \frac{1}{2}ra + \frac{1}{2}rb + \frac{1}{2}rc$$
$$= \frac{1}{2}r(a + b + c) = rs$$
$$\therefore r = \sqrt{\frac{(s-a)(s-b)(s-c)}{s}}$$

where $s = \frac{1}{2}(a + b + c)$.

EXERCISES

1. An art design consists of an equilateral triangle with 8-in. sides, the circle circumscribed about this triangle and the circle inscribed in this triangle. Find the radii of these two circles.

Ans. $\dfrac{8\sqrt{3}}{3}$; $\dfrac{4\sqrt{3}}{3}$ in. resp.

2. A piece of tin is triangular with sides 6, 7, and 10 in., respectively. Find the radius of the largest circular piece that can be cut from this triangle. *Ans.* 1.797 in.

3. A midget automobile track is the arc of a circle that must pass through the vertices of a triangle with sides 3, 6, and 8 rods, respectively. Find the radius of this circular track. *Ans.* 4.709 rods.

Suggestion.—Use [**99**] to find an angle.

4. Find the radius of the largest circular gas tank that can be constructed on a triangular lot whose sides are 80, 75, and 95 ft., respectively, and locate the center by giving the distance from the ends of the 80-ft. side to the points of tangency on the other sides.

Ans. 23.24 ft.; 30 ft.; 50 ft.

5. Derive the formula $K = \sqrt{s(s-a)(s-b)(s-c)}$ for the area of a triangle by using formulas [**108**], [**76**], [**99**], and [**102**].

439. Resultant of forces.—If two forces, represented by the vectors PQ and PS, Fig. 360, act upon a body at point P, then

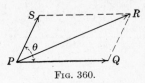

Fig. 360.

the combined effect of these forces is the same as that of the force represented by the vector PR, where PR is the diagonal of the parallelogram of which PQ and PS are two sides.

The force PR is called the **resultant** of the forces PQ and PS.

The resultant of any number of forces is a single force that will produce the same effect as the combined effect of all the given forces.

The resultant of any number of given forces can be found by finding the resultant of any two of the given forces, then the resultant of a third force and the first resultant, continuing till all the forces are used.

Thus, if a, b, c, and d, Fig. 361, are four forces acting at the point P, r_1 is the resultant of a and b, r_2 the resultant of r_1 and c, and r_3 the resultant of r_2 and d. Therefore r_3 is the resultant of a, b, c, and d.

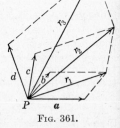

Fig. 361.

440. Computations of a resultant.—If two forces act at *right angles* to each other, their resultant is evidently equal in magnitude to the *square root of the sum of the squares of their respective magnitudes*.

Thus, in Fig. 362, $r = \sqrt{a^2 + b^2}$. Also the direction of r can be found, for tan $QPR = \dfrac{b}{a}$.

If two forces act at any angle θ to each other, their resultant can be found by using the law of cosines, Art. 430, and is equal in magnitude to the *square root of the sum of the squares of their respective magnitudes increased by twice their product times the cosine of the angle between the two forces.*

Thus, in Fig. 363, $r = \sqrt{a^2 + b^2 - 2ab \cos \varphi}$ by the cosine law. But $\varphi = 180° - \theta$, and $\cos \varphi = \cos (180° - \theta) = -\cos \theta$ by Art. 414. Substituting this value for $\cos \varphi$,

$$r = \sqrt{a^2 + b^2 + 2ab \cos \theta}$$

The angle between the resultant and either force can be found by the law of sines, Art. 429.

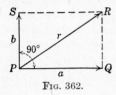

Fig. 362.

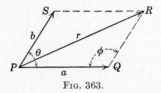

Fig. 363.

If any number of forces are in equilibrium, their resultant is zero.

Velocities can be combined in exactly the same manner as forces.

EXERCISES

1. Find the magnitude and direction of the resultant force F if a force F_1 of 40 lb. and a force F_2 of 60 lb. each act on an object in the following manner:

(1) In the same direction.

> *Ans.* 100 lb. in the same directions of F_1 and F_2.

(2) In opposite directions.   *Ans.* 20 lb. in the directions of F_2.

(3) At an angle of 90°

Ans. 20 $\sqrt{13}$ lb. in the direction such that the angle between F_2 and F is $\tan^{-1} (\frac{2}{3})$.

(4) At an angle of 30°.

Ans. 96.7 lb. in the direction such that the angle between F_2 and F is $\sin^{-1} \left(\dfrac{20}{96.7} \right)$.

2. A car is stuck in a snowbank. A force of 500 lb. acting toward the north and another force of 700 lb. acting toward the northeast are just sufficient to move the car. Find the resultant force in both magnitude and direction that is moving the car.

Ans. 1111 $+$ lb. in direction such that the angle that it makes with the smallest force is $\sin^{-1}(\frac{500}{1111} \sin 135°)$.

3. If in Exercise 2 one of the forces is 410 lb. and the other is 320 lb. and if they are acting at an angle of $51°37'$, find the resultant force both in magnitude and direction that is moving the car.

Ans. $658+$ lb. $22°23.8'$ with the first force.

4. A force F_1 of 128 lb. and another force of F_2 that is unknown are acting on a spring balance that registers 200 lb. If the angle between F_1 and the direction that the balance is noted to move is $18°24'$, find the magnitude and direction of F_2.   *Ans.* $88.3+$ lb. $45°37.3'$ with F_1.

5. A force F_1 of 470 lb. and another force F_2 of 520 lb. are acting on a balance that registers 938 lb. Find the angle between the forces F_1 and F_2.   *Ans.* $37°19.4'$.

6. Two equal forces act at an angle A on an object. Find the magnitude and direction of these two forces.   *Ans.* $\sqrt{2(1 + \cos A)}$; $\frac{1}{2}A$.

7. An airplane at an altitude of 1600 ft. and moving at the rate of 100 miles per hour in a direction due east drops a bomb. Disregarding the resistance of the air, where will the bomb strike the ground if during its fall it is acted upon by a wind of 40 miles per hour from a direction 30° east of south?

Solution.—To find the number of seconds that it is falling, use equation of Exercise 45, page 459, $\frac{1}{2}gt$; $= 1600$, where $g = 32$. This gives $t = 10$, the time in seconds.

It would move east from the starting point as far as the airplane travels in 10 sec. if the wind is not considered. This is

$$\frac{100 \times 5280 \times 10}{60 \times 60} = 1467 \text{ ft.}$$

During 10 sec. the wind would carry the bomb

$$\frac{40 \times 5280 \times 10}{60 \times 60} = 586.7 \text{ ft.}$$

The resultant of these displacements is

$$\sqrt{1467^2 + 586.7^2 + 2 \times 1467 \times 586.7 \times \cos 120°} = 1279 \text{ ft.}$$

By the sine law the direction is found to be N $66°36'$ E.

8. An automobile is traveling N 54° W at 27 miles per hour, and the wind is blowing from the NE at 30 miles per hour. What velocity and direction does the wind appear to have to the chauffeur?

Ans. 37.09 miles per hour from N $59'$ W.

9. A train is running at 30 miles per hour in a direction S 55° W, and the engine leaves a steam track in the direction N 80° E. The wind is known to be blowing from the NE; find its velocity.

Ans. 22 miles per hour.

10. In a river flowing due south at the rate of $3\frac{1}{2}$ miles per hour, a boat is drifted by a wind blowing from the southwest at the rate of 20 miles per hour. Determine the position of the boat after 40 min. if resistance reduces the effect of the wind 70 %. *Ans.* 2.87 miles N 80°14.5′ E.

11. Three forces of 18, 22, and 27 lb., respectively, and in the same plane are in equilibrium. Find the angles that they make with one another. Check by noting that the sum of the angles is 360°.

12. Four forces are acting on the origin of a system of rectangular axes. One of 200 lb. acts along the negative x-axis; one of 100 lb. acts along the positive x-axis; one of 50 lb. acts at an angle of 60° with the x-axis; and one of r lb. acts at an angle θ with the x-axis. If the forces are in equilibrium, find r and θ. *Ans.* 86.6 lb.; −30°.

Suggestion.—The sum of all forces acting north equals the sum of all forces acting south, similarly for the forces acting east and west.

13. A force of 100 lb. acts on an object. It is desired to resolve this force into two components F_1 and F_2. If F_1 makes an angle of 25°,

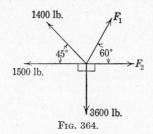

FIG. 364.

and F_2 makes 35°, respectively, with the direction of the original 100-lb. force, find the magnitude of F_1 and F_2.

Ans. $F_1 = 66.2$ lb.; $F_2 = 48.8$ lb.

14. The system of five forces as shown in Fig. 364 is known to be in equilibrium. Find the magnitude of the two unknown forces F_1 and F_2.

Ans. $F_1 = 3014$ lb.; $F_2 = 983$ lb.

TABLES

TABLE I.—SUMMARY OF FORMULAS

[1] $A = ab$, rectangle, parallelogram.

[2] $a = A \div b$, rectangle, parallelogram.

[3] $b = A \div a$, rectangle, parallelogram.

[4] $A = \frac{1}{2}ab$, triangle.

[5] $a = 2A \div b$, triangle.

[6] $b = 2A \div a$, triangle.

[7] $A = \sqrt{s(s-a)(s-b)(s-c)}$, where $s = \frac{1}{2}(a + b + c)$, triangle.

[8] $A = \frac{1}{2}(B + b) \times a$, trapezoid.

[9] $c = \sqrt{a^2 + b^2}$, right triangle.

[10] $a = \sqrt{c^2 - b^2}$, right triangle.

[11] $b = \sqrt{c^2 - a^2}$, right triangle.

[12] $l:1 = t:T$, tapers.

[13] $x = \dfrac{D - d}{2} \times \dfrac{L}{l}$, tapers.

[14] $D_1 = D - \dfrac{1.732}{N}$, sharp V-threads.

[15] $D_1 = D - \dfrac{1.299}{N}$, U. S. S. threads.

[16] $r = \dfrac{(\frac{1}{2}w)^2 + h^2}{2h}$, segment of circle.

[17] $h = r - \sqrt{r^2 - (\frac{1}{2}w)^2}$, segment of circle.

[18] $w = 2\sqrt{h(2r - h)}$, segment of circle.

[19] $C = \pi d$, circle.

[20] $d = C \div \pi$, circle.

[21] $C = 2\pi r$, circle.

[22] $2r = C \div \pi$, circle.

[23] $A = \frac{1}{2}Cr$, circle.

[24] $A = \pi r^2$, circle.

[25] $A = \frac{1}{4}\pi d^2 = 0.7854\,d^2$, circle.

[26] $r = \sqrt{A \div \pi}$, circle.

[27] $d = \sqrt{A \div \frac{1}{4}\pi}$, circle.

[28] $A_r = A - a = \pi R^2 - \pi r^2 = \pi(R^2 - r^2) = \pi(R + r)(R - r)$, ring.

[29(a)] $A = \dfrac{\theta}{360} \times \pi r^2$, sector.

[29(b)] $A = \frac{1}{2}\,\text{arc} \cdot r$, sector.

[30(a)] $A = \dfrac{2}{3}\,hw + \dfrac{h^3}{2w}$, segment.

TABLE I.—SUMMARY OF FORMULAS—*(Continued)*

[30(b)] $A = \dfrac{4}{3} h^2 \sqrt{\dfrac{2r}{h} - 0.608}$, segment.

[31] $A = \pi ab$, ellipse.

[32(a)] $P = \pi(a + b)$, ellipse.

[32(b)] $P = \pi[\frac{3}{2}(a + b) - \sqrt{ab}]$, ellipse.

[32(c)] $P = \pi \sqrt{2(a^2 + b^2)}$, ellipse.

[33] $S = ph$, prism.

[34] $T = ph + 2A$, prism.

[35] $T = 6a^2$, cube.

[36] $p = S \div h$, prism.

[37] $h = S \div p$, prism.

[38] $V = Ah$, prism.

[39] $V = a^3$, cube.

[40] $h = V \div A$, prism.

[41] $A = V \div h$, prism.

[42] $S = Ch = \pi dh = 2\pi rh$, cylinder.

[43] $V = Ah = \pi r^2 h = \frac{1}{4}\pi d^2 h$, cylinder.

[44] $h = V \div A = V \div \pi r^2$, cylinder.

[45] $A = V \div h$, cylinder.

[46] $V = \pi R^2 h - \pi r^2 h = \pi h(R^2 - r^2) = \pi h(R + r)(R - r)$, cylinder.

[47] $S = \frac{1}{2}ps$, pyramid or cone.

[48] $T = \frac{1}{2}ps + A$, pyramid or cone.

[49] $S = \frac{1}{2}(P + p) \times s$, frustum.

[50] $T = \frac{1}{2}(P + p) \times s + B + b$, frustum.

[51] $V = \frac{1}{3}Ah$, pyramid or cone.

[52] $V = \frac{1}{3}h(B + b + \sqrt{Bb})$, frustum.

[53] $V = \frac{1}{3}\pi h(R^2 + r^2 + Rr)$, frustum of cone.

[54] $V = \frac{1}{12}\pi h(D^2 + d^2 + Dd)$, frustum of cone.

[55] $S = 4\pi r^2 = \pi d^2$, sphere.

[56] $V = \frac{1}{3}Sr = \frac{4}{3}\pi r^3 = \frac{1}{6}\pi d^3$, sphere.

[57] $Z = 2\pi rh$, area of zone.

[58] $V = \frac{1}{2}\pi h(r_1^2 + r_2^2) + \frac{1}{6}\pi h^3$, volume of segment.

[59] $A = 2\pi R \times 2\pi r = 4\pi^2 Rr$, solid ring.

[60] $V = 2\pi R \times \pi r^2 = 2\pi^2 Rr^2$, solid ring.

[61] $V = \frac{1}{6}h(B_1 + 4M + B_2)$, prismatoid.

[62] $\sin^2 \theta + \cos^2 \theta = 1$.

[63] $\sec^2 \theta = 1 + \tan^2 \theta$.

[64] $\csc^2 \theta = 1 + \cot^2 \theta$.

TABLE I.—SUMMARY OF FORMULAS—(*Continued*)

[65] $\sin \theta = \dfrac{1}{\csc \theta}$ or $\csc \theta = \dfrac{1}{\sin \theta}$.

[66] $\cos \theta = \dfrac{1}{\sec \theta}$ or $\sec \theta = \dfrac{1}{\cos \theta}$.

[67] $\tan \theta = \dfrac{1}{\cot \theta}$ or $\cot \theta = \dfrac{1}{\tan \theta}$.

[68] $\tan \theta = \dfrac{\sin \theta}{\cos \theta}$.

[69] $\cot \theta = \dfrac{\cos \theta}{\sin \theta}$.

[70] $\sin (A + B) = \sin A \cos B + \cos A \sin B$.

[71] $\sin (A - B) = \sin A \cos B - \cos A \sin B$.

[72] $\cos (A + B) = \cos A \cos B - \sin A \sin B$.

[73] $\cos (A - B) = \cos A \cos B + \sin A \sin B$.

[74] $\tan (A + B) = \dfrac{\tan A + \tan B}{1 - \tan A \tan B}$.

[75] $\tan (A - B) = \dfrac{\tan A - \tan B}{1 + \tan A \tan B}$.

[76] $\sin 2A = 2 \sin A \cos A$.

[77] $\cos 2A = \cos^2 A - \sin^2 A = 1 - 2 \sin^2 A = 2 \cos^2 A - 1$.

[78] $\tan 2A = \dfrac{2 \tan A}{1 - \tan^2 A}$.

[79] $\sin A = \pm \sqrt{\dfrac{1 - \cos 2A}{2}}$.

[80] $\cos A = \pm \sqrt{\dfrac{1 + \cos 2A}{2}}$.

[81] $\tan A = \pm \sqrt{\dfrac{1 - \cos 2A}{1 + \cos 2A}} = \dfrac{\sin 2A}{1 + \cos 2A} = \dfrac{1 - \cos 2A}{\sin 2A}$.

[82] $\sin A \cos B = \frac{1}{2} \sin (A + B) + \frac{1}{2} \sin (A - B)$.

[83] $\cos A \sin B = \frac{1}{2} \sin (A + B) - \frac{1}{2} \sin (A - B)$.

[84] $\cos A \cos B = \frac{1}{2} \cos (A + B) + \frac{1}{2} \cos (A - B)$.

[85] $\sin A \sin B = - \frac{1}{2} \cos (A + B) + \frac{1}{2} \cos (A - B)$.

[86] $\sin A + \sin B = 2 \sin \frac{1}{2}(A + B) \cos \frac{1}{2}(A - B)$.

[87] $\sin A - \sin B = 2 \cos \frac{1}{2}(A + B) \sin \frac{1}{2}(A - B)$.

[88] $\cos A + \cos B = 2 \cos \frac{1}{2}(A + B) \cos \frac{1}{2}(A - B)$.

[89] $\cos A - \cos B = -2 \sin \frac{1}{2}(A + B) \sin \frac{1}{2}(A - B)$.

[90] $\dfrac{a}{\sin A} = \dfrac{b}{\sin B} = \dfrac{c}{\sin C}$.

TABLE I.—SUMMARY OF FORMULAS—(*Continued*)

[91] $a^2 = b^2 + c^2 - 2bc \cos A.$

[92] $b^2 = a^2 + c^2 - 2ac \cos B.$

[93] $c^2 = a^2 + b^2 - 2ab \cos C.$

[94] $\cos A = \dfrac{b^2 + c^2 - a^2}{2bc}.$

[95] $\cos B = \dfrac{a^2 + c^2 - b^2}{2ac}.$

[96] $\cos C = \dfrac{a^2 + b^2 - c^2}{2ab}.$

Mollweide's equations for checking triangles.

[97] $\dfrac{a - b}{c} = \dfrac{\sin \frac{1}{2}(A - B)}{\cos \frac{1}{2}C}.$

[98] $\dfrac{a + b}{c} = \dfrac{\cos \frac{1}{2}(A - B)}{\sin \frac{1}{2}C}.$

Let $s = \dfrac{a + b + c}{2}.$

[99] $\sin \dfrac{1}{2} A = \sqrt{\dfrac{(s - b)(s - c)}{bc}}.$

[100] $\sin \dfrac{1}{2} B = \sqrt{\dfrac{(s - a)(s - c)}{ac}}.$

[101] $\sin \dfrac{1}{2} C = \sqrt{\dfrac{(s - a)(s - b)}{ab}}.$

[102] $\cos \dfrac{1}{2} A = \sqrt{\dfrac{s(s - a)}{bc}}.$

[103] $\cos \dfrac{1}{2} B = \sqrt{\dfrac{s(s - b)}{ac}}.$

[104] $\cos \dfrac{1}{2} C = \sqrt{\dfrac{s(s - c)}{ab}}.$

Let $r = \sqrt{\dfrac{(s - a)(s - b)(s - c)}{s}}.$

[105] $\tan \dfrac{1}{2} A = \dfrac{r}{s - a}.$

[106] $\tan \dfrac{1}{2} B = \dfrac{r}{s - b}.$

[107] $\tan \dfrac{1}{2} C = \dfrac{r}{s - c}.$

[108] Area of a triangle $= \frac{1}{2}bc \sin A = \frac{1}{2}ac \sin B = \frac{1}{2}ab \sin C.$

[109] Area of a triangle $= \sqrt{s(s - a)(s - b)(s - c)}.$

TABLE II.—USEFUL NUMBERS

1 cu. ft. of water weighs 62.5 lb. (approx.) = 1000 oz.

1 gal. of water weighs $8\frac{1}{3}$ lb. (approx.).

1 atmosphere pressure = 14.7 lb. per sq. in. = 2116 lb. per square foot.

1 atmosphere pressure = 760 mm. of mercury.

A column of water 2.3 ft. high = a pressure of 1 lb. per square inch.

1 gal. = 231 cu. in. (by law of Congress).

1 cu. ft. = $7\frac{1}{2}$ gal. (approx.) or, better, 7.48 gal.

1 cu. ft. = $\frac{4}{5}$ bu (approx.).

1 bbl. = 4.211 − cu. ft. (approx.).

1 bu. = 2150.42 cu. in. (by law of Congress) = 1.24446 − cu. ft.

1 bu. = $\frac{5}{4}$ cu. ft. (approx.).

1 perch = $24\frac{3}{4}$ cu. ft. but usually taken 25 cu. ft.

1 in. = 25.4001 mm. (approx.).

1 ft. = 30.4801 cm.

1 m. = 39.37 in. (by law of Congress).

1 lb. (avoirdupois) = 7000 grains (by law of Congress).

1 lb. (troy or apothecaries) = 5760 grains.

1 gram = 15.432 grains.

1 kg. = 2.20462 lb. (avoirdupois).

1 liter = 1.05668 qt. (liquid) = 0.90808 qt. (dry).

1 qt. (liquid) = 946.358 cc. = 0.946358 liter, or cu. dm.

1 qt. (dry) = 1101.228 cc. = 1.101228 liters, or cu. dm.

$\pi = 3.14159265358979+ = 3.1416 = \frac{355}{113} = 3\frac{1}{7}$ (all approx.).

1 radian = 57°17′ 44.8″ = 57.2957795° +.

1° = 0.01745329 + radian.

Base of Napierian logarithms = e = 2.718281828 . . . .

$\log_{10} e$ = 0.43429448 . . . .

$\log_e 10$ = 2.30258509 . . . .

1 horsepower-second = 550 ft.-lb.

1 horsepower-minute = 33,000 ft.-lb.

$\sqrt{2}$ = 1.4142136.	$\sqrt{3}$ = 1.7320508.
$\sqrt{5}$ = 2.2360680.	$\sqrt{6}$ = 2.4494897.
$\sqrt[3]{2}$ = 1.2599210.	$\sqrt[3]{3}$ = 1.4422496.

TABLE III.—Decimal and Fractional Equivalents of Parts of an Inch

8ths and 16ths	32nds	64ths	
1 = .125	1 = .03125	1 = .015625	33 = .515625
2 = .250	3 = .09375	3 = .046875	35 = .546875
3 = .375	5 = .15625	5 = .078125	37 = .578125
4 = .500	7 = .21875	7 = .109375	39 = .609375
5 = .625	9 = .28125	9 = .140625	41 = .640625
6 = .750	11 = .34375	11 = .171875	43 = .671875
7 = .875	13 = .40625	13 = .203125	45 = .703125
16ths	15 = .46875	15 = .234375	47 = .734375
1 = .0625	17 = .53125	17 = .265625	49 = .765625
3 = .1875	19 = .59375	19 = .296875	51 = .796875
5 = .3125	21 = .65625	21 = .328125	53 = .828125
7 = .4375	23 = .71875	23 = .359375	55 = .859375
9 = .5625	25 = .78125	25 = .390625	57 = .890625
11 = .6875	27 = .84375	27 = .421875	59 = .921875
13 = .8125	29 = .90625	29 = .453125	61 = .953125
15 = .9375	31 = .96875	31 = .484375	63 = .984375

TABLE IV.—ENGLISH INCHES INTO MILLIMETERS

In.	0	1/16	1/8	3/16	1/4	5/16	3/8	7/16	1/2	9/16	5/8	11/16	3/4	13/16	7/8	15/16
0	0.0	1.6	3.2	4.8	6.4	7.9	9.5	11.1	12.7	14.3	15.9	17.5	19.1	20.6	22.2	23.8
1	25.4	27.0	28.6	30.2	31.7	33.3	34.9	36.5	38.1	39.7	41.3	42.9	44.4	46.0	47.6	49.2
2	50.8	52.4	54.0	55.6	57.1	58.7	60.3	61.9	63.5	65.1	66.7	68.3	69.8	71.4	73.0	74.6
3	76.2	77.8	79.4	81.0	82.5	84.1	85.7	87.3	88.9	90.5	92.1	93.7	95.2	96.8	98.4	100.0
4	101.6	103.2	104.8	106.4	108.0	109.5	111.1	112.7	114.3	115.9	117.5	119.1	120.7	122.2	123.8	125.4
5	127.0	128.6	130.2	131.8	133.4	134.9	136.5	138.1	139.7	141.3	142.9	144.5	146.1	147.6	149.2	150.8
6	152.4	154.0	155.6	157.2	158.8	160.3	161.9	163.5	165.1	166.7	168.3	169.9	171.5	173.0	174.6	176.2
7	177.8	179.4	181.0	182.6	184.2	185.7	187.3	188.9	190.5	192.1	193.7	195.3	196.9	198.4	200.0	201.6
8	203.2	204.8	206.4	208.0	209.6	211.1	212.7	214.3	215.9	217.5	219.1	220.7	222.3	223.8	225.4	227.0
9	228.6	230.2	231.8	233.4	235.0	236.5	238.1	239.7	241.3	242.9	244.5	246.1	247.7	249.2	250.8	252.4
10	254.0	255.6	257.2	258.8	260.4	261.9	263.5	265.1	266.7	268.3	269.9	271.5	273.1	274.6	276.2	277.8
11	279.4	281.0	282.6	284.2	285.7	287.3	288.9	290.5	292.1	293.7	295.3	296.9	298.4	300.0	301.6	303.2
12	304.8	306.4	308.0	309.6	311.1	312.7	314.3	315.9	317.5	319.1	320.7	322.3	323.8	325.4	327.0	328.6
13	330.2	331.8	333.4	335.0	336.5	338.1	339.7	341.3	342.9	344.5	346.1	347.7	349.2	350.8	352.4	354.0
14	355.6	357.2	358.8	360.4	361.9	363.5	365.1	366.7	368.3	369.9	371.5	373.1	374.6	376.2	377.8	379.4
15	381.0	382.6	384.2	385.8	387.3	388.9	390.5	392.1	393.7	395.3	396.9	398.5	400.0	401.6	403.2	404.8
16	406.4	408.0	409.6	411.2	412.7	414.3	415.9	417.5	419.1	420.7	422.3	423.9	425.4	427.0	428.6	430.2
17	431.8	433.4	435.0	436.6	438.1	439.7	441.3	442.9	444.5	446.1	447.7	449.3	450.8	452.4	454.0	455.6
18	457.2	458.8	460.4	462.0	463.5	465.1	466.7	468.3	469.9	471.5	473.1	474.7	476.2	477.8	479.4	481.0
19	482.6	484.2	485.8	487.4	488.9	490.5	492.1	493.7	495.3	496.9	498.5	500.1	501.6	503.2	504.8	506.4
20	508.0	509.6	511.2	512.8	514.3	515.9	517.5	519.1	520.7	522.3	523.9	525.5	527.0	528.6	530.2	531.8
21	533.4	535.0	536.6	538.2	539.7	541.3	542.9	544.5	546.1	547.7	549.3	550.9	552.4	554.0	555.6	557.2
22	558.8	560.4	562.0	563.6	565.1	566.7	568.3	569.9	571.5	573.1	574.7	576.3	577.8	579.4	581.0	582.6
23	584.2	585.8	587.4	589.0	590.5	592.1	593.7	595.3	596.9	598.5	600.1	601.7	603.2	604.8	606.4	608.0

39.37 in. = 1 m. = 10 dm. = 100 cm. = 1000 mm.

TABLE V.—U. S. STANDARD AND SHARP V THREADS

Diameter of screw	Threads per inch	Depth U. S. S.	Depth sharp V	Root dia. U. S. S.	Root dia. sharp V
$\frac{1}{4}$	20	.03247	.04330	.1850	.1634
$\frac{5}{16}$	18	.03608	.04811	.2403	.2163
$\frac{3}{8}$	16	.04059	.05412	.2936	.2668
$\frac{7}{16}$	14	.04639	.06178	.3447	.3139
$\frac{1}{2}$	13	.04996	.06661	.4001	.3668
$\frac{9}{16}$	12	.05412	.07216	.4542	.4182
$\frac{5}{8}$	11	.05905	.07873	.5069	.4675
$\frac{3}{4}$	10	.06495	.08660	.6201	.5768
$\frac{7}{8}$	9	.07216	.09622	.7307	.6826
1	8	.08119	.10825	.8376	.7835
$1\frac{1}{8}$	7	.09277	.12371	.9394	.8776
$1\frac{1}{4}$	7	.09277	.12371	1.0644	1.0026
$1\frac{3}{8}$	6	.10825	.14433	1.1585	1.0863
$1\frac{1}{2}$	6	.10825	.14433	1.2835	1.2113
$1\frac{5}{8}$	$5\frac{1}{2}$	.11809	.15745	1.3888	1.3101
$1\frac{3}{4}$	5	.12990	.17325	1.4902	1.4035
$1\frac{7}{8}$	5	.12990	.17325*	1.6152	1.5285
2	$4\frac{1}{2}$	.14433	.19244	1.7113	1.6151
$2\frac{1}{4}$	$4\frac{1}{2}$	.14433	.19244	1.9613	1.8651
$2\frac{1}{2}$	4	.16238	.21650	2.1752	2.0670
$2\frac{3}{4}$	4	.16238	.21650	2.4252	2.3170
3	$3\frac{1}{2}$	.18557	.24742	2.6288	2.5052
$3\frac{1}{4}$	$3\frac{1}{2}$	.18557	.24742	2.8788	2.7552
$3\frac{1}{2}$	$3\frac{1}{4}$	.19985	.26647	3.1003	2.9671
$3\frac{3}{4}$	3	.21666	.28866	3.3167	3.1727
4	3	.21666	.28866	3.5667	3.4227
$4\frac{1}{4}$	$2\frac{7}{8}$	.2259	.3012	3.7982	3.6476
$4\frac{1}{2}$	$2\frac{3}{4}$	.2362	.3149	4.0276	3.8712
$4\frac{3}{4}$	$2\frac{5}{8}$	.2474	.3299	4.2551	4.0901
5	$2\frac{1}{2}$	.2598	.3465	4.4804	4.3070
$5\frac{1}{4}$	$2\frac{1}{2}$	.2598	.3465	4.7304	4.5500
$5\frac{1}{2}$	$2\frac{3}{8}$	.2735	.3647	4.9530	4.7707
$5\frac{3}{4}$	$2\frac{3}{8}$	.2735	.3647	5.2030	5.0207
6	$2\frac{1}{4}$	.2887	.3849	5.4226	5.2302

TABLE VI.—STANDARD GAGES FOR WIRE AND SHEET METALS
Diameter or thickness given in decimals of an inch

Number of gage	Birmingham wire gage	American, Brown and Sharp (B. & S.)	United States standard plate iron steel	British Imperial	American Steel and Wire Co.
0000000	....	....	..5	.5	
000000	....	....	.46875	.464	
00000	....	....	.4375	.432	
0000	.454	.46	.40625	.400	.3938
000	.425	.409642	.375	.372	.3625
00	.380	.364796	.34375	.348	.3310
0	.340	.324861	.3125	.324	.3065
1	.300	.289297	.28125	.300	.2830
2	.284	.257627	.265625	.276	.2625
3	.259	.229423	.25	.252	.2437
4	.238	.204307	.234375	.232	.2253
5	.220	.181940	.21875	.212	.2070
6	.203	.162023	.203125	.192	.1920
7	.180	.144285	.1875	.176	.1770
8	.165	.128490	.171875	.160	.1620
9	.148	.114423	.15625	.144	.1483
10	.134	.101897	.140625	.128	.1350
11	.120	.090742	.125	.116	.1205
12	.109	.080808	.109375	.104	.1055
13	.095	.071962	.09375	.092	.0915
14	.083	.064084	.078125	.080	.0800
15	.072	.057068	.0703125	.072	.0720
16	.065	.050821	.0625	.064	.0625
17	.058	.045257	.05625	.056	.0540
18	.049	.040303	.05	.048	.0475
19	.042	.035890	.04375	.040	.0410
20	.035	.031961	.0375	.036	.0348
21	.032	.028462	.034375	.032	.03175
22	.028	.025346	.03125	.028	.0286
23	.025	.022572	.028125	.024	.0258
24	.022	.020101	.025	.022	.0230
25	.020	.017900	.021875	.020	.0204
26	.018	.015941	.01875	.018	.0181
27	.016	.014195	.0171875	.0164	.0173
28	.014	.012641	.015625	.0148	.0162
29	.013	.011257	.0140625	.0136	.0150
30	.012	.010025	.0125	.0124	.0140
31	.010	.008928	.0109375	.0116	.0132
32	.009	.007950	.01015625	.0108	.0128
33	.008	.007080	.009375	.0100	.0118
34	.007	.006305	.00859375	.0092	.0104
35	.005	.005615	.0078125	.0084	.0095
36	.004	.005000	.00703125	.0076	.0090
37	....	.004453	.006640625	.0068	
38	....	.003965	.00625	.0060	
39	....	.003531	....	.0052	
40	....	.003144	....	.0048	

TABLE VII.—SPECIFIC GRAVITIES AND WEIGHTS OF SUBSTANCES

Name of substance	Pounds per cu in.	Pounds per cu. ft.	Specific gravity
Air	.....	0.0795	
Aluminum	.....	162	2.6
Anthracite coal, broken	.....	52 to 60	
Antimony	.....	418	6.7
Asphaltum	.....	87.3	1.4
Beech wood	.....	46	.73
Birch wood	.....	41	.65
Brass, cast (copper and zinc)	.....	506	8.1
Brass, rolled	.....	525	8.4
Brick, common	.....	125	
Brick, pressed	.....	150	
Chalk	.....	156	2.5
Coal, bituminous, broken	.....	47 to 56	
Coke, loose	.....	23 to 32	
Corundum	.....	....	3.9
Copper, cast	.....	542	8.6 to 8.8
Copper, rolled	.319	555	8.8 to 9
Cork	.....	15	.24
Ebony wood	.....	76	1.23
Elm wood	.....	35	.56
Flint	.....	162	2.6
Glass	.....	186	2.5 to 3.45
Gold	.695	....	19.3
Granite	.....	170	2.56 to 2.88
Hickory wood	.....	53	.85
Ice	.....	57.5	.92
Iron, cast	.26	450	6.7 to 7.4
Iron, wrought	.28	480	7.69
Lead	.412	712	11.42
Marble	.....	168.7	2.7
Maple wood	.....	49	.79
Mercury	.49	....	13.6
Nickel	.318	....	8.8
Oak wood, red	.....	46	.73 to .75
Pine wood, white	.....	28	.45
Pine wood, yellow	.....	38	.61
Platinum	.....	....	21.5
Quartz	.....	165	2.65
Silver	.379	655	10.5
Steel	.29	490	7.85
Tin	.....	459	7.2 to 7.5
Zinc	.....	438	6.8 to 7.2
Water, distilled, at 32° F.	.....	62.417	
Water, distilled, at 62° F.	.....	62.355	1
Water, distilled, at 212° F.	.....	59.7	

SPECIFIC GRAVITIES REFERRED TO AIR

Air	1
Oxygen	1.11
Hydrogen	0.07
Chlorine gas	2.44

SPECIFIC GRAVITIES REFERRED TO HYDROGEN

Hydrogen	1
Air	14.53
Oxygen	15.95
Coal gas	6

TABLE VIII.—STRENGTH OF MATERIALS

Material	Ultimate tensile strength, pounds per sq. in.	Ultimate compressive strength, pounds per sq. in.	Coefficient of linear expansion, for 1 deg. F.
Hard steel	100,000	120,000	0.0000065
Structural steel	60,000	60,000	0.0000065
Wrought iron	50,000	50,000	0.0000067
Cast iron	20,000	90,000	0.0000062
Copper	30,000	....	0.0000089
Timber, with grain	8,000 to 25,000	4,000 to 12,000	0.0000028
Concrete	300	3,000	0.0000055
Granite	....	11,000	0.0000050
Brick	....	3,000	0.0000050

In the column of ultimate tensile strengths, are given the pulls necessary to break a rod of one square inch cross section of the given material.

In the column of ultimate compressive strengths, are given the weights necessary to cause a support of one square inch cross section to give way under the pressure.

In the column of coefficient of linear expansion, are given the fractional parts of their length, bars of the different materials will increase when the temperature rises one degree Fahrenheit.

TABLE IX.—SQUARE ROOTS

N.	0	1	2	3	4	5	6	7	8	9	1	2	3	4	5	6	7	8	9
1.0	1.000	1.005	1.010	1.015	1.020	1.025	1.030	1.034	1.039	1.044	0	1	1	2	2	3	3	4	4
1.1	1.049	1.054	1.058	1.063	1.068	1.072	1.077	1.082	1.086	1.091	0	1	1	2	2	3	3	4	4
1.2	1.095	1.100	1.105	1.109	1.114	1.118	1.122	1.127	1.131	1.136	0	1	1	2	2	3	3	4	4
1.3	1.140	1.145	1.149	1.153	1.158	1.162	1.166	1.170	1.175	1.179	0	1	1	2	2	3	3	3	4
1.4	1.183	1.187	1.192	1.196	1.200	1.204	1.208	1.212	1.217	1.221	0	1	1	2	2	2	3	3	4
1.5	1.225	1.229	1.233	1.237	1.241	1.245	1.249	1.253	1.257	1.261	0	1	1	2	2	2	3	3	4
1.6	1.265	1.269	1.273	1.277	1.281	1.285	1.288	1.292	1.296	1.300	0	1	1	2	2	2	3	3	4
1.7	1.304	1.308	1.311	1.315	1.319	1.323	1.327	1.330	1.334	1.338	0	1	1	2	2	2	3	3	3
1.8	1.342	1.345	1.349	1.353	1.356	1.360	1.364	1.367	1.371	1.375	0	1	1	1	2	2	3	3	3
1.9	1.378	1.382	1.386	1.389	1.393	1.396	1.400	1.404	1.407	1.411	0	1	1	1	2	2	3	3	3
2.0	1.414	1.418	1.421	1.425	1.428	1.432	1.435	1.439	1.442	1.446	0	1	1	1	2	2	2	3	3
2.1	1.449	1.453	1.456	1.459	1.463	1.466	1.470	1.473	1.476	1.480	0	1	1	1	2	2	2	3	3
2.2	1.483	1.487	1.490	1.493	1.497	1.500	1.503	1.507	1.510	1.513	0	1	1	1	2	2	2	3	3
2.3	1.517	1.520	1.523	1.526	1.530	1.533	1.536	1.539	1.543	1.546	0	1	1	1	2	2	2	3	3
2.4	1.549	1.552	1.556	1.559	1.562	1.565	1.568	1.572	1.575	1.578	0	1	1	1	2	2	2	3	3
2.5	1.581	1.584	1.587	1.591	1.594	1.597	1.600	1.603	1.606	1.609	0	1	1	1	2	2	2	3	3
2.6	1.612	1.616	1.619	1.622	1.625	1.628	1.631	1.634	1.637	1.640	0	1	1	1	2	2	2	2	3
2.7	1.643	1.646	1.649	1.652	1.655	1.658	1.661	1.664	1.667	1.670	0	1	1	1	2	2	2	2	3
2.8	1.673	1.676	1.679	1.682	1.685	1.688	1.691	1.694	1.697	1.700	0	1	1	1	1	2	2	2	3
2.9	1.703	1.706	1.709	1.712	1.715	1.718	1.720	1.723	1.726	1.729	0	1	1	1	1	2	2	2	3
3.0	1.732	1.735	1.738	1.741	1.744	1.746	1.749	1.752	1.755	1.758	0	1	1	1	1	2	2	2	3
3.1	1.761	1.764	1.766	1.769	1.772	1.775	1.778	1.780	1.783	1.786	0	1	1	1	1	2	2	2	3
3.2	1.789	1.792	1.794	1.797	1.800	1.803	1.806	1.808	1.811	1.814	0	1	1	1	1	2	2	2	2
3.3	1.817	1.819	1.822	1.825	1.828	1.830	1.833	1.836	1.838	1.841	0	1	1	1	1	2	2	2	2
3.4	1.844	1.847	1.849	1.852	1.855	1.857	1.860	1.863	1.865	1.868	0	1	1	1	1	2	2	2	2
3.5	1.871	1.873	1.876	1.879	1.881	1.884	1.887	1.889	1.892	1.895	0	1	1	1	1	2	2	2	2
3.6	1.897	1.900	1.903	1.905	1.908	1.910	1.913	1.916	1.918	1.921	0	1	1	1	1	2	2	2	2
3.7	1.924	1.926	1.929	1.931	1.934	1.936	1.939	1.942	1.944	1.947	0	1	1	1	1	2	2	2	2
3.8	1.949	1.952	1.954	1.957	1.960	1.962	1.965	1.967	1.970	1.972	0	1	1	1	1	2	2	2	2
3.9	1.975	1.977	1.980	1.982	1.985	1.987	1.990	1.992	1.995	1.997	0	1	1	1	1	2	2	2	2
4.0	2.000	2.002	2.005	2.007	2.010	2.012	2.015	2.017	2.020	2.022	0	0	1	1	1	1	2	2	2
4.1	2.025	2.027	2.030	2.032	2.035	2.037	2.040	2.042	2.045	2.047	0	0	1	1	1	1	2	2	2
4.2	2.049	2.052	2.054	2.057	2.059	2.062	2.064	2.066	2.069	2.071	0	0	1	1	1	1	2	2	2
4.3	2.074	2.076	2.078	2.081	2.083	2.086	2.088	2.090	2.093	2.095	0	0	1	1	1	1	2	2	2
4.4	2.098	2.100	2.102	2.105	2.107	2.110	2.112	2.114	2.117	2.119	0	0	1	1	1	1	2	2	2
4.5	2.121	2.124	2.126	2.128	2.131	2.133	2.135	2.138	2.140	2.142	0	0	1	1	1	1	2	2	2
4.6	2.145	2.147	2.149	2.152	2.154	2.156	2.159	2.161	2.163	2.166	0	0	1	1	1	1	2	2	2
4.7	2.168	2.170	2.173	2.175	2.177	2.179	2.182	2.184	2.186	2.189	0	0	1	1	1	1	2	2	2
4.8	2.191	2.193	2.195	2.198	2.200	2.202	2.205	2.207	2.209	2.211	0	0	1	1	1	1	2	2	2
4.9	2.214	2.216	2.218	2.220	2.223	2.225	2.227	2.229	2.232	2.234	0	0	1	1	1	1	2	2	2
5.0	2.236	2.238	2.241	2.243	2.245	2.247	2.249	2.252	2.254	2.256	0	0	1	1	1	1	2	2	2
5.1	2.258	2.261	2.263	2.265	2.267	2.269	2.272	2.274	2.276	2.278	0	0	1	1	1	1	2	2	2
5.2	2.280	2.283	2.285	2.287	2.289	2.291	2.293	2.296	2.298	2.300	0	0	1	1	1	1	2	2	2
5.3	2.302	2.304	2.307	2.309	2.311	2.313	2.315	2.317	2.319	2.322	0	0	1	1	1	1	2	2	2
5.4	2.324	2.326	2.328	2.330	2.332	2.335	2.337	2.339	2.341	2.343	0	0	1	1	1	1	1	2	2

| N. | 0 | 1 | 2 | 3 | 4 | 5 | 6 | 7 | 8 | 9 | 1 | 2 | 3 | 4 | 5 | 6 | 7 | 8 | 9 |

TABLE IX.—SQUARE ROOTS—*Continued*

N.	0	1	2	3	4	5	6	7	8	9	1	2	3	4	5	6	7	8	9
5.5	2.345	2.347	2.349	2.352	2.354	2.356	2.358	2.360	2.362	2.364	0	0	1	1	1	1	1	2	2
5.6	2.366	2.369	2.371	2.373	2.375	2.377	2.379	2.381	2.383	2.385	0	0	1	1	1	1	1	2	2
5.7	2.387	2.390	2.392	2.394	2.396	2.398	2.400	2.402	2.404	2.406	0	0	1	1	1	1	1	2	2
5.8	2.408	2.410	2.412	2.415	2.417	2.419	2.421	2.423	2.425	2.427	0	0	1	1	1	1	1	2	2
5.9	2.429	2.431	2.433	2.435	2.437	2.439	2.441	2.443	2.445	2.447	0	0	1	1	1	1	1	2	2
6.0	2.449	2.452	2.454	2.456	2.458	2.460	2.462	2.464	2.466	2.468	0	0	1	1	1	1	1	2	2
6.1	2.470	2.472	2.474	2.476	2.478	2.480	2.482	2.484	2.486	2.488	0	0	1	1	1	1	1	2	2
6.2	2.490	2.492	2.494	2.496	2.498	2.500	2.502	2.504	2.506	2.508	0	0	1	1	1	1	1	2	2
6.3	2.510	2.512	2.514	2.516	2.518	2.520	2.522	2.524	2.526	2.528	0	0	1	1	1	1	1	2	2
6.4	2.530	2.532	2.534	2.536	2.538	2.540	2.542	2.544	2.546	2.548	0	0	1	1	1	1	1	2	2
6.5	2.550	2.551	2.553	2.555	2.557	2.559	2.561	2.563	2.565	2.567	0	0	1	1	1	1	1	2	2
6.6	2.569	2.571	2.573	2.575	2.577	2.579	2.581	2.583	2.585	2.587	0	0	1	1	1	1	1	2	2
6.7	2.588	2.590	2.592	2.594	2.596	2.598	2.600	2.602	2.604	2.606	0	0	1	1	1	1	1	2	2
6.8	2.608	2.610	2.612	2.613	2.615	2.617	2.619	2.621	2.623	2.625	0	0	1	1	1	1	1	2	2
6.9	2.627	2.629	2.631	2.632	2.634	2.636	2.638	2.640	2.642	2.644	0	0	1	1	1	1	1	2	2
7.0	2.646	2.648	2.650	2.651	2.653	2.655	2.657	2.659	2.661	2.663	0	0	1	1	1	1	1	1	2
7.1	2.665	2.666	2.668	2.670	2.672	2.674	2.676	2.678	2.680	2.681	0	0	1	1	1	1	1	1	2
7.2	2.683	2.685	2.687	2.689	2.691	2.693	2.694	2.696	2.698	2.700	0	0	1	1	1	1	1	1	2
7.3	2.702	2.704	2.706	2.707	2.700	2.711	2.713	2.715	2.717	2.718	0	0	1	1	1	1	1	1	2
7.4	2.720	2.722	2.724	2.726	2.728	2.729	2.731	2.733	2.735	2.737	0	0	1	1	1	1	1	1	2
7.5	2.793	2.740	2.742	2.744	2.746	2.748	2.750	2.751	2.753	2.755	0	0	1	1	1	1	1	1	2
7.6	2.757	2.759	2.760	2.762	2.764	2.766	2.768	2.769	2.771	2.773	0	0	1	1	1	1	1	1	2
7.7	2.775	2.777	2.778	2.780	2.782	2.784	2.786	2.787	2.789	2.791	0	0	1	1	1	1	1	1	2
7.8	2.793	2.795	2.796	2.798	2.800	2.802	2.804	2.805	2.807	2.809	0	0	1	1	1	1	1	1	2
7.9	2.811	2.812	2.814	2.816	2.818	2.820	2.821	2.823	2.825	2.827	0	0	1	1	1	1	1	1	2
8.0	2.828	2.830	2.832	2.834	2.835	2.837	2.839	2.841	2.843	2.844	0	0	1	1	1	1	1	1	2
8.1	2.846	2.848	2.850	2.851	2.853	2.855	2.857	2.858	2.860	2.862	0	0	1	1	1	1	1	1	2
8.2	2.864	2.865	2.867	2.869	2.871	2.872	2.874	2.876	2.877	2.879	0	0	1	1	1	1	1	1	2
8.3	2.881	2.883	2.884	2.886	2.888	2.890	2.891	2.893	2.895	2.897	0	0	1	1	1	1	1	1	2
8.4	2.898	2.900	2.902	2.903	2.905	2.907	2.909	2.910	2.912	2.914	0	0	1	1	1	1	1	1	2
8.5	2.915	2.917	2.919	2.921	2.922	2.924	2.926	2.927	2.929	2.931	0	0	1	1	1	1	1	1	2
8.6	2.933	2.934	2.936	2.938	2.939	2.941	2.943	2.944	2.946	2.948	0	0	1	1	1	1	1	1	2
8.7	2.950	2.951	2.953	2.955	2.956	2.958	2.960	2.961	2.963	2.965	0	0	1	1	1	1	1	1	2
8.8	2.966	2.968	2.970	2.972	2.973	2.975	2.977	2.978	2.980	2.982	0	0	1	1	1	1	1	1	2
8.9	2.983	2.985	2.987	2.988	2.990	2.992	2.993	2.995	2.997	2.998	0	0	1	1	1	1	1	1	2
9.0	3.000	3.002	3.003	3.005	3.007	3.008	3.010	3.012	3.013	3.015	0	0	0	1	1	1	1	1	1
9.1	3.017	3.018	3.020	3.022	3.023	3.025	3.027	3.028	3.030	3.032	0	0	0	1	1	1	1	1	1
9.2	3.033	3.035	3.036	3.038	3.040	3.041	3.043	3.045	3.046	3.048	0	0	0	1	1	1	1	1	1
9.3	3.050	3.051	3.053	3.055	3.056	3.058	3.059	3.061	3.063	3.064	0	0	0	1	1	1	1	1	1
9.4	3.066	3.068	3.069	3.071	3.072	3.074	3.076	3.077	3.079	3.081	0	0	0	1	1	1	1	1	1
9.5	3.082	3.084	3.085	3.087	3.089	3.090	3.092	3.094	3.095	3.097	0	0	0	1	1	1	1	1	1
9.6	3.098	3.100	3.102	3.103	3.105	3.106	3.108	3.110	3.111	3.113	0	0	0	1	1	1	1	1	1
9.7	3.114	3.116	3.118	3.119	3.121	3.122	3.124	3.126	3.127	3.129	0	0	0	1	1	1	1	1	1
9.8	3.130	3.132	3.134	3.135	3.137	3.138	3.140	3.142	3.143	3.145	0	0	0	1	1	1	1	1	1
9.9	3.146	3.148	3.150	3.151	3.153	3.154	3.156	3.158	3.159	3.161	0	0	0	1	1	1	1	1	1
N.	0	1	2	3	4	5	6	7	8	9	1	2	3	4	5	6	7	8	9

TABLE IX.—SQUARE ROOTS—*Continued*

N.	0	1	2	3	4	5	6	7	8	9	1	2	3	4	5	6	7	8	9
10	3.162	3.178	3.194	3.209	3.225	3.240	3.256	3.271	3.286	3.302	2	3	5	6	8	9	11	12	14
11	3.317	3.332	3.347	3.362	3.376	3.391	3.406	3.421	3.435	3.450	1	3	4	6	7	9	10	12	13
12	3.464	3.479	3.493	3.507	3.521	3.536	3.550	3.564	3.578	3.592	1	3	4	6	7	8	10	11	13
13	3.606	3.619	3.633	3.647	3.661	3.674	3.688	3.701	3.715	3.728	1	3	4	5	7	8	10	11	12
14	3.742	3.755	3.768	3.782	3.795	3.808	3.821	3.834	3.847	3.860	1	3	4	5	7	8	9	11	12
15	3.873	3.886	3.899	3.912	3.924	3.937	3.950	3.962	3.975	3.987	1	3	4	5	6	8	9	10	11
16	4.000	4.012	4.025	4.037	4.050	4.062	4.074	4.087	4.099	4.111	1	2	4	5	6	7	9	10	11
17	4.123	4.135	4.14	4.159	4.171	4.183	4.195	4.207	4.219	4.231	1	2	4	5	6	7	8	10	11
18	4.243	4.254	4.266	4.278	4.290	4.301	4.313	4.324	4.336	4.347	1	2	3	5	6	7	8	9	10
19	4.359	4.370	4.382	4.393	4.405	4.416	4.427	4.438	4.450	4.461	1	2	3	5	6	7	8	9	10
20	4.472	4.483	4.494	4.506	4.517	5.528	4.539	4.550	4.561	4.572	1	2	3	4	6	7	8	9	10
21	4.583	4.593	4.604	4.615	4.626	4.637	4.648	4.658	4.669	4.680	1	2	3	4	5	6	8	9	10
22	4.690	4.701	4.712	4.722	4.733	4.743	4.754	4.764	4.775	4.785	1	2	3	4	5	6	7	8	9
23	4.796	4.806	4.817	4.827	4.837	4.848	4.858	4.868	4.879	4.889	1	2	3	4	5	6	7	8	9
24	4.899	4.909	4.919	4.930	4.940	4.950	4.960	4.970	4.980	4.990	1	2	3	4	5	6	7	8	9
25	5.000	5.010	5.020	5.030	5.040	5.050	5.060	5.070	5.079	5.089	1	2	3	4	5	6	7	8	9
25	5.099	5.109	5.119	5.128	5.138	5.148	5.158	5.167	5.177	5.187	1	2	3	4	5	6	7	8	9
27	5.196	5.206	5.215	5.225	5.235	5.244	5.254	5.263	5.273	5.282	1	2	3	4	5	6	7	8	9
28	5.292	5.301	5.310	5.320	5.329	5.339	5.348	5.357	5.367	5.376	1	2	3	4	5	6	7	7	8
29	5.385	5.394	5.404	5.413	5.422	5.431	5.441	5.450	5.459	5.468	1	2	3	4	5	5	6	7	8
30	5.477	5.486	5.495	5.505	5.514	5.523	5.532	5.541	5.550	5.559	1	2	3	4	4	5	6	7	8
31	5.568	5.577	5.586	5.595	5.604	5.612	5.621	5.630	5.639	5.648	1	2	3	3	4	5	6	7	8
32	5.657	5.666	5.675	5.683	5.692	5.701	5.710	5.718	5.727	5.736	1	2	3	3	4	5	6	7	8
33	5.745	5.753	5.762	5.771	5.779	5.788	5.797	5.805	5.814	5.822	1	2	3	3	4	5	6	7	8
34	5.831	5.840	5.848	5.857	5.865	5.874	5.882	5.891	5.899	5.908	1	2	3	3	4	5	6	7	8
35	5.916	5.925	5.933	5.941	5.950	5.958	5.967	5.975	5.983	5.992	1	2	2	3	4	5	6	7	8
36	6.000	6.008	6.017	6.025	6.033	6.042	6.050	6.058	6.066	6.075	1	2	2	3	4	5	6	7	7
37	6.083	6.091	6.099	6.107	6.116	6.124	6.132	6.140	6.148	6.156	1	2	2	3	4	5	6	7	7
38	6.164	6.173	6.181	6.189	6.197	6.205	6.213	6.221	6.229	6.237	1	2	2	3	4	5	6	6	7
39	6.245	6.253	6.261	6.269	6.277	6.285	6.293	6.301	6.309	6.317	1	2	2	3	4	5	6	6	7
40	6.325	6.332	6.340	6.348	6.356	6.364	6.372	6.380	6.387	6.395	1	2	2	3	4	5	6	6	7
41	6.403	6.411	6.419	6.427	6.434	6.442	6.450	6.458	6.465	6.473	1	2	2	3	4	5	5	6	7
42	6.481	6.488	6.496	6.504	6.512	6.519	6.527	6.535	6.542	6.550	1	2	2	3	4	5	5	6	7
43	6.557	6.565	6.573	6.580	6.588	6.595	6.603	6.611	6.618	6.626	1	2	2	3	4	5	5	6	7
44	6.633	6.641	6.648	6.656	6.663	6.671	6.678	6.686	6.693	6.701	1	2	2	3	4	5	5	6	7
45	6.708	6.716	6.723	6.731	6.738	6.745	6.753	6.760	6.768	6.775	1	1	2	3	4	4	5	6	7
46	6.782	6.790	6.797	6.804	6.812	6.819	6.826	6.834	6.841	6.848	1	1	2	3	4	4	5	6	7
47	6.856	6.863	6.870	6.877	6.885	6.892	6.899	6.907	6.914	6.921	1	1	2	3	4	4	5	6	7
48	6.928	6.935	6.943	6.950	6.957	6.964	6.971	6.979	6.986	6.993	1	1	2	3	4	4	5	6	6
49	7.000	7.007	7.014	7.021	7.029	7.036	7.043	7.050	7.057	7.064	1	1	2	3	4	4	5	6	6
50	7.071	7.078	7.085	7.092	7.099	7.106	7.113	7.120	7.127	7.134	1	1	2	3	4	4	5	6	6
51	7.141	7.148	7.155	7.162	7.169	7.176	7.183	7.190	7.197	7.204	1	1	2	3	4	4	5	6	6
52	7.211	7.218	7.225	7.232	7.239	7.246	7.253	7.259	7.266	7.273	1	1	2	3	3	4	5	6	6
53	7.280	7.287	7.294	7.301	7.308	7.314	7.321	7.328	7.335	7.342	1	1	2	3	3	4	5	5	6
54	7.348	7.355	7.362	7.369	7.376	7.382	7.389	7.396	7.403	7.409	1	1	2	3	3	4	5	5	6
N.	0	1	2	3	4	5	6	7	8	9	1	2	3	4	5	6	7	8	9

TABLE IX.—SQUARE ROOTS—Continued

N.	0	1	2	3	4	5	6	7	8	9	1	2	3	4	5	6	7	8	9
55	7.416	7.423	7.430	7.436	7.443	7.450	7.457	7.463	7.470	7.477	1	1	2	3	3	4	5	5	6
56	7.483	7.490	7.497	7.503	7.510	7.517	7.523	7.530	7.537	7.543	1	1	2	3	3	4	5	5	6
57	7.550	7.556	7.563	7.570	7.576	7.583	7.589	7.596	7.603	7.609	1	1	2	3	3	4	5	5	6
58	7.616	7.622	7.629	7.635	7.642	7.649	7.655	7.662	7.668	7.675	1	1	2	3	3	4	5	5	6
59	7.681	7.688	7.694	7.701	7.707	7.714	7.720	7.727	7.733	7.740	1	1	2	3	3	4	4	5	6
60	7.746	7.752	7.759	7.765	7.772	7.778	7.785	7.791	7.797	7.804	1	1	2	3	3	4	4	5	6
61	7.810	7.817	7.823	7.829	7.836	7.842	7.849	7.855	7.861	7.868	1	1	2	3	3	4	4	5	6
62	7.874	7.880	7.887	7.893	7.899	7.906	7.912	7.918	7.925	7.931	1	1	2	3	3	4	4	5	6
63	7.937	7.944	7.950	7.956	7.962	7.969	7.975	7.981	7.987	7.994	1	1	2	3	3	4	4	5	6
64	8.000	8.006	8.012	8.019	8.025	8.031	8.037	8.044	8.050	8.056	1	1	2	2	3	4	4	5	6
65	8.062	8.068	8.075	8.081	8.087	8.093	8.099	8.106	8.112	8.118	1	1	2	2	3	4	4	5	5
66	8.124	8.130	8.136	8.142	8.149	8.155	8.161	8.167	8.173	8.179	1	1	2	2	3	4	4	5	5
67	8.185	8.191	8.198	8.204	8.210	8.216	8.222	8.228	8.234	8.240	1	1	2	2	3	4	4	5	5
68	8.246	8.252	8.258	8.264	8.270	8.276	8.283	8.289	8.295	8.301	1	1	2	2	3	4	4	5	5
69	8.307	8.313	8.319	8.325	8.331	8.337	8.343	8.340	8.355	8.361	1	1	2	2	3	4	4	5	5
70	8.367	8.373	8.379	8.385	8.390	8.396	8.402	8.408	8.414	8.420	1	1	2	2	3	4	4	5	5
71 I	8.426	8.432	8.438	8.444	8.450	8.456	8.462	8.468	8.473	8.479	1	1	2	2	3	4	4	5	5
72	8.485	8.491	8.497	8.503	8.509	8.515	8.521	8.526	8.532	8.538	1	1	2	2	3	3	4	5	5
73	8.544	8.550	8.556	8.562	8.567	8.573	8.579	8.585	8.591	8.597	1	1	2	2	3	3	4	5	5
74	8.602	8.608	8.614	8.620	8.626	8.631	8.637	8.643	8.649	8.654	1	1	2	2	3	3	4	5	5
75	8.660	8.666	8.672	8.678	8.683	8.689	8.695	8.701	8.706	8.712	1	1	2	2	3	3	4	5	5
76	8.718	8.724	8.729	8.735	8.741	8.746	8.752	8.758	8.764	8.769	1	1	2	2	3	3	4	5	5
77	8.775	8.781	8.786	8.792	8.798	8.803	8.809	8.815	8.820	8.826	1	1	2	2	3	3	4	4	5
78	8.832	8.837	8.843	8.849	8.854	8.860	8.866	8.871	8.877	8.883	1	1	2	2	3	3	4	4	5
79	8.888	8.894	8.899	8.905	8.911	8.916	8.922	8.927	8.933	8.939	1	1	2	2	3	3	4	4	5
80	8.944	8.950	8.955	8.961	8.967	8.972	8.978	8.983	8.989	8.994	1	1	2	2	3	3	4	4	5
81	9.000	9.006	9.011	9.017	9.022	9.028	9.033	9.039	9.044	9.050	1	1	2	2	3	3	4	4	5
82	9.055	9.061	9.066	9.072	9.077	9.083	9.088	9.094	9.009	9.105	1	1	2	2	3	3	4	4	5
83	9.110	9.116	9.121	9.127	9.132	9.138	9.143	9.149	9.154	9.160	1	1	2	2	3	3	4	4	5
84	9.165	9.171	9.176	9.182	9.187	9.192	9.198	9.203	9.209	9.214	1	1	2	2	3	3	4	4	5
85	9.220	9.225	9.230	9.236	9.241	9.247	9.252	9.257	9.263	9.268	1	1	2	2	3	3	4	4	5
86	9.274	9.279	9.284	9.290	9.295	9.301	9.306	9.311	9.317	9.322	1	1	2	2	3	3	4	4	5
87	9.327	9.333	9.338	9.343	9.349	9.354	9.359	9.365	9.370	9.375	1	1	2	2	3	3	4	4	5
88	9.381	9.386	9.391	9.397	9.402	9.407	9.413	9.418	9.423	9.429	1	1	2	2	3	3	4	4	5
89	9.434	9.439	9.445	9.450	9.455	9.460	9.466	9.471	9.476	9.482	1	1	2	2	3	3	4	4	5
90	9.487	9.492	9.497	9.503	9.508	9.513	9.518	9.524	9.529	9.534	1	1	2	2	3	3	4	4	5
91	9.539	9.545	9.550	9.555	9.560	9.566	9.571	9.576	9.581	9.586	1	1	2	2	3	3	4	4	5
92	9.592	9.597	9.602	9.607	9.612	9.618	9.623	9.628	9.633	9.638	1	1	2	2	3	3	4	4	5
93	9.644	9.649	9.654	9.659	9.664	9.670	9.675	9.680	9.685	9.690	1	1	2	2	3	3	4	4	5
94	9.695	9.701	9.706	9.711	9.716	9.721	9.726	9.731	9.737	9.742	1	1	2	2	3	3	4	4	5
95	9.747	9.752	9.757	9.762	9.767	9.772	9.778	9.783	9.788	9.793	1	1	2	2	3	3	4	4	5
96	0.798	9.803	9.808	9.813	9.818	9.823	9.829	9.834	9.839	9.844	1	1	2	2	3	3	4	4	5
97	9.849	9.854	9.859	9.864	9.869	9.874	9.879	9.884	9.889	9.894	1	1	2	2	3	3	4	4	5
98	9.899	9.905	9.910	9.915	9.920	9.925	9.930	9.935	9.940	9.945	1	1	1	2	2	3	3	4	4
99	9.950	9.955	9.960	9.965	9.970	9.975	9.980	9.985	9.990	9.995	0	1	1	2	2	3	3	4	4
N.	0	1	2	3	4	5	6	7	8	9	1	2	3	4	5	6	7	8	9

TABLE X.—COMMON LOGARITHMS

N.	0	1	2	3	4	5	6	7	8	9
10	0000	0043	0086	0128	0170	0212	0253	0294	0334	0374
11	0414	0453	0492	0531	0569	0607	0645	0682	0719	0755
12	0792	0828	0864	0899	0934	0969	1004	1038	1072	1106
13	1139	1173	1206	1239	1271	1303	1335	1367	1399	1430
14	1461	1492	1523	1553	1584	1614	1644	1673	1703	1732
15	1761	1790	1818	1847	1875	1903	1931	1959	1987	2014
16	2041	2068	2095	2122	2148	2175	2201	2227	2253	2279
17	2304	2330	2355	2380	2405	2430	2455	2480	2504	2529
18	2553	2577	2601	2625	2648	2672	2695	2718	2742	2765
19	2788	2810	2833	2856	2878	2900	2923	2945	2967	2989
20	3010	3032	3054	3075	3096	3118	3139	3160	3181	3201
21	3222	3243	3263	3284	3304	3324	3345	3365	3385	3404
22	3424	3444	3464	3483	3502	3522	3541	3560	3579	3598
23	3617	3636	3655	3674	3692	3711	3729	3747	3766	3784
24	3802	3820	3838	3856	3874	3892	3909	3927	3945	3962
25	3979	3997	4014	4031	4048	4065	4082	4099	4116	4133
26	4150	4166	4183	4200	4216	4232	4249	4265	4281	4298
27	4314	4330	4346	4362	4378	4393	4409	4425	4440	4456
28	4472	4487	4502	4518	4533	4548	4564	4579	4594	4609
29	4624	4639	4654	4669	4683	4698	4713	4728	4742	4757
30	4771	4786	4800	4814	4829	4843	4857	4871	4886	4900
31	4914	4928	4942	4955	4969	4983	4997	5011	5024	5038
32	5051	5065	5079	5092	5105	5119	5132	5145	5159	5172
33	5185	5198	5211	5224	5237	5250	5263	5276	5289	5302
34	5315	5328	5340	5353	5366	5378	5391	5403	5416	5428
35	5441	5453	5465	5478	5490	5502	5514	5527	5539	5551
36	5563	5575	5587	5599	5611	5623	5635	5647	5658	5670
37	5682	5694	5705	5717	5729	5740	5752	5763	5775	5786
38	5798	5809	5821	5832	5843	5855	5866	5877	5888	5899
39	5911	5922	5933	5944	5955	5966	5977	5988	5999	6010
40	6021	6031	6042	6053	6064	6075	6085	6096	6107	6117
41	6128	6138	6149	6160	6170	6180	6191	6201	6212	6222
42	6232	6243	6253	6263	6274	6284	6294	6304	6314	6325
43	6335	6345	6355	6365	6375	6385	6395	6405	6415	6425
44	6435	6444	6454	6464	6474	6484	6493	6503	6513	6522
45	6532	6542	6551	6561	6571	6580	6590	6599	6609	6618
46	6628	6637	6646	6656	6665	6675	6684	6693	6702	6712
47	6721	6730	6739	6749	6758	6767	6776	6785	6794	6803
48	6812	6821	6830	6839	6848	6857	6866	6875	6884	6893
49	6902	6911	6920	6928	6937	6946	6955	6964	6972	6981
50	6990	6998	7007	7016	7024	7033	7042	7050	7059	7067
51	7076	7084	7093	7101	7110	7118	7126	7135	7143	7152
52	7160	7168	7177	7185	7193	7202	7210	7218	7226	7235
53	7243	7251	7259	7267	7275	7284	7292	7300	7308	7316
54	7324	7332	7340	7348	7356	7364	7372	7380	7388	7396
N.	0	1	2	3	4	5	6	7	8	9

TABLE X.—COMMON LOGARITHMS—*Continued*

N.	0	1	2	3	4	5	6	7	8	9
55	7404	7412	7419	7427	7435	7448	7451	7459	7466	7474
56	7482	7490	7497	7505	7513	7520	7528	7536	7543	7551
57	7559	7566	7574	7582	7589	7597	7604	7612	7619	7627
58	7634	7642	7649	7657	7664	7672	7679	7686	7694	7701
59	7709	7716	7723	7731	7738	7745	7752	7760	7767	7774
60	7782	7789	7796	7803	7810	7818	7825	7832	7839	7846
61	7853	7860	7868	7875	7882	7889	7896	7903	7910	7917
62	7924	7931	7938	7945	7952	7959	7966	7973	7980	7987
63	7993	8000	8007	8014	8021	8028	8035	8041	8048	8055
64	8062	8069	8075	8082	8089	8096	8102	8109	8116	8122
65	8129	8136	8142	8149	8156	8162	8169	8176	8182	8189
66	8195	8202	8209	8215	8222	8228	8235	8241	8248	8254
67	8261	8267	8274	8280	8287	8293	8299	8306	8312	8319
68	8325	8331	8338	8344	8351	8357	8363	8370	8376	8382
69	8388	8395	8401	8407	8414	8420	8426	8432	8439	8445
70	8451	8457	8463	8470	8476	8482	8488	8494	8500	8506
71	8513	8519	8525	8531	8537	8543	8549	8555	8561	8567
72	8573	8579	8585	8591	8597	8603	8609	8615	8621	8627
73	8633	8639	8645	8651	8657	8663	8669	8675	8681	8686
74	8692	8698	8704	8710	8716	8722	8727	8733	8739	8745
75	8751	8756	8762	8768	8774	8779	8785	8791	8797	8802
76	8808	8814	8820	8825	8831	8837	8842	8848	8854	8859
77	8865	8871	8876	8882	8887	8893	8899	8904	8910	8915
78	8921	8927	8932	8938	8943	8949	8954	8960	8965	8971
79	8976	8982	8987	8993	8998	9004	9009	9015	9020	9025
80	9031	9036	9042	9047	9053	9058	9063	9069	9074	9079
81	9085	9090	9096	9101	9106	9112	9117	9122	9128	9133
82	9138	9143	9149	9154	9159	9165	9170	9175	9180	9186
83	9191	9196	9201	9206	9212	9217	9222	9227	9232	9238
84	9243	9248	9253	9258	9263	9269	9274	9279	9284	9289
85	9294	9299	9304	9309	9315	9320	9325	9330	9335	9340
86	9345	9350	9355	9360	9365	9370	9375	9380	9385	9390
87	9395	9400	9405	9410	9415	9420	9425	9430	9435	9440
88	9445	9450	9455	9460	9465	9469	9474	9479	9484	9489
89	9494	9499	9504	9509	9513	9518	9523	9528	9533	9538
90	9542	9547	9552	9557	9562	9566	9571	9576	9581	9586
91	9590	9595	9600	9605	9609	9614	9619	9624	9628	9633
92	9638	9643	9647	9652	9657	9661	9666	9671	9675	9680
93	9685	9689	9694	9699	9703	9708	9713	9717	9722	9727
94	9731	9736	9741	9745	9750	9754	9759	9763	9768	9773
95	9777	9782	9786	9791	9795	9800	9805	9809	9814	9818
96	9823	9827	9832	9836	9841	9845	9850	9854	9859	9863
97	9868	9872	9877	9881	9886	9890	9894	9899	9903	9908
98	9912	9917	9921	9926	9930	9934	9939	9943	9948	9952
99	9956	9961	9965	9969	9974	9978	9983	9987	9991	9996
N.	0	1	2	3	4	5	6	7	8	9

TABLE XI.—TRIGONOMETRIC FUNCTIONS

Angles	Sines		Cosines		Tangents		Cotangents		Angles
	Nat.	Log.	Nat.	Log.	Nat.	Log.	Nat.	Log.	
0° 00′	.0000	∞	1.0000	0.0000	.0000	∞	0	∞	90° 00′
10	.0029	7.4637	1.0000	0000	.0029	7.4637	343.77	2.5363	50
20	.0058	7648	1.0000	0000	.0058	7648	171.89	2352	40
30	.0087	9408	1.0000	0000	.0087	9409	114.59	0591	30
40	.0116	8.0658	.9999	0000	.0116	8.0658	85.940	1.9342	20
50	.0145	1627	.9999	0000	.0145	1627	68.750	8373	10
1° 00′	.0175	8.2419	.9998	9.9999	.0175	8.2419	57.290	1.7581	89° 00′
10	.0204	3088	.9998	9999	.0204	3089	49.104	6911	50
20	.0233	3668	.9997	9999	.0233	3669	42.964	6331	40
30	.0262	4179	.9997	9999	.0262	4181	38.188	5819	30
40	.0291	4637	.9996	9998	.0291	4638	34.368	5362	20
50	.0320	5050	.9995	9998	.0320	5053	31.242	4947	10
2° 00′	.0349	8.5428	.9994	9.9997	.0349	8.5431	28.636	1.4569	88° 00′
10	.0378	5776	.9993	9997	.0378	5779	26.432	4221	50
20	.0407	6097	.9992	9996	.0407	6101	24.542	3899	40
30	.0436	6397	.9990	9996	.0437	6401	22.904	3599	30
40	.0465	6677	.9989	9995	.0466	6682	21.470	3318	20
50	.0494	6940	.9988	9995	.0495	6945	20.206	3055	10
3° 00′	.0523	8.7188	.9986	9.9994	.0524	8.7194	19.081	1.2806	87° 00′
10	.0552	7423	.9985	9993	.0553	7429	18.075	2571	50
20	.0581	7645	.9983	9993	.0582	7652	17.169	2348	40
30	.0610	7857	.9981	9992	.0612	7865	16.350	2135	30
40	.0640	8059	.9980	9991	.0641	8067	15.605	1933	20
50	.0669	8251	.9978	9990	.0670	8261	14.924	1739	10
4° 00′	.0698	8.8436	.9976	9.9989	.0699	8.8446	14.301	1.1554	86° 00′
10	.0727	8613	.9974	9989	.0729	8624	13.727	1376	50
20	.0756	8783	.9971	9988	.0758	8795	13.197	1205	40
30	.0785	8946	.9969	9987	.0787	8960	12.706	1040	30
40	.0814	9104	.9967	9986	.0816	9118	12.251	0882	20
50	.0843	9256	.9964	9985	.0846	9272	11.826	0728	10
5° 00′	.0872	8.9403	.9962	9.9983	.0875	8.9420	11.430	1.0580	85° 00′
10	.0901	9545	.9959	9982	.0904	9563	11.059	0437	50
20	.0929	9682	.9957	9981	.0934	9701	10.712	0299	40
30	.0958	9816	.9954	9980	.0963	9836	10.385	0164	30
40	.0987	9945	.9951	9979	.0992	9966	10.078	0034	20
50	.1016	9.0070	.9948	9977	.1022	9.0093	9.7882	0.9907	10
6° 00′	.1045	9.0192	.9945	9.9976	.1051	9.0216	9.5144	0.9784	84° 00′
10	.1074	0311	.9942	9975	.1080	0336	9.2553	9664	50
20	.1103	0426	.9939	9973	.1110	0453	9.0098	9547	40
30	.1132	0539	.9936	9972	.1139	0567	8.7769	9433	30
40	.1161	0648	.9932	9971	.1169	0678	8.5555	9322	20
50	.1190	0755	.9929	9969	.1198	0786	8.3450	9214	10
7° 00′	.1219	9.0859	.9925	9.9968	.1228	9.0891	8.1443	0.9109	83° 00′
10	.1248	0961	.9922	9966	.1257	0995	7.9530	9005	50
20	.1276	1060	.9918	9964	.1287	1096	7.7704	8904	40
30	.1305	1157	.9914	9963	.1317	1194	7.5958	8806	30
40	.1334	1252	.9911	9961	.1346	1291	7.4287	8709	20
50	.1363	1345	.9907	9959	.1376	1385	7.2687	8615	10
8° 00′	.1392	9.1436	.9903	9.9958	.1405	9.1478	7.1154	0.8522	82° 00′
10	.1421	1525	.9899	9956	.1435	1569	6.9682	8431	50
20	.1449	1612	.9894	9954	.1465	1658	6.8269	8342	40
30	.1478	1697	.9890	9952	.1495	1745	6.6912	8255	30
40	.1507	1781	.9886	9950	.1524	1831	6.5606	8169	20
50	.1536	1863	.9881	9948	.1554	1915	6.4348	8085	10
9° 00′	.1564	9.1943	.9877	9.9946	.1584	9.1997	6.3138	0.8003	81° 00′
	Nat.	Log.	Nat.	Log.	Nat.	Log.	Nat.	Log.	
Angles	Cosines		Sines		Cotangents		Tangents		Angles

TABLE XI.—TRIGONOMETRIC FUNCTIONS—*Continued*

Angles	Sines		Cosines		Tangents		Cotangents		Angles
	Nat.	Log.	Nat.	Log.	Nat.	Log.	Nat.	Log.	
9° 00′	.1564	9.1943	.9877	9.9946	.1584	9.1997	6.3138	0.8003	81° 00′
10	.1593	2022	.9872	9944	.1614	2078	6.1970	7922	50
20	.1622	2100	.9868	9942	.1644	2158	6.0844	7842	40
30	.1650	2176	.9863	9940	.1673	2236	5.9758	7764	30
40	.1679	2251	.9858	9938	.1703	2313	5.8707	7687	20
50	.1708	2324	.9853	9936	.1733	2389	5.7694	7611	10
10° 00′	.1736	9.2397	.9848	9.9934	.1763	9.2463	5.6713	0.7537	80° 00′
10	.1765	2468	.9843	9931	.1793	2536	5.5764	7464	50
20	.1794	2538	.9838	9929	.1823	2609	5.4845	7391	40
30	.1822	2606	.9833	9927	.1853	2680	5.3955	7320	30
40	.1851	2674	.9827	9924	.1883	2750	5.3093	7250	20
50	.1880	2740	.9822	9922	.1914	2819	5.2257	7181	10
11° 00′	.1908	9.2806	.9816	9.9919	.1944	9.2887	5.1446	0.7113	79° 00′
10	.1937	2870	.9811	9917	.1974	2953	5.0658	7047	50
20	.1965	2934	.9805	9914	.2004	3020	4.9894	6980	40
30	.1994	2997	.9799	9912	.2035	3085	4.9152	6915	30
40	.2022	3058	.9793	9909	.2065	3149	4.8430	6851	20
50	.2051	3119	.9787	9907	.2095	3212	4.7729	6788	10
12° 00′	.2079	9.3179	.9781	9.9904	.2126	9.3275	4.7046	0.6725	78° 00′
10	.2108	3238	.9775	9901	.2156	3336	4.6382	6664	50
20	.2136	3296	.9769	9899	.2186	3397	4.5736	6603	40
30	.2164	3353	.9763	9896	.2217	3458	4.5107	6542	30
40	.2193	3410	.9757	9893	.2247	3517	4.4494	6483	20
50	.2221	3466	.9750	9890	.2278	3576	4.3897	6424	10
13° 00′	.2250	9.3521	.9744	9.9887	.2309	9.3634	4.3315	0.6366	77° 00′
10	.2278	3575	.9737	9884	.2339	3691	4.2747	6309	50
20	.2306	3629	.9730	9881	.2370	3748	4.2193	6252	40
30	.2334	3682	.9724	9878	.2401	3804	4.1653	6196	30
40	.2363	3734	.9717	9875	.2432	3859	4.1126	6141	20
50	.2391	3786	.9710	9872	.2462	3914	4.0611	6086	10
14° 00′	.2419	9.3837	.9703	9.9869	.2493	9.3968	4.0108	0.6032	76° 00′
10	.2447	3887	.9696	9866	.2524	4021	3.9617	5979	50
20	.2476	3937	.9689	9863	.2555	4074	3.9136	5926	40
30	.2504	3986	.9681	9859	.2586	4127	3.8667	5873	30
40	.2532	4035	.9674	9856	.2617	4178	3.8208	5822	20
50	.2560	4083	.9667	9853	.2648	4230	3.7760	5770	10
15° 00′	.2588	9.4130	.9659	9.9849	.2679	9.4281	3.7321	0.5719	75° 00′
10	.2616	4177	.9652	9846	.2711	4331	3.6891	5669	50
20	.2644	4223	.9644	9843	.2742	4381	3.6470	5619	40
30	.2672	4269	.9636	9839	.2773	4430	3.6059	5570	30
40	.2700	4314	.9628	9836	.2805	4479	3.5656	5521	20
50	.2728	4359	.9621	9832	.2836	4527	3.5261	5473	10
16° 00′	.2756	9.4403	.9613	9.9828	.2867	9.4575	3.4874	0.5425	74° 00′
10	.2784	4447	.9605	9825	.2899	4622	3.4495	5378	50
20	.2812	4491	.9596	9821	.2931	4669	3.4124	5331	40
30	.2840	4533	.9588	9817	.2962	4716	3.3759	5284	30
40	.2868	4576	.9580	9814	.2994	4762	3.3402	5238	20
50	.2896	4618	.9572	9810	.3026	4808	3.3052	5192	10
17° 00′	.2924	9.4659	.9563	9.9806	.3057	9.4853	3.2709	0.5147	73° 00′
10	.2952	4700	.9555	9802	.3089	4898	3.2371	5102	50
20	.2979	4741	.9546	9798	.3121	4943	3.2041	5057	40
30	.3007	4781	.9537	9794	.3153	4987	3.1716	5013	30
40	.3035	4821	.9528	9790	.3185	5031	3.1397	4969	20
50	.3062	4861	.9520	9786	.3217	5075	3.1084	4925	10
18° 00′	.3090	9.4900	.9511	9.9782	.3249	9.5118	3.0777	0.4882	72° 00′
	Nat.	Log.	Nat.	Log.	Nat.	Log.	Nat.	Log.	
Angles	Cosines		Sines		Cotangents		Tangents		Angles

TABLE XI.—TRIGONOMETRIC FUNCTIONS—*Continued*

Angles	Sines		Cosines		Tangents		Cotangents		Angles
	Nat.	Log.	Nat.	Log.	Nat.	Log.	Nat.	Log.	
18° 00'	.3090	9.4900	.9511	9.9782	.3249	9.5118	3.0777	0.4882	72° 00'
10	.3118	4939	.9502	9778	.3281	5161	3.0475	4839	50
20	.3145	4977	.9492	9774	.3314	5203	3.0178	4797	40
30	.3173	5015	.9483	9770	.3346	5245	2.9887	4755	30
40	.3201	5052	.9474	9765	.3378	5287	2.9600	4713	20
50	.3228	5090	.9465	9761	.3411	5329	2.9319	4671	10
19° 00'	.3256	9.5126	.9455	9.9757	.3443	9.5370	2.9042	0.4630	71° 00'
10	.3283	5163	.9446	9752	.3476	5411	2.8770	4589	50
20	.3311	5199	.9436	9748	.3508	5451	2.8502	4549	40
30	.3338	5235	.9426	9743	.3541	5491	2.8239	4509	30
40	.3365	5270	.9417	9739	.3574	5531	2.7980	4469	20
50	.3393	5306	.9407	9734	.3607	5571	2.7725	4429	10
20° 00'	.3420	9.5341	.9397	9.9730	.3640	9.5611	2.7475	0.4389	70° 00'
10	.3448	5375	.9387	9725	.3673	5650	2.7228	4350	50
20	.3475	5409	.9377	9721	.3706	5689	2.6985	4311	40
30	.3502	5443	.9367	9716	.3739	5727	2.6746	4273	30
40	.3529	5477	.9356	9711	.3772	5766	2.6511	4234	20
50	.3557	5510	.9346	9706	.3805	5804	2.6279	4196	10
21° 00'	.3584	9.5543	.9336	9.9702	.3839	9.5842	2.6051	0.4158	69° 00'
10	.3611	5576	.9325	9697	.3872	5879	2.5826	4121	50
20	.3638	5609	.9315	9692	.3906	5917	2.5605	4083	40
30	.3665	5641	.9304	9687	.3939	5954	2.5386	4046	30
40	.3692	5673	.9293	9682	.3973	5991	2.5172	4009	20
50	.3719	5704	.9283	9677	.4006	6028	2.4960	3972	10
22° 00'	.3746	9.5736	.9272	9.9672	.4040	9.6064	2.4751	0.3936	68° 00'
10	.3773	5767	.9261	9667	.4074	6100	2.4545	3900	50
20	.3800	5798	.9250	9661	.4108	6136	2.4342	3864	40
30	.3827	5828	.9239	9656	.4142	6172	2.4142	3828	30
40	.3854	5859	.9228	9651	.4176	6208	2.3945	3792	20
50	.3881	5889	.9216	9646	.4210	6243	2.3750	3757	10
23° 00'	.3907	9.5919	.9205	9.9640	.4245	9.6279	2.3559	0.3721	67° 00'
10	.3934	5948	.9194	9635	.4279	6314	2.3369	3686	50
20	.3961	5978	.9182	9629	.4314	6348	2.3183	3652	40
30	.3987	6007	.9171	9624	.4348	6383	2.2998	3617	30
40	.4014	6036	.9159	9618	.4383	6417	2.2817	3583	20
50	.4041	6065	.9147	9613	.4417	6452	2.2637	3548	10
24° 00'	.4067	9.6093	.9135	9.9607	.4452	9.6486	2.2460	0.3514	66° 00'
10	.4094	6121	.9124	9602	.4487	6520	2.2286	3480	50
20	.4120	6149	.9122	9596	.4522	6553	2.2113	3447	40
30	.4147	6177	.9100	9590	.4557	6587	2.1943	3413	30
40	.4173	6205	.9088	9584	.4592	6620	2.1775	3380	20
50	.4200	6232	.9075	9579	.4628	6654	2.1609	3346	10
25° 00'	.4226	9.6259	.9063	9.9573	.4663	9.6687	2.1445	0.3313	65° 00'
10	.4253	6286	.9051	9567	.4699	6720	2.1283	3280	50
20	.4279	6313	.9038	9561	.4734	6752	2.1123	3248	40
30	.4305	6340	.9026	9555	.4770	6785	2.0965	3215	30
40	.4331	6366	.9013	9549	.4806	6817	2.0809	3183	20
50	.4358	6392	.9001	9543	.4841	6850	2.0655	3150	10
26° 00'	.4384	9.6418	.8988	9.9537	.4877	9.6882	2.0503	0.3118	64° 00'
10	.4410	6444	.8975	9530	.4913	6914	2.0353	3086	50
20	.4436	6470	.8962	9524	.4950	6946	2.0204	3054	40
30	.4462	6495	.8949	9518	.4986	6977	2.0057	3023	30
40	.4488	6521	.8936	9512	.5022	7009	1.9912	2991	20
50	.4514	6546	.8923	9505	.5059	7040	1.9768	2960	10
27° 00'	.4540	9.6570	.8910	9.9499	.5095	9.7072	1.9626	0.2928	63° 00'
	Nat.	Log.	Nat.	Log.	Nat.	Log.	Nat.	Log.	
Angles	Cosines		Sines		Cotangents		Tangents		Angles

TABLE XI.—TRIGONOMETRIC FUNCTIONS—*Continued*

Angles	Sines		Cosines		Tangents		Cotangents		Angles
	Nat.	Log.	Nat.	Log.	Nat.	Log.	Nat.	Log.	
27° 00	.4540	9.6570	.8910	9.9499	.5095	9.7072	1.9626	0.2928	63° 00'
10	.4566	6595	.8897	9492	.5132	7103	1.9486	2897	50
20	.4592	6620	.8884	9486	.5169	7134	1.9347	2866	40
30	.4617	6644	.8870	9479	.5206	7165	1.9210	2835	30
40	.4643	6668	.8857	9473	.5243	7196	1.9074	2804	20
50	.4669	6692	.8843	9466	.5280	7226	1.8940	2774	10
28° 00'	.4695	9.6716	.8829	9.9459	.5317	9.7257	1.8807	0.2743	62° 00'
10	.4720	6740	.8816	9453	.5354	7287	1.8676	2713	50
20	.4746	6763	.8802	9446	.5392	7317	1.8546	2683	40
30	.4772	6787	.8788	9439	.5430	7348	1.8418	2652	30
40	.4797	6810	.8774	9432	.5467	7378	1.8291	2622	20
50	.4823	6833	.8760	9425	.5505	7408	1.8165	2592	10
29° 00'	.4848	9.6856	.8746	9.9418	.5543	9.7438	1.8040	0.2562	61° 00'
10	.4874	6878	.8732	9411	.5581	7467	1.7917	2533	50
20	.4899	6901	.8718	9404	.5619	7497	1.7796	2503	40
30	.4924	6923	.8704	9397	.5658	7526	1.7675	2474	30
40	.4950	6946	.8689	9390	.5696	7556	1.7556	2444	20
50	.4975	6968	.8675	9383	.5735	7585	1.7437	2415	10
30° 00'	.5000	9.6990	.8660	9.9375	.5774	9.7614	1.7321	0.2386	60° 00'
10	.5025	7012	.8646	9368	.5812	7644	1.7205	2356	50
20	.5050	7033	.8631	9361	.5851	7673	1.7090	2327	40
30	.5075	7055	.8616	9353	.5890	7701	1.6977	2299	30
40	.5100	7076	.8601	9346	.5930	7730	1.6864	2270	20
50	.5125	7097	.8587	9338	.5969	7759	1.6753	2241	10
31° 00'	.5150	9.7118	.8572	9.9331	.6009	9.7788	1.6643	0.2212	59° 00'
10	.5175	7139	.8557	9323	.6048	7816	1.6534	2184	50
20	.5200	7160	.8542	9315	.6088	7845	1.6426	2155	40
30	.5225	7181	.8526	9308	.6128	7873	1.6319	2127	30
40	.5250	7201	.8511	9300	.6168	7902	1.6212	2098	20
50	.5275	7222	.8496	9292	.6208	7930	1.6107	2070	10
32° 00'	.5299	9.7242	.8480	9.9284	.6249	9.7958	1.6003	0.2042	58° 00'
10	.5324	7262	.8465	9276	.6289	7986	1.5900	2014	50
20	.5348	7282	.8450	9268	.6330	8014	1.5798	1986	40
30	.5373	7302	.8434	9260	.6371	8042	1.5697	1958	30
40	.5398	7322	.8418	9252	.6412	8070	1.5597	1930	20
50	.5422	7342	.8403	9244	.6453	8097	1.5497	1903	10
33° 00'	.5446	9.7361	.8387	9.9236	.6494	9.8125	1.5399	0.1875	57° 00'
10	.5471	7380	.8371	9228	.6536	8153	1.5301	1847	50
20	.5495	7400	.8355	9219	.6577	8180	1.5204	1820	40
30	.5519	7419	.8339	9211	.6619	8208	1.5108	1792	30
40	.5544	7438	.8323	9203	.6661	8235	1.5013	1765	20
50	.5568	7457	.8307	9194	.6703	8263	1.4919	1737	10
34° 00'	.5592	9.7476	.8290	9.9186	.6745	9.8290	1.4826	0.1710	56° 00'
10	.5616	7494	.8274	9177	.6787	8317	1.4733	1683	50
20	.5640	7513	.8258	9169	.6830	8344	1.4641	1656	40
30	.5664	7531	.8241	9160	.6873	8371	1.4550	1629	30
40	.5688	7550	.8225	9151	.6916	8398	1.4460	1602	20
50	.5712	7568	.8208	9142	.6959	8425	1.4370	1575	10
35° 00'	.5736	9.7586	.8192	9.9134	.7002	9.8452	1.4281	0.1548	55° 00'
10	.5760	7604	.8175	9125	.7046	8479	1.4193	1521	50
20	.5783	7622	.8158	9116	.7089	8506	1.4106	1494	40
30	.5807	7640	.8141	9107	.7133	8533	1.4019	1467	30
40	.5831	7657	.8124	9098	.7177	8559	1.3934	1441	20
50	.5854	7675	.8107	9089	.7221	8586	1.3848	1414	10
36° 00'	.5878	9.7692	.8090	9.9080	.7265	9.8613	1.3764	0.1387	54° 00'
	Nat.	Log.	Nat.	Log.	Nat.	Log.	Nat.	Log.	
Angles	Cosines		Sines		Cotangents		Tangents		Angles

TABLE XI.—TRIGONOMETRIC FUNCTIONS—*Continued*

Angles	Sines		Cosines		Tangents		Cotangents		Angles
	Nat.	Log.	Nat.	Log.	Nat.	Log.	Nat.	Log.	
36° 00'	.5878	9.7692	.8090	9.9080	.7265	9.8613	1.3764	0.1387	54° 00'
10	.5901	7710	.8073	9070	.7310	8639	1.3680	1361	50
20	.5925	7727	.8056	9061	.7355	8666	1.3597	1334	40
30	.5948	7744	.8039	9052	.7400	8692	1.3514	1308	30
40	.5972	7761	.8021	9042	.7445	8718	1.3432	1282	20
50	.5995	7778	.8004	9033	.7490	8745	1.3351	1255	10
37° 00'	.6018	9.7795	.7986	9.9023	.7536	9.8771	1.3270	0.1229	53° 00'
10	.6041	7811	.7969	9014	.7581	8797	1.3190	1203	50
20	.6065	7828	.7951	9004	.7627	8824	1.3111	1176	40
30	.6088	7844	.7934	8995	.7673	8850	1.3032	1150	30
40	.6111	7861	.7916	8985	.7720	8876	1.2954	1124	20
50	.6134	7877	.7898	8975	.7766	8902	1.2876	1098	10
38° 00'	.6157	9.7893	.7880	9.8965	.7813	9.8928	1.2799	0.1072	52° 00'
10	.6180	7910	.7862	8955	.7860	8954	1.2723	1046	50
20	.6202	7926	.7844	8945	.7907	8980	1.2647	1020	40
30	.6225	7941	.7826	8935	.7954	9006	1.2572	0994	30
40	.6248	7957	.7808	8925	.8002	9032	1.2497	0968	20
50	.6271	7973	.7790	8915	.8050	9058	1.2423	0942	10
39° 00'	.6293	9.7989	.7771	9.8905	.8098	9.9084	1.2349	0.0916	51° 00'
10	.6316	8004	.7753	8895	.8146	9110	1.2276	0890	50
20	.6338	8020	.7735	8884	.8195	9135	1.2203	0865	40
30	.6361	8035	.7716	8874	.8243	9161	1.2131	0839	30
40	.6383	8050	.7698	8864	.8292	9187	1.2059	0813	20
50	.6406	8066	.7679	8853	.8342	9212	1.1988	0788	10
40° 00'	.6428	9.8081	.7660	9.8843	.8391	9.9238	1.1918	0.0762	50° 00'
10	.6450	8096	.7642	8832	.8441	9264	1.1847	0736	50
20	.6472	8111	.7623	8821	.8491	9289	1.1778	0711	40
30	.6494	8125	.7604	8810	.8541	9315	1.1708	0685	30
40	.6517	8140	.7585	8800	.8591	9341	1.1640	0659	20
50	.6539	8155	.7566	8789	.8642	9366	1.1571	0634	10
41° 00'	.6561	9.8169	.7547	9.8778	.8693	9.9392	1.1504	0.0608	49° 00'
10	.6583	8184	.7528	8767	.8744	9417	1.1436	0583	50
20	.6604	8198	.7509	8756	.8796	9443	1.1369	0557	40
30	.6626	8213	.7490	8745	.8847	9468	1.1303	0532	30
40	.6648	8227	.7470	8733	.8899	9494	1.1237	0506	20
50	.6670	8241	.7451	8722	.8952	9519	1.1171	0481	10
42° 00'	.6691	9.8255	.7431	9.8711	.9004	9.9544	1.1106	0.0456	48° 00'
10	.6713	8269	.7412	8699	.9057	9570	1.1041	0430	50
20	.6734	8283	.7392	8688	.9110	9595	1.0977	0405	40
30	.6756	8297	.7373	8676	.9163	9621	1.0913	0379	30
40	.6777	8311	.7353	8665	.9217	9646	1.0850	0354	20
50	.6799	8324	.7333	8653	.9271	9671	1.0786	0329	10
43° 00'	.6820	9.8338	.7314	9.8641	.9325	9.9697	1.0724	0.0303	47° 00'
10	.6841	8351	.7294	8629	.9380	9722	1.0661	0278	50
20	.6862	8365	.7274	8618	.9435	9747	1.0599	0253	40
30	.6884	8378	.7254	8606	.9490	9772	1.0538	0228	30
40	.6905	8391	.7234	8594	.9545	9798	1.0477	0202	20
50	.6926	8405	.7214	8582	.9601	9823	1.0416	0177	10
44° 00'	.6947	9.8418	.7193	9.8569	.9657	9.9848	1.0355	0.0152	46° 00'
10	.6967	8431	.7173	8557	.9713	9874	1.0295	0126	50
20	.6988	8444	.7153	8545	.9770	9899	1.0235	0101	40
30	.7009	8457	.7133	8532	.9827	9924	1.0176	0076	30
40	.7030	8469	.7112	8520	.9884	9949	1.0117	0051	20
50	.7050	8482	.7092	8507	.9942	9975	1.0058	0025	10
45° 00'	.7071	9.8495	.7071	9.8495	1.0000	0.0000	1.0000	0.0000	45° 00'
	Nat.	Log.	Nat.	Log.	Nat.	Log.	Nat.	Log.	
Angles	Cosines		Sines		Cotangents		Tangents		Angles

INDEX